PEARSON CUSTOM
MATHEMATICS

University of Florida
Survey of Calculus II
MAC2234

PEARSON

This special edition published in cooperation with Pearson Learning Solutions.

Printed in the United States of America.

V092

Please visit our website at *www.pearsonlearningsolutions.com.*

Attention bookstores: For permission to return any unsold stock, contact us at *pe-uscustomreturns@pearson.com.*

Pearson Learning Solutions, 501 Boylston Street, Suite 900, Boston, MA 02116
A Pearson Education Company
www.pearsoned.com

ISBN 10: 1-269-23434-X
ISBN 13: 978-1-269-23434-4

Table of Contents

Integration

If we know the rate at which a quantity is changing, we can find the total change over a period of time by integrating. An exercise in Section 3 illustrates how this process can be used to estimate the number of cars that cross the Tappan Zee Bridge in New York state each day, given information about how the rate of cars per hour varies with time. This same concept allows us to determine how far a car has gone, given its speed as a function of time; how much a culture of bacteria will grow; or how much consumers benefit by buying a product at the price determined by supply and demand.

Maureen Plainfield/ Shutterstock

U p to this point in calculus you have probably solved problems such as

$$f(x) = x^5; \text{find } f'(x).$$

In this chapter you will be asked to solve problems that are the reverse of these, that is, problems of the form

$$f'(x) = 5x^4; \text{find } f(x).$$

The derivative and its applications, are part of what is called *differential calculus*. This chapter is devoted to the other main branch of calculus, *integral calculus*. Integrals have many applications: finding areas; determining the lengths of curved paths; solving complicated probability problems; and calculating the location of an object (such as the distance of a space shuttle from Earth) when its velocity and initial position are known. The Fundamental Theorem of Calculus presented later in this chapter, will reveal a surprisingly close connection between differential and integral calculus.

| Antiderivatives

APPLY IT If an object is thrown from the top of the Willis Tower in Chicago, how fast is it going when it hits the ground?
Using antiderivatives, we will answer this question in Example 11.

Functions used in applications in previous chapters have provided information about a *total amount* of a quantity, such as cost, revenue, profit, temperature, gallons of oil, or distance. Derivatives of these functions provided information about the rate of change of these quantities and allowed us to answer important questions about the extrema of the functions. It is not always possible to find ready-made functions that provide information about the total amount of a quantity, but it is often possible to collect enough data to come up with a function that gives the *rate of change* of a quantity. We know that derivatives give the rate of change when the total amount is known. The reverse of finding a derivative is known as **antidifferentiation**. The goal is to find an *antiderivative, defined as follows.*

> Antiderivative
> If $F'(x) = f(x)$, then $F(x)$ is an **antiderivative** of $f(x)$.

EXAMPLE 1 Antiderivative

(a) If $F(x) = 10x$, then $F'(x) = 10$, so $F(x) = 10x$ is an antiderivative of $f(x) = 10$.
(b) For $F(x) = x^2$, $F'(x) = 2x$, making $F(x) = x^2$ an antiderivative of $f(x) = 2x$.

EXAMPLE 2 Antiderivative

Find an antiderivative of $f(x) = 5x^4$.

SOLUTION To find a function $F(x)$ whose derivative is $5x^4$, work backwards. Recall that the derivative of x^n is nx^{n-1}. If

$$nx^{n-1} \text{ is } 5x^4,$$

then $n - 1 = 4$ and $n = 5$, so x^5 is an antiderivative of $5x^4$.   TRY YOUR TURN 1

YOUR TURN 1 Find an antiderivative $f(x) = 8x^7$.

EXAMPLE 3 Population

Suppose a population is growing at a rate given by $f(x) = e^x$, where x is time in years from some initial date. Find a function giving the population at time x.

SOLUTION Let the population function be $F(x)$. Then

$$f(x) = F'(x) = e^x.$$

The derivative of the function defined by $F(x) = e^x$ is $F'(x) = e^x$, so one possible population function with the given growth rate is $F(x) = e^x$.

The function from Example 1(b), defined by $F(x) = x^2$, is not the only function whose derivative is $f(x) = 2x$. For example,

$$F(x) = x^2, \qquad G(x) = x^2 + 2, \qquad \text{and} \qquad H(x) = x^2 - 4$$

are all antiderivatives of $f(x) = 2x$, and any two of them differ only by a constant. These three functions, shown in Figure 1, have the same derivative, $f(x) = 2x$, and the slopes of their tangent lines at any particular value of x are the same. In fact, for any real number C, the function $F(x) = x^2 + C$ has $f(x) = 2x$ as its derivative. This means that there is a *family* or *class* of functions having $2x$ as a derivative. As the next theorem states, if two functions $F(x)$ and $G(x)$ are antiderivatives of $f(x)$, then $F(x)$ and $G(x)$ can differ only by a constant.

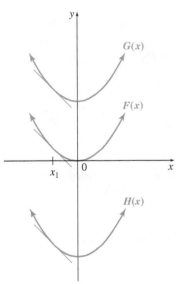

Slopes of the tangent lines at $x = x_1$ are the same.

FIGURE 1

If $F(x)$ and $G(x)$ are both antiderivatives of a function $f(x)$ on an interval, then there is a constant C such that

$$F(x) - G(x) = C.$$

(Two antiderivatives of a function can differ only by a constant.) The arbitrary real number C is called an integration constant.

The family of all antiderivatives of the function f is indicated by

$$\int f(x)\, dx = F(x) + C.$$

The symbol $\int$ is the **integral sign**, $f(x)$ is the **integrand**, and $\int f(x)\, dx$ is called an **indefinite integral**, the most general antiderivative of f.

Indefinite Integral
If $F'(x) = f(x)$, then
$$\int f(x)\,dx = F(x) + C,$$
for any real number C.

For example, using this notation,
$$\int 2x\,dx = x^2 + C.$$

The dx in the indefinite integral indicates that $\int f(x)\,dx$ is the "integral of $f(x)$ *with respect to* x" just as the symbol dy/dx denotes the "derivative of y with respect to x." For example, in the indefinite integral $\int 2ax\,dx$, dx indicates that a is to be treated as a constant and x as the variable, so that
$$\int 2ax\,dx = \int a(2x)\,dx = ax^2 + C.$$
On the other hand,
$$\int 2ax\,da = a^2x + C = xa^2 + C.$$
A more complete interpretation of dx will be discussed later.

The symbol $\int f(x)\,dx$ was created by G. W. Leibniz (1646–1716) in the latter part of the seventeenth century. The $\int$ is an elongated S from *summa*, the Latin word for *sum*. The word *integral* as a term in the calculus was coined by Jakob Bernoulli (1654–1705), a Swiss mathematician who corresponded frequently with Leibniz. The relationship between sums and integrals will be clarified in a later section.

Finding an antiderivative is the reverse of finding a derivative. Therefore, each rule for derivatives leads to a rule for antiderivatives. For example, the power rule for derivatives tells us that
$$\frac{d}{dx}x^5 = 5x^4.$$
Consequently,
$$\int 5x^4\,dx = x^5 + C,$$
the result found in Example 2. Note that the derivative of x^n is found by multiplying x by n and reducing the exponent on x by 1. To find an indefinite integral—that is, to undo what was done—*increase* the exponent by 1 and *divide* by the new exponent, $n + 1$.

FOR REVIEW

Recall that $\dfrac{d}{dx}x^n = nx^{n-1}$.

Power Rule
For any real number $n \neq -1$,
$$\int x^n\,dx = \frac{x^{n+1}}{n+1} + C.$$

(The antiderivative of $f(x) = x^n$ for $n \neq -1$ is found by increasing the exponent n by 1 and dividing x raised to the new power by the new value of the exponent.)

This rule can be verified by differentiating the expression on the right above:
$$\frac{d}{dx}\left(\frac{x^{n+1}}{n+1} + C\right) = \frac{n+1}{n+1}x^{(n+1)-1} + 0 = x^n.$$

(If $n = -1$, the expression in the denominator is 0, and the above rule cannot be used. Finding an antiderivative for this case is discussed later.)

EXAMPLE 4   Power Rule

Use the power rule to find each indefinite integral.

(a) $\int t^3 \, dt$

SOLUTION   Use the power rule with $n = 3$.

$$\int t^3 \, dt = \frac{t^{3+1}}{3+1} + C = \frac{t^4}{4} + C$$

To check the solution, find the derivative of $t^4/4 + C$. The derivative is t^3, the original function.

(b) $\int \frac{1}{t^2} \, dt$

SOLUTION   First, write $1/t^2$ as t^{-2}. Then

$$\int \frac{1}{t^2} \, dt = \int t^{-2} \, dt = \frac{t^{-2+1}}{-2+1} + C = \frac{t^{-1}}{-1} + C = -\frac{1}{t} + C.$$

Verify the solution by differentiating $-(1/t) + C$ to get $1/t^2$.

(c) $\int \sqrt{u} \, du$

SOLUTION   Since $\sqrt{u} = u^{1/2}$,

$$\int \sqrt{u} \, du = \int u^{1/2} \, du = \frac{u^{3/2}}{3/2} + C = \frac{2}{3} u^{3/2} + C.$$

To check this, differentiate $(2/3)u^{3/2} + C$; the derivative is $u^{1/2}$, the original function.

(d) $\int dx$

YOUR TURN 2

Find $\int \frac{1}{t^4} \, dt$.

SOLUTION   Write dx as $1 \cdot dx$, and use the fact that $x^0 = 1$ for any nonzero number x to get

$$\int dx = \int 1 \, dx = \int x^0 \, dx = \frac{x^1}{1} + C = x + C. \qquad \text{TRY YOUR TURN 2}$$

As shown earlier, the derivative of the product of a constant and a function is the product of the constant and the derivative of the function. A similar rule applies to indefinite integrals. Also, since derivatives of sums or differences are found term by term, indefinite integrals also can be found term by term.

─ FOR REVIEW ─

Recall that $\dfrac{d}{dx}[f(x) \pm g(x)] = [f'(x) \pm g'(x)]$ and $\dfrac{d}{dx}[kf(x)] = kf'(x)$.

Constant Multiple Rule and Sum or Difference Rule

If all indicated integrals exist,

$$\int k \cdot f(x) \, dx = k \int f(x) \, dx, \qquad \text{for any real number } k,$$

and

$$\int [f(x) \pm g(x)] \, dx = \int f(x) \, dx \pm \int g(x) \, dx.$$

(The antiderivative of a constant times a function is the constant times the antiderivative of the function. The antiderivative of a sum or difference of functions is the sum or difference of the antiderivatives.)

| CAUTION | The constant multiple rule requires k to be a *number*. The rule does not apply to a *variable*. For example,

$$\int x\sqrt{x-1}\,dx \neq x\int \sqrt{x-1}\,dx.$$

EXAMPLE 5 Rules of Integration

Use the rules to find each integral.

(a) $\int 2v^3\,dv$

SOLUTION By the constant multiple rule and the power rule,

$$\int 2v^3\,dv = 2\int v^3\,dv = 2\left(\frac{v^4}{4}\right) + C = \frac{v^4}{2} + C.$$

Because C represents any real number, it is not necessary to multiply it by 2 in the next-to-last step.

(b) $\int \frac{12}{z^5}\,dz$

SOLUTION Rewrite $12/z^5$ as $12z^{-5}$, then find the integral.

$$\int \frac{12}{z^5}\,dz = \int 12z^{-5}\,dz = 12\int z^{-5}\,dz = 12\left(\frac{z^{-4}}{-4}\right) + C$$

$$= -3z^{-4} + C = \frac{-3}{z^4} + C$$

(c) $\int (3z^2 - 4z + 5)\,dz$

SOLUTION By extending the sum and difference rules to more than two terms, we get

$$\int (3z^2 - 4z + 5)\,dz = 3\int z^2\,dz - 4\int z\,dz + 5\int dz$$

$$= 3\left(\frac{z^3}{3}\right) - 4\left(\frac{z^2}{2}\right) + 5z + C$$

$$= z^3 - 2z^2 + 5z + C.$$

YOUR TURN 3

Find $\int (6x^2 + 8x - 9)\,dx.$

Only one constant C is needed in the answer; the three constants from integrating term by term are combined.   TRY YOUR TURN 3

Remember to check your work by taking the derivative of the result. For instance, in Example 5(c) check that $z^3 - 2z^2 + 5z + C$ is the required indefinite integral by taking the derivative

$$\frac{d}{dz}(z^3 - 2z^2 + 5z + C) = 3z^2 - 4z + 5,$$

which agrees with the original information.

EXAMPLE 6 Rules of Integration

Use the rules to find each integral.

(a) $\displaystyle\int \frac{x^2 + 1}{\sqrt{x}}\, dx$

SOLUTION First rewrite the integrand as follows.

$$\int \frac{x^2 + 1}{\sqrt{x}}\, dx = \int \left(\frac{x^2}{\sqrt{x}} + \frac{1}{\sqrt{x}} \right) dx \qquad \text{Rewrite as a sum of fractions.}$$

$$= \int \left(\frac{x^2}{x^{1/2}} + \frac{1}{x^{1/2}} \right) dx \qquad \sqrt{a} = a^{1/2}$$

$$= \int (x^{3/2} + x^{-1/2})\, dx \qquad \text{Use } \frac{a^m}{a^n} = a^{m-n}.$$

Now find the antiderivative.

$$\int (x^{3/2} + x^{-1/2})\, dx = \frac{x^{5/2}}{5/2} + \frac{x^{1/2}}{1/2} + C$$

$$= \frac{2}{5} x^{5/2} + 2x^{1/2} + C$$

(b) $\displaystyle\int (x^2 - 1)^2\, dx$

SOLUTION Square the binomial first, and then find the antiderivative.

$$\int (x^2 - 1)^2\, dx = \int (x^4 - 2x^2 + 1)\, dx$$

$$= \frac{x^5}{5} - \frac{2x^3}{3} + x + C \qquad \text{TRY YOUR TURN 4}$$

YOUR TURN 4

Find $\displaystyle\int \frac{x^3 - 2}{\sqrt{x}}\, dx$.

It was shown earlier that the derivative of $f(x) = e^x$ is $f'(x) = e^x$, and the derivative of $f(x) = a^x$ is $f'(x) = (\ln a)a^x$. Also, the derivative of $f(x) = e^{kx}$ is $f'(x) = k \cdot e^{kx}$, and the derivative of $f(x) = a^{kx}$ is $f'(x) = k(\ln a)a^{kx}$. These results lead to the following formulas for indefinite integrals of exponential functions.

Indefinite Integrals of Exponential Functions

$$\int e^x\, dx = e^x + C$$

$$\int e^{kx}\, dx = \frac{e^{kx}}{k} + C, \quad k \neq 0$$

For $a > 0$, $a \neq 1$:

$$\int a^x\, dx = \frac{a^x}{\ln a} + C$$

$$\int a^{kx}\, dx = \frac{a^{kx}}{k(\ln a)} + C, \quad k \neq 0$$

(The antiderivative of the exponential function e^x is itself. If x has a coefficient of k, we must divide by k in the antiderivative. If the base is not e, we must divide by the natural logarithm of the base.)

EXAMPLE 7 **Exponential Functions**

(a) $\int 9e^t \, dt = 9 \int e^t \, dt = 9e^t + C$

(b) $\int e^{9t} \, dt = \dfrac{e^{9t}}{9} + C$

(c) $\int 3e^{(5/4)u} \, du = 3\left(\dfrac{e^{(5/4)u}}{5/4}\right) + C$

$$= 3\left(\dfrac{4}{5}\right)e^{(5/4)u} + C$$

$$= \dfrac{12}{5} e^{(5/4)u} + C$$

(d) $\int 2^{-5x} \, dx = \dfrac{2^{-5x}}{-5(\ln 2)} + C = -\dfrac{2^{-5x}}{5(\ln 2)} + C$

The restriction $n \neq -1$ was necessary in the formula for $\int x^n \, dx$ since $n = -1$ made the denominator of $1/(n+1)$ equal to 0. To find $\int x^n \, dx$ when $n = -1$, that is, to find $\int x^{-1} \, dx$, recall the differentiation formula for the logarithmic function: The derivative of $f(x) = \ln |x|$, where $x \neq 0$, is $f'(x) = 1/x = x^{-1}$. This formula for the derivative of $f(x) = \ln |x|$ gives a formula for $\int x^{-1} \, dx$.

Indefinite Integral of x^{-1}

$$\int x^{-1} \, dx = \int \frac{1}{x} \, dx = \ln |x| + C$$

(The antiderivative of $f(x) = x^n$ for $n = -1$ is the natural logarithm of the absolute value of x.)

CAUTION Don't neglect the absolute value sign in the natural logarithm when integrating x^{-1}. If x can take on a negative value, $\ln x$ will be undefined there. Note, however, that the absolute value is redundant (but harmless) in an expression such as $\ln |x^2 + 1|$, since $x^2 + 1$ can never be negative.

EXAMPLE 8 **Integrals**

(a) $\int \dfrac{4}{x} \, dx = 4 \int \dfrac{1}{x} \, dx = 4 \ln |x| + C$

YOUR TURN 5

Find $\int \left(\dfrac{3}{x} + e^{-3x}\right) dx$.

(b) $\int \left(-\dfrac{5}{x} + e^{-2x}\right) dx = -5 \ln |x| - \dfrac{1}{2}e^{-2x} + C$ TRY YOUR TURN 5

In all these examples, the antiderivative family of functions was found. In many applications, however, the given information allows us to determine the value of the integration constant C. The next examples illustrate this idea.

EXAMPLE 9 Cost

Suppose a publishing company has found that the marginal cost at a level of production of x thousand books is given by

$$C'(x) = \frac{50}{\sqrt{x}}$$

and that the fixed cost (the cost before the first book can be produced) is $25,000. Find the cost function $C(x)$.

SOLUTION Write $50/\sqrt{x}$ as $50/x^{1/2}$ or $50x^{-1/2}$, and then use the indefinite integral rules to integrate the function.

$$C(x) = \int \frac{50}{\sqrt{x}}\, dx = \int 50x^{-1/2}\, dx = 50(2x^{1/2}) + k = 100x^{1/2} + k$$

(Here k is used instead of C to avoid confusion with the cost function $C(x)$.) To find the value of k, use the fact that $C(0)$ is 25,000.

$$C(x) = 100x^{1/2} + k$$
$$25{,}000 = 100 \cdot 0 + k$$
$$k = 25{,}000$$

With this result, the cost function is $C(x) = 100x^{1/2} + 25{,}000$.

EXAMPLE 10 Demand

Suppose the marginal revenue from a product is given by $400e^{-0.1q} + 8$, where q is the number of products produced.

(a) Find the revenue function for the product.

   SOLUTION The marginal revenue is the derivative of the revenue function, so

$$R'(q) = 400e^{-0.1q} + 8$$

$$R(q) = \int (400e^{-0.1q} + 8)\, dq$$

$$= 400\frac{e^{-0.1q}}{-0.1} + 8q + C$$

$$= -4000e^{-0.1q} + 8q + C.$$

   If $q = 0$, then $R = 0$ (no items sold means no revenue), so that

$$0 = -4000e^{-0.1(0)} + 8(0) + C$$
$$0 = -4000 + 0 + C$$
$$4000 = C.$$

   Thus, the revenue function is

$$R(q) = -4000e^{-0.1q} + 8q + 4000.$$

(b) Find the demand function for this product.

   SOLUTION Recall that $R = qp$, where p is the demand function giving the price p as a function of q. Then

$$-4000e^{-0.1q} + 8q + 4000 = qp$$

$$\frac{-4000e^{-0.1q} + 8q + 4000}{q} = p. \qquad \text{Divide by } q.$$

The demand function is $p = \dfrac{-4000e^{-0.1q} + 8q + 4000}{q}$.

In the next example, integrals are used to find the position of a particle when the acceleration of the particle is given.

EXAMPLE 11 Velocity and Acceleration

Recall that if the function $s(t)$ gives the position of a particle at time t, then its velocity $v(t)$ and its acceleration $a(t)$ are given by

$$v(t) = s'(t) \qquad \text{and} \qquad a(t) = v'(t) = s''(t).$$

(a) Suppose the velocity of an object is $v(t) = 6t^2 - 8t$ and that the object is at 5 when time is 0. Find $s(t)$.

SOLUTION Since $v(t) = s'(t)$, the function $s(t)$ is an antiderivative of $v(t)$:

$$s(t) = \int v(t)\, dt = \int (6t^2 - 8t)\, dt$$
$$= 2t^3 - 4t^2 + C$$

for some constant C. Find C from the given information that $s = 5$ when $t = 0$.

$$s(t) = 2t^3 - 4t^2 + C$$
$$5 = 2(0)^3 - 4(0)^2 + C$$
$$5 = C$$
$$s(t) = 2t^3 - 4t^2 + 5$$

Rudy Balasko/ Shutterstock

(b) Many experiments have shown that when an object is dropped, its acceleration (ignoring air resistance) is constant. This constant has been found to be approximately 32 ft per second every second; that is,

$$a(t) = -32.$$

The negative sign is used because the object is falling. Suppose an object is thrown down from the top of the 1100-ft-tall Willis Tower (formerly known as the Sears Tower) in Chicago. If the initial velocity of the object is -20 ft per second, find $s(t)$, the distance of the object from the ground at time t.

SOLUTION First find $v(t)$ by integrating $a(t)$:

$$v(t) = \int (-32)\, dt = -32t + k.$$

When $t = 0$, $v(t) = -20$:

$$-20 = -32(0) + k$$
$$-20 = k$$

and

$$v(t) = -32t - 20.$$

Be sure to evaluate the constant of integration k before integrating again to get $s(t)$. Now integrate $v(t)$ to find $s(t)$.

$$s(t) = \int (-32t - 20) \, dt = -16t^2 - 20t + C$$

Since $s(t) = 1100$ when $t = 0$, we can substitute these values into the equation for $s(t)$ to get $C = 1100$ and

$$s(t) = -16t^2 - 20t + 1100$$

as the distance of the object from the ground after t seconds.

(c) Use the equations derived in (b) to find the velocity of the object when it hit the ground and how long it took to strike the ground.

APPLY IT

SOLUTION When the object strikes the ground, $s = 0$, so

$$0 = -16t^2 - 20t + 1100.$$

To solve this equation for t, factor out the common factor of -4 and then use the quadratic formula.

$$0 = -4(4t^2 + 5t - 275)$$

$$t = \frac{-5 \pm \sqrt{25 + 4400}}{8} \approx \frac{-5 \pm 66.5}{8}$$

Only the positive value of t is meaningful here: $t \approx 7.69$. It took the object about 7.69 seconds to strike the ground. From the velocity equation, with $t = 7.69$, we find

YOUR TURN 6 Repeat Example 11(b) and 11(c) for the Burj Khalifa in Dubai, which is the tallest building in the world, standing 2717 ft. The initial velocity is -20 ft per second.

$$v(t) = -32t - 20$$
$$v(7.69) = -32(7.69) - 20 \approx -266,$$

so the object was falling (as indicated by the negative sign) at about 266 ft per second when it hit the ground.   TRY YOUR TURN 6

EXAMPLE 12 Slope

Find a function f whose graph has slope $f'(x) = 6x^2 + 4$ and goes through the point $(1, 1)$.

SOLUTION Since $f'(x) = 6x^2 + 4$,

$$f(x) = \int (6x^2 + 4) \, dx = 2x^3 + 4x + C.$$

The graph of f goes through $(1, 1)$, so C can be found by substituting 1 for x and 1 for $f(x)$.

YOUR TURN 7 Find an equation of the curve whose tangent line has slope $f'(x) = 3x^{1/2} + 4$ and goes through the point $(1, -2)$.

$$1 = 2(1)^3 + 4(1) + C$$
$$1 = 6 + C$$
$$C = -5$$

Finally, $f(x) = 2x^3 + 4x - 5$.   TRY YOUR TURN 7

EXERCISES

1. What must be true of $F(x)$ and $G(x)$ if both are antiderivatives of $f(x)$?

2. How is the antiderivative of a function related to the function?

3. In your own words, describe what is meant by an integrand.

4. Explain why the restriction $n \neq -1$ is necessary in the rule
$$\int x^n \, dx = \frac{x^{n+1}}{n+1} + C.$$

Find the following.

5. $\int 6 \, dk$

6. $\int 9 \, dy$

7. $\int (2z + 3) \, dz$

8. $\int (3x - 5) \, dx$

9. $\int (6t^2 - 8t + 7) \, dt$

10. $\int (5x^2 - 6x + 3) \, dx$

11. $\int (4z^3 + 3z^2 + 2z - 6) \, dz$

12. $\int (16y^3 + 9y^2 - 6y + 3) \, dy$

13. $\int (5\sqrt{z} + \sqrt{2}) \, dz$

14. $\int (t^{1/4} + \pi^{1/4}) \, dt$

15. $\int 5x(x^2 - 8) \, dx$

16. $\int x^2(x^4 + 4x + 3) \, dx$

17. $\int (4\sqrt{v} - 3v^{3/2}) \, dv$

18. $\int (15x\sqrt{x} + 2\sqrt{x}) \, dx$

19. $\int (10u^{3/2} - 14u^{5/2}) \, du$

20. $\int (56t^{5/2} + 18t^{7/2}) \, dt$

21. $\int \left(\frac{7}{z^2}\right) dz$

22. $\int \left(\frac{4}{x^3}\right) dx$

23. $\int \left(\frac{\pi^3}{y^3} - \frac{\sqrt{\pi}}{\sqrt{y}}\right) dy$

24. $\int \left(\sqrt{u} + \frac{1}{u^2}\right) du$

25. $\int (-9t^{-2.5} - 2t^{-1}) \, dt$

26. $\int (10x^{-3.5} + 4x^{-1}) \, dx$

27. $\int \frac{1}{3x^2} \, dx$

28. $\int \frac{2}{3x^4} \, dx$

29. $\int 3e^{-0.2x} \, dx$

30. $\int -4e^{0.2v} \, dv$

31. $\int \left(\frac{-3}{x} + 4e^{-0.4x} + e^{0.1}\right) dx$

32. $\int \left(\frac{9}{x} - 3e^{-0.4x}\right) dx$

33. $\int \frac{1 + 2t^3}{4t} \, dt$

34. $\int \frac{2y^{1/2} - 3y^2}{6y} \, dy$

35. $\int (e^{2u} + 4u) \, du$

36. $\int (v^2 - e^{3v}) \, dv$

37. $\int (x + 1)^2 \, dx$

38. $\int (2y - 1)^2 \, dy$

39. $\int \frac{\sqrt{x} + 1}{\sqrt[3]{x}} \, dx$

40. $\int \frac{1 - 2\sqrt[3]{z}}{\sqrt[3]{z}} \, dz$

41. $\int 10^x \, dx$

42. $\int 3^{2x} \, dx$

43. Find an equation of the curve whose tangent line has a slope of
$$f'(x) = x^{2/3},$$
given that the point $(1, 3/5)$ is on the curve.

44. The slope of the tangent line to a curve is given by
$$f'(x) = 6x^2 - 4x + 3.$$
If the point $(0, 1)$ is on the curve, find an equation of the curve.

APPLICATIONS

Business and Economics

Cost Find the cost function for each marginal cost function.

45. $C'(x) = 4x - 5$;   fixed cost is $8

46. $C'(x) = 0.2x^2 + 5x$;   fixed cost is $10

47. $C'(x) = 0.03e^{0.01x}$;   fixed cost is $8

48. $C'(x) = x^{1/2}$;   16 units cost $45

49. $C'(x) = x^{2/3} + 2$;   8 units cost $58

50. $C'(x) = x + 1/x^2$;   2 units cost $5.50

51. $C'(x) = 5x - 1/x$;   10 units cost $94.20

52. $C'(x) = 1.2^x(\ln 1.2)$;   2 units cost $9.44

Demand Find the demand function for each marginal revenue function. Recall that if no items are sold, the revenue is 0.

53. $R'(x) = 175 - 0.02x - 0.03x^2$

54. $R'(x) = 50 - 5x^{2/3}$

55. $R'(x) = 500 - 0.15\sqrt{x}$

56. $R'(x) = 600 - 5e^{0.0002x}$

57. Text Messaging The approximate rate of change in the number (in billions) of monthly text messages is given by
$$f'(t) = 7.50t - 16.8,$$
where t represents the number of years since 2000. In 2005 ($t = 5$) there were approximately 9.8 billion monthly text messages. *Source: Cellular Telecommunication & Internet Association.*

a. Find the function that gives the total number (in billions) of monthly text messages in year t.

b. According to this function, how many monthly text messages were there in 2009? Compare this with the actual number of 152.7 billion.

58. Profit The marginal profit of a small fast-food stand is given, in thousands of dollars, by
$$P'(x) = \sqrt{x} + \frac{1}{2},$$
where x is the sales volume in thousands of hamburgers. The "profit" is $-$1000 when no hamburgers are sold. Find the profit function.

59. Profit The marginal profit in dollars on Brie cheese sold at a cheese store is given by

$$P'(x) = x(50x^2 + 30x),$$

where x is the amount of cheese sold, in hundreds of pounds. The "profit" is $-\$40$ when no cheese is sold.

a. Find the profit function.

b. Find the profit from selling 200 lb of Brie cheese.

Life Sciences

60. Biochemical Excretion If the rate of excretion of a biochemical compound is given by

$$f'(t) = 0.01e^{-0.01t},$$

the total amount excreted by time t (in minutes) is $f(t)$.

a. Find an expression for $f(t)$.

b. If 0 units are excreted at time $t = 0$, how many units are excreted in 10 minutes?

61. Flour Beetles A model for describing the population of adult flour beetles involves evaluating the integral

$$\int \frac{g(x)}{x}\,dx,$$

where $g(x)$ is the per-unit-abundance growth rate for a population of size x. The researchers consider the simple case in which $g(x) = a - bx$ for positive constants a and b. Find the integral in this case. *Source: Ecology.*

62. Concentration of a Solute According to Fick's law, the diffusion of a solute across a cell membrane is given by

$$c'(t) = \frac{kA}{V}[C - c(t)], \tag{1}$$

where A is the area of the cell membrane, V is the volume of the cell, $c(t)$ is the concentration inside the cell at time t, C is the concentration outside the cell, and k is a constant. If c_0 represents the concentration of the solute inside the cell when $t = 0$, then it can be shown that

$$c(t) = (c_0 - C)e^{-kAt/V} + C. \tag{2}$$

a. Use the last result to find $c'(t)$.

b. Substitute back into Equation (1) to show that (2) is indeed the correct antiderivative of (1).

63. Cell Growth Under certain conditions, the number of cancer cells $N(t)$ at time t increases at a rate

$$N'(t) = Ae^{kt},$$

where A is the rate of increase at time 0 (in cells per day) and k is a constant.

a. Suppose $A = 50$, and at 5 days, the cells are growing at a rate of 250 per day. Find a formula for the number of cells after t days, given that 300 cells are present at $t = 0$.

b. Use your answer from part a to find the number of cells present after 12 days.

64. Blood Pressure The rate of change of the volume $V(t)$ of blood in the aorta at time t is given by

$$V'(t) = -kP(t),$$

where $P(t)$ is the pressure in the aorta at time t and k is a constant that depends upon properties of the aorta. The pressure in the aorta is given by

$$P(t) = P_0e^{-mt},$$

where P_0 is the pressure at time $t = 0$ and m is another constant. Letting V_0 be the volume at time $t = 0$, find a formula for $V(t)$.

Social Sciences

65. Bachelor's Degrees The number of bachelor's degrees conferred in the United States has been increasing steadily in recent decades. Based on data from the National Center for Education Statistics, the rate of change of the number of bachelor's degrees (in thousands) can be approximated by the function

$$B'(t) = 0.06048t^2 - 1.292t + 15.86,$$

where t is the number of years since 1970. *Source: National Center for Education Statistics.*

a. Find $B(t)$, given that about 839,700 degrees were conferred in 1970 ($t = 0$).

b. Use the formula from part a to project the number of bachelor's degrees that will be conferred in 2015 ($t = 45$).

66. Degrees in Dentistry The number of degrees in dentistry (D.D.S. or D.M.D.) conferred to females in the United States has been increasing steadily in recent decades. Based on data from the National Center for Education Statistics, the rate of change of the number of bachelor's degrees can be approximated by the function

$$D'(t) = 29.25e^{0.03572t},$$

where t is the number of years since 1980. *Source: National Center for Education Statistics.*

a. Find $D(t)$, given that about 700 degrees in dentistry were conferred to females in 1980 ($t = 0$).

b. Use the formula from part a to project the number of degrees in dentistry that will be conferred to females in 2015 ($t = 35$).

Physical Sciences

Exercises 67–71 refer to Example 11 in this section.

67. Velocity For a particular object, $a(t) = 5t^2 + 4$ and $v(0) = 6$. Find $v(t)$.

68. Distance Suppose $v(t) = 9t^2 - 3\sqrt{t}$ and $s(1) = 8$. Find $s(t)$.

69. Time An object is dropped from a small plane flying at 6400 ft. Assume that $a(t) = -32$ ft per second and $v(0) = 0$. Find $s(t)$. How long will it take the object to hit the ground?

70. Distance Suppose $a(t) = 18t + 8$, $v(1) = 15$, and $s(1) = 19$. Find $s(t)$.

71. Distance Suppose $a(t) = (15/2)\sqrt{t} + 3e^{-t}$, $v(0) = -3$, and $s(0) = 4$. Find $s(t)$.

72. Motion Under Gravity Show that an object thrown from an initial height h_0 with an initial velocity v_0 has a height at time t given by the function

$$h(t) = \tfrac{1}{2}gt^2 + v_0 t + h_0,$$

where g is the acceleration due to gravity, a constant with value -32 ft/sec^2.

73. Rocket A small rocket was launched straight up from a platform. After 5 seconds, the rocket reached a maximum height of 412 ft. Find the initial velocity and height of the rocket. (*Hint:* See the previous exercise.)

74. Rocket Science In the 1999 movie *October Sky*, Homer Hickum was accused of launching a rocket that started a forest fire. Homer proved his innocence by showing that his rocket could not have flown far enough to reach where the fire started. He used the following reasoning.

a. Using the fact that $a(t) = -32$ (see Example 11(b)), find $v(t)$ and $s(t)$, given $v(0) = v_0$ and $s(0) = 0$.

(The initial velocity was unknown, and the initial height was 0 ft.)

b. Homer estimated that the rocket was in the air for 14 seconds. Use $s(14) = 0$ to find v_0.

c. If the rocket left the ground at a 45° angle, the velocity in the horizontal direction would be equal to v_0, the velocity in the vertical direction, so the distance traveled horizontally would be $v_0 t$. (The rocket left the ground at a steeper angle, so this would overestimate the distance from starting to landing point.) Find the distance the rocket would travel horizontally during its 14-second flight.

YOUR TURN ANSWERS

1. x^8 or $x^8 + C$

2. $-\dfrac{1}{3t^3} + C$

3. $2x^3 + 4x^2 - 9x + C$

4. $\dfrac{2}{7}x^{7/2} - 4x^{1/2} + C$

5. $3\ln|x| - \dfrac{1}{3}e^{-3x} + C$

6. $s(t) = -16t^2 - 20t + 2717$; 12.42 sec; 417 ft/sec

7. $f(x) = 2x^{3/2} + 4x - 8$

2 Substitution

APPLY IT If a formula for the marginal revenue is known, how can a formula for the total revenue be found?
Using the method of substitution, this question will be answered in Exercise 39.

Recall all the rules you've learned for finding derivatives of elementary functions By correctly applying those rules, you can take the derivative of any function involving powers of x, exponential functions, and logarithmic functions, combined in any way using the operations of arithmetic (addition, subtraction, multiplication, division, and exponentiation). By contrast, finding the antiderivative is much more complicated. There are a large number of techniques—more than we can cover in this text. Furthermore, for some functions all possible techniques fail. In the last section we saw how to integrate a few simple functions. In this section we introduce a technique known as *substitution* that will greatly expand the set of functions you can integrate.

The substitution technique depends on the idea of a differential. If $u = f(x)$, the *differential* of u, written du, is defined as

$$du = f'(x)\, dx.$$

For example, if $u = 2x^3 + 1$, then $du = 6x^2\, dx$. In this chapter we will only use differentials as a convenient notational device when finding an antiderivative such as

$$\int (2x^3 + 1)^4 6x^2\, dx.$$

The function $(2x^3 + 1)^4 6x^2$ might remind you of the result when using the chain rule to take the derivative. We will now use differentials and the chain rule in reverse to find the antiderivative. Let $u = 2x^3 + 1$; then $du = 6x^2\,dx$. Now substitute u for $2x^3 + 1$ and du for $6x^2\,dx$ in the indefinite integral.

$$\int (2x^3 + 1)^4 6x^2\,dx = \int \overbrace{(2x^3 + 1)}^{u}{}^4 (\overbrace{6x^2\,dx}^{du})$$

$$= \int u^4\,du$$

With substitution we have changed a complicated integral into a simple one. This last integral can now be found by the power rule.

$$\int u^4\,du = \frac{u^5}{5} + C$$

Finally, substitute $2x^3 + 1$ for u in the antiderivative to get

$$\int (2x^3 + 1)^4 6x^2\,dx = \frac{(2x^3 + 1)^5}{5} + C.$$

We can check the accuracy of this result by using the chain rule to take the derivative. We get

$$\frac{d}{dx}\left[\frac{(2x^3 + 1)^5}{5} + C\right] = \frac{1}{5} \cdot 5(2x^3 + 1)^4(6x^2) + 0$$

$$= (2x^3 + 1)^4 6x^2.$$

This method of integration is called **integration by substitution**. As shown above, it is simply the chain rule for derivatives in reverse. The results can always be verified by differentiation.

EXAMPLE 1   Substitution

Find $\int 6x(3x^2 + 4)^7\,dx$.

SOLUTION   If we choose $u = 3x^2 + 4$, then $du = 6x\,dx$ and the integrand can be written as the product of $(3x^2 + 4)^7$ and $6x\,dx$. Now substitute.

$$\int 6x(3x^2 + 4)^7\,dx = \int (3x^2 + 4)^7(6x\,dx) = \int u^7\,du$$

Find this last indefinite integral.

$$\int u^7\,du = \frac{u^8}{8} + C$$

Now replace u with $3x^2 + 4$.

$$\int 6x(3x^2 + 4)^7\,dx = \frac{u^8}{8} + C = \frac{(3x^2 + 4)^8}{8} + C$$

To verify this result, find the derivative.

$$\frac{d}{dx}\left[\frac{(3x^2 + 4)^8}{8} + C\right] = \frac{8}{8}(3x^2 + 4)^7(6x) + 0 = (3x^2 + 4)^7(6x)$$

YOUR TURN 1

Find $\int 8x(4x^2 + 8)^6\,dx$.

The derivative is the original function, as required.   TRY YOUR TURN 1

EXAMPLE 2 Substitution

Find $\int x^2 \sqrt{x^3 + 1}\, dx$.

SOLUTION

Method 1
Modifying the Integral

An expression raised to a power is usually a good choice for u, so because of the square root or 1/2 power, let $u = x^3 + 1$; then $du = 3x^2\, dx$. The integrand does not contain the constant 3, which is needed for du. To take care of this, multiply by 3/3, placing 3 inside the integral sign and 1/3 outside.

$$\int x^2 \sqrt{x^3 + 1}\, dx = \frac{1}{3} \int 3x^2 \sqrt{x^3 + 1}\, dx = \frac{1}{3} \int \sqrt{x^3 + 1}\, (3x^2\, dx)$$

Now substitute u for $x^3 + 1$ and du for $3x^2\, dx$, and then integrate.

$$\frac{1}{3} \int \sqrt{x^3 + 1}\, (3x^2 dx) = \frac{1}{3} \int \sqrt{u}\, du = \frac{1}{3} \int u^{1/2}\, du$$

$$= \frac{1}{3} \cdot \frac{u^{3/2}}{3/2} + C = \frac{2}{9} u^{3/2} + C$$

Since $u = x^3 + 1$,

$$\int x^2 \sqrt{x^3 + 1}\, dx = \frac{2}{9}(x^3 + 1)^{3/2} + C.$$

Method 2
Eliminating the Constant

As in Method 1, we let $u = x^3 + 1$, so that $du = 3x^2\, dx$. Since there is no 3 in the integral, we divide the equation for du by 3 to get

$$\frac{1}{3}\, du = x^2\, dx.$$

We then substitute u for $x^3 + 1$ and $du/3$ for $x^2\, dx$ to get

$$\int \sqrt{u}\, \frac{1}{3}\, du = \frac{1}{3} \int u^{1/2}\, du$$

YOUR TURN 2

Find $\int x^3 \sqrt{3x^4 + 10}\, dx$.

and proceed as we did in Method 1. The two methods are just slightly different ways of doing the same thing, but some people prefer one method over the other.

TRY YOUR TURN 2

The substitution method given in the examples above *will not always work*. For example, you might try to find

$$\int x^3 \sqrt{x^3 + 1}\, dx$$

by substituting $u = x^3 + 1$, so that $du = 3x^2\, dx$. However, there is no *constant* that can be inserted inside the integral sign to give $3x^2$ alone. This integral, and a great many others, cannot be evaluated by substitution.

With practice, choosing u will become easy if you keep two principles in mind.

1. u should equal some expression in the integral that, when replaced with u, tends to make the integral simpler.

2. u must be an expression whose derivative—disregarding any constant multiplier, such as the 3 in $3x^2$—is also present in the integral.

The substitution should include as much of the integral as possible, as long as its derivative is still present. In Example 1, we could have chosen $u = 3x^2$, but $u = 3x^2 + 4$

is better, because it has the same derivative as $3x^2$ and captures more of the original integral. If we carry this reasoning further, we might try $u = (3x^2 + 4)^4$, but this is a poor choice, for $du = 4(3x^2 + 4)^3(6x)\, dx$, an expression not present in the original integral.

EXAMPLE 3 Substitution

Find $\int \dfrac{x + 3}{(x^2 + 6x)^2}\, dx$.

SOLUTION Let $u = x^2 + 6x$, so that $du = (2x + 6)\, dx = 2(x + 3)\, dx$. The integral is missing the 2, so multiply by $2 \cdot (1/2)$, putting 2 inside the integral sign and $1/2$ outside.

$$\int \frac{x + 3}{(x^2 + 6x)^2}\, dx = \frac{1}{2} \int \frac{2(x + 3)}{(x^2 + 6x)^2}\, dx$$

$$= \frac{1}{2} \int \frac{du}{u^2} = \frac{1}{2} \int u^{-2}\, du = \frac{1}{2} \cdot \frac{u^{-1}}{-1} + C = \frac{-1}{2u} + C$$

Substituting $x^2 + 6x$ for u gives

$$\int \frac{x + 3}{(x^2 + 6x)^2}\, dx = \frac{-1}{2(x^2 + 6x)} + C. \qquad \text{TRY YOUR TURN 3}$$

YOUR TURN 3

Find $\int \dfrac{x + 1}{(4x^2 + 8x)^3}\, dx$.

In Example 3, the quantity $x^2 + 6x$ was raised to a power in the denominator. When such an expression is not raised to a power, the function can often be integrated using the fact that

$$\frac{d}{dx} \ln |f(x)| = \frac{1}{f(x)} \cdot f'(x).$$

This suggests that such integrals can be solved by letting u equal the expression in the denominator, as long as the derivative of the denominator is present in the numerator (disregarding any constant multiplier as usual). The next example illustrates this idea.

EXAMPLE 4 Substitution

Find $\int \dfrac{(2x - 3)\, dx}{x^2 - 3x}$.

SOLUTION Let $u = x^2 - 3x$, so that $du = (2x - 3)\, dx$. Then

$$\int \frac{(2x - 3)\, dx}{x^2 - 3x} = \int \frac{du}{u} = \ln |u| + C = \ln |x^2 - 3x| + C.$$

TRY YOUR TURN 4

YOUR TURN 4

Find $\int \dfrac{x + 3}{x^2 + 6x}\, dx$.

Recall that if $f(x)$ is a function, then by the chain rule, the derivative of the exponential function $y = e^{f(x)}$ is

$$\frac{d}{dx} e^{f(x)} = e^{f(x)} \cdot f'(x).$$

This suggests that the antiderivative of a function of the form $e^{f(x)}$ can be found by letting u be the exponent, as long as $f'(x)$ is also present in the integral (disregarding any constant multiplier as usual).

EXAMPLE 5   Substitution

Find $\int x^2 e^{x^3}\, dx$.

SOLUTION   Let $u = x^3$, the exponent on e. Then $du = 3x^2\, dx$. Multiplying by $3/3$ gives

$$\int x^2 e^{x^3}\, dx = \frac{1}{3}\int e^{x^3}(3x^2\, dx)$$

$$= \frac{1}{3}\int e^u\, du = \frac{1}{3}e^u + C = \frac{1}{3}e^{x^3} + C. \quad \text{TRY YOUR TURN 5}$$

YOUR TURN 5
Find $\int x^3 e^{x^4}\, dx$.

The techniques in the preceding examples can be summarized as follows.

Substitution

Each of the following forms can be integrated using the substitution $u = f(x)$.

Form of the Integral	Result
1. $\displaystyle\int [f(x)]^n f'(x)\, dx, \quad n \neq -1$	$\displaystyle\int u^n\, du = \frac{u^{n+1}}{n+1} + C = \frac{[f(x)]^{n+1}}{n+1} + C$
2. $\displaystyle\int \frac{f'(x)}{f(x)}\, dx$	$\displaystyle\int \frac{1}{u}\, du = \ln|u| + C = \ln|f(x)| + C$
3. $\displaystyle\int e^{f(x)} f'(x)\, dx$	$\displaystyle\int e^u\, du = e^u + C = e^{f(x)} + C$

The next example shows a more complicated integral in which none of the previous forms apply, but for which substitution still works.

EXAMPLE 6   Substitution

Find $\int x\sqrt{1 - x}\, dx$.

SOLUTION   Let $u = 1 - x$. To get the x outside the radical in terms of u, solve $u = 1 - x$ for x to get $x = 1 - u$. Then $dx = -du$ and we can substitute as follows.

$$\int x\sqrt{1 - x}\, dx = \int (1 - u)\sqrt{u}(-du) = \int (u - 1)u^{1/2}\, du$$

$$= \int (u^{3/2} - u^{1/2})\, du = \frac{2}{5}u^{5/2} - \frac{2}{3}u^{3/2} + C$$

$$= \frac{2}{5}(1 - x)^{5/2} - \frac{2}{3}(1 - x)^{3/2} + C$$

TRY YOUR TURN 6

YOUR TURN 6
Find $\int x\sqrt{3 + x}\, dx$

The substitution method is useful if the integral can be written in one of the following forms, where u is some function of x.

Substitution Method

In general, for the types of problems we are concerned with, there are three cases. We choose u to be one of the following:

1. the quantity under a root or raised to a power;
2. the quantity in the denominator;
3. the exponent on e.

Remember that some integrands may need to be rearranged to fit one of these cases.

Integration

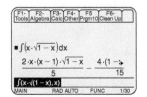

TECHNOLOGY NOTE

FIGURE 2

Some calculators, such as the TI-89 and TI-Nspire CAS, can find indefinite integrals automatically. Many computer algebra systems, such as Maple, Matlab, and Mathematica, also do this. The website www.wolframalpha.com can also be used to symbolically determine indefinite integrals and derivatives of functions. Figure 2 shows the integral in Example 6 performed on a TI-89. The answer looks different but is algebraically equivalent to the answer found in Example 6.

EXAMPLE 7   Demand

The research department for a hardware chain has determined that at one store the marginal price of x boxes per week of a particular type of nails is

$$p'(x) = \frac{-4000}{(2x + 15)^3}.$$

Find the demand equation if the weekly demand for this type of nails is 10 boxes when the price of a box of nails is $4.

SOLUTION   To find the demand function, first integrate $p'(x)$ as follows.

$$p(x) = \int p'(x)\, dx = \int \frac{-4000}{(2x + 15)^3}\, dx$$

Let $u = 2x + 15$. Then $du = 2\, dx$, and

$$p(x) = \frac{-4000}{2} \int (2x + 15)^{-3}\, 2\, dx \qquad \text{Multiply by 2/2.}$$

$$= -2000 \int u^{-3}\, du \qquad\qquad \text{Substitute.}$$

$$= (-2000)\frac{u^{-2}}{-2} + C$$

$$= \frac{1000}{u^2} + C$$

$$p(x) = \frac{1000}{(2x + 15)^2} + C. \qquad\qquad\qquad (1)$$

Find the value of C by using the given information that $p = 4$ when $x = 10$.

$$4 = \frac{1000}{(2 \cdot 10 + 15)^2} + C$$

$$4 = \frac{1000}{35^2} + C$$

$$4 \approx 0.82 + C$$

$$3.18 \approx C$$

Replacing C with 3.18 in Equation (1) gives the demand function,

$$p(x) = \frac{1000}{(2x + 15)^2} + 3.18.$$

With a little practice, you will find you can skip the substitution step for integrals such as that shown in Example 7, in which the derivative of u is a constant. Recall from the chain rule that when you differentiate a function, such as $p(x) = 1000/(2x + 15)^2 + 3.18$

Integration

in the previous example, you multiply by 2, the derivative of $(2x + 15)$. So when taking the antiderivative, simply divide by 2:

$$\int -4000(2x + 15)^{-3}\,dx = \frac{-4000}{2} \cdot \frac{(2x + 15)^{-2}}{-2} + C$$
$$= \frac{1000}{(2x + 15)^2} + C.$$

CAUTION This procedure is valid because of the constant multiple rule presented in the previous section, which says that constant multiples can be brought into or out of integrals, just as they can with derivatives. This procedure is *not* valid with any expression other than a constant.

EXAMPLE 8 Popularity Index

To determine the top 100 popular songs of each year since 1956, Jim Quirin and Barry Cohen developed a function that represents the rate of change on the charts of *Billboard* magazine required for a song to earn a "star" on the *Billboard* "Hot 100" survey. They developed the function

$$f(x) = \frac{A}{B + x},$$

where $f(x)$ represents the rate of change in position on the charts, x is the position on the "Hot 100" survey, and A and B are positive constants. The function

$$F(x) = \int f(x)\,dx$$

is defined as the "Popularity Index." Find $F(x)$. *Source: Chartmasters' Rock 100.*

SOLUTION Integrating $f(x)$ gives

$$F(x) = \int f(x)\,dx$$
$$= \int \frac{A}{B + x}\,dx$$
$$= A\int \frac{1}{B + x}\,dx.$$

Let $u = B + x$, so that $du = dx$. Then

$$F(x) = A\int \frac{1}{u}\,du = A \ln u + C$$
$$= A \ln(B + x) + C.$$

(The absolute value bars are not necessary, since $B + x$ is always positive here.)

2 EXERCISES

1. Integration by substitution is related to what differentiation method? What type of integrand suggests using integration by substitution?

2. The following integrals may be solved using substitution. Choose a function u that may be used to solve each problem. Then find du.

a. $\int (3x^2 - 5)^4\, 2x\,dx$

b. $\int \sqrt{1 - x}\,dx$

c. $\int \frac{x^2}{2x^3 + 1}\,dx$

d. $\int 4x^3 e^{x^4}\,dx$

Use substitution to find each indefinite integral.

3. $\int 4(2x + 3)^4\, dx$

4. $\int (-4t + 1)^3\, dt$

5. $\int \dfrac{2\, dm}{(2m + 1)^3}$

6. $\int \dfrac{3\, du}{\sqrt{3u - 5}}$

7. $\int \dfrac{2x + 2}{(x^2 + 2x - 4)^4}\, dx$

8. $\int \dfrac{6x^2\, dx}{(2x^3 + 7)^{3/2}}$

9. $\int z\sqrt{4z^2 - 5}\, dz$

10. $\int r\sqrt{5r^2 + 2}\, dr$

11. $\int 3x^2 e^{2x^3}\, dx$

12. $\int re^{-r^2}\, dr$

13. $\int (1 - t)e^{2t - t^2}\, dt$

14. $\int (x^2 - 1)e^{x^3 - 3x}\, dx$

15. $\int \dfrac{e^{1/z}}{z^2}\, dz$

16. $\int \dfrac{e^{\sqrt{y}}}{2\sqrt{y}}\, dy$

17. $\int \dfrac{t}{t^2 + 2}\, dt$

18. $\int \dfrac{-4x}{x^2 + 3}\, dx$

19. $\int \dfrac{x^3 + 2x}{x^4 + 4x^2 + 7}\, dx$

20. $\int \dfrac{t^2 + 2}{t^3 + 6t + 3}\, dt$

21. $\int \dfrac{2x + 1}{(x^2 + x)^3}\, dx$

22. $\int \dfrac{y^2 + y}{(2y^3 + 3y^2 + 1)^{2/3}}\, dy$

23. $\int p(p + 1)^5\, dp$

24. $\int 4r\sqrt{8 - r}\, dr$

25. $\int \dfrac{u}{\sqrt{u - 1}}\, du$

26. $\int \dfrac{2x}{(x + 5)^6}\, dx$

27. $\int (\sqrt{x^2 + 12x})(x + 6)\, dx$ **28.** $\int (\sqrt{x^2 - 6x})(x - 3)\, dx$

29. $\int \dfrac{(1 + 3\ln x)^2}{x}\, dx$

30. $\int \dfrac{\sqrt{2 + \ln x}}{x}\, dx$

31. $\int \dfrac{e^{2x}}{e^{2x} + 5}\, dx$

32. $\int \dfrac{1}{x(\ln x)}\, dx$

33. $\int \dfrac{\log x}{x}\, dx$

34. $\int \dfrac{(\log_2 (5x + 1))^2}{5x + 1}\, dx$

35. $\int x8^{3x^2 + 1}\, dx$

36. $\int \dfrac{10^{5\sqrt{x} + 2}}{\sqrt{x}}\, dx$

37. Stan and Ollie work on the integral
$$\int 3x^2 e^{x^3}\, dx.$$
Stan lets $u = x^3$ and proceeds to get
$$\int e^u\, du = e^u + C = e^{x^3} + C.$$
Ollie tries $u = e^{x^3}$ and proceeds to get
$$\int du = u + C = e^{x^3} + C.$$
Discuss which procedure you prefer, and why.

38. Stan and Ollie work on the integral
$$\int 2x(x^2 + 2)\, dx.$$

Stan lets $u = x^2 + 2$ and proceeds to get
$$\int u\, du = \dfrac{u^2}{2} + C = \dfrac{(x^2 + 2)^2}{2} + C.$$

Ollie multiplies out the function under the integral and gets
$$\int (2x^3 + 4x)\, dx = \dfrac{x^4}{2} + 2x^2 + C.$$

How can they both be right?

APPLICATIONS

Business and Economics

39. APPLY IT **Revenue** The marginal revenue (in thousands of dollars) from the sale of x MP3 players is given by
$$R'(x) = 4x(x^2 + 27{,}000)^{-2/3}.$$

a. Find the total revenue function if the revenue from 125 players is $29,591.

b. How many players must be sold for a revenue of at least $40,000?

40. Debt A company incurs debt at a rate of
$$D'(t) = 90(t + 6)\sqrt{t^2 + 12t}$$
dollars per year, where t is the amount of time (in years) since the company began. By the fourth year the company had accumulated $16,260 in debt.

a. Find the total debt function.

b. How many years must pass before the total debt exceeds $40,000?

41. Cost A company has found that the marginal cost (in thousands of dollars) to produce x central air conditioning units is
$$C'(x) = \dfrac{60x}{5x^2 + e},$$
where x is the number of units produced.

a. Find the cost function, given that the company incurs a fixed cost of $10,000 even if no units are built.

b. The company will seek a new source of investment income if the cost is more than $20,000 to produce 5 units. Should they seek this new source?

42. Profit The rate of growth of the profit (in millions of dollars) from a new technology is approximated by
$$P'(x) = xe^{-x^2},$$
where x represents time measured in years. The total profit in the third year that the new technology is in operation is $10,000.

a. Find the total profit function.

b. What happens to the total amount of profit in the long run?

43. Transportation According to data from the Bureau of Transportation Statistics, the rate of change in the number of local transit vehicles (buses, light rail, etc.), in thousands, in the United States from 1970 to the present can be approximated by

$$f'(t) = 4.0674 \times 10^{-4}t(t - 1970)^{0.4},$$

where t is the year. **Source: National Transportation Statistics 2006.**

a. Using the fact that in 1970 there were 61,298 such vehicles, find a formula giving the approximate number of local transit vehicles as a function of time.

b. Use the answer to part a to forecast the number of local transit vehicles in the year 2015.

Life Sciences

44. Outpatient Visits According to data from the American Hospital Association, the rate of change in the number of hospital outpatient visits, in millions, in the United States each year from 1980 to the present can be approximated by

$$f'(t) = 0.001483t(t - 1980)^{0.75},$$

where t is the year. **Source: Hospital Statistics.**

a. Using the fact that in 1980 there were 262,951,000 outpatient visits, find a formula giving the approximate number of outpatient visits as a function of time.

b. Use the answer to part a to forecast the number of outpatient visits in the year 2015.

YOUR TURN ANSWERS

1. $\dfrac{(4x^2 + 8)^7}{7} + C$

2. $\dfrac{(3x^4 + 10)^{3/2}}{18} + C$

3. $-\dfrac{1}{16(4x^2 + 8x)^2} + C$

4. $\frac{1}{2} \ln|x^2 + 6x| + C$

5. $\frac{1}{4}e^{x^4} + C$

6. $\frac{2}{5}(3 + x)^{5/2} - 2(3 + x)^{3/2} + C$

3 Area and the Definite Integral

APPLY IT If we know how the rate that oil is leaking from a machine varies with time, how can we estimate the total amount of leakage over a certain period of time?

We will answer this question in Example 3 using a method introduced in this section.

To calculate the areas of geometric figures such as rectangles, squares, triangles, and circles, we use specific formulas. In this section we consider the problem of finding the area of a figure or region that is bounded by curves, such as the shaded region in Figure 3.

The brilliant Greek mathematician Archimedes (about 287 B.C.–212 B.C.) is considered one of the greatest mathematicians of all time. His development of a rigorous method known as *exhaustion* to derive results was a forerunner of the ideas of integral calculus. Archimedes used a method that would later be verified by the theory of integration. His method involved viewing a geometric figure as a sum of other figures. For example, he thought of a plane surface area as a figure consisting of infinitely many parallel line segments. Among the results established by Archimedes' method was the fact that the area of a segment of a parabola (shown in color in Figure 3) is equal to 4/3 the area of a triangle with the same base and the same height.

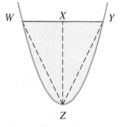

Area of parabolic segment

$= \frac{4}{3}$ (area of triangle WYZ)

FIGURE 3

EXAMPLE 1 Approximation of Area

Consider the region bounded by the y-axis, the x-axis, and the graph of $f(x) = \sqrt{4 - x^2}$, shown in Figure 4.

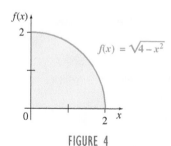

FIGURE 4

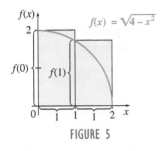

FIGURE 5

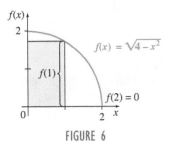

FIGURE 6

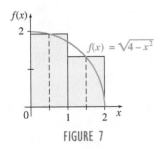

FIGURE 7

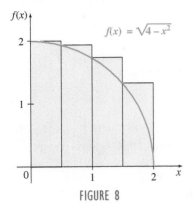

FIGURE 8

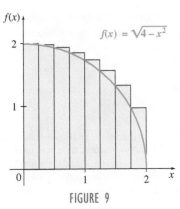

FIGURE 9

(a) Approximate the area of the region using two rectangles. Determine the height of the rectangle by the value of the function at the *left* endpoint.

SOLUTION A very rough approximation of the area of this region can be found by using two rectangles whose heights are determined by the value of the function at the left endpoints, as in Figure 5. The height of the rectangle on the left is $f(0) = 2$ and the height of the rectangle on the right is $f(1) = \sqrt{3}$. The width of each rectangle is 1, making the total area of the two rectangles

$$1 \cdot f(0) + 1 \cdot f(1) = 2 + \sqrt{3} \approx 3.7321 \text{ square units.}$$

Note that $f(x)$ is a decreasing function, and that we will overestimate the area when we evaluate the function at the left endpoint to determine the height of the rectangle in that interval.

(b) Repeat part (a) using the value of the function at the *right* endpoint to determine the height of the rectangle.

SOLUTION Using the right endpoints, as in Figure 6, the area of the two rectangles is

$$1 \cdot f(1) + 1 \cdot f(2) = \sqrt{3} + 0 \approx 1.7321 \text{ square units.}$$

Note that we underestimate the area of this particular region when we use the right endpoints.

    If the left endpoint gives an answer too big and the right endpoint an answer too small, it seems reasonable to average the two answers. This produces the method called the *trapezoidal rule*, discussed in more detail later in this chapter. In this example, we get

$$\frac{3.7321 + 1.7321}{2} = 2.7321 \text{ square units.}$$

(c) Repeat part (a) using the value of the function at the *midpoint* of each interval to determine the height of the rectangle.

SOLUTION In Figure 7, the rectangles are drawn with height determined by the midpoint of each interval. This method is called the **midpoint rule**, and gives

$$1 \cdot f(0.5) + 1 \cdot f(1.5) = \sqrt{3.75} + \sqrt{1.75} \approx 3.2594 \text{ square units.}$$

(d) We can improve the accuracy of the previous approximations by increasing the number of rectangles. Repeat part (a) using four rectangles.

SOLUTION Divide the interval from $x = 0$ to $x = 2$ into four equal parts, each of width $1/2$. The height of each rectangle is given by the value of f at the left side of the rectangle, as shown in Figure 8. The area of each rectangle is the width, $1/2$, multiplied by the height. The total area of the four rectangles is

$$\frac{1}{2} \cdot f(0) + \frac{1}{2} \cdot f\left(\frac{1}{2}\right) + \frac{1}{2} \cdot f(1) + \frac{1}{2} \cdot f\left(1\frac{1}{2}\right)$$

$$= \frac{1}{2}(2) + \frac{1}{2}\left(\frac{\sqrt{15}}{2}\right) + \frac{1}{2}(\sqrt{3}) + \frac{1}{2}\left(\frac{\sqrt{7}}{2}\right)$$

$$= 1 + \frac{\sqrt{15}}{4} + \frac{\sqrt{3}}{2} + \frac{\sqrt{7}}{4} \approx 3.4957 \text{ square units.}$$

This approximation looks better, but it is still greater than the actual area.

(e) Repeat part (a) using eight rectangles.

SOLUTION Divide the interval from $x = 0$ to $x = 2$ into 8 equal parts, each of width $1/4$ (see Figure 9). The total area of all of these rectangles is

$$\frac{1}{4} \cdot f(0) + \frac{1}{4} \cdot f\left(\frac{1}{4}\right) + \frac{1}{4} \cdot f\left(\frac{1}{2}\right) + \frac{1}{4} \cdot f\left(\frac{3}{4}\right) + \frac{1}{4} \cdot f(1)$$

$$+ \frac{1}{4} \cdot f\left(\frac{5}{4}\right) + \frac{1}{4} \cdot f\left(\frac{3}{2}\right) + \frac{1}{4} \cdot f\left(\frac{7}{4}\right)$$

$$\approx 3.3398 \text{ square units.}$$

The process used in Example 1 of approximating the area under a curve by using more and more rectangles to get a better and better approximation can be generalized. To do this, divide the interval from $x = 0$ to $x = 2$ into n equal parts. Each of these n intervals has width

$$\frac{2 - 0}{n} = \frac{2}{n},$$

so each rectangle has width $2/n$ and height determined by the function value at the left side of the rectangle, or the right side, or the midpoint. We could also average the left and right side values as before. Using a computer or graphing calculator to find approximations to the area for several values of n gives the results in the following table.

	Approximations to the Area			
n	Left Sum	Right Sum	Trapezoidal	Midpoint
2	3.7321	1.7321	2.7321	3.2594
4	3.4957	2.4957	2.9957	3.1839
8	3.3398	2.8398	3.0898	3.1567
10	3.3045	2.9045	3.1045	3.1524
20	3.2285	3.0285	3.1285	3.1454
50	3.1783	3.0983	3.1383	3.1426
100	3.1604	3.1204	3.1404	3.1419
500	3.1455	3.1375	3.1415	3.1416

The numbers in the last four columns of this table represent approximations to the area under the curve, above the x-axis, and between the lines $x = 0$ and $x = 2$. As n becomes larger and larger, all four approximations become better and better, getting closer to the actual area. In this example, the exact area can be found by a formula from plane geometry. Write the given function as

$$y = \sqrt{4 - x^2},$$

then square both sides to get

$$y^2 = 4 - x^2$$
$$x^2 + y^2 = 4,$$

the equation of a circle centered at the origin with radius 2. The region in Figure 4 is the quarter of this circle that lies in the first quadrant. The actual area of this region is one-quarter of the area of the entire circle, or

$$\frac{1}{4}\pi(2)^2 = \pi \approx 3.1416.$$

As the number of rectangles increases without bound, the sum of the areas of these rectangles gets closer and closer to the actual area of the region, π. This can be written as

$$\lim_{n \to \infty} (\text{sum of areas of } n \text{ rectangles}) = \pi.$$

(The value of π was originally found by a process similar to this.)*

---

*The number π is the ratio of the circumference of a circle to its diameter. It is an example of an *irrational number*, and as such it cannot be expressed as a terminating or repeating decimal. Many approximations have been used for π over the years. A passage in the Bible (1 Kings 7:23) indicates a value of 3. The Egyptians used the value 3.16, and Archimedes showed that its value must be between 22/7 and 223/71. A Hindu writer, Brahmagupta, used $\sqrt{10}$ as its value in the seventh century. The search for the digits of π has continued into modern times. Fabrice Bellard, using a desktop computer, recently computed the value to nearly 2.7 trillion digits.

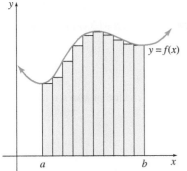

Ten rectangles of equal width

(a)

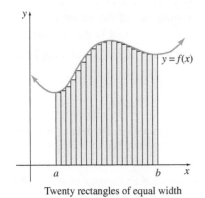

Twenty rectangles of equal width

(b)

FIGURE 10

Notice in the previous table that for a particular value of n, the midpoint rule gave the best answer (the one closest to the true value of $\pi \approx 3.1416$), followed by the trapezoidal rule, followed by the left and right sums. In fact, the midpoint rule with $n = 20$ gives a value (3.1454) that is slightly more accurate than the left sum with $n = 500$ (3.1455). It is usually the case that the midpoint rule gives a more accurate answer than either the left or the right sum.

Now we can generalize to get a method of finding the area bounded by the curve $y = f(x)$, the x-axis, and the vertical lines $x = a$ and $x = b$, as shown in Figure 10. To approximate this area, we could divide the region under the curve first into 10 rectangles (Figure 10(a)) and then into 20 rectangles (Figure 10(b)). The sum of the areas of the rectangles gives an approximation to the area under the curve when $f(x) \geq 0$. In the next section we will consider the case in which $f(x)$ might be negative.

To develop a process that would yield the *exact* area, begin by dividing the interval from a to b into n pieces of equal width, using each of these n pieces as the base of a rectangle (see Figure 11). Let x_1 be an arbitrary point in the first interval, x_2 be an arbitrary point in the second interval, and so on, up to the nth interval. In the graph of Figure 11, the symbol Δx is used to represent the width of each of the intervals. Since the length of the entire interval is $b - a$, each of the n pieces has length

$$\Delta x = \frac{b - a}{n}.$$

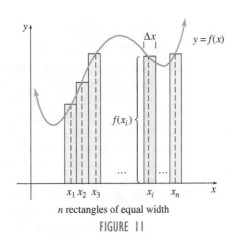

n rectangles of equal width

FIGURE 11

The pink rectangle is an arbitrary rectangle called the ith rectangle. Its area is the product of its length and width. Since the width of the ith rectangle is Δx and the length of the ith rectangle is given by the height $f(x_i)$,

$$\text{Area of the } i\text{th rectangle} = f(x_i) \cdot \Delta x.$$

The total area under the curve is approximated by the sum of the areas of all n of the rectangles. With sigma notation, the approximation to the total area becomes

$$\text{Area of all } n \text{ rectangles} = \sum_{i=1}^{n} f(x_i) \cdot \Delta x.$$

The exact area is defined to be the limit of this sum (if the limit exists) as the number of rectangles increases without bound:

$$\text{Exact area} = \lim_{n \to \infty} \sum_{i=1}^{n} f(x_i)\Delta x.$$

Whenever this limit exists, regardless of whether $f(x)$ is positive or negative, we will call it the *definite integral* of $f(x)$ from a to b. It is written as follows.

The Definite Integral

If f is defined on the interval $[a, b]$, the **definite integral** of f from a to b is given by

$$\int_a^b f(x)\, dx = \lim_{n \to \infty} \sum_{i=1}^{n} f(x_i)\Delta x,$$

provided the limit exists, where $\Delta x = (b - a)/n$ and x_i is *any* value of x in the ith interval.*

The definite integral can be approximated by

$$\sum_{i=1}^{n} f(x_i)\Delta x.$$

If $f(x) \geq 0$ on the interval $[a, b]$, the definite integral gives the area under the curve between $x = a$ and $x = b$. In the midpoint rule, x_i is the midpoint of the ith interval. We may also let x_i be the left endpoint, the right endpoint, or any other point in the ith interval.

In Example 1, the area bounded by the x-axis, the curve $y = \sqrt{4 - x^2}$, and the lines $x = 0$ and $x = 2$ could be written as the definite integral

$$\int_0^2 \sqrt{4 - x^2}\, dx = \pi.$$

NOTE   Notice that unlike the indefinite integral, which is a set of *functions*, the definite integral represents a *number*. The next section will show how antiderivatives are used in finding the definite integral and, thus, the area under a curve.

Keep in mind that finding the definite integral of a function can be thought of as a mathematical process that gives the sum of an infinite number of individual parts (within certain limits). The definite integral represents area only if the function involved is *nonnegative* ($f(x) \geq 0$) at every x-value in the interval $[a, b]$. There are many other interpretations of the definite integral, and all of them involve this idea of approximation by appropriate sums. In the next section we will consider the definite integral when $f(x)$ might be negative.

As indicated in this definition, although the left endpoint of the ith interval has been used to find the height of the ith rectangle, any number in the ith interval can be used. (A more general definition is possible in which the rectangles do not necessarily all have the same width.) The b above the integral sign is called the **upper limit** of integration, and the a is the **lower limit** of integration. This use of the word *limit* has nothing to do with the limit of the sum; it refers to the limits, or boundaries, on x.

TECHNOLOGY NOTE

Some calculators have a built-in function for evaluating the definite integral. For example, the TI-84 Plus uses the `fnInt` command, found in the MATH menu, as shown in Figure 12(a). Figure 12(b) shows the command used for Example 1 and gives the answer 3.141593074, with an error of approximately 0.0000004.

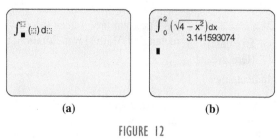

(a)   (b)

FIGURE 12

*The sum in the definition of the definite integral is an example of a Riemann sum, named for the German mathematician Georg Riemann (1826–1866), who at the age of 20 changed his field of study from theology and the classics to mathematics. Twenty years later he died of tuberculosis while traveling in Italy in search of a cure. The concepts of *Riemann sum* and *Riemann integral* are still studied in rigorous calculus textbooks.

| EXAMPLE 2 | Approximation of Area |

Approximate $\int_0^4 2x \, dx$, the area of the region under the graph of $f(x) = 2x$, above the x-axis, and between $x = 0$ and $x = 4$, by using four rectangles of equal width whose heights are the values of the function at the midpoint of each subinterval.

Method 1
Calculating by Hand

SOLUTION

We want to find the area of the shaded region in Figure 13. The heights of the four rectangles given by $f(x_i)$ for $i = 1, 2, 3,$ and 4 are as follows.

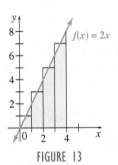

FIGURE 13

Rectangle Heights		
i	x_i	$f(x_i)$
1	$x_1 = 0.5$	$f(0.5) = 1.0$
2	$x_2 = 1.5$	$f(1.5) = 3.0$
3	$x_3 = 2.5$	$f(2.5) = 5.0$
4	$x_4 = 3.5$	$f(3.5) = 7.0$

The width of each rectangle is $\Delta x = (4 - 0)/4 = 1$. The sum of the areas of the four rectangles is

$$\sum_{i=1}^{4} f(x_i)\Delta x = f(x_1)\Delta x + f(x_2)\Delta x + f(x_3)\Delta x + f(x_4)\Delta x$$
$$= f(0.5)\Delta x + f(1.5)\Delta x + f(2.5)\Delta x + f(3.5)\Delta x$$
$$= 1(1) + 3(1) + 5(1) + 7(1)$$
$$= 16.$$

Using the formula for the area of a triangle, $A = (1/2)bh$, with b, the length of the base, equal to 4 and h, the height, equal to 8, gives

$$A = \frac{1}{2}bh = \frac{1}{2}(4)(8) = 16,$$

the exact value of the area. The approximation equals the exact area in this case because our use of the midpoints of each subinterval distributed the error evenly above and below the graph.

Method 2
Graphing Calculator

A graphing calculator can be used to organize the information in this example. For example, the `seq` feature in the LIST OPS menu of the TI-84 Plus calculator can be used to store the values of i in the list L_1. Using the STAT EDIT menu, the entries for x_i can be generated by entering the formula $-.5 + L_1$ as the heading of L_2. Similarly, entering the formula for $f(x_i)$, $2 * L_2$, at the top of list L_3 will generate the values of $f(x_i)$ in L_3. (The entries are listed automatically when the formula is entered.) Then the `sum` feature in the LIST MATH menu can be used to add the values in L_3. The resulting screens are shown in Figure 14.

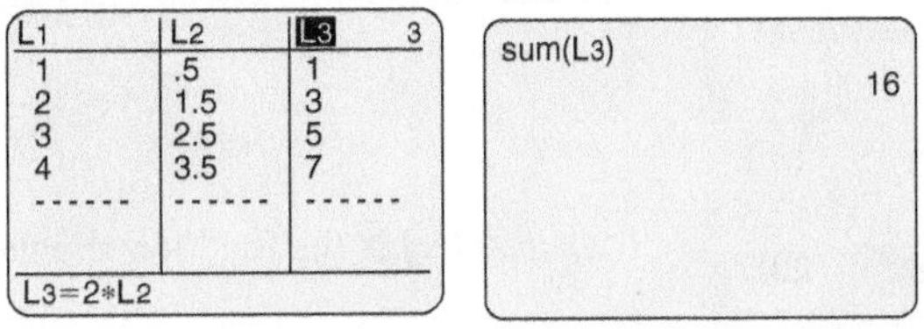

L1	L2	L3	3
1	.5	1	
2	1.5	3	
3	2.5	5	
4	3.5	7	
------	------	------	

L3=2*L2

sum(L3)	
	16

(a)   (b)

FIGURE 14

Method 3
Spreadsheet

YOUR TURN 1 Repeat Example 1 to approximate

$$\int_1^5 4x\,dx.$$

The calculations in this example can also be done on a spreadsheet. In Microsoft Excel, for example, store the values of i in column A. Put the command "=A1−.5" into B1; copying this formula into the rest of column B gives the values of x_i. Similarly, use the formula for $f(x_i)$ to fill column C. Column D is the product of Column C and Δx. Sum column D to get the answer.

TRY YOUR TURN 1

Total Change

Suppose the function $f(x) = x^2 + 20$ gives the marginal cost of some item at a particular x-value. Then $f(2) = 24$ gives the rate of change of cost at $x = 2$. That is, a unit change in x (at this point) will produce a change of 24 units in the cost function. Also, $f(3) = 29$ means that each unit of change in x (when $x = 3$) will produce a change of 29 units in the cost function.

To find the *total* change in the cost function as x changes from 2 to 3, we could divide the interval from 2 to 3 into n equal parts, using each part as the base of a rectangle as we did above. The area of each rectangle would approximate the change in cost at the x-value that is the left endpoint of the base of the rectangle. Then the sum of the areas of these rectangles would approximate the net total change in cost from $x = 2$ to $x = 3$. The limit of this sum as $n \to \infty$ would give the exact total change.

This result produces another application of the definite integral: the area of the region under the graph of the marginal cost function $f(x)$ that is above the x-axis and between $x = a$ and $x = b$ gives the *net total change in the cost* as x goes from a to b.

Total Change in $F(x)$

If $f(x)$ gives the rate of change of $F(x)$ for x in $[a, b]$, then the **total change** in $F(x)$ as x goes from a to b is given by

$$\lim_{n \to \infty} \sum_{i=1}^{n} f(x_i)\Delta x = \int_a^b f(x)\,dx.$$

In other words, the total change in a quantity can be found from the function that gives the rate of change of the quantity, using the same methods used to approximate the area under a curve.

EXAMPLE 3 Oil Leakage

APPLY IT Figure 15 shows the rate that oil is leaking from a machine in a large factory (in cubic centimeters per hour) with specific rates over a 12-hour period given in the table. Approximate the total amount of leakage over a 12-hour shift.

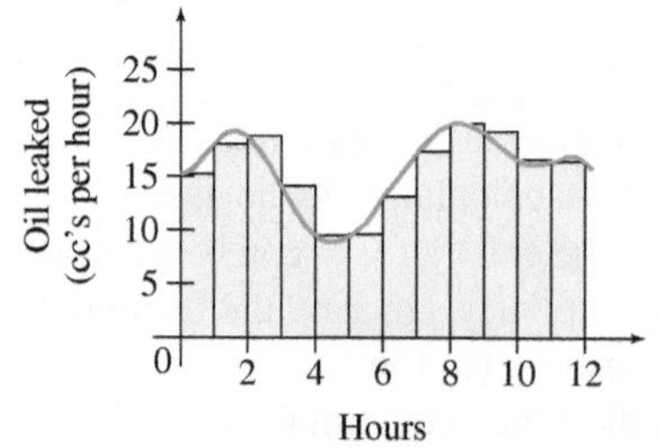

SOLUTION Use approximating rectangles, dividing the interval from 0 to 12 into 12 equal subdivisions. Each subinterval has width 1. Using the left endpoint of each subinterval and the table to determine the height of the rectangle, as shown, the approximation becomes

$$1 \cdot 15.2 + 1 \cdot 18.0 + 1 \cdot 18.8 + 1 \cdot 14.1 + 1 \cdot 9.5 + 1 \cdot 9.6 + 1 \cdot 13.1 + 1 \cdot 17.3$$
$$+ 1 \cdot 20.0 + 1 \cdot 19.2 + 1 \cdot 16.6 + 1 \cdot 16.4 = 187.8.$$

About 187.8 cubic centimeters of oil leak during this time. Mathematically, we could write

$$\int_0^{12} f(x)\,dx \approx 187.8,$$

where $f(x)$ is the function shown in Figure 15.

Recall, velocity is the rate of change in distance from time a to time b. Thus the area under the velocity function defined by $v(t)$ from $t = a$ to $t = b$ gives the distance traveled in that time period.

FIGURE 15

Oil Leakage (cc's per hour)			
x	y	x	y
0	15.2	6	13.1
1	18.0	7	17.3
2	18.8	8	20.0
3	14.1	9	19.2
4	9.5	10	16.6
5	9.6	11	16.4

EXAMPLE 4 Total Distance

A driver traveling on a business trip checks the speedometer each hour. The table shows the driver's velocity at several times.

Approximate the total distance traveled during the 3-hour period using the left endpoint of each interval, then the right endpoint.

Velocity				
Time (hr)	0	1	2	3
Velocity (mph)	0	52	58	60

YOUR TURN 2 Repeat Example 4 for a driver traveling at the following velocities at various times.

Time (hr)	0	0.5	1	1.5	2
Velocity (mph)	0	50	56	40	48

SOLUTION Using left endpoints, the total distance is

$$0 \cdot 1 + 52 \cdot 1 + 58 \cdot 1 = 110.$$

With right endpoints, we get

$$52 \cdot 1 + 58 \cdot 1 + 60 \cdot 1 = 170.$$

Again, left endpoints give a total that is too small, while right endpoints give a total that is too large. The average, 140 miles, is a better estimate of the total distance traveled.

TRY YOUR TURN 2

Before discussing further applications of the definite integral, we need a more efficient method for evaluating it. This method will be developed in the next section.

3 EXERCISES

1. Explain the difference between an indefinite integral and a definite integral.

2. Complete the following statement.

$$\int_0^4 (x^2 + 3)\, dx = \lim_{n \to \infty} \underline{\quad\quad}, \text{ where } \Delta x = \underline{\quad\quad}, \text{ and } x_i$$

is _____.

3. Let $f(x) = 2x + 5$, $x_1 = 0$, $x_2 = 2$, $x_3 = 4$, $x_4 = 6$, and $\Delta x = 2$.

a. Find $\sum_{i=1}^{4} f(x_i)\Delta x$.

b. The sum in part a approximates a definite integral using rectangles. The height of each rectangle is given by the value of the function at the left endpoint. Write the definite integral that the sum approximates.

4. Let $f(x) = 1/x$, $x_1 = 1/2$, $x_2 = 1$, $x_3 = 3/2$, $x_4 = 2$, and $\Delta x = 1/2$.

a. Find $\sum_{i=1}^{4} f(x_i)\Delta x$.

b. The sum in part a approximates a definite integral using rectangles. The height of each rectangle is given by the value of the function at the left endpoint. Write the definite integral that the sum approximates.

In Exercises 5–12, approximate the area under the graph of $f(x)$ and above the x-axis using the following methods with $n = 4$. (a) Use left endpoints. (b) Use right endpoints. (c) Average the answers in parts a and b. (d) Use midpoints.

5. $f(x) = 2x + 5$ from $x = 2$ to $x = 4$

6. $f(x) = 3x + 2$ from $x = 1$ to $x = 3$

7. $f(x) = -x^2 + 4$ from $x = -2$ to $x = 2$

8. $f(x) = x^2$ from $x = 1$ to $x = 5$

9. $f(x) = e^x + 1$ from $x = -2$ to $x = 2$

10. $f(x) = e^x - 1$ from $x = 0$ to $x = 4$

11. $f(x) = \dfrac{2}{x}$ from $x = 1$ to $x = 9$

12. $f(x) = \dfrac{1}{x}$ from $x = 1$ to $x = 3$

13. Consider the region below $f(x) = x/2$, above the x-axis, and between $x = 0$ and $x = 4$. Let x_i be the midpoint of the ith subinterval.

a. Approximate the area of the region using four rectangles.

b. Find $\int_0^4 f(x)\, dx$ by using the formula for the area of a triangle.

14. Consider the region below $f(x) = 5 - x$, above the x-axis, and between $x = 0$ and $x = 5$. Let x_i be the midpoint of the ith subinterval.

a. Approximate the area of the region using five rectangles.

b. Find $\int_0^5 (5 - x)\,dx$ by using the formula for the area of a triangle.

15. Find $\int_0^4 f(x)\,dx$ for each graph of $y = f(x)$.

a.

b.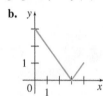

16. Find $\int_0^6 f(x)\,dx$ for each graph of $y = f(x)$, where $f(x)$ consists of line segments and circular arcs.

a.

b.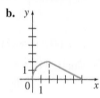

Find the exact value of each integral using formulas from geometry.

17. $\int_{-4}^{0} \sqrt{16 - x^2}\,dx$

18. $\int_{-3}^{3} \sqrt{9 - x^2}\,dx$

19. $\int_{2}^{5} (1 + 2x)\,dx$

20. $\int_{1}^{3} (5 + x)\,dx$

 21. In this exercise, we investigate the value of $\int_0^1 x^2\,dx$ using larger and larger values of n in the definition of the definite integral.

a. First let $n = 10$, so $\Delta x = 0.1$. Fill a list on your calculator with values of x^2 as x goes from 0.1 to 1. (On a TI-84 Plus, use the command `seq(X^2,X,.1,1,.1)→L1`.)

b. Sum the values in the list formed in part a, and multiply by 0.1, to estimate $\int_0^1 x^2\,dx$ with $n = 10$. (On a TI-84 Plus, use the command `.1*sum(L1)`.)

c. Repeat parts a and b with $n = 100$.

d. Repeat parts a and b with $n = 500$.

e. Based on your answers to parts b through d, what do you estimate the value of $\int_0^1 x^2\,dx$ to be?

 22. Repeat Exercise 21 for $\int_0^1 x^3\,dx$.

 23. The booklet *All About Lawns* published by Ortho Books gives the following instructions for measuring the area of an irregularly shaped region. (See figure in the next column.) *Source: All About Lawns.*

Irregular Shapes

(within 5% accuracy)

Measure a long (L) axis of the area. Every 10 feet along the length line, measure the width at right angles to the length line. Total widths and multiply by 10.

Area $= (\overline{A_1 A_2} + \overline{B_1 B_2} + \overline{C_1 C_2}$ **etc.**$) \times 10$

$A = (40' + 60' + 32') \times 10$

$A = 132' \times 10'$

$A = 1320$ square feet

How does this method relate to the discussion in this section?

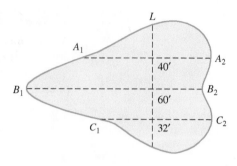

APPLICATIONS

In Exercises 24–28, estimate the area under each curve by summing the area of rectangles. Use the left endpoints, then the right endpoints, then give the average of those answers.

Business and Economics

24. Electricity Consumption The following graph shows the rate of use of electrical energy (in millions of kilowatts) in a certain city on a very hot day. Estimate the total usage of electricity on that day. Let the width of each rectangle be 2 hours.

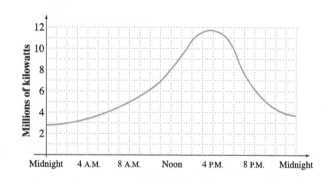

25. Wind Energy Consumption The following graph shows the U.S. wind energy consumption (trillion BTUs) for various years. Estimate the total consumption for the 12-year period from 1997 to 2009 using rectangles of width 3 years. *Source: Annual Energy Review.*

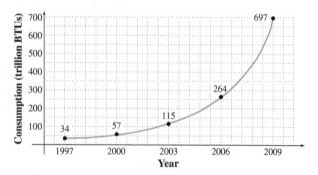

Life Sciences

26. Oxygen Inhalation The graph on the next page shows the rate of inhalation of oxygen (in liters per minute) by a person riding a bicycle very rapidly for 10 minutes. Estimate the total volume of oxygen inhaled in the first 20 minutes after the beginning of the ride. Use rectangles with widths of 1 minute.

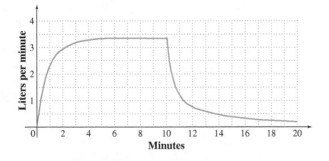

27. Foot-and-Mouth Epidemic In 2001, the United Kingdom suffered an epidemic of foot-and-mouth disease. The graph below shows the reported number of cattle (red) and pigs (blue) that were culled each month from mid-February through mid-October in an effort to stop the spread of the disease. *Source: Department of Environment, Food and Rural Affairs, United Kingdom.*

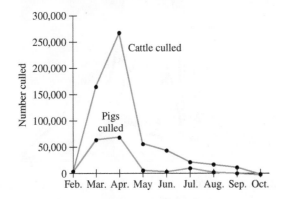

a. Estimate the total number of cattle that were culled from mid-February through mid-October and compare this with 581,801, the actual number of cattle that were culled. Use rectangles that are one month in width, starting with mid-February.

b. Estimate the total number of pigs that were culled from mid-February through mid-October and compare this with 146,145, the actual number of pigs that were culled. Use rectangles that are one month in width starting with mid-February.

Social Sciences

28. Automobile Accidents The graph shows the number of fatal automobile accidents in California for various years. Estimate the total number of accidents in the 8-year period from 2000 to 2008 using rectangles of width 2 years. *Source: California Highway Patrol.*

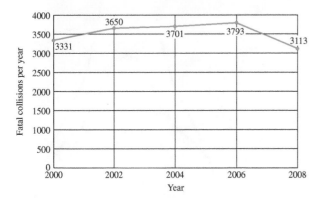

Physical Sciences

Distance The next two graphs are from the Road & Track website. The curves show the velocity at t seconds after the car accelerates from a dead stop. To find the total distance traveled by the car in reaching 130 mph, we must estimate the definite integral

$$\int_0^T v(t)\,dt,$$

where T represents the number of seconds it takes for the car to reach 130 mph.

Use the graphs to estimate this distance by adding the areas of rectangles and using the midpoint rule. To adjust your answer to miles per hour, divide by 3600 (the number of seconds in an hour). You then have the number of miles that the car traveled in reaching 130 mph. Finally, multiply by 5280 ft per mile to convert the answer to feet. *Source: Road & Track.*

29. Estimate the distance traveled by the Lamborghini Gallardo LP560-4 using the graph below. Use rectangles with widths of 3 seconds, except for the last rectangle, which should have a width of 2 seconds. The circle marks the point where the car has gone a quarter mile. Does this seem correct?

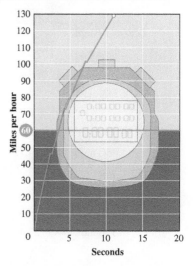

30. Estimate the distance traveled by the Alfa Romeo 8C Competizione using the graph below. Use rectangles with widths of 4 seconds, except for the last rectangle, which should have a width of 3.5 seconds. The circle marks the point where the car has gone a quarter mile. Does this seem correct?

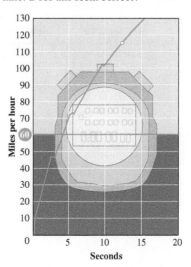

Distance When data are given in tabular form, you may need to vary the size of the interval to calculate the area under the curve. The next two exercises include data from *Car and Driver* magazine. To estimate the total distance traveled by the car (in feet) during the time it took to reach its maximum velocity, estimate the area under the velocity versus time graph, as in the previous two exercises. Use the left endpoint for each time interval (the velocity at the beginning of that interval) and then the right endpoint (the velocity at the end of the interval). Finally, average the two answers together. Calculating and adding up the areas of the rectangles is most easily done on a spreadsheet or graphing calculator. As in the previous two exercises, you will need to multiply by a conversion factor of $5280/3600 = 22/15$, since the velocities are given in miles per hour, but the time is in seconds, and we want the answer in feet. *Source: Car and Driver.*

31. Estimate the distance traveled by the Mercedes-Benz S550, using the table below.

Acceleration	Seconds
Zero to 30 mph	2.0
40 mph	2.9
50 mph	4.1
60 mph	5.3
70 mph	6.9
80 mph	8.7
90 mph	10.7
100 mph	13.2
110 mph	16.1
120 mph	19.3
130 mph	23.4

32. Estimate the distance traveled by the Chevrolet Malibu Maxx SS, using the table below.

Acceleration	Seconds
Zero to 30 mph	2.4
40 mph	3.5
50 mph	5.1
60 mph	6.9
70 mph	8.9
80 mph	11.2
90 mph	14.9
100 mph	19.2
110 mph	24.4

Heat Gain The following graphs show the typical heat gain, in BTUs per hour per square foot, for windows (one with plain glass and one that is triple glazed) in Pittsburgh in June, one facing east and one facing south. The horizontal axis gives the time of the day. Estimate the total heat gain per square foot by summing the areas of rectangles. Use rectangles with widths of 2 hours, and let the function value at the midpoint of the subinterval give the height of the rectangle. *Source: Sustainable by Design.*

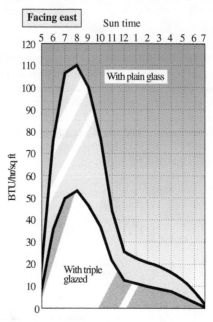

33. a. Estimate the total heat gain per square foot for a plain glass window facing east.

   b. Estimate the total heat gain per square foot for a triple glazed window facing east.

34. a. Estimate the total heat gain per square foot for a plain glass window facing south.

   b. Estimate the total heat gain per square foot for a triple glazed window facing south.

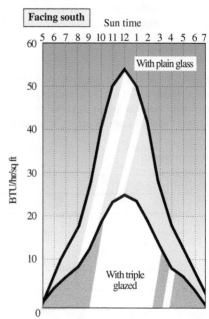

35. Automobile Velocity Two cars start from rest at a traffic light and accelerate for several minutes. The graph shows their velocities (in feet per second) as a function of time (in seconds). Car A is the one that initially has greater velocity. *Source: Stephen Monk.*

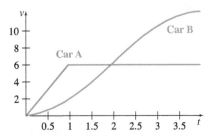

a. How far has car A traveled after 2 seconds? (*Hint*: Use formulas from geometry.)

b. When is car A farthest ahead of car B?

c. Estimate the farthest that car A gets ahead of car B. For car A, use formulas from geometry. For car B, use $n = 4$ and the value of the function at the midpoint of each interval.

d. Give a rough estimate of when car B catches up with car A.

36. Distance Musk the friendly pit bull has escaped again! Here is her velocity during the first 4 seconds of her romp.

t (sec)	0	1	2	3	4
v (ft/sec)	0	8	13	17	18

Give two estimates for the total distance Musk traveled during her 4-second trip, one using the left endpoint of each interval and one using the right endpoint.

Courtesy of Raymond N. Greenwell

37. Distance The speed of a particle in a test laboratory was noted every second for 3 seconds. The results are shown in the following table. Use the left endpoints and then the right endpoints to estimate the total distance the particle moved in the first three seconds.

t (sec)	0	1	2	3
v (ft/sec)	10	6.5	6	5.5

38. Running In 1987, Canadian Ben Johnson set a world record in the 100-m sprint. (The record was later taken away when he was found to have used an anabolic steroid to enhance his performance.) His speed at various times in the race is given in the following table*. *Source: Information Graphics.*

Time (sec)	Speed (mph)
0	0
1.84	12.9
3.80	23.8
6.38	26.3
7.23	26.3
8.96	26.0
9.83	25.7

Gary Kemper/AP Images

a. Use the information in the table and left endpoints to estimate the distance that Johnson ran in miles. You will first need to calculate Δt for each interval. At the end, you will need to divide by 3600 (the number of seconds in an hour), since the speed is in miles per hour.

b. Repeat part a, using right endpoints.

c. Wait a minute; we know that the distance Johnson ran is 100 m. Divide this by 1609, the number of meters in a mile, to find how far Johnson ran in miles. Is your answer from part a or part b closer to the true answer? Briefly explain why you think this answer should be more accurate.

39. Traffic The following graph shows the number of vehicles per hour crossing the Tappan Zee Bridge, which spans the Hudson River north of New York City. The graph shows the number of vehicles traveling eastbound (into the city) and westbound (out of the city) as a function of time. *Source: The New York Times.*

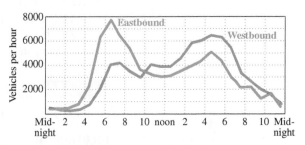

Source: New York Metropolitan Transportation Council

*The world record of 9.58 seconds is currently held by Usain Bolt of Jamaica.

a. Using midpoints on intervals of one hour, estimate the total number of vehicles that cross the bridge going eastbound each day.

b. Repeat the instructions for part a for vehicles going westbound.

c. Discuss whether the answers to parts a and b should be equal, and try to explain any discrepancies.

1. 48
2. Left endpoint estimate is 73 miles, right endpoint estimate is 97 miles, and average is 85 miles.

4 The Fundamental Theorem of Calculus

APPLY IT If we know how the rate of consumption of natural gas varies over time, how can we compute the total amount of natural gas used?
We will answer this question in Example 7.

In the first section of this chapter, you learned about antiderivatives. In the previous section, you learned about the definite integral. In this section, we connect these two separate topics and present one of the most powerful theorems of calculus.

We have seen that, if $f(x) \geq 0$,

$$\int_a^b f(x)\, dx$$

gives the area between the graph of $f(x)$ and the x-axis, from $x = a$ to $x = b$. The definite integral was defined and evaluated in the previous section using the limit of a sum. In that section, we also saw that if $f(x)$ gives the rate of change of $F(x)$, the definite integral $\int_a^b f(x)\, dx$ gives the total change of $F(x)$ as x changes from a to b. If $f(x)$ gives the rate of change of $F(x)$, then $F(x)$ is an antiderivative of $f(x)$. Writing the total change in $F(x)$ from $x = a$ to $x = b$ as $F(b) - F(a)$ shows the connection between antiderivatives and definite integrals. This relationship is called the **Fundamental Theorem of Calculus**.

Fundamental Theorem of Calculus
Let f be continuous on the interval $[a, b]$, and let F be *any* antiderivative of f. Then

$$\int_a^b f(x)\, dx = F(b) - F(a) = F(x)\Big|_a^b.$$

The symbol $F(x)|_a^b$ is used to represent $F(b) - F(a)$. It is important to note that the Fundamental Theorem does not require $f(x) > 0$. The condition $f(x) > 0$ is necessary only when using the Fundamental Theorem to find area. Also, note that the Fundamental Theorem does not *define* the definite integral; it just provides a method for evaluating it.

EXAMPLE 1 **Fundamental Theorem of Calculus**

First find $\int 4t^3\, dt$ and then find $\int_1^2 4t^3\, dt$.

SOLUTION By the power rule given earlier, the indefinite integral is

$$\int 4t^3\, dt = t^4 + C.$$

By the Fundamental Theorem, the value of the definite integral $\int_1^2 4t^3\, dt$ is found by evaluating $t^4\big|_1^2$, with no constant C required.

YOUR TURN 1 Find $\displaystyle\int_1^3 3x^2 dx.$

$$\int_1^2 4t^3\, dt = t^4\bigg|_1^2 = 2^4 - 1^4 = 15 \qquad \text{TRY YOUR TURN 1}$$

Example 1 illustrates the difference between the definite integral and the indefinite integral. A definite integral is a real number; an indefinite integral is a family of functions in which all the functions are antiderivatives of a function f.

NOTE No constant C is needed, as it is for the indefinite integral, because even if C were added to an antiderivative F, it would be eliminated in the final answer:

$$\int_a^b f(x)\, dx = (F(x) + C)\bigg|_a^b$$
$$= (F(b) + C) - (F(a) + C)$$
$$= F(b) - F(a).$$

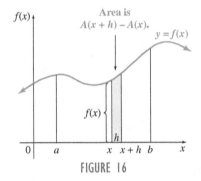

FIGURE 16

In other words, any antiderivative will give the same answer, so for simplicity, we choose the one with $C = 0$.

To see why the Fundamental Theorem of Calculus is true for $f(x) > 0$ when f is continuous, look at Figure 16. Define the function $A(x)$ as the area between the x-axis and the graph of $y = f(x)$ from a to x. We first show that A is an antiderivative of f; that is $A'(x) = f(x)$.

To do this, let h be a small positive number. Then $A(x + h) - A(x)$ is the shaded area in Figure 16. This area can be approximated with a rectangle having width h and height $f(x)$. The area of the rectangle is $h \cdot f(x)$, and

$$A(x + h) - A(x) \approx h \cdot f(x).$$

Dividing both sides by h gives

$$\frac{A(x + h) - A(x)}{h} \approx f(x).$$

This approximation improves as h gets smaller and smaller. Taking the limit on the left as h approaches 0 gives an exact result.

$$\lim_{h \to 0} \frac{A(x + h) - A(x)}{h} = f(x)$$

This limit is simply $A'(x)$, so

$$A'(x) = f(x).$$

This result means that A is an antiderivative of f, as we set out to show.

$A(b)$ is the area under the curve from a to b, and $A(a) = 0$, so the area under the curve can be written as $A(b) - A(a)$. From the previous section, we know that the area under the curve is also given by $\int_a^b f(x)\, dx$. Putting these two results together gives

$$\int_a^b f(x)\, dx = A(b) - A(a)$$

$$= A(x)\bigg|_a^b$$

where A is an antiderivative of f. From the note after Example 1, we know that any antiderivative will give the same answer, which proves the Fundamental Theorem of Calculus.

The Fundamental Theorem of Calculus certainly deserves its name, which sets it apart as the most important theorem of calculus. It is the key connection between differential calculus and integral calculus, which originally were developed separately without knowledge of this connection between them.

The variable used in the integrand does not matter; each of the following definite integrals represents the number $F(b) - F(a)$.

$$\int_a^b f(x)\, dx = \int_a^b f(t)\, dt = \int_a^b f(u)\, du$$

Key properties of definite integrals are listed below. Some of them are just restatements of properties from Section 1.

Properties of Definite Integrals

If all indicated definite integrals exist,

1. $\displaystyle\int_a^a f(x)\, dx = 0;$

2. $\displaystyle\int_a^b k \cdot f(x)\, dx = k \cdot \int_a^b f(x)\, dx$ for any real constant k
   (constant multiple of a function);

3. $\displaystyle\int_a^b [f(x) \pm g(x)]\, dx = \int_a^b f(x)\, dx \pm \int_a^b g(x)\, dx$
   (sum or difference of functions);

4. $\displaystyle\int_a^b f(x)\, dx = \int_a^c f(x)\, dx + \int_c^b f(x)\, dx$ for any real number c;

5. $\displaystyle\int_a^b f(x)\, dx = -\int_b^a f(x)\, dx.$

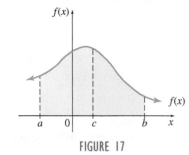

FIGURE 17

For $f(x) \geq 0$, since the distance from a to a is 0, the first property says that the "area" under the graph of f bounded by $x = a$ and $x = a$ is 0. Also, since $\int_a^c f(x)\, dx$ represents the blue region in Figure 17 and $\int_c^b f(x)\, dx$ represents the pink region,

$$\int_a^b f(x)\, dx = \int_a^c f(x)\, dx + \int_c^b f(x)\, dx,$$

as stated in the fourth property. While the figure shows $a < c < b$, the property is true for any value of c where both $f(x)$ and $F(x)$ are defined.

An algebraic proof is given here for the third property; proofs of the other properties are left for the exercises. If $F(x)$ and $G(x)$ are antiderivatives of $f(x)$ and $g(x)$, respectively,

$$\int_a^b [f(x) + g(x)]\, dx = [F(x) + G(x)]\Big|_a^b$$
$$= [F(b) + G(b)] - [F(a) + G(a)]$$
$$= [F(b) - F(a)] + [G(b) - G(a)]$$
$$= \int_a^b f(x)\, dx + \int_a^b g(x)\, dx.$$

Integration

EXAMPLE 2 Fundamental Theorem of Calculus

Find $\int_2^5 (6x^2 - 3x + 5)\, dx$.

SOLUTION Use the properties above and the Fundamental Theorem, along with properties from Section 1.

$$\int_2^5 (6x^2 - 3x + 5)\, dx = 6\int_2^5 x^2\, dx - 3\int_2^5 x\, dx + 5\int_2^5 dx$$

$$= 2x^3\Big|_2^5 - \frac{3}{2}x^2\Big|_2^5 + 5x\Big|_2^5$$

$$= 2(5^3 - 2^3) - \frac{3}{2}(5^2 - 2^2) + 5(5 - 2)$$

$$= 2(125 - 8) - \frac{3}{2}(25 - 4) + 5(3)$$

$$= 234 - \frac{63}{2} + 15 = \frac{435}{2}$$

TRY YOUR TURN 2

YOUR TURN 2

Find $\int_3^5 (2x^3 - 3x + 4)\, dx$.

EXAMPLE 3 Fundamental Theorem of Calculus

$$\int_1^2 \frac{dy}{y} = \ln |y|\,\Big|_1^2 = \ln |2| - \ln |1|$$

$$= \ln 2 - \ln 1 \approx 0.6931 - 0 = 0.6931 \quad \text{TRY YOUR TURN 3}$$

YOUR TURN 3

Find $\int_1^3 \frac{2}{y}\, dy$.

EXAMPLE 4 Substitution

Evaluate $\int_0^5 x\sqrt{25 - x^2}\, dx$.

SOLUTION

Method 1
Changing the Limits

Use substitution. Let $u = 25 - x^2$, so that $du = -2x\, dx$. With a definite integral, the limits should be changed, too. The new limits on u are found as follows.

If $x = 5$, then $u = 25 - 5^2 = 0$.
If $x = 0$, then $u = 25 - 0^2 = 25$.

Then

$$\int_0^5 x\sqrt{25 - x^2}\, dx = -\frac{1}{2}\int_0^5 \sqrt{25 - x^2}(-2x\, dx) \quad \text{Multiply by } -2/-2.$$

$$= -\frac{1}{2}\int_{25}^0 \sqrt{u}\, du \quad \text{Substitute and change limits.}$$

$$= -\frac{1}{2}\int_{25}^0 u^{1/2}\, du \quad \sqrt{u} = u^{1/2}$$

$$= -\frac{1}{2} \cdot \frac{u^{3/2}}{3/2}\Big|_{25}^0 \quad \text{Use the power rule.}$$

$$= -\frac{1}{2} \cdot \frac{2}{3}[0^{3/2} - 25^{3/2}]$$

$$= -\frac{1}{3}(-125) = \frac{125}{3}.$$

37

Method 2
Evaluating the Antiderivative

An alternative method that some people prefer is to evaluate the antiderivative first and then calculate the definite integral. To evaluate the antiderivative in this example, ignore the limits on the original integral and use the substitution $u = 25 - x^2$, so that $du = -2x\,dx$. Then

$$\int x\sqrt{25 - x^2}\,dx = -\frac{1}{2}\int \sqrt{25 - x^2}(-2x\,dx)$$

$$= -\frac{1}{2}\int \sqrt{u}\,du$$

$$= -\frac{1}{2}\int u^{1/2}\,du$$

$$= -\frac{1}{2}\frac{u^{3/2}}{3/2} + C$$

$$= -\frac{u^{3/2}}{3} + C$$

$$= -\frac{(25 - x^2)^{3/2}}{3} + C.$$

We will ignore the constant C because it doesn't affect the answer, as we mentioned in the Note following Example 1.

Then, using the Fundamental Theorem of Calculus, we have

$$\int_0^5 x\sqrt{25 - x^2}\,dx = -\frac{(25 - x^2)^{3/2}}{3}\Big|_0^5$$

$$= 0 - \left[-\frac{(25)^{3/2}}{3}\right]$$

$$= \frac{125}{3}.$$

YOUR TURN 4 Evaluate
$$\int_0^4 2x\sqrt{16 - x^2}\,dx.$$

TRY YOUR TURN 4

CAUTION Don't confuse these two methods. In Method 1, we never return to the original variable or the original limits of integration. In Method 2, it is essential to return to the original variable and to not change the limits. When using Method 1, we recommend labeling the limits with the appropriate variable to avoid confusion, so the substitution in Example 4 becomes

$$\int_{x=0}^{x=5} x\sqrt{25 - x^2}\,dx = -\frac{1}{2}\int_{u=25}^{u=0} \sqrt{u}\,du.$$

The Fundamental Theorem of Calculus is a powerful tool, but it has a limitation. The problem is that not every function has an antiderivative in terms of the functions and operations you have seen so far. One example of an integral that cannot be evaluated by the Fundamental Theorem of Calculus for this reason is

$$\int_a^b e^{-x^2/2}\,dx,$$

yet this integral is crucial in probability and statistics. Such integrals may be evaluated by numerical integration, which is covered in the last section of this chapter. Fortunately for you, all the integrals in this section can be antidifferentiated using the techniques presented in the first two sections of this chapter.

Area In the previous section we saw that, if $f(x) \geq 0$ in $[a, b]$, the definite integral $\int_a^b f(x)\,dx$ gives the area below the graph of the function $y = f(x)$, above the x-axis, and between the lines $x = a$ and $x = b$.

Integration

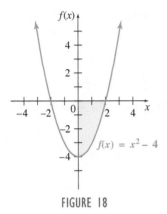

FIGURE 18

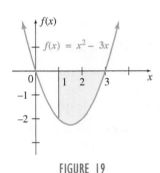

FIGURE 19

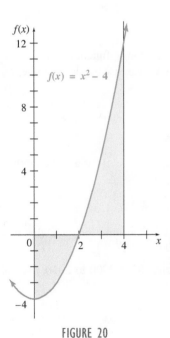

FIGURE 20

YOUR TURN 5 Repeat Example 6 for the function $f(x) = x^2 - 9$ from $x = 0$ to $x = 6$.

To see how to work around the requirement that $f(x) \geq 0$, look at the graph of $f(x) = x^2 - 4$ in Figure 18. The area bounded by the graph of f, the x-axis, and the vertical lines $x = 0$ and $x = 2$ lies below the x-axis. Using the Fundamental Theorem gives

$$\int_0^2 (x^2 - 4)\, dx = \left(\frac{x^3}{3} - 4x\right)\Bigg|_0^2$$

$$= \left(\frac{8}{3} - 8\right) - (0 - 0) = -\frac{16}{3}.$$

The result is a negative number because $f(x)$ is negative for values of x in the interval $[0, 2]$. Since Δx is always positive, if $f(x) < 0$ the product $f(x) \cdot \Delta x$ is negative, so $\int_0^2 f(x)\, dx$ is negative. Since area is nonnegative, the required area is given by $|-16/3|$ or $16/3$. Using a definite integral, the area could be written as

$$\left| \int_0^2 (x^2 - 4)\, dx \right| = \left| -\frac{16}{3} \right| = \frac{16}{3}.$$

EXAMPLE 5 Area

Find the area of the region between the x-axis and the graph of $f(x) = x^2 - 3x$ from $x = 1$ to $x = 3$.

SOLUTION The region is shown in Figure 19. Since the region lies below the x-axis, the area is given by

$$\left| \int_1^3 (x^2 - 3x)\, dx \right|.$$

By the Fundamental Theorem,

$$\int_1^3 (x^2 - 3x)\, dx = \left(\frac{x^3}{3} - \frac{3x^2}{2}\right)\Bigg|_1^3 = \left(\frac{27}{3} - \frac{27}{2}\right) - \left(\frac{1}{3} - \frac{3}{2}\right) = -\frac{10}{3}.$$

The required area is $|-10/3| = 10/3$.

EXAMPLE 6 Area

Find the area between the x-axis and the graph of $f(x) = x^2 - 4$ from $x = 0$ to $x = 4$.

SOLUTION Figure 20 shows the required region. Part of the region is below the x-axis. The definite integral over that interval will have a negative value. To find the area, integrate the negative and positive portions separately and take the absolute value of the first result before combining the two results to get the total area. Start by finding the point where the graph crosses the x-axis. This is done by solving the equation

$$x^2 - 4 = 0.$$

The solutions of this equation are 2 and -2. The only solution in the interval $[0, 4]$ is 2. The total area of the region in Figure 19 is

$$\left| \int_0^2 (x^2 - 4)\, dx \right| + \int_2^4 (x^2 - 4)\, dx = \left| \left(\frac{1}{3}x^3 - 4x\right)\Bigg|_0^2 \right| + \left(\frac{1}{3}x^3 - 4x\right)\Bigg|_2^4$$

$$= \left| \frac{8}{3} - 8 \right| + \left(\frac{64}{3} - 16\right) - \left(\frac{8}{3} - 8\right)$$

$$= 16.$$

TRY YOUR TURN 5

39

Incorrectly using one integral over the entire interval to find the area in Example 6 would have given

$$\int_0^4 (x^2 - 4)\,dx = \left(\frac{x^3}{3} - 4x\right)\Big|_0^4 = \left(\frac{64}{3} - 16\right) - 0 = \frac{16}{3},$$

which is not the correct area. This definite integral does not represent any area but is just a real number.

For instance, if $f(x)$ in Example 6 represents the annual rate of profit of a company, then 16/3 represents the total profit for the company over a 4-year period. The integral between 0 and 2 is $-16/3$; the negative sign indicates a loss for the first two years. The integral between 2 and 4 is 32/3, indicating a profit. The overall profit is $32/3 - 16/3 = 16/3$, although the total shaded area is $32/3 + |-16/3| = 16$.

Finding Area

In summary, to find the area bounded by $f(x)$, $x = a$, $x = b$, and the x-axis, use the following steps.

1. Sketch a graph.

2. Find any x-intercepts of $f(x)$ in $[a, b]$. These divide the total region into subregions.

3. The definite integral will be *positive* for subregions above the x-axis and *negative* for subregions below the x-axis. Use separate integrals to find the (positive) areas of the subregions.

4. The total area is the sum of the areas of all of the subregions.

In the last section, we saw that the area under a rate of change function $f'(x)$ from $x = a$ to $x = b$ gives the total value of $f(x)$ on $[a, b]$. Now we can use the definite integral to solve these problems.

EXAMPLE 7   Natural Gas Consumption

The yearly rate of consumption of natural gas (in trillions of cubic feet) for a certain city is

$$C'(t) = t + e^{0.01t},$$

where t is time in years and $t = 0$ corresponds to 2000. At this consumption rate, what was the total amount the city used in the 10-year period of 2000 to 2010?

APPLY IT   **SOLUTION**   To find the consumption over the 10-year period from 2000 to 2010, use the definite integral.

$$\int_0^{10} (t + e^{0.01t})\,dt = \left(\frac{t^2}{2} + \frac{e^{0.01t}}{0.01}\right)\Big|_0^{10}$$
$$= (50 + 100e^{0.1}) - (0 + 100)$$
$$\approx -50 + 100(1.10517) \approx 60.5$$

Therefore, a total of about 60.5 trillion ft^3 of natural gas was used from 2000 to 2010 at this consumption rate.

4 EXERCISES

Evaluate each definite integral.

1. $\displaystyle\int_{-2}^{4} (-3)\, dp$

2. $\displaystyle\int_{-4}^{1} \sqrt{2}\, dx$

3. $\displaystyle\int_{-1}^{2} (5t - 3)\, dt$

4. $\displaystyle\int_{-2}^{2} (4z + 3)\, dz$

5. $\displaystyle\int_{0}^{2} (5x^2 - 4x + 2)\, dx$

6. $\displaystyle\int_{-2}^{3} (-x^2 - 3x + 5)\, dx$

7. $\displaystyle\int_{0}^{2} 3\sqrt{4u + 1}\, du$

8. $\displaystyle\int_{3}^{9} \sqrt{2r - 2}\, dr$

9. $\displaystyle\int_{0}^{4} 2(t^{1/2} - t)\, dt$

10. $\displaystyle\int_{0}^{4} -(3x^{3/2} + x^{1/2})\, dx$

11. $\displaystyle\int_{1}^{4} (5y\sqrt{y} + 3\sqrt{y})\, dy$

12. $\displaystyle\int_{4}^{9} (4\sqrt{r} - 3r\sqrt{r})\, dr$

13. $\displaystyle\int_{4}^{6} \frac{2}{(2x - 7)^2}\, dx$

14. $\displaystyle\int_{1}^{4} \frac{-3}{(2p + 1)^2}\, dp$

15. $\displaystyle\int_{1}^{5} (6n^{-2} - n^{-3})\, dn$

16. $\displaystyle\int_{2}^{3} (3x^{-3} - 5x^{-4})\, dx$

17. $\displaystyle\int_{-3}^{-2} \left(2e^{-0.1y} + \frac{3}{y}\right)\, dy$

18. $\displaystyle\int_{-2}^{-1} \left(\frac{-2}{t} + 3e^{0.3t}\right)\, dt$

19. $\displaystyle\int_{1}^{2} \left(e^{4u} - \frac{1}{(u + 1)^2}\right)\, du$

20. $\displaystyle\int_{0.5}^{1} (p^3 - e^{4p})\, dp$

21. $\displaystyle\int_{-1}^{0} y(2y^2 - 3)^5\, dy$

22. $\displaystyle\int_{0}^{3} m^2(4m^3 + 2)^3\, dm$

23. $\displaystyle\int_{1}^{64} \frac{\sqrt{z} - 2}{\sqrt[3]{z}}\, dz$

24. $\displaystyle\int_{1}^{8} \frac{3 - y^{1/3}}{y^{2/3}}\, dy$

25. $\displaystyle\int_{1}^{2} \frac{\ln x}{x}\, dx$

26. $\displaystyle\int_{1}^{3} \frac{\sqrt{\ln x}}{x}\, dx$

27. $\displaystyle\int_{0}^{8} x^{1/3}\sqrt{x^{4/3} + 9}\, dx$

28. $\displaystyle\int_{1}^{2} \frac{3}{x(1 + \ln x)}\, dx$

29. $\displaystyle\int_{0}^{1} \frac{e^{2t}}{(3 + e^{2t})^2}\, dt$

30. $\displaystyle\int_{0}^{1} \frac{e^{2z}}{\sqrt{1 + e^{2z}}}\, dz$

In Exercises 31–40, use the definite integral to find the area between the x-axis and f(x) over the indicated interval. Check first to see if the graph crosses the x-axis in the given interval.

31. $f(x) = 2x - 14; \quad [6, 10]$

32. $f(x) = 4x - 32; \quad [5, 10]$

33. $f(x) = 2 - 2x^2; \quad [0, 5]$

34. $f(x) = 9 - x^2; \quad [0, 6]$

35. $f(x) = x^3; \quad [-1, 3]$

36. $f(x) = x^3 - 2x; \quad [-2, 4]$

37. $f(x) = e^x - 1; \quad [-1, 2]$

38. $f(x) = 1 - e^{-x}; \quad [-1, 2]$

39. $f(x) = \dfrac{1}{x} - \dfrac{1}{e}; \quad [1, e^2]$

40. $f(x) = 1 - \dfrac{1}{x}; \quad [e^{-1}, e]$

Find the area of each shaded region.

41.
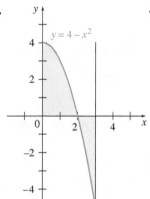

42.
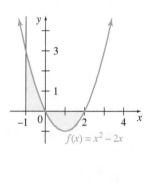

43.
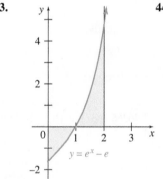

44.
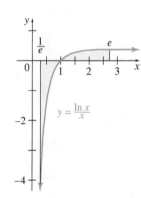

45. Assume $f(x)$ is continuous for $g \leq x \leq c$ as shown in the figure. Write an equation relating the three quantities

$$\int_{a}^{b} f(x)\, dx, \qquad \int_{a}^{c} f(x)\, dx, \qquad \int_{b}^{c} f(x)\, dx.$$

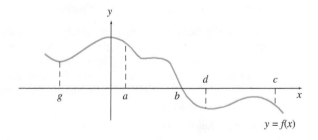

46. Is the equation you wrote for Exercise 45 still true

a. if b is replaced by d?

b. if b is replaced by g?

47. The graph of $f(x)$, shown here, consists of two straight line segments and two quarter circles. Find the value of $\int_0^{16} f(x)\,dx$.

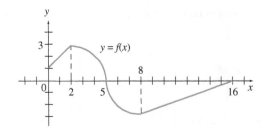

Use the Fundamental Theorem to show that the following are true.

48. $\displaystyle\int_a^b kf(x)\,dx = k\int_a^b f(x)\,dx$

49. $\displaystyle\int_a^b f(x)\,dx = \int_a^c f(x)\,dx + \int_c^b f(x)\,dx$

50. $\displaystyle\int_a^b f(x)\,dx = -\int_b^a f(x)\,dx$

51. Use Exercise 49 to find $\int_{-1}^4 f(x)\,dx$, given

$$f(x) = \begin{cases} 2x + 3 & \text{if } x \le 0 \\ -\dfrac{x}{4} - 3 & \text{if } x > 0. \end{cases}$$

52. You are given $\int_0^1 e^{x^2}\,dx = 1.46265$ and $\int_0^2 e^{x^2}\,dx = 16.45263$. Use this information to find

a. $\displaystyle\int_{-1}^1 e^{x^2}\,dx$;

b. $\displaystyle\int_1^2 e^{x^2}\,dx$.

53. Let $g(t) = t^4$ and define $f(x) = \displaystyle\int_c^x g(t)\,dt$ with $c = 1$.

a. Find a formula for $f(x)$.

b. Verify that $f'(x) = g(x)$. The fact that

$$\frac{d}{dx}\int_c^x g(t)\,dt = g(x)$$

is true for all continuous functions g is an alternative version of the Fundamental Theorem of Calculus.

c. Let us verify the result in part b for a function whose antiderivative cannot be found. Let $g(t) = e^{t^2}$ and let $c = 0$. Use the integration feature on a graphing calculator to find $f(x)$ for $x = 1$ and $x = 1.01$. Then use the definition of the derivative with $h = 0.01$ to approximate $f'(1)$, and compare it with $g(1)$.

54. Consider the function $f(x) = x(x^2 + 3)^7$.

a. Use the Fundamental Theorem of Calculus to evaluate $\displaystyle\int_{-5}^5 f(x)\,dx$.

b. Use symmetry to describe how the integral from part a could be evaluated without using substitution or finding an antiderivative.

APPLICATIONS

Business and Economics

55. Profit Karla Harby Communications, a small company of science writers, found that its rate of profit (in thousands of dollars) after t years of operation is given by

$$P'(t) = (3t + 3)(t^2 + 2t + 2)^{1/3}.$$

a. Find the total profit in the first three years.

b. Find the profit in the fourth year of operation.

c. What is happening to the annual profit over the long run?

56. Worker Efficiency A worker new to a job will improve his efficiency with time so that it takes him fewer hours to produce an item with each day on the job, up to a certain point. Suppose the rate of change of the number of hours it takes a worker in a certain factory to produce the xth item is given by

$$H'(x) = 20 - 2x.$$

a. What is the total number of hours required to produce the first 5 items?

b. What is the total number of hours required to produce the first 10 items?

Life Sciences

57. Pollution Pollution from a factory is entering a lake. The rate of concentration of the pollutant at time t is given by

$$P'(t) = 140t^{5/2},$$

where t is the number of years since the factory started introducing pollutants into the lake. Ecologists estimate that the lake can accept a total level of pollution of 4850 units before all the fish life in the lake ends. Can the factory operate for 4 years without killing all the fish in the lake?

58. Spread of an Oil Leak An oil tanker is leaking oil at the rate given (in barrels per hour) by

$$L'(t) = \frac{80\ln(t + 1)}{t + 1},$$

where t is the time (in hours) after the tanker hits a hidden rock (when $t = 0$).

a. Find the total number of barrels that the ship will leak on the first day.

b. Find the total number of barrels that the ship will leak on the second day.

c. What is happening over the long run to the amount of oil leaked per day?

59. Tree Growth After long study, tree scientists conclude that a eucalyptus tree will grow at the rate of $0.6 + 4/(t + 1)^3$ ft per year, where t is time (in years).

a. Find the number of feet that the tree will grow in the second year.

b. Find the number of feet the tree will grow in the third year.

60. Growth of a Substance The rate at which a substance grows is given by

$$R'(x) = 150e^{0.2x},$$

where x is the time (in days). What is the total accumulated growth during the first 3.5 days?

61. Drug Reaction For a certain drug, the rate of reaction in appropriate units is given by

$$R'(t) = \frac{5}{t + 1} + \frac{2}{\sqrt{t + 1}},$$

where t is time (in hours) after the drug is administered. Find the total reaction to the drug over the following time periods.

a. From $t = 1$ to $t = 12$ **b.** From $t = 12$ to $t = 24$

62. Human Mortality If $f(x)$ is the instantaneous death rate for members of a population at time x, then the number of individuals who survive to age T is given by

$$F(T) = \int_0^T f(x)\,dx.$$

In 1825 the biologist Benjamin Gompertz proposed that $f(x) = kb^x$. Find a formula for $F(T)$. *Source: Philosophical Transactions of the Royal Society of London.*

63. Cell Division Let the expected number of cells in a culture that have an x percent probability of undergoing cell division during the next hour be denoted by $n(x)$.

a. Explain why $\int_{20}^{30} n(x)\,dx$ approximates the total number of cells with a 20% to 30% chance of dividing during the next hour.

b. Give an integral representing the number of cells that have less than a 60% chance of dividing during the next hour.

c. Let $n(x) = \sqrt{5x + 1}$ give the expected number of cells (in millions) with x percent probability of dividing during the next hour. Find the number of cells with a 5 to 10% chance of dividing.

64. Bacterial Growth A population of *E. coli* bacteria will grow at a rate given by

$$w'(t) = (3t + 2)^{1/3},$$

where w is the weight (in milligrams) after t hours. Find the change in weight of the population from $t = 0$ to $t = 3$.

65. Blood Flow In an example from an earlier chapter, the velocity v of the blood in a blood vessel was given as

$$v = k(R^2 - r^2),$$

where R is the (constant) radius of the blood vessel, r is the distance of the flowing blood from the center of the blood vessel, and k is a constant. Total blood flow (in millimeters per minute) is given by

$$Q(R) = \int_0^R 2\pi v r\,dr.$$

a. Find the general formula for Q in terms of R by evaluating the definite integral given above.

b. Evaluate $Q(0.4)$.

66. Rams' Horns The average annual increment in the horn length (in centimeters) of bighorn rams born since 1986 can be approximated by

$$y = 0.1762x^2 - 3.986x + 22.68,$$

where x is the ram's age (in years) for x between 3 and 9. Integrate to find the total increase in the length of a ram's horn during this time. *Source: Journal of Wildlife Management.*

67. Beagles The daily energy requirements of female beagles who are at least 1 year old change with respect to time according to the function

$$E(t) = 753t^{-0.1321},$$

where $E(t)$ is the daily energy requirement (in $kJ/W^{0.67}$), where W is the dog's weight (in kilograms) for a beagle that is t years old. *Source: Journal of Nutrition.*

a. Assuming 365 days in a year, show that the energy requirement for a female beagle that is t days old is given by

$$E(t) = 1642t^{-0.1321}.$$

b. Using the formula from part a, determine the total energy requirements (in $kJ/W^{0.67}$) for a female beagle between her first and third birthday.

68. Sediment The density of sediment (in grams per cubic centimeter) at the bottom of Lake Coeur d'Alene, Idaho, is given by

$$p(x) = p_0 e^{0.0133x},$$

where x is the depth (in centimeters) and p_0 is the density at the surface. The total mass of a square-centimeter column of sediment above a depth of h cm is given by

$$\int_0^h p(x)\,dx.$$

If $p_0 = 0.85$ g per cm^3, find the total mass above a depth of 100 cm. *Source: Mathematics Teacher.*

Social Sciences

69. Age Distribution The U.S. Census Bureau gives an age distribution that is approximately modeled (in millions) by the function

$$f(x) = 40.2 + 3.50x - 0.897x^2$$

where x varies from 0 to 9 decades. The population of a given age group can be found by integrating this function over the interval for that age group. *Source: Ralph DeMarr and the U.S. Census Bureau.*

a. Find the integral of $f(x)$ over the interval [0, 9]. What does this integral represent?

b. Baby boomers are those born between 1945 and 1965, that is, those in the range of 4.5 to 6.5 decades in 2010. Estimate the number of baby boomers.

Integration

70. Income Distribution Based on data from the U.S. Census Bureau, an approximate family income distribution for the United States is given by the function

$$f(x) = 0.0353x^3 - 0.541x^2 + 3.78x + 4.29,$$

where x is the annual income in units of $10,000, with $0 \le x \le 10$. For example, $x = 0.5$ represents an annual family income of $5000. (*Note*: This function does not give a good representation for family incomes over $100,000.) The percent of the families with an income in a given range can be found by integrating this function over that range. Find the percentage of families with an income between $25,000 and $50,000. *Source: Ralph DeMarr and the U.S. Census Bureau.*

Physical Sciences

71. Oil Consumption Suppose that the rate of consumption of a natural resource is $c'(t)$, where

$$c'(t) = ke^{rt}.$$

Here t is time in years, r is a constant, and k is the consumption in the year when $t = 0$. In 2010, an oil company sold 1.2 billion barrels of oil. Assume that $r = 0.04$.

a. Write $c'(t)$ for the oil company, letting $t = 0$ represent 2010.

b. Set up a definite integral for the amount of oil that the company will sell in the next 10 years.

c. Evaluate the definite integral of part b.

d. The company has about 20 billion barrels of oil in reserve. To find the number of years that this amount will last, solve the equation

$$\int_0^T 1.2e^{0.04t}\,dt = 20.$$

e. Rework part d, assuming that $r = 0.02$.

72. Oil Consumption The rate of consumption of oil (in billions of barrels) by the company in Exercise 71 was given as

$$1.2e^{0.04t},$$

where $t = 0$ corresponds to 2010. Find the total amount of oil used by the company from 2010 to year T. At this rate, how much will be used in 5 years?

YOUR TURN ANSWERS

1. 26
2. 256
3. 2 ln 3 or ln 9
4. 128/3
5. 54

5 The Area Between Two Curves

APPLY IT If an executive knows how the savings from a new manufacturing process decline over time and how the costs of that process will increase, how can she compute when the net savings will cease and what the total savings will be?

We will answer this question in Example 4.

Many important applications of integrals require finding the area between two graphs. The method used in previous sections to find the area between the graph of a function and the x-axis from $x = a$ to $x = b$ can be generalized to find such an area. For example, the area between the graphs of $f(x)$ and $g(x)$ from $x = a$ to $x = b$ in Figure 21(a) is the same as the area under the graph of $f(x)$, shown in Figure 21(b), minus the area under the graph of $g(x)$ (see Figure 21(c)). That is, the area between the graphs is given by

$$\int_a^b f(x)\,dx - \int_a^b g(x)\,dx,$$

44

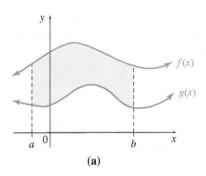
(a)

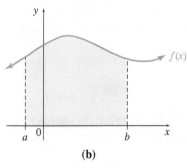
(b)

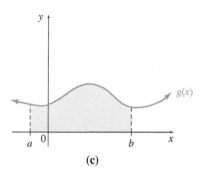
(c)

FIGURE 21

which can be written as

$$\int_a^b [f(x) - g(x)]\, dx.$$

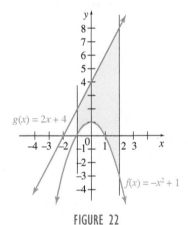

FIGURE 22

> **Area Between Two Curves**
> If f and g are continuous functions and $f(x) \geq g(x)$ on $[a, b]$, then the area between the curves $f(x)$ and $g(x)$ from $x = a$ to $x = b$ is given by
>
> $$\int_a^b [f(x) - g(x)]\, dx.$$

EXAMPLE 1 Area

Find the area bounded by $f(x) = -x^2 + 1$, $g(x) = 2x + 4$, $x = -1$, and $x = 2$.

SOLUTION A sketch of the four equations is shown in Figure 22. In general, it is not necessary to spend time drawing a detailed sketch, but only to know whether the two functions intersect, and which function is greater between the intersections. To find out, set the two functions equal.

$$-x^2 + 1 = 2x + 4$$
$$0 = x^2 + 2x + 3$$

Verify by the quadratic formula that this equation has no real roots. Since the graph of f is a parabola opening downward that does not cross the graph of g (a line), the parabola must be entirely under the line, as shown in Figure 22. Therefore $g(x) \geq f(x)$ for x in the interval $[-1, 2]$, and the area is given by

$$\int_{-1}^2 [g(x) - f(x)]\, dx = \int_{-1}^2 [(2x + 4) - (-x^2 + 1)]\, dx$$

$$= \int_{-1}^2 (2x + 4 + x^2 - 1)\, dx$$

$$= \int_{-1}^2 (x^2 + 2x + 3)\, dx$$

$$= \frac{x^3}{3} + x^2 + 3x \Big|_{-1}^2$$

$$= \left(\frac{8}{3} + 4 + 6\right) - \left(\frac{-1}{3} + 1 - 3\right)$$

$$= \frac{8}{3} + 10 + \frac{1}{3} + 2$$

$$= 15.$$

YOUR TURN 1 Repeat Example 1 for $f(x) = 4 - x^2$, $g(x) = x + 2$, $x = -2$, and $x = 1$.

TRY YOUR TURN 1

NOTE It is not necessary to draw the graphs to determine which function is greater. Since the functions in the previous example do not intersect, we can evaluate them at *any* point to make this determination. For example, $f(0) = 1$ and $g(0) = 4$. Because $g(x) > f(x)$ at $x = 4$, and the two functions are continuous and never intersect, $g(x) > f(x)$ for all x.

EXAMPLE 2   Area

Find the area between the curves $y = x^{1/2}$ and $y = x^3$.

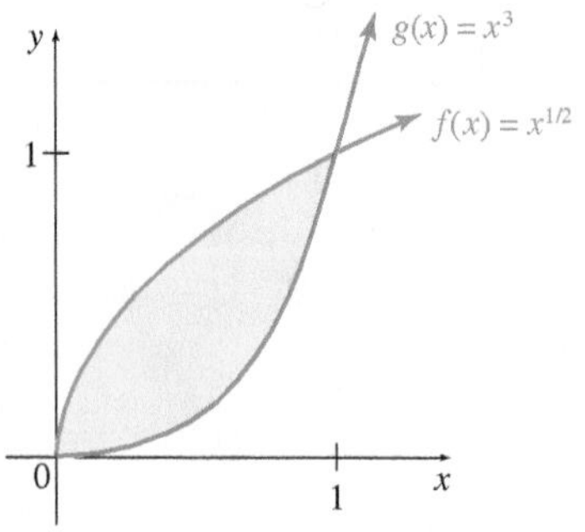

SOLUTION Let $f(x) = x^{1/2}$ and $g(x) = x^3$. As before, set the two equal to find where they intersect.

$$x^{1/2} = x^3$$
$$0 = x^3 - x^{1/2}$$
$$0 = x^{1/2}(x^{5/2} - 1)$$

The only solutions are $x = 0$ and $x = 1$. Verify that the graph of f is concave downward, while the graph of g is concave upward, so the graph of f must be greater between 0 and 1. (This may also be verified by taking a point between 0 and 1, such as 0.5, and verifying that $0.5^{1/2} > 0.5^3$.) The graph is shown in Figure 23.

The area between the two curves is given by

$$\int_a^b [f(x) - g(x)]\, dx = \int_0^1 (x^{1/2} - x^3)\, dx.$$

Using the Fundamental Theorem,

$$\int_0^1 (x^{1/2} - x^3)\, dx = \left(\frac{x^{3/2}}{3/2} - \frac{x^4}{4}\right)\Big|_0^1$$
$$= \left(\frac{2}{3}x^{3/2} - \frac{x^4}{4}\right)\Big|_0^1$$
$$= \frac{2}{3}(1) - \frac{1}{4}$$
$$= \frac{5}{12}.$$

TRY YOUR TURN 2

FIGURE 23

y-axis labeled with $g(x) = x^3$ *and* $f(x) = x^{1/2}$

YOUR TURN 2 Repeat Example 2 for $y = x^{1/4}$ and $y = x^2$.

TECHNOLOGY NOTE A graphing calculator is very useful in approximating solutions of problems involving the area between two curves. First, it can be used to graph the functions and identify any intersection points. Then it can be used to approximate the definite integral that represents the area. (A function that gives a numerical approximation to the integral is located in the MATH menu of a TI-84 Plus calculator.) Figure 24 shows the results of using these steps for Example 2. The second window shows that the area closely approximates 5/12.

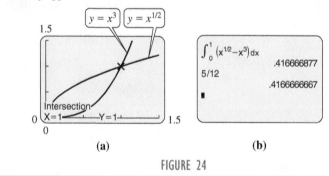

(a)   (b)

FIGURE 24

The difference between two integrals can be used to find the area between the graphs of two functions even if one graph lies below the x-axis. In fact, if $f(x) \geq g(x)$ for all values of x in the interval $[a, b]$, then the area between the two graphs is always given by

$$\int_a^b [f(x) - g(x)]\, dx.$$

To see this, look at the graphs in Figure 25(a), where $f(x) \geq g(x)$ for x in $[a, b]$. Suppose a constant C is added to both functions, with C large enough so that both graphs lie above the x-axis, as in Figure 25(b). The region between the graphs is not changed. By the work above, this area is given by $\int_a^b [f(x) - g(x)] dx$ regardless of where the graphs of $f(x)$ and $g(x)$ are located. As long as $f(x) \geq g(x)$ on $[a, b]$, then the area between the graphs from $x = a$ to $x = b$ will equal $\int_a^b [f(x) - g(x)] dx$.

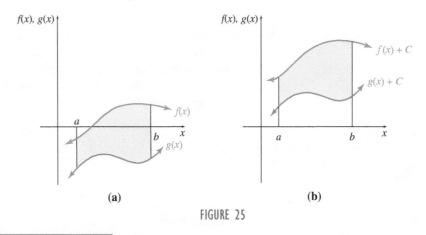

(a)   (b)

FIGURE 25

EXAMPLE 3 Area

Find the area of the region enclosed by $y = x^2 - 2x$ and $y = x$ on $[0, 4]$.

SOLUTION Verify that the two graphs cross at $x = 0$ and $x = 3$. Because the first graph is a parabola opening upward, the parabola must be below the line between 0 and 3 and above the line between 3 and 4. See Figure 26. (The greater function could also be identified by checking a point between 0 and 3, such as 1, and a point between 3 and 4, such as 3.5. For each of these values of x, we could calculate the corresponding value of y for the two functions and see which is greater.) Because the graphs cross at $x = 3$, the area is found by taking the sum of two integrals as follows.

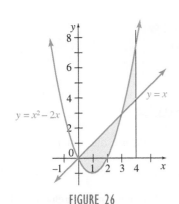

FIGURE 26

$$\text{Area} = \int_0^3 [x - (x^2 - 2x)] \, dx + \int_3^4 [(x^2 - 2x) - x] \, dx$$

$$= \int_0^3 (-x^2 + 3x) \, dx + \int_3^4 (x^2 - 3x) \, dx$$

$$= \left(\frac{-x^3}{3} + \frac{3x^2}{2} \right) \Big|_0^3 + \left(\frac{x^3}{3} - \frac{3x^2}{2} \right) \Big|_3^4$$

$$= \left(-9 + \frac{27}{2} - 0 \right) + \left(\frac{64}{3} - 24 - 9 + \frac{27}{2} \right)$$

$$= \frac{19}{3}$$

YOUR TURN 3 Repeat Example 3 for $y = x^2 - 3x$ and $y = 2x$ on $[0, 6]$.

TRY YOUR TURN 3

In the remainder of this section we will consider some typical applications that require finding the area between two curves.

EXAMPLE 4 Savings

A company is considering a new manufacturing process in one of its plants. The new process provides substantial initial savings, with the savings declining with time t (in years) according to the rate-of-savings function

$$S'(t) = 100 - t^2,$$

47

where $S'(t)$ is in thousands of dollars per year. At the same time, the cost of operating the new process increases with time t (in years), according to the rate-of-cost function (in thousands of dollars per year)

$$C'(t) = t^2 + \frac{14}{3}t.$$

(a) For how many years will the company realize savings?

SOLUTION Figure 27 shows the graphs of the rate-of-savings and rate-of-cost functions. The rate of cost (marginal cost) is increasing, while the rate of savings (marginal savings) is decreasing. The company should use this new process until the difference between these quantities is zero; that is, until the time at which these graphs intersect. The graphs intersect when

$$C'(t) = S'(t),$$

or

$$t^2 + \frac{14}{3}t = 100 - t^2.$$

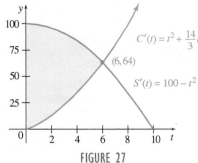

FIGURE 27

Solve this equation as follows.

$$0 = 2t^2 + \frac{14}{3}t - 100$$

$$0 = 3t^2 + 7t - 150 \qquad \text{Multiply by } \tfrac{3}{2}.$$

$$= (t - 6)(3t + 25) \qquad \text{Factor.}$$

Set each factor equal to 0 separately to get

$$t = 6 \qquad \text{or} \qquad t = -25/3.$$

Only 6 is a meaningful solution here. The company should use the new process for 6 years.

(b) What will be the net total savings during this period?

SOLUTION Since the total savings over the 6-year period is given by the area under the rate-of-savings curve and the total additional cost is given by the area under the rate-of-cost curve, the net total savings over the 6-year period is given by the area between the rate-of-cost and the rate-of-savings curves and the lines $t = 0$ and $t = 6$. This area can be evaluated with a definite integral as follows.

$$\text{Total savings} = \int_0^6 \left[(100 - t^2) - \left(t^2 + \frac{14}{3}t \right) \right] dt$$

$$= \int_0^6 \left(100 - \frac{14}{3}t - 2t^2 \right) dt$$

$$= \left(100t - \frac{7}{3}t^2 - \frac{2}{3}t^3 \right) \Big|_0^6$$

$$= 100(6) - \frac{7}{3}(36) - \frac{2}{3}(216) = 372$$

The company will save a total of $372,000 over the 6-year period.

The answer to a problem will not always be an integer. Suppose in solving the quadratic equation in Example 4 we found the solutions to be $t = 6.7$ and $t = -7.3$. It may not be realistic to use a new process for 6.7 years; it may be necessary to choose between 6 years and 7 years. Since the mathematical model produces a result that is not in the domain of the function in this case, it is necessary to find the total savings after 6 years and after 7 years and then select the best result.

Consumers' Surplus

The market determines the price at which a product is sold. As indicated earlier, the point of intersection of the demand curve and the supply curve for a product gives the equilibrium price. At the equilibrium price, consumers will purchase the same amount of the product that the manufacturers want to sell. Some consumers, however, would be willing to spend more for an item than the equilibrium price. The total of the differences between the equilibrium price of the item and the higher prices that individuals would be willing to pay is thought of as savings realized by those individuals and is called the **consumers' surplus**.

To calculate the total amount that consumers would be willing to pay for q_0 items, first consider the simple case in which everyone is willing to pay exactly p_0, the equilibrium price. Then the total amount everyone would pay would be the price times the quantity, or $p_0 q_0$, which is the green area in Figure 28. In fact, this is the exact total that everyone together pays when the item sells for p_0. Now divide the interval from 0 to q_0 into n intervals, each of width $\Delta q = q_0/n$. Each interval represents Δq people. Specifically, we will assume that the people represented by the ith interval, where i is a number between 1 and n, are those who are willing to pay a price $p_i = D(q_i)$ for the item, where q_i is some quantity on that interval. Then the total amount those people would be willing to pay would be $D(q_i)\Delta q$. The total amount that everyone together would be willing to pay is

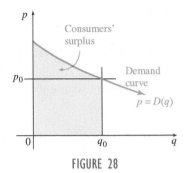

FIGURE 28

$$\sum_{i=1}^{n} D(q_i)\Delta q.$$

In a more realistic situation, the demand curve changes continuously, so we find the total amount that everyone would be willing to pay by taking the limit as n goes to infinity:

$$\lim_{n \to \infty} \sum_{i=1}^{n} D(q_i)\Delta q = \int_{0}^{q_0} D(q)\,dq.$$

This quantity, which represents the total amount consumers are willing to spend for q_0 items, is the area under the demand curve in Figure 28. The pink shaded area represents the difference between what consumers would be willing to pay and what they actually pay, or the consumers' surplus.

As the figure suggests, the consumers' surplus is given by an area between the two curves $p = D(q)$ and $p = p_0$, so its value can be found with a definite integral as follows.

Consumers' Surplus
If $D(q)$ is a demand function with equilibrium price p_0 and equilibrium demand q_0, then

$$\textbf{Consumers' surplus} = \int_{0}^{q_0} [D(q) - p_0]\,dq.$$

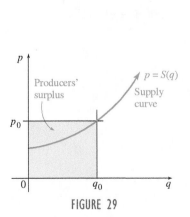

FIGURE 29

Similarly, if some manufacturers would be willing to supply a product at a price *lower* than the equilibrium price p_0, the total of the differences between the equilibrium price and the lower prices at which the manufacturers would sell the product is considered added income for the manufacturers and is called the **producers' surplus**. Figure 29 shows the (green shaded) total area under the supply curve from $q = 0$ to $q = q_0$, which is the minimum total amount the manufacturers are willing to realize from the sale of q_0 items. The total area under the line $p = p_0$ is the amount actually realized. The difference between these two areas, the producers' surplus, is also given by a definite integral.

Producers' Surplus

If $S(q)$ is a supply function with equilibrium price p_0 and equilibrium supply q_0, then

$$\text{Producers' surplus} = \int_0^{q_0} [p_0 - S(q)] \, dq.$$

EXAMPLE 5   Consumers' and Producers' Surplus

Suppose the price (in dollars per ton) for oat bran is

$$D(q) = 400 - e^{q/2},$$

when the demand for the product is q tons. Also, suppose the function

$$S(q) = e^{q/2} - 1$$

gives the price (in dollars per ton) when the supply is q tons. Find the consumers' surplus and the producers' surplus.

SOLUTION   Begin by finding the equilibrium quantity. This is done by setting the two equations equal.

$$e^{q/2} - 1 = 400 - e^{q/2}$$

$$2e^{q/2} = 401$$

$$e^{q/2} = \frac{401}{2}$$

$$q/2 = \ln\left(\frac{401}{2}\right)$$

$$q = 2\ln\left(\frac{401}{2}\right) \approx 10.60163$$

The result can be further rounded to 10.60 tons as long as this rounded value is not used in future calculations. At the equilibrium point where the supply and demand are both 10.60 tons, the price is

$$S(10.60163) = e^{10.60163/2} - 1 \approx 199.50,$$

or $199.50. Verify that this same answer is found by computing $D(10.60163)$. The consumers' surplus, represented by the area shown in Figure 30, is

$$\int_0^{10.60163} [(400 - e^{q/2}) - 199.50] \, dq = \int_0^{10.60163} [200.5 - e^{q/2}] \, dq.$$

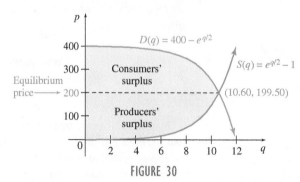

FIGURE 30

Evaluating the definite integral gives

$$\left. (200.5q - 2e^{q/2}) \right|_0^{10.60163} = [200.5(10.60163) - 2e^{10.60163/2}] - (0 - 2)$$
$$\approx 1726.63.$$

Here the consumers' surplus is $1726.63. The producers' surplus, also shown in Figure 30, is given by

$$\int_0^{10.60163} [199.50 - (e^{q/2} - 1)]\, dq = \int_0^{10.60163} [200.5 - e^{q/2}]\, dq,$$

which is exactly the same as the expression found for the consumers' surplus, so the producers' surplus is also $1726.63.   TRY YOUR TURN 4

YOUR TURN 4 Repeat Example 5 when $D(q) = 600 - e^{q/3}$ and $S(q) = e^{q/3} - 100$.

NOTE In general, the producers' surplus and consumers' surplus are not the same, as they are in Example 5.

5 EXERCISES

Find the area between the curves in Exercises 1–24.

1. $x = -2$, $x = 1$, $y = 2x^2 + 5$, $y = 0$

2. $x = 1$, $x = 2$, $y = 3x^3 + 2$, $y = 0$

3. $x = -3$, $x = 1$, $y = x^3 + 1$, $y = 0$

4. $x = -3$, $x = 0$, $y = 1 - x^2$, $y = 0$

5. $x = -2$, $x = 1$, $y = 2x$, $y = x^2 - 3$

6. $x = 0$, $x = 6$, $y = 5x$, $y = 3x + 10$

7. $y = x^2 - 30$, $y = 10 - 3x$

8. $y = x^2 - 18$, $y = x - 6$

9. $y = x^2$, $y = 2x$

10. $y = x^2$, $y = x^3$

11. $x = 1$, $x = 6$, $y = \dfrac{1}{x}$, $y = \dfrac{1}{2}$

12. $x = 0$, $x = 4$, $y = \dfrac{1}{x+1}$, $y = \dfrac{x-1}{2}$

13. $x = -1$, $x = 1$, $y = e^x$, $y = 3 - e^x$

14. $x = -1$, $x = 2$, $y = e^{-x}$, $y = e^x$

15. $x = -1$, $x = 2$, $y = 2e^{2x}$, $y = e^{2x} + 1$

16. $x = 2$, $x = 4$, $y = \dfrac{x-1}{4}$, $y = \dfrac{1}{x-1}$

17. $y = x^3 - x^2 + x + 1$, $y = 2x^2 - x + 1$

18. $y = 2x^3 + x^2 + x + 5$, $y = x^3 + x^2 + 2x + 5$

19. $y = x^4 + \ln(x + 10)$, $y = x^3 + \ln(x + 10)$

20. $y = x^5 - 2\ln(x + 5)$, $y = x^3 - 2\ln(x + 5)$

21. $y = x^{4/3}$, $y = 2x^{1/3}$

22. $y = \sqrt{x}$, $y = x\sqrt{x}$

23. $x = 0$, $x = 3$, $y = 2e^{3x}$, $y = e^{3x} + e^6$

24. $x = 0$, $x = 3$, $y = e^x$, $y = e^{4-x}$

📈 **In Exercises 25 and 26, use a graphing calculator to find the values of x where the curves intersect and then to find the area between the two curves.**

25. $y = e^x$, $y = -x^2 - 2x$

26. $y = \ln x$, $y = x^3 - 5x^2 + 6x - 1$

APPLICATIONS

Business and Economics

27. **Net Savings** Suppose a company wants to introduce a new machine that will produce a rate of annual savings (in dollars) given by

$$S'(x) = 150 - x^2,$$

where x is the number of years of operation of the machine, while producing a rate of annual costs (in dollars) of

$$C'(x) = x^2 + \frac{11}{4}x.$$

a. For how many years will it be profitable to use this new machine?

b. What are the net total savings during the first year of use of the machine?

c. What are the net total savings over the entire period of use of the machine?

28. Net Savings A new smog-control device will reduce the output of sulfur oxides from automobile exhausts. It is estimated that the rate of savings (in millions of dollars per year) to the community from the use of this device will be approximated by

$$S'(x) = -x^2 + 4x + 8,$$

after x years of use of the device. The new device cuts down on the production of sulfur oxides, but it causes an increase in the production of nitrous oxides. The rate of additional costs (in millions of dollars per year) to the community after x years is approximated by

$$C'(x) = \frac{3}{25}x^2.$$

a. For how many years will it pay to use the new device?

b. What will be the net savings over this period of time?

29. Profit Canham Enterprises had an expenditure rate of $E'(x) = e^{0.1x}$ dollars per day and an income rate of $I'(x) = 98.8 - e^{0.1x}$ dollars per day on a particular job, where x was the number of days from the start of the job. The company's profit on that job will equal total income less total expenditures. Profit will be maximized if the job ends at the optimum time, which is the point where the two curves meet. Find the following.

a. The optimum number of days for the job to last

b. The total income for the optimum number of days

c. The total expenditures for the optimum number of days

d. The maximum profit for the job

30. Net Savings A factory of Hollis Sherman Industries has installed a new process that will produce an increased rate of revenue (in thousands of dollars per year) of

$$R'(t) = 104 - 0.4e^{t/2},$$

where t is time measured in years. The new process produces additional costs (in thousands of dollars per year) at the rate of

$$C'(t) = 0.3e^{t/2}.$$

a. When will it no longer be profitable to use this new process?

b. Find the net total savings.

31. Producers' Surplus Find the producers' surplus if the supply function for pork bellies is given by

$$S(q) = q^{5/2} + 2q^{3/2} + 50.$$

Assume supply and demand are in equilibrium at $q = 16$.

32. Producers' Surplus Suppose the supply function for concrete is given by

$$S(q) = 100 + 3q^{3/2} + q^{5/2},$$

and that supply and demand are in equilibrium at $q = 9$. Find the producers' surplus.

33. Consumers' Surplus Find the consumers' surplus if the demand function for grass seed is given by

$$D(q) = \frac{200}{(3q + 1)^2},$$

assuming supply and demand are in equilibrium at $q = 3$.

34. Consumers' Surplus Find the consumers' surplus if the demand function for extra virgin olive oil is given by

$$D(q) = \frac{32,000}{(2q + 8)^3},$$

and if supply and demand are in equilibrium at $q = 6$.

35. Consumers' and Producers' Surplus Suppose the supply function for oil is given (in dollars) by

$$S(q) = q^2 + 10q,$$

and the demand function is given (in dollars) by

$$D(q) = 900 - 20q - q^2.$$

a. Graph the supply and demand curves.

b. Find the point at which supply and demand are in equilibrium.

c. Find the consumers' surplus.

d. Find the producers' surplus.

36. Consumers' and Producers' Surplus Suppose the supply function for a certain item is given by

$$S(q) = (q + 1)^2,$$

and the demand function is given by

$$D(q) = \frac{1000}{q + 1}.$$

a. Graph the supply and demand curves.

b. Find the point at which supply and demand are in equilibrium.

c. Find the consumers' surplus.

d. Find the producers' surplus.

37. Consumers' and Producers' Surplus Suppose that with the supply and demand for oil as in Exercise 35, the government sets the price at $264 per unit.

a. Use the supply function to calculate the quantity that will be produced at the new price.

b. Find the consumers' surplus for the new price, using the quantity found in part a in place of the equilibrium quantity. How much larger is this than the consumers' surplus in Exercise 35?

c. Find the producers' surplus for the new price, using the quantity found in part a in place of the equilibrium quantity. How much smaller is this than the producers' surplus in Exercise 35?

d. Calculate the difference between the total of the consumers' and producers' surplus under the equilibrium price and under the government price. Economists refer to this loss as the *welfare cost* of the government's setting the price.

e. Because of the welfare cost calculated in part d, many economists argue that it is bad economics for the government to set prices. Others point to the increase in the consumers' surplus, calculated in part b, as a justification for such government action. Discuss the pros and cons of this issue.

38. Fuel Economy In an article in the December 1994 *Scientific American* magazine, the authors estimated future gas use. Without a change in U.S. policy, auto fuel use is forecasted to rise along the projection shown at the right in the figure below. The shaded band predicts gas use if the technologies for increased fuel economy are phased in by the year 2010. The moderate estimate (center curve) corresponds to an average of 46 mpg for all cars on the road. *Source: Scientific American.*

a. Discuss the interpretation of the shaded area and other regions of the graph that pertain to the topic in this section.

b. According to the Energy Information Administration, the U.S. gasoline consumption in 2010 was 9,030,000 barrels per day. Discuss how this affects the areas considered in part a. *Source: U.S. Energy Information Administration.*

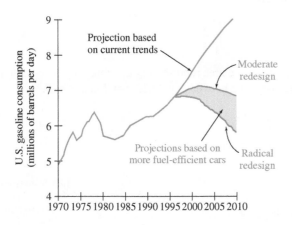

Life Sciences

39. Pollution Pollution begins to enter a lake at time $t = 0$ at a rate (in gallons per hour) given by the formula

$$f(t) = 10(1 - e^{-0.5t}),$$

where t is the time (in hours). At the same time, a pollution filter begins to remove the pollution at a rate

$$g(t) = 0.4t$$

as long as pollution remains in the lake.

a. How much pollution is in the lake after 12 hours?

b. Use a graphing calculator to find the time when the rate that pollution enters the lake equals the rate the pollution is removed.

c. Find the amount of pollution in the lake at the time found in part b.

d. Use a graphing calculator to find the time when all the pollution has been removed from the lake.

40. Pollution Repeat the steps of Exercise 39, using the functions

$$f(t) = 15(1 - e^{-0.05t})$$

and

$$g(t) = 0.3t.$$

Social Sciences

41. Distribution of Income Suppose that all the people in a country are ranked according to their incomes, starting at the bottom. Let x represent the fraction of the community making the lowest income $(0 \le x \le 1)$; $x = 0.4$, therefore, represents the lower 40% of all income producers. Let $I(x)$ represent the proportion of the total income earned by the lowest x of all people. Thus, $I(0.4)$ represents the fraction of total income earned by the lowest 40% of the population. The curve described by this function is known as a *Lorenz curve*. Suppose

$$I(x) = 0.9x^2 + 0.1x.$$

Find and interpret the following.

a. $I(0.1)$ **b.** $I(0.4)$

If income were distributed uniformly, we would have $I(x) = x$. The area under this line of complete equality is $1/2$. As $I(x)$ dips further below $y = x$, there is less equality of income distribution. This inequality can be quantified by the ratio of the area between $I(x)$ and $y = x$ to $1/2$. This ratio is called the *Gini index of income inequality* and equals $2\int_0^1 [x - I(x)]\, dx$.

c. Graph $I(x) = x$ and $I(x) = 0.9x^2 + 0.1x$, for $0 \le x \le 1$, on the same axes.

d. Find the area between the curves.

e. For U.S. families, the Gini index was 0.386 in 1968 and 0.466 in 2008. Describe how the distribution of family incomes has changed over this time. *Source: U.S. Census.*

Physical Sciences

42. Metal Plate A worker sketches the curves $y = \sqrt{x}$ and $y = x/2$ on a sheet of metal and cuts out the region between the curves to form a metal plate. Find the area of the plate.

YOUR TURN ANSWERS

1. 9/2   **2.** 7/15

3. 71/3   **4.** $5103.83; $5103.83

6 Numerical Integration

APPLY IT **If the velocity of a vehicle is known only at certain points in time, how can the total distance traveled by the vehicle be estimated?**
Using numerical integration, we will answer this question in Example 3 of this section.

Some integrals cannot be evaluated by any technique. One solution to this problem was presented in Section 3 of this chapter, in which the area under a curve was approximated by summing the areas of rectangles. This method is seldom used in practice because better methods exist that are more accurate for the same amount of work. These methods are referred to as **numerical integration** methods. We discuss two such methods here: the trapezoidal rule and Simpson's rule.

Trapezoidal Rule
Recall, the trapezoidal rule was mentioned briefly in Section 3, where we found approximations with it by averaging the sums of rectangles found by using left endpoints and then using right endpoints. In this section we derive an explicit formula for the trapezoidal rule in terms of function values.* To illustrate the derivation of the trapezoidal rule, consider the integral

$$\int_1^5 \frac{1}{x}\, dx.$$

The shaded region in Figure 31 shows the area representing that integral, the area under the graph $f(x) = 1/x$, above the x-axis, and between the lines $x = 1$ and $x = 5$.

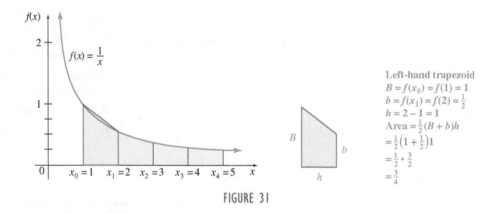

FIGURE 31

Note that this function can be integrated using the Fundamental Theorem of Calculus. Since $\int (1/x)\, dx = \ln |x| + C$,

$$\int_1^5 \frac{1}{x}\, dx = \ln |x| \Big|_1^5 = \ln 5 - \ln 1 = \ln 5 - 0 = \ln 5 \approx 1.609438.$$

We can also approximate the integral using numerical integration. As shown in the figure, if the area under the curve is approximated with trapezoids rather than rectangles, the approximation should be improved.

As in earlier work, to approximate this area we divide the interval $[1, 5]$ into subintervals of equal widths. To get a first approximation to $\ln 5$ by the trapezoidal rule, find the sum of the

*In American English a trapezoid is a four-sided figure with two parallel sides, contrasted with a trapezium, which has no parallel sides. In British English, however, it is just the opposite. What Americans call a trapezoid is called a trapezium in Great Britain.

n	Trapezoidal Approximation
6	1.64360
8	1.62897
10	1.62204
20	1.61262
100	1.60957
1000	1.60944

Approximations to $\int_1^5 \frac{1}{x}\, dx$

areas of the four trapezoids shown in Figure 31. From geometry, the area of a trapezoid is half the product of the sum of the bases and the altitude. Each of the trapezoids in Figure 31 has altitude 1. (In this case, the bases of the trapezoid are vertical and the altitudes are horizontal.) Adding the areas gives

$$\ln 5 = \int_1^5 \frac{1}{x}\, dx \approx \frac{1}{2}\left(\frac{1}{1} + \frac{1}{2}\right)(1) + \frac{1}{2}\left(\frac{1}{2} + \frac{1}{3}\right)(1) + \frac{1}{2}\left(\frac{1}{3} + \frac{1}{4}\right)(1) + \frac{1}{2}\left(\frac{1}{4} + \frac{1}{5}\right)(1)$$

$$= \frac{1}{2}\left(\frac{3}{2} + \frac{5}{6} + \frac{7}{12} + \frac{9}{20}\right) \approx 1.68333.$$

To get a better approximation, divide the interval $[1, 5]$ into more subintervals. Generally speaking, the larger the number of subintervals, the better the approximation. The results for selected values of n are shown to 5 decimal places. When $n = 1000$, the approximation agrees with the true value of $\ln 5 \approx 1.609438$ to 5 decimal places.

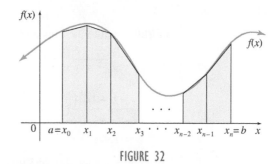

FIGURE 32

Generalizing from this example, let f be a continuous function on an interval $[a, b]$. Divide the interval from a to b into n equal subintervals by the points $a = x_0, x_1, x_2, \ldots, x_n = b$, as shown in Figure 32. Use the subintervals to make trapezoids that approximately fill in the region under the curve. The approximate value of the definite integral $\int_a^b f(x)\, dx$ is given by the sum of the areas of the trapezoids, or

$$\int_a^b f(x)\, dx \approx \frac{1}{2}[f(x_0) + f(x_1)]\left(\frac{b - a}{n}\right) + \frac{1}{2}[f(x_1) + f(x_2)]\left(\frac{b - a}{n}\right)$$

$$+ \cdots + \frac{1}{2}[f(x_{n-1}) + f(x_n)]\left(\frac{b - a}{n}\right)$$

$$= \left(\frac{b - a}{n}\right)\left[\frac{1}{2}f(x_0) + \frac{1}{2}f(x_1) + \frac{1}{2}f(x_1) + \frac{1}{2}f(x_2) + \frac{1}{2}f(x_2) + \cdots + \frac{1}{2}f(x_{n-1}) + \frac{1}{2}f(x_n)\right]$$

$$= \left(\frac{b - a}{n}\right)\left[\frac{1}{2}f(x_0) + f(x_1) + f(x_2) + \cdots + f(x_{n-1}) + \frac{1}{2}f(x_n)\right].$$

This result gives the following rule.

Trapezoidal Rule

Let f be a continuous function on $[a, b]$ and let $[a, b]$ be divided into n equal subintervals by the points $a = x_0, x_1, x_2, \ldots, x_n = b$. Then, by the **trapezoidal rule**,

$$\int_a^b f(x)\, dx \approx \left(\frac{b - a}{n}\right)\left[\frac{1}{2}f(x_0) + f(x_1) + \cdots + f(x_{n-1}) + \frac{1}{2}f(x_n)\right].$$

EXAMPLE 1 **Trapezoidal Rule**

Use the trapezoidal rule with $n = 4$ to approximate

$$\int_0^2 \sqrt{x^2 + 1}\, dx.$$

SOLUTION

Method 1
Calculating by Hand

Here $a = 0$, $b = 2$, and $n = 4$, with $(b - a)/n = (2 - 0)/4 = 1/2$ as the altitude of each trapezoid. Then $x_0 = 0$, $x_1 = 1/2$, $x_2 = 1$, $x_3 = 3/2$, and $x_4 = 2$. Now find the corresponding function values. The work can be organized into a table, as follows.

		Calculations for Trapezoidal Rule
i	x_i	$f(x_i)$
0	0	$\sqrt{0^2 + 1} = 1$
1	1/2	$\sqrt{(1/2)^2 + 1} \approx 1.11803$
2	1	$\sqrt{1^2 + 1} \approx 1.41421$
3	3/2	$\sqrt{(3/2)^2 + 1} \approx 1.80278$
4	2	$\sqrt{2^2 + 1} \approx 2.23607$

Substitution into the trapezoidal rule gives

$$\int_0^2 \sqrt{x^2 + 1}\, dx$$

$$\approx \frac{2 - 0}{4}\left[\frac{1}{2}(1) + 1.11803 + 1.41421 + 1.80278 + \frac{1}{2}(2.23607)\right]$$

$$\approx 2.97653.$$

The approximation 2.97653 found above using the trapezoidal rule with $n = 4$ differs from the true value of 2.95789 by 0.01864. As mentioned above, this error would be reduced if larger values were used for n. For example, if $n = 8$, the trapezoidal rule gives an answer of 2.96254, which differs from the true value by 0.00465. Techniques for estimating such errors are considered in more advanced courses.

Method 2
Graphing Calculator

Just as we used a graphing calculator to approximate area using rectangles, we can also use it for the trapezoidal rule. As before, put the values of i in L_1 and the values of x_i in L_2. In the heading for L_3, put $\sqrt{(L_2^2 + 1)}$. Using the fact that $(b - a)/n = (2 - 0)/4 = 0.5$, the command $.5*(.5*L_3(1)+\text{sum}(L_3,2,4)+.5*L_3(5))$ gives the result 2.976528589.

Method 3
Spreadsheet

The trapezoidal rule can also be done on a spreadsheet. In Microsoft Excel, for example, store the values of 0 through n in column A. After putting the left endpoint in E1 and Δx in E2, put the command "=\$E\$1+A1*\$E\$2" into B1; copying this formula into the rest of column B gives the values of x_i. Similarly, use the formula for $f(x_i)$ to fill column C. Using the fact that $n = 5$ in this example, the command "\$E\$2*(.5*C1+sum(C2:C4)+.5*C5)" gives the result 2.976529.

YOUR TURN 1 Use the trapezoidal rule with $n = 4$ to approximate $\displaystyle\int_1^3 \sqrt{x^2 + 3}\, dx$.

TRY YOUR TURN 1

The trapezoidal rule is not widely used because its results are not very accurate. In fact, the midpoint rule discussed earlier in this chapter is usually more accurate than the trapezoidal rule. We will now consider a method that usually gives more accurate results than either the trapezoidal or midpoint rule.

Simpson's Rule

Another numerical method, *Simpson's rule*, approximates consecutive portions of the curve with portions of parabolas rather than the line segments of the trapezoidal rule. Simpson's rule usually gives a better approximation than the trapezoidal rule for the same number of subintervals. As shown in Figure 33, one parabola is fitted

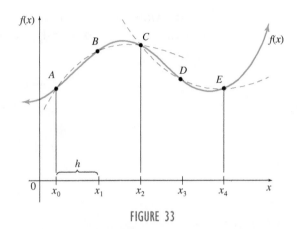

FIGURE 33

through points A, B, and C, another through C, D, and E, and so on. Then the sum of of the areas under these parabolas will approximate the area under the graph of the function. Because of the way the parabolas overlap, it is necessary to have an even number of intervals, and therefore an odd number of points, to apply Simpson's rule.

If h, the length of each subinterval, is $(b - a)/n$, the area under the parabola through points A, B, and C can be found by a definite integral. The details are omitted; the result is

$$\frac{h}{3}[f(x_0) + 4f(x_1) + f(x_2)].$$

Similarly, the area under the parabola through points C, D, and E is

$$\frac{h}{3}[f(x_2) + 4f(x_3) + f(x_4)].$$

When these expressions are added, the last term of one expression equals the first term of the next. For example, the sum of the two areas given above is

$$\frac{h}{3}[f(x_0) + 4f(x_1) + 2f(x_2) + 4f(x_3) + f(x_4)].$$

This illustrates the origin of the pattern of the terms in the following rule.

Simpson's Rule

Let f be a continuous function on $[a, b]$ and let $[a, b]$ be divided into an even number n of equal subintervals by the points $a = x_0, x_1, x_2, \ldots, x_n = b$. Then by **Simpson's rule**,

$$\int_a^b f(x)\, dx \approx \left(\frac{b - a}{3n}\right)[f(x_0) + 4f(x_1) + 2f(x_2) + 4f(x_3) + \cdots$$
$$+ 2f(x_{n-2}) + 4f(x_{n-1}) + f(x_n)].$$

Thomas Simpson (1710–1761), a British mathematician, wrote texts on many branches of mathematics. Some of these texts went through as many as ten editions. His name became attached to this numerical method of approximating definite integrals even though the method preceded his work.

CAUTION   In Simpson's rule, n (the number of subintervals) must be even.

EXAMPLE 2 Simpson's Rule

Use Simpson's rule with $n = 4$ to approximate

$$\int_0^2 \sqrt{x^2 + 1}\, dx,$$

which was approximated by the trapezoidal rule in Example 1.

SOLUTION As in Example 1, $a = 0$, $b = 2$, and $n = 4$, and the endpoints of the four intervals are $x_0 = 0$, $x_1 = 1/2$, $x_2 = 1$, $x_3 = 3/2$, and $x_4 = 2$. The table of values is also the same.

Calculations for Simpson's Rule		
i	x_i	$f(x_i)$
0	0	1
1	1/2	1.11803
2	1	1.41421
3	3/2	1.80278
4	2	2.23607

Since $(b - a)/(3n) = 2/12 = 1/6$, substituting into Simpson's rule gives

YOUR TURN 2 Use Simpson's rule with $n = 4$ to approximate $\int_1^3 \sqrt{x^2 + 3}\,dx$.

$$\int_0^2 \sqrt{x^2 + 1}\,dx \approx \frac{1}{6}[1 + 4(1.11803) + 2(1.41421) + 4(1.80278) + 2.23607] \approx 2.95796.$$

This differs from the true value by 0.00007, which is less than the trapezoidal rule with $n = 8$. If $n = 8$ for Simpson's rule, the approximation is 2.95788, which differs from the true value by only 0.00001.   **TRY YOUR TURN 2**

NOTE

1. Just as we can use a graphing calculator or a spreadsheet for the trapezoidal rule, we can also use such technology for Simpson's rule.
2. Let M represent the midpoint rule approximation and T the trapezoidal rule approximation, using n subintervals in each. Then the formula $S = (2M + T)/3$ gives the Simpson's rule approximation with $2n$ subintervals.

Numerical methods make it possible to approximate

$$\int_a^b f(x)\,dx$$

even when $f(x)$ is not known. The next example shows how this is done.

EXAMPLE 3   Total Distance

As mentioned earlier, the velocity $v(t)$ gives the rate of change of distance $s(t)$ with respect to time t. Suppose a vehicle travels an unknown distance. The passengers keep track of the velocity at 10-minute intervals (every 1/6 of an hour) with the following results.

Velocity of a Vehicle							
Time in Hours, t	1/6	2/6	3/6	4/6	5/6	1	7/6
Velocity in Miles per Hour, $v(t)$	45	55	52	60	64	58	47

What is the total distance traveled in the 60-minute period from $t = 1/6$ to $t = 7/6$?

APPLY IT   **SOLUTION**   The distance traveled in t hours is $s(t)$, with $s'(t) = v(t)$. The total distance traveled between $t = 1/6$ and $t = 7/6$ is given by

$$\int_{1/6}^{7/6} v(t)\,dt.$$

Even though this integral cannot be evaluated since we do not have an expression for $v(t)$, either the trapezoidal rule or Simpson's rule can be used to approximate its value and give the total distance traveled. In either case, let $n = 6$, $a = t_0 = 1/6$, and $b = t_6 = 7/6$. By the trapezoidal rule,

$$\int_{1/6}^{7/6} v(t)\, dt \approx \frac{7/6 - 1/6}{6}\left[\frac{1}{2}(45) + 55 + 52 + 60 + 64 + 58 + \frac{1}{2}(47)\right]$$

$$\approx 55.83.$$

By Simpson's rule,

$$\int_{1/6}^{7/6} v(t)\, dt \approx \frac{7/6 - 1/6}{3(6)}[45 + 4(55) + 2(52) + 4(60) + 2(64) + 4(58) + 47]$$

$$= \frac{1}{18}(45 + 220 + 104 + 240 + 128 + 232 + 47) \approx 56.44.$$

The distance traveled in the 1-hour period was about 56 miles.

As already mentioned, Simpson's rule generally gives a better approximation than the trapezoidal rule. As n increases, the two approximations get closer and closer. For the same accuracy, however, a smaller value of n generally can be used with Simpson's rule so that less computation is necessary. Simpson's rule is the method used by many calculators that have a built-in integration feature.

The branch of mathematics that studies methods of approximating definite integrals (as well as many other topics) is called *numerical* analysis. Numerical integration is useful even with functions whose antiderivatives can be determined if the antidifferentiation is complicated and a computer or calculator programmed with Simpson's rule is handy. You may want to program your calculator for both the trapezoidal rule and Simpson's rule.

6 EXERCISES

In Exercises 1–10, use $n = 4$ to approximate the value of the given integrals by the following methods: (a) the trapezoidal rule, and (b) Simpson's rule. (c) Find the exact value by integration.

1. $\int_0^2 (3x^2 + 2)\, dx$

2. $\int_0^2 (2x^2 + 1)\, dx$

3. $\int_{-1}^3 \frac{3}{5 - x}\, dx$

4. $\int_1^5 \frac{6}{2x + 1}\, dx$

5. $\int_{-1}^2 (2x^3 + 1)\, dx$

6. $\int_0^3 (2x^3 + 1)\, dx$

7. $\int_1^5 \frac{1}{x^2}\, dx$

8. $\int_2^4 \frac{1}{x^3}\, dx$

9. $\int_0^1 4xe^{-x^2}\, dx$

10. $\int_0^4 x\sqrt{2x^2 + 1}\, dx$

11. Find the area under the semicircle $y = \sqrt{4 - x^2}$ and above the x-axis by using $n = 8$ with the following methods.

   a. The trapezoidal rule   **b.** Simpson's rule

   c. Compare the results with the area found by the formula for the area of a circle. Which of the two approximation techniques was more accurate?

12. Find the area between the x-axis and the upper half of the ellipse $4x^2 + 9y^2 = 36$ by using $n = 12$ with the following methods.

   a. The trapezoidal rule   **b.** Simpson's rule

   (*Hint:* Solve the equation for y and find the area of the semiellipse.)

   c. Compare the results with the actual area, $3\pi \approx 9.4248$ (which can be found by methods not considered in this text). Which approximation technique was more accurate?

13. Suppose that $f(x) > 0$ and $f''(x) > 0$ for all x between a and b, where $a < b$. Which of the following cases is true of a trapezoidal approximation T for the integral $\int_a^b f(x)\, dx$? Explain.

a. $T < \int_a^b f(x)dx$ **b.** $T > \int_a^b f(x)dx$

c. Can't say which is larger

14. Refer to Exercise 13. Which of the three cases applies to these functions?

a. $f(x) = x^2$; $[0, 3]$ **b.** $f(x) = \sqrt{x}$; $[0, 9]$

c.

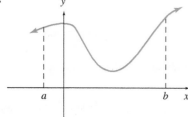

Exercises **15–18** require both the trapezoidal rule and Simpson's rule. They can be worked without calculator programs if such programs are not available, although they require more calculation than the other problems in this exercise set.

Error Analysis The difference between the true value of an integral and the value given by the trapezoidal rule or Simpson's rule is known as the error. In numerical analysis, the error is studied to determine how large n must be for the error to be smaller than some specified amount. For both rules, the error is inversely proportional to a power of n, the number of subdivisions. In other words, the error is roughly k/n^p, where k is a constant that depends on the function and the interval, and p is a power that depends only on the method used. With a little experimentation, you can find out what the power p is for the trapezoidal rule and for Simpson's rule.

15. a. Find the exact value of $\int_0^1 x^4\, dx$.

b. Approximate the integral in part a using the trapezoidal rule with $n = 4, 8, 16$, and 32. For each of these answers, find the absolute value of the error by subtracting the trapezoidal rule answer from the exact answer found in part a.

c. If the error is k/n^p, then the error times n^p should be approximately a constant. Multiply the errors in part b times n^p for $p = 1, 2$, etc., until you find a power p yielding the same answer for all four values of n.

16. Based on the results of Exercise 15, what happens to the error in the trapezoidal rule when the number of intervals is doubled?

17. Repeat Exercise 15 using Simpson's rule.

18. Based on the results of Exercise 17, what happens to the error in Simpson's rule when the number of intervals is doubled?

19. For the integral in Exercise 7, apply the midpoint rule with $n = 4$ and Simpson's rule with $n = 8$ to verify the formula $S = (2M + T)/3$.

20. Repeat the instructions of Exercise 19 using the integral in Exercise 8.

APPLICATIONS

Business and Economics

21. Total Sales A sales manager presented the following results at a sales meeting.

Year, x	1	2	3	4	5	6	7
Rate of Sales, $f(x)$	0.4	0.6	0.9	1.1	1.3	1.4	1.6

Find the total sales over the given period as follows.

a. Plot these points. Connect the points with line segments.

b. Use the trapezoidal rule to find the area bounded by the broken line of part a, the x-axis, the line $x = 1$, and the line $x = 7$.

c. Approximate the same area using Simpson's rule.

22. Total Cost A company's marginal costs (in hundreds of dollars per year) were as follows over a certain period.

Year, x	1	2	3	4	5	6	7
Marginal Cost, $f(x)$	9.0	9.2	9.5	9.4	9.8	10.1	10.5

Repeat parts a–c of Exercise 21 for these data to find the total cost over the given period.

Life Sciences

23. Drug Reaction Rate The reaction rate to a new drug is given by

$$y = e^{-t^2} + \frac{1}{t+1},$$

where t is time (in hours) after the drug is administered. Find the total reaction to the drug from $t = 1$ to $t = 9$ by letting $n = 8$ and using the following methods.

a. The trapezoidal rule **b.** Simpson's rule

24. Growth Rate The growth rate of a certain tree (in feet) is given by

$$y = \frac{2}{t+2} + e^{-t^2/2},$$

where t is time (in years). Find the total growth from $t = 1$ to $t = 7$ by using $n = 12$ with the following methods.

a. The trapezoidal rule **b.** Simpson's rule

Blood Level Curves In the study of bioavailability in pharmacy, a drug is given to a patient. The level of concentration of the drug is then measured periodically, producing blood level curves such as the ones shown in the figure.

The areas under the curves give the total amount of the drug available to the patient for each milliliter of blood. Use the trapezoidal rule with $n = 10$ to find the following areas. *Source: Basics of Bioavailability.*

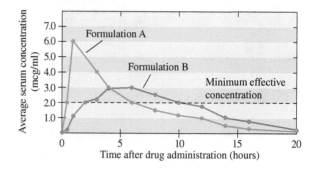

25. Find the total area under the curve for Formulation A. What does this area represent?

26. Find the total area under the curve for Formulation B. What does this area represent?

27. Find the area between the curve for Formulation A and the minimum effective concentration line. What does your answer represent?

28. Find the area between the curve for Formulation B and the minimum effective concentration line. What does this area represent?

29. Calves The daily milk consumption (in kilograms) for calves can be approximated by the function

$$y = b_0 w^{b_1} e^{-b_2 w},$$

where w is the age of the calf (in weeks) and b_0, b_1, and b_2 are constants. *Source: Animal Production.*

a. The age in days is given by $t = 7w$. Use this fact to convert the function above to a function in terms of t.

b. For a group of Angus calves, $b_0 = 5.955$, $b_1 = 0.233$, and $b_2 = 0.027$. Use the trapezoidal rule with $n = 10$, and then Simpson's rule with $n = 10$, to find the total amount of milk consumed by one of these calves over the first 25 weeks of life.

c. For a group of Nelore calves, $b_0 = 8.409$, $b_1 = 0.143$, and $b_2 = 0.037$. Use the trapezoidal rule with $n = 10$, and then Simpson's rule with $n = 10$, to find the total amount of milk consumed by one of these calves over the first 25 weeks of life.

30. Foot-and-Mouth Epidemic In 2001, the United Kingdom suffered an epidemic of foot-and-mouth disease. The graph below shows the reported number of cattle (red) and pigs (blue) that were culled each month from mid-February through mid-October in an effort to stop the spread of the disease. In section 7.3 on Area and the Definite Integral we estimated the number of cattle and pigs that were culled using rectangles. *Source: Department of Environment, Food and Rural Affairs, United Kingdom.*

a. Estimate the total number of cattle that were culled from mid-February through mid-October and compare this with 581,801, the actual number of cattle that were culled. Use Simpson's rule with interval widths of one month starting with mid-February.

b. Estimate the total number of pigs that were culled from mid-February through mid-October and compare this with 146,145, the actual number of pigs that were culled. Use Simpson's rule with interval widths of one month starting with mid-February.

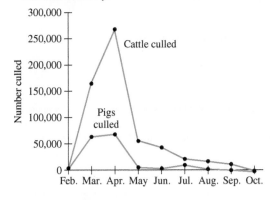

Social Sciences

31. Educational Psychology The results from a research study in psychology were as follows.

Number of Hours of Study, x	1	2	3	4	5	6	7
Rate of Extra Points Earned on a Test, $f(x)$	4	7	11	9	15	16	23

Repeat parts a–c of Exercise 21 for these data.

Physical Sciences

32. Chemical Formation The following table shows the results from a chemical experiment.

Concentration of Chemical A, x	1	2	3	4	5	6	7
Rate of Formation of Chemical B, $f(x)$	12	16	18	21	24	27	32

Repeat parts a–c of Exercise 21 for these data.

If you have a program for Simpson's rule in your graphing calculator, use it with $n = 20$ for Exercises 33–35.

33. Total Revenue An electronics company analyst has determined that the rate per month at which revenue comes in from the calculator division is given by

$$R(x) = 105e^{0.01x} + 32,$$

where x is the number of months the division has been in operation. Find the total revenue between the 12th and 36th months.

34. Milk Consumption The average individual daily milk consumption for herds of Charolais, Angus, and Hereford calves can be described by a mathematical function. Here we write the consumption in Kg/day as a function of the age of the calf in days (t) as

$$M(t) = 3.922t^{0.242}e^{-0.00357t}, \quad 7 \le t \le 182.$$

Find the total amount of milk consumed from 7 to 182 days for a calf. *Source: Animal Production.*

35. Probability The most important function in probability and statistics is the density function for the standard normal distribution, which is the familiar bell-shaped curve. The function is

$$f(x) = \frac{1}{\sqrt{2\pi}} e^{-x^2/2}.$$

a. The area under this curve between $x = -1$ and $x = 1$ represents the probability that a normal random variable is within 1 standard deviation of the mean. Find this probability.

b. Find the area under this curve between $x = -2$ and $x = 2$, which represents the probability that a normal random variable is within 2 standard deviations of the mean.

c. Find the probability that a normal random variable is within 3 standard deviations of the mean.

YOUR TURN ANSWERS

1. 5.3552   **2.** 5.3477

CHAPTER REVIEW

SUMMARY

The derivative, is one of the two main ideas of calculus. This chapter deals with integration, the second main idea. There are two aspects of integration. The first is indefinite integration, or finding an antiderivative; the second is definite integration, which can be used to find the area under a curve. The Fundamental Theorem of Calculus unites these two ideas by showing that

the way to find the area under a curve is to use the antiderivative. Substitution is a technique for finding antiderivatives. Numerical integration can be used to find the definite integral when finding an antiderivative is not feasible. The idea of the definite integral can also be applied to finding the area between two curves.

Antidifferentiation Formulas

Power Rule $\int x^n \, dx = \dfrac{x^{n+1}}{n+1} + C, \; n \neq -1$

Constant Multiple Rule $\int k \cdot f(x) \, dx = k \int f(x) \, dx, \quad \text{for any real number } k$

Sum or Difference Rule $\int [f(x) \pm g(x)] \, dx = \int f(x) \, dx \pm \int g(x) \, dx$

Integration of x^{-1} $\int x^{-1} \, dx = \ln |x| + C$

Integration of Exponential Functions $\int e^{kx} \, dx = \dfrac{e^{kx}}{k} + C, \; k \neq 0$

Substitution Method Choose u to be one of the following:

1. the quantity under a root or raised to a power;
2. the quantity in the denominator;
3. the exponent on e.

Definite Integrals

Definition of the Definite Integral $\int_a^b f(x) \, dx = \lim\limits_{n \to \infty} \sum\limits_{i=1}^n f(x_i)\Delta x$, where $\Delta x = (b-a)/n$ and x_i is any value of x in the ith interval. If $f(x)$ gives the rate of change of $F(x)$ for x in $[a, b]$, then this represents the total change in $F(x)$ as x goes from a to b.

Properties of Definite Integrals

1. $\int_a^a f(x) \, dx = 0$
2. $\int_a^b k \cdot f(x) \, dx = k \int_a^b f(x) \, dx, \quad \text{for any real number } k.$
3. $\int_a^b [f(x) \pm g(x)] \, dx = \int_a^b f(x) \, dx \pm \int_a^b g(x) \, dx$
4. $\int_a^b f(x) \, dx = \int_a^c f(x) \, dx + \int_c^b f(x) \, dx, \quad \text{for any real number } c$
5. $\int_a^b f(x) \, dx = -\int_b^a f(x) \, dx$

Fundamental Theorem of Calculus $\int_a^b f(x) \, dx = F(x)|_a^b = F(b) - F(a)$, where f is continuous on $[a, b]$ and F is any antiderivative of f

Area Between Two Curves $\int_a^b [f(x) - g(x)] \, dx$, where f and g are continuous functions and $f(x) \geq g(x)$ on $[a, b]$

Consumers' Surplus	$\int_0^{q_0}[D(q) - p_0]\,dq$, where D is the demand function and p_0 and q_0 are the equilibrium price and demand
Producers' Surplus	$\int_0^{q_0}[p_0 - S(q)]\,dq$, where S is the supply function and p_0 and q_0 are the equilibrium price and supply
Trapezoidal Rule	$\int_a^b f(x)\,dx \approx \left(\dfrac{b-a}{n}\right)\left[\dfrac{1}{2}f(x_0) + f(x_1) + \cdots + f(x_{n-1}) + \dfrac{1}{2}f(x_n)\right]$
Simpson's Rule	$\int_a^b f(x)\,dx \approx \left(\dfrac{b-a}{3n}\right)[f(x_0) + 4f(x_1) + 2f(x_2) + \cdots + 4f(x_{n-1}) + f(x_n)]$

KEY TERMS

1
antidifferentiation
antiderivative
integral sign
integrand
indefinite integral

2
integration by substitution

3
midpoint rule
definite integral
limits of integration
total change

4
Fundamental Theorem
of Calculus

5
consumers' surplus
producers' surplus

6
numerical integration
trapezoidal rule
Simpson's rule

REVIEW EXERCISES

CONCEPT CHECK

Determine whether each of the following statements is true or false, and explain why.

1. The indefinite integral is another term for the family of all antiderivatives of a function.

2. The indefinite integral of x^n is $x^{n+1}/(n+1) + C$ for all real numbers n.

3. The indefinite integral $\int xf(x)\,dx$ is equal to $x\int f(x)\,dx$.

4. The velocity function is an antiderivative of the acceleration function.

5. Substitution can often be used to turn a complicated integral into a simpler one.

6. The definite integral gives the instantaneous rate of change of a function.

7. The definite integral gives an approximation to the area under a curve.

8. The definite integral of a positive function is the limit of the sum of the areas of rectangles.

9. The Fundamental Theorem of Calculus gives a relationship between the definite integral and an antiderivative of a function.

10. The definite integral of a function is always a positive quantity.

11. The area between two distinct curves is always a positive quantity.

12. The consumers' surplus and the producers' surplus equal each other.

13. In the trapezoidal rule, the number of subintervals must be even.

14. Simpson's rule usually gives a better approximation than the trapezoidal rule.

PRACTICE AND EXPLORATION

15. Explain the differences between an indefinite integral and a definite integral.

16. Explain under what circumstances substitution is useful in integration.

17. Explain why the limits of integration are changed when u is substituted for an expression in x in a definite integral.

18. Describe the type of integral for which numerical integration is useful.

In Exercises 19–40, find each indefinite integral.

19. $\int (2x + 3)\,dx$

20. $\int (5x - 1)\,dx$

21. $\int (x^2 - 3x + 2)\,dx$

22. $\int (6 - x^2)\,dx$

23. $\int 3\sqrt{x}\,dx$

24. $\int \dfrac{\sqrt{x}}{2}\,dx$

25. $\int (x^{1/2} + 3x^{-2/3})\,dx$

26. $\int (2x^{4/3} + x^{-1/2})\,dx$

27. $\int \dfrac{-4}{x^3}\,dx$

28. $\int \dfrac{5}{x^4}\,dx$

29. $\int -3e^{2x}\,dx$

30. $\int 5e^{-x}\,dx$

31. $\int xe^{3x^2}\,dx$

32. $\int 2xe^{x^2}\,dx$

33. $\int \dfrac{3x}{x^2 - 1}\,dx$

34. $\int \dfrac{-x}{2 - x^2}\,dx$

35. $\int \dfrac{x^2\,dx}{(x^3 + 5)^4}$

36. $\int (x^2 - 5x)^4(2x - 5)\,dx$

37. $\int \dfrac{x^3}{e^{3x^4}}\,dx$

38. $\int e^{3x^2 + 4}x\,dx$

39. $\int \dfrac{(3 \ln x + 2)^4}{x}\,dx$

40. $\int \dfrac{\sqrt{5 \ln x + 3}}{x}\,dx$

41. Let $f(x) = 3x + 1$, $x_1 = -1$, $x_2 = 0$, $x_3 = 1$, $x_4 = 2$, and $x_5 = 3$. Find $\sum_{i=1}^{5} f(x_i)$.

42. Find $\int_0^4 f(x)\,dx$ for each graph of $y = f(x)$.

a.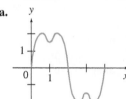

b.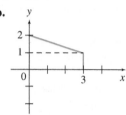

43. Approximate the area under the graph of $f(x) = 2x + 3$ and above the x-axis from $x = 0$ to $x = 4$ using four rectangles. Let the height of each rectangle be the function value on the left side.

44. Find $\int_0^4 (2x + 3)\,dx$ by using the formula for the area of a trapezoid: $A = (1/2)(B + b)h$, where B and b are the lengths of the parallel sides and h is the distance between them. Compare with Exercise 43.

45. In Exercises 29 and 30 of the section on Area and the Definite Integral, you calculated the distance that a car traveled by estimating the integral $\int_0^T v(t)\,dt$.

  a. Let $s(t)$ represent the mileage reading on the odometer. Express the distance traveled between $t = 0$ and $t = T$ using the function $s(t)$.

  b. Since your answer to part a and the original integral both represent the distance traveled by the car, the two can be set equal. Explain why the resulting equation is a statement of the Fundamental Theorem of Calculus.

46. What does the Fundamental Theorem of Calculus state?

Find each definite integral.

47. $\int_1^2 (3x^2 + 5)\,dx$

48. $\int_1^6 (2x^2 + x)\,dx$

49. $\int_1^5 (3x^{-1} + x^{-3})\,dx$

50. $\int_1^3 (2x^{-1} + x^{-2})\,dx$

51. $\int_0^1 x\sqrt{5x^2 + 4}\,dx$

52. $\int_0^2 x^2(3x^3 + 1)^{1/3}\,dx$

53. $\int_0^2 3e^{-2x}\,dx$

54. $\int_1^5 \dfrac{5}{2}e^{0.4x}\,dx$

55. Use the substitution $u = 4x^2$ and the equation of a semicircle to evaluate

$$\int_0^{1/2} x\sqrt{1 - 16x^4}\,dx.$$

56. Use the substitution $u = x^2$ and the equation of a semicircle to evaluate

$$\int_0^{\sqrt{2}} 4x\sqrt{4 - x^4}\,dx.$$

In Exercises 57 and 58, use substitution to change the integral into one that can be evaluated by a formula from geometry, and then find the value of the integral.

57. $\int_1^{e^5} \dfrac{\sqrt{25 - (\ln x)^2}}{x}\,dx$

58. $\int_1^{\sqrt{7}} 2x\sqrt{36 - (x^2 - 1)^2}\,dx$

In Exercises 59–62, find the area between the x-axis and $f(x)$ over each of the given intervals.

59. $f(x) = \sqrt{4x - 3}$; $[1, 3]$

60. $f(x) = (3x + 2)^6$; $[-2, 0]$

61. $f(x) = xe^{x^2}$; $[0, 2]$

62. $f(x) = 1 + e^{-x}$; $[0, 4]$

Find the area of the region enclosed by each group of curves.

63. $f(x) = 5 - x^2$, $g(x) = x^2 - 3$

64. $f(x) = x^2 - 4x$, $g(x) = x - 6$

65. $f(x) = x^2 - 4x$, $g(x) = x + 6$, $x = -2$, $x = 4$

66. $f(x) = 5 - x^2$, $g(x) = x^2 - 3$, $x = 0$, $x = 4$

Use the trapezoidal rule with $n = 4$ to approximate the value of each integral. Then find the exact value and compare the two answers.

67. $\int_1^3 \dfrac{\ln x}{x}\,dx$

68. $\int_2^{10} \dfrac{x\,dx}{x - 1}$

69. $\int_0^1 e^x\sqrt{e^x + 4}\,dx$

70. $\int_0^2 xe^{-x^2}\,dx$

Use Simpson's rule with $n = 4$ to approximate the value of each integral. Compare your answers with the answers to Exercises 67–70.

71. $\int_1^3 \dfrac{\ln x}{x}\,dx$

72. $\int_2^{10} \dfrac{x\,dx}{x - 1}$

73. $\int_0^1 e^x\sqrt{e^x + 4}\,dx$

74. $\int_0^2 xe^{-x^2}\,dx$

75. Find the area of the region between the graphs of $y = \sqrt{x - 1}$ and $2y = x - 1$ from $x = 1$ to $x = 5$ in three ways.

  a. Use antidifferentiation.

  b. Use the trapezoidal rule with $n = 4$.

  c. Use Simpson's rule with $n = 4$.

76. Find the area of the region between the graphs of $y = \dfrac{1}{x + 1}$ and $y = \dfrac{x + 2}{2}$ from $x = 0$ to $x = 4$ in three ways.

  a. Use antidifferentiation.

  b. Use the trapezoidal rule with $n = 4$.

  c. Use Simpson's rule with $n = 4$.

77. Let $f(x) = [x(x-1)(x+1)(x-2)(x+2)]^2$.

    a. Find $\int_{-2}^{2} f(x)\,dx$ using the trapezoidal rule with $n = 4$.

    b. Find $\int_{-2}^{2} f(x)\,dx$ using Simpson's rule with $n = 4$.

    c. Without evaluating $\int_{-2}^{2} f(x)\,dx$, explain why your answers to parts a and b cannot possibly be correct.

    d. Explain why the trapezoidal rule and Simpson's rule with $n = 4$ give incorrect answers for $\int_{-2}^{2} f(x)\,dx$ with this function.

78. Given $\displaystyle\int_{0}^{2} f(x)\,dx = 3$ and $\displaystyle\int_{2}^{4} f(x)\,dx = 5$, calculate

$$\int_{0}^{2} f(2x)\,dx.$$ Choose one of the following. *Source: Society of Actuaries.*

    a. 3/2   **b.** 3   **c.** 4   **d.** 6   **e.** 8

APPLICATIONS

Business and Economics

Cost Find the cost function for each of the marginal cost functions in Exercises 79 and 80.

79. $C'(x) = 3\sqrt{2x - 1}$; 13 units cost $270.

80. $C'(x) = \dfrac{8}{2x + 1}$; fixed cost is $18.

81. **Investment** The curve shown gives the rate that an investment accumulates income (in dollars per year). Use rectangles of width 2 units and height determined by the function value at the midpoint to find the total income accumulated over 10 years.

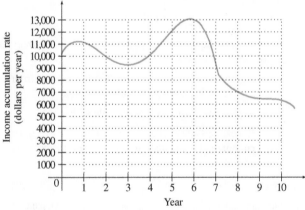

82. **Utilization of Reserves** A manufacturer of electronic equipment requires a certain rare metal. He has a reserve supply of 4,000,000 units that he will not be able to replace. If the rate at which the metal is used is given by

$$f(t) = 100{,}000e^{0.03t},$$

where t is time (in years), how long will it be before he uses up the supply? (*Hint:* Find an expression for the total amount used in t years and set it equal to the known reserve supply.)

83. **Sales** The rate of change of sales of a new brand of tomato soup (in thousands of dollars per month) is given by

$$S'(x) = 3\sqrt{2x + 1} + 3,$$

where x is the time (in months) that the new product has been on the market. Find the total sales after 4 months.

84. **Productivity** The function defined by

$$f'(x) = -0.1624x + 3.4909$$

approximates marginal U.S. nonfarm productivity from 2000–2009. Productivity is measured as total output per hour compared to a measure of 100 for 2000, and x is the number of years since 2000. *Source: Bureau of Labor Statistics.*

    a. Give the function that describes total productivity in year x.

    b. Use your function from part a to find productivity at the end of 2008. In 2009, productivity actually measured 122.3. How does your value using the function compare with this?

85. **Producers' and Consumers' Surplus** Suppose that the supply function for some commodity is

$$S(q) = q^2 + 5q + 100$$

and the demand function for the commodity is

$$D(q) = 350 - q^2.$$

    a. Find the producers' surplus.

    b. Find the consumers' surplus.

86. **Net Savings** A company has installed new machinery that will produce a savings rate (in thousands of dollars per year) of

$$S'(x) = 225 - x^2,$$

where x is the number of years the machinery is to be used. The rate of additional costs (in thousands of dollars per year) to the company due to the new machinery is expected to be

$$C'(x) = x^2 + 25x + 150.$$

For how many years should the company use the new machinery? Find the net savings (in thousands of dollars) over this period.

87. **Oil Production** The following table shows the amount of crude oil (in billions of barrels) produced in the United States in recent years. *Source: U.S. Energy Information Administration.*

Year	Crude Oil Produced
2000	2.131
2001	2.118
2002	2.097
2003	2.073
2004	1.983
2005	1.890
2006	1.862
2007	1.848
2008	1.812
2009	1.938

In this exercise we are interested in the total amount of crude oil produced over the 9-year period from mid-2000 to mid-2009, using the data for the 10 years above.

a. One approach is to sum up the numbers in the second column, but only count half of the first and last numbers. Give the answer to this calculation.

b. Approximate the amount of crude oil produced over the 9-year period 2000–2009 by taking the average of the left endpoint sum and the right endpoint sum. Explain why this is equivalent to the calculation done in part a.

c. Explain why the answer from part a is the same as using the trapezoidal rule to approximate the amount of crude oil produced over the 9-year period 2000–2009.

d. Find the equation of the least squares line for this data, letting $x = 0$ correspond to 2000. Then integrate this equation over the interval [0, 9] to estimate the amount of crude oil produced over this time period. Compare with your answer to part a.

88. Inventory At time $t = 0$, a store has 19 units of a product in inventory. The cumulative number of units sold is given by $S(t) = e^{3t} - 1$, where t is measured in weeks. The inventory will be replenished when it drops to 1 unit. The cost of carrying inventory until then is 15 per unit per week (prorated for a portion of a week). Calculate the inventory carrying cost that will be incurred before the inventory is replenished. Choose one of the following. *Source: Society of Actuaries.*

a. 90   **b.** 199   **c.** 204   **d.** 210   **e.** 294

Life Sciences

89. Population Growth The rate of change of the population of a rare species of Australian spider for one year is given by

$$f'(t) = 100 - t\sqrt{0.4t^2 + 1},$$

where $f(t)$ is the number of spiders present at time t (in months). Find the total number of additional spiders in the first 10 months.

90. Infection Rate The rate of infection of a disease (in people per month) is given by the function

$$I'(t) = \frac{100t}{t^2 + 1},$$

where t is the time (in months) since the disease broke out. Find the total number of infected people over the first four months of the disease.

91. Insect Cannibalism In certain species of flour beetles, the larvae cannibalize the unhatched eggs. In calculating the population cannibalism rate per egg, researchers needed to evaluate the integral

$$\int_0^A c(x)\, dx,$$

where A is the length of the larval stage and $c(x)$ is the cannibalism rate per egg per larva of age x. The minimum value of A for the flour beetle *Tribolium castaneum* is 17.6 days, which is the value we will use. The function $c(x)$ starts at day 0 with a value of 0, increases linearly to the value 0.024 at day 12, and then stays constant. *Source: Journal of Animal Ecology.* Find the values of the integral using

a. formulas from geometry;

b. the Fundamental Theorem of Calculus.

92. Insulin in Sheep A research group studied the effect of a large injection of glucose in sheep fed a normal diet compared with sheep that were fasting. A graph of the plasma insulin levels (in pM—pico molars, or 10^{-12} of a molar) for both groups is shown below. The red graph designates the fasting sheep and the green graph the sheep fed a normal diet. The researchers compared the area under the curves for the two groups. *Source: Endocrinology.*

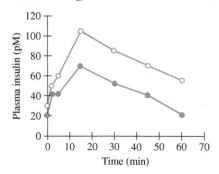

a. For the fasting sheep, estimate the area under the curve using rectangles, first by using the left endpoints, then the right endpoints, and then averaging the two. Note that the width of the rectangles will vary.

b. Repeat part a for the sheep fed a normal diet.

c. How much higher is the area under the curve for the fasting sheep compared with the normal sheep?

93. Milk Production Researchers report that the average amount of milk produced (in kilograms per day) by a 4- to 5-year-old cow weighing 700 kg can be approximated by

$$y = 1.87t^{1.49}e^{-0.189(\ln t)^2},$$

where t is the number of days into lactation. *Source: Journal of Dairy Science.*

a. Approximate the total amount of milk produced from $t = 1$ to $t = 321$ using the trapezoidal rule with $n = 8$.

b. Repeat part a using Simpson's rule with $n = 8$.

c. Repeat part a using the integration feature of a graphing calculator, and compare your answer with the answers to parts a and b.

Social Sciences

94. Automotive Accidents The table on the next page shows the amount of property damage (in dollars) due to automobile accidents in California in recent years. In this exercise we are interested in the total amount of property damage due to automobile accidents over the 8-year period from mid-2000 to mid-2008, using the data for the 9 years. *Source: The California Highway Patrol.*

a. One approach is to sum up the numbers in the second column, but only count half of the first and last numbers. Give the answer to this calculation.

b. Approximate the amount of property damage over the 8-year period 2000–2008 by taking the average of the left endpoint sum and the right endpoint sum. Explain why this is equivalent to the calculation done in part a.

Year	Property Damage ($)
2000	309,569
2001	317,567
2002	335,869
2003	331,055
2004	331,208
2005	330,195
2006	325,453
2007	313,357
2008	278,986

c. Explain why the answer from part a is the same as using the trapezoidal rule to approximate the amount of property damage over the 8-year period 2000–2008.

d. Find the equation of the least squares line for this data, letting $x = 0$ correspond to 2000. Then integrate this equation over the interval $[0, 8]$ to estimate the amount of property damage over this time period. Compare with your answer to part a.

Physical Sciences

95. Linear Motion A particle is moving along a straight line with velocity $v(t) = t^2 - 2t$. Its distance from the starting point after 3 seconds is 8 cm. Find $s(t)$, the distance of the particle from the starting point after t seconds.

EXTENDED APPLICATION

ESTIMATING DEPLETION DATES FOR MINERALS

t is becoming more and more obvious that the earth contains only a finite quantity of minerals. The "easy and cheap" sources of minerals are being used up, forcing an ever more expensive search for new sources. For example, oil from the North Slope of Alaska would never have been used in the United States during the 1930s because a great deal of Texas and California oil was readily available.

We said in an earlier chapter that population tends to follow an exponential growth curve. Mineral usage also follows such a curve. Thus, if q represents the rate of consumption of a certain mineral at time t, while q_0 represents consumption when $t = 0$, then

$$q = q_0 e^{kt},$$

where k is the growth constant. For example, the world consumption of petroleum in 1970 was 16,900 million barrels. During this period energy use was growing rapidly, and by 1975 annual world consumption had risen to 21,300 million barrels. We can use these two values to make a rough estimate of the constant k, and we find that over this 5-year span the average value of k was about 0.047, representing 4.7% annual growth. If we let $t = 0$ correspond to the base year 1970, then

$$q = 16,900 e^{0.047t}$$

is the rate of consumption at time t, assuming that all the trends of the early 1970s have continued. In 1970 a reasonable guess would have put the total amount of oil in provable reserves or likely to be discovered in the future at 1,500,000 million barrels. At the 1970–1975 rate of consumption, in how many years after 1970 would you expect the world's reserves to be depleted? We can use the integral calculus of this chapter to find out. *Source: Energy Information Administration.*

To begin, we need to know the total quantity of petroleum that would be used between time $t = 0$ and some future time $t = T$. Figure 34 on the following page shows a typical graph of the function $q = q_0 e^{kt}$.

Following the work we did in Section 3, divide the time interval from $t = 0$ to $t = T$ into n subintervals. Let each subinterval have width Δt. Let the rate of consumption for the ith subinterval be approximated by q_i^*. Thus, the approximate total consumption for the subinterval is given by

$$q_i^* \cdot \Delta t,$$

and the total consumption over the interval from time $t = 0$ to $t = T$ is approximated by

$$\sum_{i=1}^{n} q_i^* \cdot \Delta t.$$

67

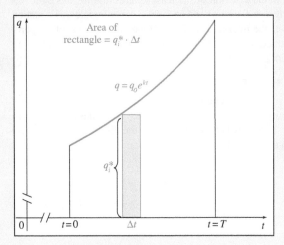

FIGURE 34

The limit of this sum as Δt approaches 0 gives the total consumption from time $t = 0$ to $t = T$. That is,

$$\text{Total consumption} = \lim_{\Delta t \to 0} \sum q_i^* \cdot \Delta t.$$

We have seen, however, that this limit is the definite integral of the function $q = q_0 e^{kt}$ from $t = 0$ to $t = T$, or

$$\text{Total consumption} = \int_0^T q_0 e^{kt} \, dt.$$

We can now evaluate this definite integral.

$$\int_0^T q_0 e^{kt} \, dt = q_0 \int_0^T e^{kt} \, dt = q_0 \left(\frac{e^{kt}}{k} \right) \Big|_0^T$$

$$= \frac{q_0}{k} e^{kt} \Big|_0^T = \frac{q_0}{k} e^{kT} - \frac{q_0}{k} e^0$$

$$= \frac{q_0}{k} e^{kT} - \frac{q_0}{k}(1)$$

$$= \frac{q_0}{k}(e^{kT} - 1) \qquad \qquad \text{(1)}$$

Now let us return to the numbers we gave for petroleum. We said that $q_0 = 16{,}900$ million barrels, where q_0 represents consumption in the base year of 1970. We have $k = 0.047$ with total petroleum reserves estimated at $1{,}500{,}000$ million barrels. Thus, using Equation (1) we have

$$1{,}500{,}000 = \frac{16{,}900}{0.047}(e^{0.047T} - 1).$$

Multiply both sides of the equation by 0.047.

$$70{,}500 = 16{,}900(e^{0.047T} - 1)$$

Divide both sides of the equation by 16,900.

$$4.2 = e^{0.047T} - 1$$

Add 1 to both sides.

$$5.2 = e^{0.047T}$$

Take natural logarithms of both sides.

$$\ln 5.2 = \ln e^{0.047T}$$
$$= 0.047T$$

Finally,

$$T = \frac{\ln 5.2}{0.047} \approx 35.$$

By this result, petroleum reserves would only last 35 years after 1970, that is, until about 2005.

In fact, in the early 1970s some analysts were predicting that reserves would be exhausted before the end of the century, and this was a reasonable guess. But since 1970, more reserves have been discovered. One way to refine our model is to look at the historical data over a longer time span. The following table gives average world annual petroleum consumption in millions of barrels at 5-year intervals from 1970 to 2000. *Source: Energy Information Administration.*

Year	World Consumption (in millions of barrels)
1970	16,900
1975	21,300
1980	22,900
1985	22,200
1990	24,300
1995	25,700
2000	27,900
2005	30,400

The first step in comparing this data with our exponential model is to estimate a value for the growth constant k. One simple way of doing this is to solve the equation

$$30{,}400 = 16{,}900 \cdot e^{k \cdot 35}.$$

Using natural logarithms just as we did in estimating the time to depletion for $k = 0.036$, we find that

$$k = \frac{\ln\left(\dfrac{30{,}400}{16{,}900}\right)}{35} \approx 0.017.$$

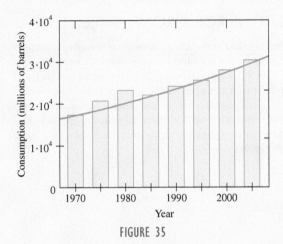

FIGURE 35

So the data from the Bureau of Transportation Statistics suggests a growth constant of about 1.7%. We can check the fit by plotting the function $16{,}900 \cdot e^{0.017t}$ along with a bar graph of the consumption data, shown in Figure 35. The fit looks reasonably good, but over this short range of 35 years, the exponential model is close to a linear model, and the growth in consumption is certainly not smooth.

The exponential model rests on the assumption of a constant growth rate. As already noted, we might expect instead that the growth rate would change as the world comes closer to exhausting its reserves. In particular, scarcity might drive up the price of oil and thus reduce consumption. We can use integration to explore an alternative model in which the factor k changes over time, so that k becomes $k(t)$, a function of time.

As an illustration, we explore a model in which the growth constant k declines toward 0 over time. We'll use 1970 as our base year, so the variable t will count years since 1970. We need a simple positive function $k(t)$ that tends toward 0 as t gets large. To get some numbers to work with, assume that the growth rate was 2% in 1970 and declined to 1% by 1995. There are many possible choices for the function $k(t)$, but a convenient one is

$$k(t) = \frac{0.5}{t + 25}.$$

Using integration to turn the instantaneous rate of consumption into the total consumption up to time T, we can write

$$\text{Total consumption} = 16{,}900 \int_0^T e^{k(t) \cdot t}\, dt$$
$$= 16{,}900 \int_0^T e^{0.5t/(t + 25)}\, dt.$$

We'd like to find out when the world will use up its estimated reserves, but as just noted, the estimates have increased since the 1970s. It is estimated that the current global petroleum reserves are 3,000,000 million barrels. *Source: Geotimes.* So we need to solve

$$3{,}000{,}000 = 16{,}900 \int_0^T e^{0.5t/(t + 25)}\, dt \qquad (2)$$

But this problem is much harder to solve than the corresponding problem for constant growth, because *there is no formula for evaluating this definite integral!* The function

$$g(t) = e^{0.5t/(t + 25)}$$

doesn't have an antiderivative that we can write down in terms of functions that we know how to compute.

Here the numerical integration techniques discussed in Section 6 come to the rescue. We can use one of the integration rules to *approximate* the integral numerically for various values of T, and with some trial and error we can estimate how long the reserves will last. If you have a calculator or computer algebra system that does numerical integration, you can pick some T values and evaluate the right-hand side of Equation (2). Here are the results produced by one computer algebra system:

> For $T = 120$ the integral is about 2,797,000.
>
> For $T = 130$ the integral is about 3,053,000.
>
> For $T = 140$ the integral is about 3,311,000.

So using this model we would estimate that starting in 1970 the petroleum reserves would last for about 130 years, that is, until 2100.

Our integration tools are essential in building and exploring models of resource use, but the difference in our two predictions (35 years vs. 130 years) illustrates the difficulty of making accurate predictions. A model that performs well on historical data may not take the changing dynamics of resource use into account, leading to forecasts that are either unduly gloomy or too optimistic.

EXERCISES

1. Find the number of years that the estimated petroleum reserves would last if used at the same rate as in the base year.

2. How long would the estimated petroleum reserves last if the growth constant was only 2% instead of 4.7%?

Estimate the length of time until depletion for each mineral.

3. Bauxite (the ore from which aluminum is obtained): estimated reserves in base year 15,000,000 thousand tons; rate of consumption in base year 63,000 thousand tons; growth constant 6%

4. Bituminous coal: estimated world reserves 2,000,000 million tons; rate of consumption in base year 2200 million tons; growth constant 4%

5. **a.** Verify that the function $k(t)$ defined on the previous page has the right values at $k = 0$ and $k = 25$.

   b. Find a similar function that has $k(0) = 0.03$ and $k(25) = 0.02$.

6. **a.** Use the function you defined in Exercise 5 b to write an integral for world petroleum consumption from 1970 until T years after 1970.

   b. If you have access to a numerical integrator, compute some values of your integral and estimate the time required to exhaust the reserve of 3,000,000 million barrels.

7. A reasonable assumption is that over time scarcity might drive up the price of oil and thus reduce consumption. Comment on the fact that the rate of oil consumption actually increased in 2002, connecting current events and economic forecasts to the short-term possibility of a reduction in consumption.

8. Develop a spreadsheet that shows the time to exhaustion for various values of k.

9. Go to the website WolframAlpha.com and enter "integrate." Follow the instructions to find the time to exhaustion for various values of k. Discuss how the solution compares with the solutions provided by a graphing calculator and by Microsoft Excel.

DIRECTIONS FOR GROUP PROJECT

Suppose that you and three other students are spending a summer as interns for a local congresswoman. During your internship you realize that the information contained in your calculus class could be used to help with a new bill under consideration. The primary purpose of the bill is to require, by law, that all cars manufactured after a certain date get at least 60 miles per gallon of gasoline. Prepare a report that uses the information above to make a case for or against a bill of this nature.

ANSWERS TO SELECTED EXERCISES

Exercises 1

1. They differ only by a constant.

5. $6k + C$ **7.** $z^2 + 3z + C$

9. $2t^3 - 4t^2 + 7t + C$

11. $z^4 + z^3 + z^2 - 6z + C$

13. $10z^{3/2}/3 + \sqrt{2}z + C$

For exercises . . .	5–24, 27,28,	25,26, 29–32, 35,36, 41,42, 60,63, 66	33,34, 37–40, 61	43,44	45–52, 57–59, 65	53–56	67–74
Refer to example . . .	4,5	7,8	6	12	9	10	11

15. $5x^4/4 - 20x^2 + C$

17. $8v^{3/2}/3 - 6v^{5/2}/5 + C$

19. $4u^{5/2} - 4u^{7/2} + C$ **21.** $-7/z + C$ **23.** $-\pi^3/(2y^2) - 2\sqrt{\pi y} + C$ **25.** $6t^{-1.5} - 2\ln|t| + C$ **27.** $-1/(3x) + C$

29. $-15e^{-0.2x} + C$ **31.** $-3\ln|x| - 10e^{-0.4x} + e^{0.1}x + C$ **33.** $(1/4)\ln|t| + t^3/6 + C$ **35.** $e^{2u}/2 + 2u^2 + C$

37. $x^3/3 + x^2 + x + C$ **39.** $6x^{7/6}/7 + 3x^{2/3}/2 + C$ **41.** $10^x/(\ln 10) + C$ **43.** $f(x) = 3x^{5/3}/5$

45. $C(x) = 2x^2 - 5x + 8$ **47.** $C(x) = 3e^{0.01x} + 5$ **49.** $C(x) = 3x^{5/3}/5 + 2x + 114/5$

51. $C(x) = 5x^2/2 - \ln|x| - 153.50$ **53.** $p = 175 - 0.01x - 0.01x^2$ **55.** $p = 500 - 0.1\sqrt{x}$

57. a. $f(t) = 3.75t^2 - 16.8t + 0.05$ **b.** Approximately 152.6 billion monthly text messages **59. a.** $P(x) = 25x^4/2 + 10x^3 - 40$

b. \$240 **61.** $a\ln x - bx + C$ **63. a.** $N(t) = 155.3e^{0.3219t} + 144.7$ **b.** 7537

65. a. $B(t) = 0.02016t^3 - 0.6460t^2 + 15.86t + 839.7$ **b.** About 2,082,000 **67.** $v(t) = 5t^3/3 + 4t + 6$

69. $s(t) = -16t^2 + 6400$; 20 sec **71.** $s(t) = 2t^{5/2} + 3e^{-t} + 1$ **73.** 160 ft/sec, 12 ft

Exercises 2

3. $2(2x + 3)^5/5 + C$

5. $-(2m + 1)^{-2}/2 + C$

7. $-(x^2 + 2x - 4)^{-3}/3 + C$

For exercises . . .	3,4,29, 33,34	5–8, 21,22	9,10,27, 28,30	11–16, 31,35, 36	17–20, 32	23–26	39–44
Refer to example . . .	1	3	2	5	4	6	7

9. $(4z^2 - 5)^{3/2}/12 + C$ **11.** $e^{2x^3}/2 + C$ **13.** $e^{2t-t^2}/2 + C$ **15.** $-e^{1/z} + C$ **17.** $[\ln(t^2 + 2)]/2 + C$

19. $[\ln(x^4 + 4x^2 + 7)]/4 + C$ **21.** $-1/[2(x^2 + x)^2] + C$ **23.** $(p + 1)^7/7 - (p + 1)^6/6 + C$

25. $2(u - 1)^{3/2}/3 + 2(u - 1)^{1/2} + C$ **27.** $(x^2 + 12x)^{3/2}/3 + C$ **29.** $(1 + 3\ln x)^3/9 + C$ **31.** $(1/2)\ln(e^{2x} + 5) + C$

33. $(\ln 10)(\log x)^2/2 + C$ **35.** $8^{3x^2+1}/(6\ln 8) + C$ **39. a.** $R(x) = 6(x^2 + 27,000)^{1/3} - 180$ **b.** 150 players

41. a. $C(x) = 6\ln(5x^2 + e) + 4$ **b.** Yes **43. a.** $f(t) = 4.0674 \times 10^{-4}[(t - 1970)^{2.4}/2.4 +$

$1970(t - 1970)^{1.4}/1.4] + 61.298$ **b.** About 181,000

Exercises 3

3. a. 88 **b.** $\int_0^8 (2x + 5)\, dx$

For exercises . . .	5–14,17–22	15,16,24–30, 33–35,39	31,32,36–38
Refer to example . . .	1,2	3	4

5. a. 21 **b.** 23 **c.** 22 **d.** 22 **7. a.** 10 **b.** 10 **c.** 10 **d.** 11 **9. a.** 8.22 **b.** 15.48 **c.** 11.85 **d.** 10.96 **11. a.** 6.70

b. 3.15 **c.** 4.93 **d.** 4.17 **13. a.** 4 **b.** 4 **15. a.** 4 **b.** 5 **17.** 4π **19.** 24 **21. b.** 0.385 **c.** 0.33835 **d.** 0.334334

e. 0.333333 **25.** Left: 1410 trillion BTUs; right: 3399 trillion BTUs; average: 2404.5 trillion BTUs **27. a.** Left: about 582,000

cases; right: about 580,000 cases; average: about 581,000 cases **b.** Left: about 146,000 cases; right: about 144,000 cases; average:

about 145,000 cases **29.** About 1300 ft; yes **31.** 2751 ft, 3153 ft, 2952 ft **33. a.** About 660 BTU/ft² **b.** About 320 BTU/ft²

35. a. 9 ft **b.** 2 sec **c.** 4.6 ft **d.** Between 3 and 3.5 sec **37.** 22.5 and 18 ft **39. a.** About 75,600 **b.** About 77,300

Exercises 4

1. -18 **3.** $-3/2$ **5.** $28/3$ **7.** 13

9. $-16/3$ **11.** 76 **13.** $4/5$ **15.** $108/25$

17. $20e^{0.3} - 20e^{0.2} + 3\ln 2 - 3\ln 3 \approx 1.353$

For exercises . . .	1–6,9–12, 15–20, 23,24	7,8,13,14, 21,22, 27–30,54	31–44,47	55–61, 63–72
Refer to example . . .	1,2,3	4	5, 6	7

19. $e^8/4 - e^4/4 - 1/6 \approx 731.4$ **21.** $91/3$

23. $447/7 \approx 63.86$ **25.** $(\ln 2)^2/2 \approx 0.2402$ **27.** 49 **29.** $1/8 - 1/[2(3 + e^2)] \approx 0.07687$ **31.** 10 **33.** 76 **35.** $41/2$

37. $e^2 - 3 + 1/e \approx 4.757$ **39.** $e - 2 + 1/e \approx 1.086$ **41.** $23/3$ **43.** $e^2 - 2e + 1 \approx 2.952$

45. $\int_a^c f(x)\,dx = \int_a^b f(x)\,dx + \int_b^c f(x)\,dx$ **47.** -8 **51.** -12 **53. a.** $x^5/5 - 1/5$ **c.** $f'(1) \approx 2.746$, and $g(1) = e \approx 2.718$

55. a. $(9000/8)(17^{4/3} - 2^{4/3}) \approx \$46,341$ **b.** $(9000/8)(26^{4/3} - 17^{4/3}) \approx \$37,477$ **c.** It is slowly increasing without bound.

57. No **59. a.** 0.8778 ft **b.** 0.6972 ft **61. a.** 18.12 **b.** 8.847 **63. b.** $\int_0^{60} n(x)\,dx$ **c.** $2(51^{3/2} - 26^{3/2})/15 \approx 30.89$ million

65. a. $Q(R) = \pi k R^4/2$ **b.** $0.04k$ mm per min **67. b.** About 505,000 kJ/W$^{0.67}$ **69. a.** About 286 million; the total population aged 0 to 90 **b.** About 64 million **71. a.** $c'(t) = 1.2e^{0.04t}$ **b.** $\int_0^{10} 1.2e^{0.04t}\, dt$ **c.** $30e^{0.4} - 30 \approx 14.75$ billion **d.** About 12.8 yr **e.** About 14.4 yr

Exercises 5

1. 21 **3.** 20 **5.** 23/3 **7.** 366.2
9. 4/3 **11.** $2\ln 2 - \ln 6 + 3/2 \approx 1.095$
13. $6\ln(3/2) - 6 + 2e^{-1} + 2e \approx 2.605$

For exercises . . .	1,2	3–6, 11–18,20, 23,24	7–10, 19,21,22, 25,26,41,42	27–30, 39,40	31–37
Refer to example . . .	1	3	2	4	5

15. $(e^{-2} + e^4)/2 - 2 \approx 25.37$ **17.** 1/2 **19.** 1/20 **21.** $3(2^{4/3})/2 - 3(2^{7/3})/7 \approx 1.620$ **23.** $(e^9 + e^6 + 1)/3 \approx 2836$
25. $-1.9241, -0.4164, 0.6650$ **27. a.** 8 yr **b.** About $148 **c.** About $771 **29. a.** 39 days **b.** $3369.18 **c.** $484.02
d. $2885.16 **31.** 12,931.66 **33.** 54
35. a.

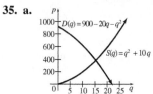

b. $(15, 375)$ **c.** $4500 **d.** $3375 **37. a.** 12 **b.** $5616, $1116 **c.** $1872, $1503
d. $387 **39. a.** About 71.25 gal **b.** About 25 hr **c.** About 105 gal **d.** About 47.91 hr
41. a. 0.019; the lower 10% of the income producers earn 1.9% of the total income of the
population. **b.** 0.184; the lower 40% of the income producers earn 18.4% of the total income of
the population. **c.**

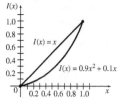

d. 0.15 **e.** Income is distributed less equally in 2008 than in 1968.

Exercises 6

1. a. 12.25 **b.** 12 **c.** 12 **3. a.** 3.35 **b.** 3.3
c. $3\ln 3 \approx 3.296$ **5. a.** 11.34 **b.** 10.5 **c.** 10.5
7. a. 0.9436 **b.** 0.8374 **c.** $4/5 = 0.8$ **9. a.** 1.236

For exercises . . .	1a–12a,15, 23a–24a,29	1b–12b,17,19,20, 23b–24b,29,30, 33–35	21,22,25–28, 31,32
Refer to example . . .	1	2	3

b. 1.265 **c.** $2 - 2e^{-1} \approx 1.264$ **11. a.** 5.991 **b.** 6.167
c. 6.283; Simpson's rule **13.** b is true. **15. a.** 0.2 **b.** 0.220703, 0.205200, 0.201302, 0.200325, 0.020703, 0.005200, 0.001302,
0.000325 **c.** $p = 2$ **17. a.** 0.2 **b.** 0.2005208, 0.2000326, 0.2000020, 0.2000001, 0.0005208, 0.0000326, 0.0000020, 0.0000001
c. $p = 4$ **19.** $M = 0.7355; S = 0.8048$

21. a.

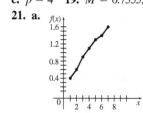

b. 6.3 **c.** 6.27 **23. a.** 1.831 **b.** 1.758 **25.** About 30 mcg(h)/ml; this represents the total
amount of drug available to the patient for each ml of blood. **27.** About 9 mcg(h)/ml; this represents the total effective amount of the drug available to the patient for each ml of blood.
29. a. $y = b_0(t/7)^{b_1}e^{-b_2 t/7}$ **b.** About 1212 kg; about 1231 kg **c.** About 1224 kg; about 1250 kg
31. a.

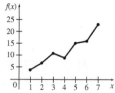

b. 71.5 **c.** 69.0 **33.** 3979 **35. a.** 0.6827 **b.** 0.9545 **c.** 0.9973

Chapter Review Exercises

1. True **2.** False **3.** False **4.** True
5. True **6.** False **7.** False **8.** True
9. True **10.** False **11.** True **12.** False
13. False **14.** True **19.** $x^2 + 3x + C$

For exercises . . .	1–4, 19–30, 79,80, 84	5,16,17, 31–40, 87,94	6–8,15, 41–43, 81,92,96	9,10, 45–62, 82,83, 89–91, 95	11,12, 63–66, 85,86	13,14, 18, 44, 67–77, 93
Refer to section . . .	1	2	3	4	5	6

21. $x^3/3 - 3x^2/2 + 2x + C$ **23.** $2x^{3/2} + C$ **25.** $2x^{3/2}/3 + 9x^{1/3} + C$ **27.** $2x^{-2} + C$ **29.** $-3e^{2x}/2 + C$ **31.** $e^{3x}/6 + C$
33. $(3\ln|x^2 - 1|)/2 + C$ **35.** $-(x^3 + 5)^{-3}/9 + C$ **37.** $-e^{-3x}/12 + C$ **39.** $(3\ln x + 2)^5/15 + C$ **41.** 20 **43.** 24
45. a. $s(T) - s(0)$ **b.** $\int_0^T v(t)\, dt = s(T) - s(0)$ is equivalent to the Fundamental Theorem with $a = 0$ and $b = T$ because $s(t)$
is an antiderivative of $v(t)$. **47.** 12 **49.** $3\ln 5 + 12/25 \approx 5.308$ **51.** 19/15 **53.** $3(1 - e^{-4})/2 \approx 1.473$ **55.** $\pi/32$
57. $25\pi/4$ **59.** 13/3 **61.** $(e^4 - 1)/2 \approx 26.80$ **63.** 64/3 **65.** 149/3 **67.** 0.5833; 0.6035 **69.** 4.187; 4.155 **71.** 0.6011
73. 4.156 **75. a.** 4/3 **b.** 1.146 **c.** 1.252 **77. a.** 0 **b.** 0 **79.** $C(x) = (2x - 1)^{3/2} + 145$ **81.** $96,000 **83.** $38,000
85. a. $916.67 **b.** $666.67 **87. a.** 17.718 billion barrels **b.** 17.718 billion barrels **d.** $y = -0.03545x + 2.1347$; 17.777
billion barrels **89.** 782 **91. a.** 0.2784 **b.** 0.2784 **93. a.** About 8208 kg **b.** About 8430 kg **c.** About 8558 kg
95. $s(t) = t^3/3 - t^2 + 8$.

SAMPLE SOURCES

Section 1

1. Exercise 57 from "US Wireless Quick Facts Year-End Figures," CTIA, International Association for the Wireless Telecommunications Industry. http://www.ctia.org/advocacy/research/index.cfm/AID/10323.
2. Exercise 61 from Dennis, Brian and Robert F. Costantino, "Analysis of Steady-State Populations with the Gamma Abundance Model: Application to *Tribolium,*" *Ecology,* Vol. 69, No. 4, Aug. 1988, pp. 1200–1213.
3. Exercise 65 from "Digest of Education Statistics," National Center for Education Statistics, Table 271. http://nces.gov/programs/digest;d08/tables/dt08_271.asp.
4. Exercise 66 from "Digest of Education Statistics," National Center for Education Statistics, Table 279. http://nces.gov/programs/digest;d08/tables/dt08_279.asp

Section 2

1. From Quirin, Jim and Barry Cohen, *Chartmasters' Rock 100,* 5th ed. Copyright 1992 by Chartmasters. Reprinted by permission.
2. Exercise 43 from *National Transportation Statistics 2006,* Bureau of Transportation Statistics.
3. Exercise 44 from *Hospital Statistics,* American Hospital Association.

Section 3

1. Exercise 23 from MacLaskey, Michael, *All About Lawns,* ed. by Alice Mace, Ortho Information Services, © 1980, p.108.
2. Exercise 25 from U.S. Energy Information Administration, Monthly Energy Review June 2010, Table 10.1, "Renewable Energy Production and Consumption by Source." www.eia.doe.gov/mer/ppdf/mer.pdf.
3. Exercise 27 from Department of Environment, Food, and Rural Affairs, Foot and Mouth Disease, http://footandmouth.csl.gov.uk.
4. Exercise 28 from California Highway Patrol, Table 1A; "Fatal Collisions by Month 1999–2008." http://www.chp.ca.gov/switrs/#section1.
5. Exercises 29 and 30 from http://www.roadandtrack.com/tests/data-panel-archive.
6. Exercises 33 and 34 from Sustainable by Design, www.susdesign.com/windowheatgain.
7. Exercise 35 based on an example given by Stephen Monk of the University of Washington.
8. Exercise 38 from Wildbur, Peter, *Information Graphics,* Van Nostrand Reinhold, 1989, pp. 126–127.
9. Exercise 39 from *The New York Times,* Jan. 27, 2006, p.86.

Section 4

1. Exercise 62 from Gompertz, Benjamin, "On the Nature of the Function Expressive of the Law of Human Mortality," *Philosophical Transactions of the Royal Society of London,* 1825.
2. Exercise 66 from Jorgenson, Jon T., et al., "Effects of Population Density on Horn Development in Bighorn Rams," *Journal of Wildlife Management,* Vol. 62, No. 3, 1998, pp. 1011–1020.
3. Exercise 67 from Finke, M., "Energy Requirements of Adult Female Beagles," *Journal of Nutrition,* Vol. 124, 1994, pp. 2604s–2608s.
4. Exercise 68 from Nord, Gail and John Nord, "Sediment in Lake Coeur d'Alene, Idaho," *Mathematics Teacher,* Vol. 91, No. 4, April 1998, pp. 292–295.
5. Exercise 69 was originally contributed by Ralph DeMarr, University of New Mexico. It was updated with information from the U.S. Census Bureau. http://www.census.gov/popest/national/asrh/2008-nat-res.html.
6. Exercise 70 was originally contributed by Ralph DeMarr, University of New Mexico. It was updated with information from the U.S. Census Bureau, Current Population Reports, Table 680, P60-235, August 2008. http://www.census.gov/prod/2008pubs/p60-235.pdf.

Section 5

1. Exercise 38 from DeCicco, John and Marc Ross, "Improving Automotive Efficiency," *Scientific American,* Vol. 271, No. 6, Dec. 1994, p. 56. Copyright © 1994 by Scientific American, Inc. All rights reserved. Oil_and_Liquid_Fuels.
2. Exercise 38b from Table 4a, U.S. Crude Oil and Liquid Fuels Supply, Consumption, and Inventories, http://www.eia.doe.gov/steo.
3. Exercise 41 from Table H-4. "Gini Ratios for Households, by Race and Hispanic Origin of Householder: 1967 to 2008," http://www.census.gov/hhes/www/income/data/historical/inequality/index.html.

Section 6

1. From Chodos, D. J. and A. R. DeSantos, *Basics of Bioavailability,* Upjohn Company, 1978.
2. Exercise 29 from Mezzadra, C., R. Paciaroni, S. Vulich, E. Villarreal, and L. Melucci, "Estimation of Milk Consumption Curve Parameters for Different Genetic Groups of Bovine Calves," *Animal Production,* Vol. 49, 1989, pp. 83–87.
3. Exercise 30 from Department of Environment, Food, and Rural Affairs, Foot and Mouth Disease, http://footandmouth.csl.gov.uk.
4. Exercise 34 from Mezzadra, C., R. Paciaroni, S. Vulich, E. Villarreal, and L. Melucci, "Estimation of Milk Consumption Curve Parameters for Different Genetic Groups of Bovine Calves, *Animal Production,* Vol. 49, 1989, pp. 83–87.

Review Exercises

1. Exercise 78 from Problem 7 from May 2003 Course 1 Examination of the *Education and Examination Committee of the Society of Actuaries.* Reprinted by permission of the Society of Actuaries.
2. Exercise 84 from Economic News Release. http://data.bls.gov/news.release/prod3.t02.htm.
3. Exercise 87 from "Annual U.S. Field Production of Crude Oil," U.S. Energy Information Administration http://www.eia.doe.gov/dnav/pet/hist/LeafHandler.ashx?n-petas-mcrfpus19f=a.
4. Exercise 88 from Problem 38 from May 2003 Course 1 Examination of the *Education and Examination Committee of the Society of Actuaries.* Reprinted by permission of the Society of Actuaries.
5. Exercise 91 from Hastings, Alan and Robert F. Costantino, "Oscillations in Population Numbers: Age-Dependent Cannibalism," *Journal of Animal Ecology,* Vol. 60, No. 2, June 1991, pp. 471–482.
6. Exercise 92 from Oliver, M. H. et al., "Material Undernutrition During the Periconceptual Period Increases Plasma Taurine Levels and Insulin Response to Glucose but not Arginine in the Late Gestation Fetal Sheep," *Endocrinology,* Vol 14, No. 10, 2001, pp. 4576–4579.
7. Exercise 93 from Freeze, Brian S. and Timothy J. Richards, "Lactation Curve Estimation for Use in Economic Optimization Models in the Dairy Industry," *Journal of Dairy Science,* Vol. 75, 1992, pp. 2984–2989.
8. Exercise 94 from Table IF "Property-Damage-Only Collisions by Month 1999–2008. The California Highway Patrol." http://www.chp.gov/switrs/#section1.

Extended Application

1. From http://www.eia.gov/totalenergy/data/annual.
2. From http://www.geotimes.org/nov02/feature_oil.html.

CREDITS

Further Techniques and Applications of Integration

It might seem that definite integrals with infinite limits have only theoretical interest, but in fact these *improper* integrals provide answers to many practical questions. An example in Section 4 models an environmental cleanup process in which the amount of pollution entering a stream decreases by a constant fraction each year. An improper integral gives the total amount of pollutant that will ever enter the river.

B.W. Folsom/ Shutterstock

Further Techniques and Applications of Integration

I
n this chapter we develop methods of integrating functions. We also show how to evaluate an integral that has one or both limits at infinity. These techniques allow us to consider applications of integration such as volumes of solids of revolution, the average value of a function, and continuous money flow.

1

Integration by Parts

APPLY IT   If we know the rate of growth of a patch of moss, how can we calculate the area the moss covers?

We will use integration by parts to answer this question in Exercise 42.

The technique of *integration by parts* often makes it possible to reduce a complicated integral to a simpler integral. We know that if u and v are both differentiable functions, then uv is also differentiable and, by the product rule for derivatives,

$$\frac{d(uv)}{dx} = u\frac{dv}{dx} + v\frac{du}{dx}.$$

This expression can be rewritten, using differentials, as

$$d(uv) = u\,dv + v\,du.$$

Integrating both sides of this last equation gives

$$\int d(uv) = \int u\,dv + \int v\,du,$$

or

$$uv = \int u\,dv + \int v\,du.$$

Rearranging terms gives the following formula.

Integration by Parts
If u and v are differentiable functions, then

$$\int u\,dv = uv - \int v\,du.$$

The process of finding integrals by this formula is called **integration by parts**. There are two ways to do integration by parts: the standard method and column integration. Both methods are illustrated in the following example.

EXAMPLE 1   **Integration by Parts**

Find $\int xe^{5x}\,dx$.

Method 1
Standard Method

SOLUTION

Although this integral cannot be found by using any method studied so far, it can be found with integration by parts. First write the expression $xe^{5x}\,dx$ as a product of two functions u and dv in such a way that $\int dv$ can be found. One way to do this is to choose the two functions x and e^{5x}. Both x and e^{5x} can be integrated, but $\int x\, dx$, which is $x^2/2$, is more complicated than x itself, while the derivative of x is 1, which is simpler than x. Since e^{5x} remains the same (except for the coefficient) whether it is integrated or differentiated, it is best here to choose

$$dv = e^{5x}\, dx \qquad \text{and} \qquad u = x.$$

Then

$$du = dx,$$

and v is found by integrating dv:

$$v = \int dv = \int e^{5x}\, dx = \frac{e^{5x}}{5}.$$

We need not introduce the constant of integration until the last step, because only one constant is needed. Now substitute into the formula for integration by parts and complete the integration.

$$\int u\, dv = uv - \int v\, du$$

$$\underbrace{\int x}_{u}\underbrace{e^{5x}\, dx}_{dv} = \underbrace{x}_{u}\underbrace{\left(\frac{e^{5x}}{5}\right)}_{v} - \int \underbrace{\frac{e^{5x}}{5}}_{v}\underbrace{dx}_{du}$$

$$= \frac{xe^{5x}}{5} - \frac{e^{5x}}{25} + C$$

$$= \frac{e^{5x}}{25}(5x - 1) + C \qquad \text{Factor out } e^{5x}/25.$$

The constant C was added in the last step. As before, check the answer by taking its derivative.

Method 2
Column Integration

A technique called **column integration**, or *tabular integration*, is equivalent to integration by parts but helps in organizing the details.* We begin by creating two columns. The first column, labeled D, contains u, the part to be differentiated in the original integral. The second column, labeled I, contains the rest of the integral: that is, the part to be integrated, but without the dx. To create the remainder of the first column, write the derivative of the function in the first row underneath it in the second row. Now write the derivative of the function in the second row underneath it in the third row. Proceed in this manner down the first column, taking derivatives until you get a 0. Form the second column in a similar manner, except take an antiderivative at each row, until the second column has the same number of rows as the first.

To illustrate this process, consider our goal of finding $\int xe^{5x}\, dx$. Here $u = x$, so e^{5x} is left for the second column. Taking derivatives down the first column and antiderivatives down the second column results in the following table.

D	I
x	e^{5x}
1	$e^{5x}/5$
0	$e^{5x}/25$

*This technique appeared in the 1988 movie *Stand and Deliver*.

Next, draw a diagonal line from each term (except the last) in the left column to the term in the row below it in the right column. Label the first such line with "+", the next with "−", and continue alternating the signs as shown.

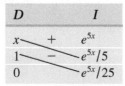

D		I
x	+	e^{5x}
1	−	$e^{5x}/5$
0		$e^{5x}/25$

Then multiply the terms on opposite ends of each diagonal line. Finally, sum up the products just formed, adding the "+" terms and subtracting the "−" terms.

$$\int xe^{5x}\,dx = x(e^{5x}/5) - 1(e^{5x}/25) + C$$

$$= \frac{xe^{5x}}{5} - \frac{e^{5x}}{25} + C$$

$$= \frac{e^{5x}}{25}(5x - 1) + C \qquad \text{Factor out } e^{5x}/25.$$

YOUR TURN 1
Find $\int xe^{-2x}\,dx$.

Compare these steps with those of Method 1 and convince yourself that the process is the same.

TRY YOUR TURN 1

Conditions for Integration by Parts
Integration by parts can be used only if the integrand satisfies the following conditions.
1. The integrand can be written as the product of two factors, u and dv.
2. It is possible to integrate dv to get v and to differentiate u to get du.
3. The integral $\int v\,du$ can be found.

EXAMPLE 2   Integration by Parts

Find $\int \ln x\,dx$ for $x > 0$.

Method 1
Standard Method

SOLUTION

No rule has been given for integrating $\ln x$, so choose

$$dv = dx \qquad \text{and} \qquad u = \ln x.$$

Then

$$v = x \qquad \text{and} \qquad du = \frac{1}{x}\,dx,$$

and, since $uv = vu$, we have

$$\int \underbrace{\ln x}_{u}\ \underbrace{dx}_{dv} = \underbrace{x \ln x}_{v \cdot u} - \int \underbrace{x \cdot \frac{1}{x}\,dx}_{v \cdot du}$$

$$= x \ln x - \int dx$$

$$= x \ln x - x + C.$$

Method 2
Column Integration

Column integration works a little differently here. As in Method 1, choose $\ln x$ as the part to differentiate. The part to be integrated must be 1. (Think of $\ln x$ as $1 \cdot \ln x$.) No matter how many times $\ln x$ is differentiated, the result is never 0. In this case, stop as soon as the natural logarithm is gone.

D	I
$\ln x$	1
$1/x$	x

Draw diagonal lines with alternating $+$ and $-$ as before. On the last line, because the left column does not contain a 0, draw a horizontal line.

D	I
$\ln x$ ⟍ $+$	1
$1/x$ —— $-$ ⟶ x	

The presence of a horizontal line indicates that the product is to be integrated, just as the original integral was represented by the first row of the two columns.

$$\int \ln x \, dx = (\ln x)x - \int \frac{1}{x} \cdot x \, dx$$

$$= x \ln x - \int dx$$

$$= x \ln x - x + C.$$

Note that when setting up the columns, a horizontal line is drawn only when a 0 does not eventually appear in the left column.

YOUR TURN 2
Find $\int \ln 2x \, dx$.

TRY YOUR TURN 2

Sometimes integration by parts must be applied more than once, as in the next example.

EXAMPLE 3 **Integration by Parts**

Find $\int (2x^2 + 5)e^{-3x} \, dx$.

Method 1
Standard Method

SOLUTION

Choose

$$dv = e^{-3x} \, dx \qquad \text{and} \qquad u = 2x^2 + 5.$$

Then

$$v = \frac{-e^{-3x}}{3} \qquad \text{and} \qquad du = 4x \, dx.$$

Substitute these values into the formula for integration by parts.

$$\int u \, dv = uv - \int v \, du$$

$$\int (2x^2 + 5)e^{-3x} \, dx = (2x^2 + 5)\left(\frac{-e^{-3x}}{3}\right) - \int \left(\frac{-e^{-3x}}{3}\right) 4x \, dx$$

$$= -(2x^2 + 5)\left(\frac{e^{-3x}}{3}\right) + \frac{4}{3}\int xe^{-3x} \, dx$$

Now apply integration by parts to the last integral, letting

$$dv = e^{-3x} \, dx \qquad \text{and} \qquad u = x,$$

so

$$v = \frac{-e^{-3x}}{3} \quad \text{and} \quad du = dx.$$

$$\int (2x^2 + 5)e^{-3x}\, dx = -(2x^2 + 5)\left(\frac{e^{-3x}}{3}\right) + \frac{4}{3}\int xe^{-3x}\, dx$$

$$= -(2x^2 + 5)\left(\frac{e^{-3x}}{3}\right) + \frac{4}{3}\left[x\left(\frac{-e^{-3x}}{3}\right) - \int\left(\frac{-e^{-3x}}{3}\right) dx\right]$$

$$= -(2x^2 + 5)\left(\frac{e^{-3x}}{3}\right) + \frac{4}{3}\left[-\frac{x}{3}e^{-3x} - \left(\frac{e^{-3x}}{9}\right)\right] + C$$

$$= -(2x^2 + 5)\left(\frac{e^{-3x}}{3}\right) - \frac{4}{9}xe^{-3x} - \frac{4}{27}e^{-3x} + C$$

$$= [-(2x^2 + 5)(9) - 4x(3) - 4]\frac{e^{-3x}}{27} + C \qquad \text{Factor out } e^{-3x}/27.$$

$$= (-18x^2 - 12x - 49)\frac{e^{-3x}}{27} + C \qquad \text{Simplify.}$$

Method 2
Column Integration

Choose $2x^2 + 5$ as the part to be differentiated, and put e^{-3x} in the integration column.

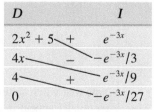

D	I
$2x^2 + 5$ +	e^{-3x}
$4x$ −	$-e^{-3x}/3$
4 +	$e^{-3x}/9$
0	$-e^{-3x}/27$

Multiplying and adding as before yields

$$\int (2x^2 + 5)e^{-3x}\, dx = (2x^2 + 5)(-e^{-3x}/3) - 4x(e^{-3x}/9) + 4(-e^{-3x}/27) + C$$

$$= (-18x^2 - 12x - 49)\frac{e^{-3x}}{27} + C.$$

YOUR TURN 3

Find $\int (3x^2 + 4)e^{2x}\, dx$.

TRY YOUR TURN 3

With the functions discussed so far in this text, choosing u and dv (or the parts to be differentiated and integrated) is relatively simple. In general, the following strategy should be used.

First see if the integration can be performed using substitution. If substitution does not work:

- See if $\ln x$ is in the integral. If it is, set $u = \ln x$ and dv equal to the rest of the integral. (Equivalently, put $\ln x$ in the D column and the rest of the function in the I column.)

- If $\ln x$ is not present, see if the integral contains x^k, where k is any positive integer, or any other polynomial. If it does, set $u = x^k$ (or the polynomial) and dv equal to the rest of the integral. (Equivalently, put x^k in the D column and the rest of the function in the I column.)

EXAMPLE 4 **Definite Integral**

Find $\int_1^e \frac{\ln x}{x^2}\, dx$.

SOLUTION First find the indefinite integral using integration by parts by the standard method. (You may wish to verify this using column integration.) Whenever $\ln x$ is present, it is selected as u, so let

$$u = \ln x \quad \text{and} \quad dv = \frac{1}{x^2}\, dx.$$

Then

$$du = \frac{1}{x} \, dx \quad \text{and} \quad v = -\frac{1}{x}.$$

Substitute these values into the formula for integration by parts, and integrate the second term on the right.

$$\int u \, dv = uv - \int v \, du$$

$$\int \frac{\ln x}{x^2} \, dx = (\ln x)\frac{-1}{x} - \int \left(-\frac{1}{x} \cdot \frac{1}{x}\right) dx$$

$$= -\frac{\ln x}{x} + \int \frac{1}{x^2} \, dx$$

$$= -\frac{\ln x}{x} - \frac{1}{x} + C$$

$$= \frac{-\ln x - 1}{x} + C$$

Now find the definite integral.

$$\int_1^e \frac{\ln x}{x^2} \, dx = \left.\frac{-\ln x - 1}{x}\right|_1^e$$

$$= \left(\frac{-1-1}{e}\right) - \left(\frac{0-1}{1}\right)$$

$$= \frac{-2}{e} + 1 \approx 0.2642411177 \quad \text{TRY YOUR TURN 4}$$

YOUR TURN 4

Find $\int_1^e x^2 \ln x \, dx$.

TECHNOLOGY NOTE

Definite integrals can be found with a graphing calculator using the function integral feature or by finding the area under the graph of the function between the limits. For example, using the `fnInt` feature of the TI-84 Plus calculator to find the integral in Example 4 gives 0.2642411177. Using the area under the graph approach gives 0.26424112, the same result rounded.

Many integrals cannot be found by the methods presented so far. For example, consider the integral

$$\int \frac{1}{4 - x^2} \, dx.$$

Substitution of $u = 4 - x^2$ will not help, because $du = -2x \, dx$, and there is no x in the numerator of the integral. We could try integration by parts, using $dv = dx$ and $u = (4 - x^2)^{-1}$. Integration gives $v = x$ and differentiation gives $du = 2x \, dx/(4 - x^2)^2$, with

$$\int \frac{1}{4 - x^2} \, dx = \frac{x}{4 - x^2} - \int \frac{2x^2}{(4 - x^2)^2} \, dx.$$

The integral on the right is more complicated than the original integral, however. A second use of integration by parts on the new integral would only make matters worse. Since we cannot choose $dv = (4 - x^2)^{-1} \, dx$ because it cannot be integrated by the methods studied so far, integration by parts is not possible for this problem.

This integration can be performed using one of the many techniques of integration beyond the scope of this text.* Tables of integrals can also be used, but technology is rapidly

*For example, see Thomas, George B., Maurice D. Weir, and Joel Hass, *Thomas' Calculus*, 12th ed., Pearson, 2010.

making such tables obsolete and even reducing the importance of techniques of integration. The following example shows how the table of integrals may be used.

EXAMPLE 5 Tables of Integrals

Find $\int \dfrac{1}{4 - x^2}\,dx$.

SOLUTION Using this formula from the table of integrals,

$$\int \frac{1}{a^2 - x^2}\,dx = \frac{1}{2a} \cdot \ln\left|\frac{a + x}{a - x}\right| + C \quad (a \neq 0)$$

with $a = 2$, gives

$$\int \frac{1}{4 - x^2}\,dx = \frac{1}{4} \cdot \ln\left|\frac{2 + x}{2 - x}\right| + C.$$

TRY YOUR TURN 5

YOUR TURN 5

Find $\int \dfrac{1}{x\sqrt{4 + x^2}}\,dx$.

TECHNOLOGY NOTE Consider how computer algebra systems and some calculators can perform integration. Using a TI-89, the answer to the above integral is

$$\frac{\ln\left(\dfrac{|x + 2|}{|x - 2|}\right)}{4}.$$

(The C is not included.) Verify that this is equivalent to the answer given in Example 5.

If you don't have a calculator or computer program that integrates symbolically, there is a Web site (http://integrals.wolfram.com), as of this writing, that finds indefinite integrals using the computer algebra system Mathematica. It includes instructions on how to enter your function. When the previous integral was entered, it returned the answer

$$\frac{1}{4}(\log(-x - 2) - \log(x - 2)).$$

Note that Mathematica does not include the C or the absolute value, and that natural logarithms are written as log. Verify that this answer is equivalent to the answer given by the TI-89 and the answer given in Example 5.

Unfortunately, there are integrals that cannot be antidifferentiated by any technique, in which case numerical integration must be used. For simplicity, all integrals to be antidifferentiated can be done with substitution or by parts, except for Exercises 23–28 in this section.

EXERCISES

Use integration by parts to find the integrals in Exercises 1–10.

1. $\int xe^x\,dx$

2. $\int (x + 6)e^x\,dx$

3. $\int (4x - 12)e^{-8x}\,dx$

4. $\int (6x + 3)e^{-2x}\,dx$

5. $\int x \ln x\,dx$

6. $\int x^3 \ln x\,dx$

7. $\int_0^1 \dfrac{2x + 1}{e^x}\,dx$

8. $\int_0^3 \dfrac{3 - x}{3e^x}\,dx$

9. $\int_1^9 \ln 3x\,dx$

10. $\int_1^2 \ln 5x\,dx$

11. Find the area between $y = (x - 2)e^x$ and the x-axis from $x = 2$ to $x = 4$.

12. Find the area between $y = (x + 1) \ln x$ and the x-axis from $x = 1$ to $x = e$.

Exercises 13–22 are mixed—some require integration by parts, while others can be integrated by using techniques discussed in the chapter on Integration.

13. $\int x^2 e^{2x}\,dx$

14. $\int \dfrac{x^2\,dx}{2x^3 + 1}$

15. $\int x^2\sqrt{x + 4}\,dx$

16. $\int (2x - 1) \ln(3x)\,dx$

17. $\int (8x + 10) \ln(5x)\,dx$

18. $\int x^3 e^{x^4}\,dx$

19. $\int_1^2 (1 - x^2)e^{2x}\, dx$

20. $\int_0^1 \dfrac{x^2\, dx}{2x^3 + 1}$

21. $\int_0^1 \dfrac{x^3\, dx}{\sqrt{3 + x^2}}$

22. $\int_0^5 x\sqrt[3]{x^2 + 2}\, dx$

Use the table of integrals, or a computer or calculator with symbolic integration capabilities, to find each indefinite integral.

23. $\int \dfrac{16}{\sqrt{x^2 + 16}}\, dx$

24. $\int \dfrac{10}{x^2 - 25}\, dx$

25. $\int \dfrac{3}{x\sqrt{121 - x^2}}\, dx$

26. $\int \dfrac{2}{3x(3x - 5)}\, dx$

27. $\int \dfrac{-6}{x(4x + 6)^2}\, dx$

28. $\int \sqrt{x^2 + 15}\, dx$

29. What rule of differentiation is related to integration by parts?

30. Explain why the two methods of solving Example 2 are equivalent.

31. Suppose that u and v are differentiable functions of x with $\int_0^1 v\, du = 4$ and the following functional values.

x	$u(x)$	$v(x)$
0	2	1
1	3	-4

Use this information to determine $\int_0^1 u\, dv$.

32. Suppose that u and v are differentiable functions of x with $\int_1^{20} v\, du = -1$ and the following functional values.

x	$u(x)$	$v(x)$
1	5	-2
20	15	6

Use this information to determine $\int_1^{20} u\, dv$.

33. Suppose we know that the functions r and s are everywhere differentiable and that $r(0) = 0$. Suppose we also know that for $0 \le x \le 2$, the area between the x-axis and the nonnegative function $h(x) = s(x)\dfrac{dr}{dx}$ is 5, and that on the same interval, the area between the x-axis and the nonnegative function $k(x) = r(x)\dfrac{ds}{dx}$ is 10. Determine $r(2)s(2)$.

34. Suppose we know that the functions u and v are everywhere differentiable and that $u(3) = 0$. Suppose we also know that for $1 \le x \le 3$, the area between the x-axis and the nonnegative function $h(x) = u(x)\dfrac{dv}{dx}$ is 15, and that on the same interval, the area between the x-axis and the nonnegative function $k(x) = v(x)\dfrac{du}{dx}$ is 20. Determine $u(1)v(1)$.

35. Use integration by parts to derive the following formula from the table of integrals.

$$\int x^n \cdot \ln |x|\, dx = x^{n+1}\left[\dfrac{\ln |x|}{n + 1} - \dfrac{1}{(n + 1)^2}\right] + C, \quad n \ne -1$$

36. Use integration by parts to derive the following formula from the table of integrals.

$$\int x^n e^{ax}\, dx = \dfrac{x^n e^{ax}}{a} - \dfrac{n}{a}\int x^{n-1}e^{ax}\, dx + C, \quad a \ne 0$$

37. a. One way to integrate $\int x\sqrt{x + 1}\, dx$ is to use integration by parts. Do so to find the antiderivative.

   b. Another way to evaluate the integral in part a is by using the substitution $u = x + 1$. Do so to find the antiderivative.

   c. Compare the results from the two methods. If they do not look the same, explain how this can happen. Discuss the advantages and disadvantages of each method.

38. Using integration by parts,

$$\int \frac{1}{x}\, dx = \int \frac{1}{x} \cdot 1\, dx$$
$$= \frac{1}{x} \cdot x - \int \left(-\frac{1}{x^2}\right)x\, dx$$
$$= 1 + \int \frac{1}{x}\, dx.$$

Subtracting $\int \frac{1}{x}\, dx$ from both sides we conclude that $0 = 1$. What is wrong with this logic? *Source: Sam Northshield.*

APPLICATIONS

Business and Economics

39. Rate of Change of Revenue The rate of change of revenue (in dollars per calculator) from the sale of x calculators is

$$R'(x) = (x + 1)\ln(x + 1).$$

Find the total revenue from the sale of the first 12 calculators. (*Hint:* In this exercise, it simplifies matters to write an antiderivative of $x + 1$ as $(x + 1)^2/2$ rather than $x^2/2 + x$.)

Life Sciences

40. Reaction to a Drug The rate of reaction to a drug is given by

$$r'(t) = 2t^2 e^{-t},$$

where t is the number of hours since the drug was administered. Find the total reaction to the drug from $t = 1$ to $t = 6$.

41. Growth of a Population The rate of growth of a microbe population is given by

$$m'(t) = 27te^{3t},$$

where t is time in days. What is the total accumulated growth during the first 2 days?

42. APPLY IT Rate of Growth The area covered by a patch of moss is growing at a rate of

$$A'(t) = \sqrt{t}\, \ln t$$

cm^2 per day, for $t \ge 1$. Find the additional amount of area covered by the moss between 4 and 9 days.

43. Thermic Effect of Food A person's metabolic rate tends to go up after eating a meal and then, after some time has passed, it returns to a resting metabolic rate. This phenomenon is known as the thermic effect of food, and the effect (in kJ per hour) for one individual is

$$F(t) = -10.28 + 175.9te^{-t/1.3},$$

where t is the number of hours that have elapsed since eating a meal. *Source: American Journal of Clinical Nutrition.* Find the total thermic energy of a meal for the next six hours after a meal by integrating the thermic effect function between $t = 0$ and $t = 6$.

44. Rumen Fermentation The rumen is the first division of the stomach of a ruminant, or cud-chewing animal. An article on the rumen microbial system reports that the fraction of the soluble material passing from the rumen without being fermented during the first hour after its ingestion could be calculated by the integral

$$\int_0^1 ke^{-kt}(1-t)dt,$$

where k measures the rate that the material is fermented. *Source: Annual Review of Ecology and Systematics.*

a. Determine the above integral, and evaluate it for the following values of k used in the article: $1/12, 1/24,$ and $1/48$ hour.

b. The fraction of intermediate material left in the rumen at 1 hour that escapes digestion by passage between 1 and 6 hours is given by

$$\int_1^6 ke^{-kt}(6-t)/5\, dt.$$

Determine this integral, and evaluate it for the values of k given in part a.

YOUR TURN ANSWERS

1. $-e^{-2x}(2x+1)/4 + C$
2. $x \ln 2x - x + C$
3. $(6x^2 - 6x + 11)e^{2x}/4 + C$
4. $(2e^3 + 1)/9$
5. $(-1/2) \ln|(2 + \sqrt{4+x^2})/x| + C$

2 Volume and Average Value

APPLY IT If we have a formula giving the price of a common stock as a function of time, how can we find the average price of the stock over a certain period of time?

We will answer this question in Example 4 using concepts developed in this section, in which we will discover how to find the average value of a function, as well as how to compute the volume of a solid.

Volume Figure 1 shows the regions below the graph of some function $y = f(x)$, above the x-axis, and between $x = a$ and $x = b$. We have seen how to use integrals to find the area of such a region. Suppose this region is revolved about the x-axis as shown in Figure 2. The resulting figure is called a **solid of revolution**. In many cases, the volume of a solid of revolution can be found by integration.

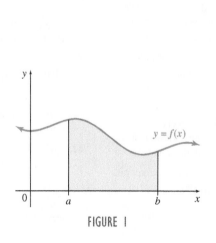

FIGURE 1

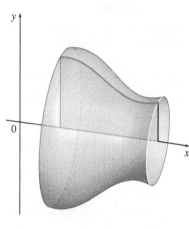

FIGURE 2

To begin, divide the interval $[a, b]$ into n subintervals of equal width Δx by the points $a = x_0, x_1, x_2, \ldots, x_i, \ldots, x_n = b$. Then think of slicing the solid into n slices of equal thickness Δx, as shown in Figure 3(a). If the slices are thin enough, each slice is very close to being a right circular cylinder, as shown in Figure 3(b). The formula for the volume of a right circular cylinder is $\pi r^2 h$, where r is the radius of the circular base and h is the height of the cylinder. As shown in Figure 4, the height of each slice is Δx. (The height is horizontal here, since the cylinder is on its side.) The radius of the circular base of each slice is $f(x_i)$. Thus, the volume of the slice is closely approximated by $\pi[f(x_i)]^2 \Delta x$. The volume of the solid of revolution will be approximated by the sum of the volumes of the slices:

$$V \approx \sum_{i=1}^{n} \pi[f(x_i)]^2 \Delta x.$$

By definition, the volume of the solid of revolution is the limit of this sum as the thickness of the slices approaches 0, or

$$V = \lim_{\Delta x \to 0} \sum_{i=1}^{n} \pi[f(x_i)]^2 \Delta x.$$

This limit, like the one discussed earlier for area, is a definite integral.

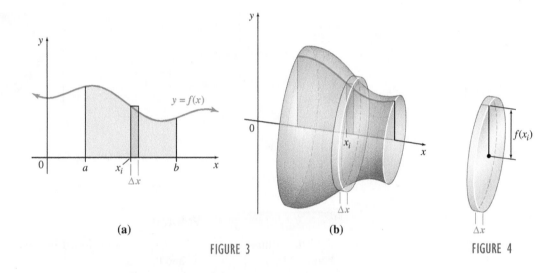

(a)   (b)

FIGURE 3   FIGURE 4

Volume of a Solid of Revolution

If $f(x)$ is nonnegative and R is the region between $f(x)$ and the x-axis from $x = a$ to $x = b$, the volume of the solid formed by rotating R about the x-axis is given by

$$V = \lim_{\Delta x \to 0} \sum_{i=1}^{n} \pi[f(x_i)]^2 \Delta x = \int_{a}^{b} \pi[f(x)]^2 \, dx.$$

The technique of summing disks to approximate volumes was originated by Johannes Kepler (1571–1630), a famous German astronomer who discovered three laws of planetary motion. He estimated volumes of wine casks used at his wedding by means of solids of revolution.

EXAMPLE 1   Volume

Find the volume of the solid of revolution formed by rotating about the x-axis the region bounded by $y = x + 1$, $y = 0$, $x = 1$, and $x = 4$.

SOLUTION The region and the solid are shown in Figure 5. Notice that the orientation of the x-axis is slightly different in Figure 5(b) than in Figure 5(a) to emphasize the three-dimensionality of the figure. Use the formula given above for the volume, with $a = 1$, $b = 4$, and $f(x) = x + 1$.

$$V = \int_1^4 \pi(x + 1)^2 \, dx = \pi\left[\frac{(x + 1)^3}{3}\right]\Big|_1^4$$

$$= \frac{\pi}{3}(5^3 - 2^3)$$

$$= \frac{117\pi}{3} = 39\pi$$

YOUR TURN 1 Find the volume of the solid of revolution formed by rotating about the x-axis the region bounded by $y = x^2 + 1$, $y = 0$, $x = -1$, and $x = 1$.

TRY YOUR TURN 1

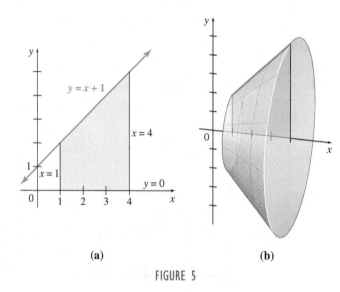

(a)

(b)

FIGURE 5

EXAMPLE 2 Volume

Find the volume of the solid of revolution formed by rotating about the x-axis the area bounded by $f(x) = 4 - x^2$ and the x-axis.

SOLUTION The region and the solid are shown in Figure 6 on the next page. Find a and b from the x-intercepts. If $y = 0$, then $x = 2$ or $x = -2$, so that $a = -2$ and $b = 2$. The volume is

$$V = \int_{-2}^{2} \pi(4 - x^2)^2 \, dx$$

$$= \int_{-2}^{2} \pi(16 - 8x^2 + x^4) \, dx$$

$$= \pi\left(16x - \frac{8x^3}{3} + \frac{x^5}{5}\right)\Big|_{-2}^{2}$$

$$= \frac{512\pi}{15}.$$

TECHNOLOGY NOTE A graphing calculator with the fnInt feature gives the value as 107.2330292, which agrees with the approximation of $512\pi/15$ to the 7 decimal places shown.

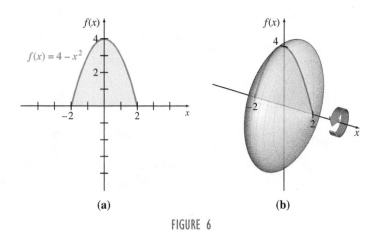

(a)   (b)

FIGURE 6

EXAMPLE 3   Volume

Find the volume of a right circular cone with height h and base radius r.

SOLUTION   Figure 7(a) shows the required cone, while Figure 7(b) shows an area that could be rotated about the x-axis to get such a cone. The cone formed by the rotation is shown in Figure 7(c). Here $y = f(x)$ is the equation of the line through $(0, 0)$ and (h, r). The slope of this line is r/h, and since the y-intercept is 0, the equation of the line is

$$y = \frac{r}{h}x.$$

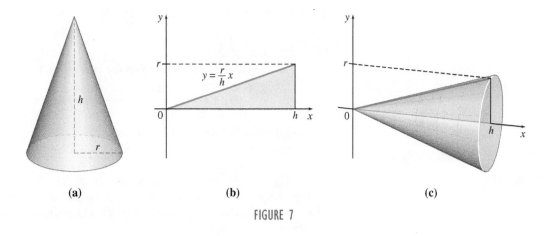

(a)   (b)   (c)

FIGURE 7

Then the volume is

$$V = \int_0^h \pi\left(\frac{r}{h}x\right)^2 dx = \pi \int_0^h \frac{r^2 x^2}{h^2}\, dx$$

$$= \pi \frac{r^2 x^3}{3h^2}\Big|_0^h \qquad \text{Since } r \text{ and } h \text{ are constants}$$

$$= \frac{\pi r^2 h}{3}.$$

This is the familiar formula for the volume of a right circular cone.

87

Average Value of a Function

The average of the n numbers $v_1, v_2, v_3, \ldots, v_i, \ldots, v_n$ is given by

$$\frac{v_1 + v_2 + v_3 + \cdots + v_n}{n} = \frac{\sum_{i=1}^{n} v_i}{n}.$$

For example, to compute an average temperature, we could take readings at equally spaced intervals and average the readings.

The average value of a function f on $[a, b]$ can be defined in a similar manner; divide the interval $[a, b]$ into n subintervals, each of width Δx. Then choose an x-value, x_i, in each subinterval, and find $f(x_i)$. The average function value for the n subintervals and the given choices of x_i is

$$\frac{f(x_1) + f(x_2) + \cdots + f(x_n)}{n} = \frac{\sum_{i=1}^{n} f(x_i)}{n}.$$

Since $(b - a)/n = \Delta x$, multiply the expression on the right side of the equation by $(b - a)/(b - a)$ and rearrange the expression to get

$$\frac{b - a}{b - a} \cdot \frac{\sum_{i=1}^{n} f(x_i)}{n} = \frac{1}{b - a} \sum_{i=1}^{n} f(x_i) \left(\frac{b - a}{n} \right) = \frac{1}{b - a} \sum_{i=1}^{n} f(x_i) \Delta x.$$

Now, take the limit as $n \to \infty$. If the limit exists, then

$$\lim_{n \to \infty} \frac{1}{b - a} \sum_{i=1}^{n} f(x_i) \Delta x = \frac{1}{b - a} \lim_{n \to \infty} \sum_{i=1}^{n} f(x_i) \Delta x = \frac{1}{b - a} \int_{a}^{b} f(x) \, dx.$$

The following definition summarizes this discussion.

Average Value of a Function

The **average value of a function** f on the interval $[a, b]$ is

$$\frac{1}{b - a} \int_{a}^{b} f(x) \, dx,$$

provided the indicated definite integral exists.

In Figure 8 the quantity $\overline{y}$ represents the average height of the irregular region. The average height can be thought of as the height of a rectangle with base $b - a$. For $f(x) \geq 0$, this rectangle has area $\overline{y}(b - a)$, which equals the area under the graph of $f(x)$ from $x = a$ to $x = b$, so that

$$\overline{y}(b - a) = \int_{a}^{b} f(x) \, dx.$$

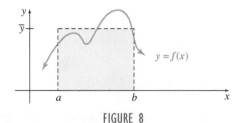

FIGURE 8

EXAMPLE 4 Average Price

A stock analyst plots the price per share of a certain common stock as a function of time and finds that it can be approximated by the function

$$S(t) = 25 - 5e^{-0.01t},$$

where t is the time (in years) since the stock was purchased. Find the average price of the stock over the first six years.

APPLY IT

SOLUTION   Use the formula for average value with $a = 0$ and $b = 6$. The average price is

$$\frac{1}{6-0}\int_0^6 (25 - 5e^{-0.01t})\, dt = \frac{1}{6}\left(25t - \frac{5}{-0.01}e^{-0.01t}\right)\Big|_0^6$$

$$= \frac{1}{6}(25t + 500e^{-0.01t})\Big|_0^6$$

$$= \frac{1}{6}(150 + 500e^{-0.06} - 500)$$

$$\approx 20.147,$$

or approximately \$20.15.

YOUR TURN 2 Find the average value of the function $f(x) = x + \sqrt{x}$ on the interval $[1, 4]$.

TRY YOUR TURN 2

2   EXERCISES

Find the volume of the solid of revolution formed by rotating about the *x*-axis each region bounded by the given curves.

1. $f(x) = x$, $y = 0$, $x = 0$, $x = 3$

2. $f(x) = 3x$, $y = 0$, $x = 0$, $x = 2$

3. $f(x) = 2x + 1$, $y = 0$, $x = 0$, $x = 4$

4. $f(x) = x - 4$, $y = 0$, $x = 4$, $x = 10$

5. $f(x) = \frac{1}{3}x + 2$, $y = 0$, $x = 1$, $x = 3$

6. $f(x) = \frac{1}{2}x + 4$, $y = 0$, $x = 0$, $x = 5$

7. $f(x) = \sqrt{x}$, $y = 0$, $x = 1$, $x = 4$

8. $f(x) = \sqrt{x + 5}$, $y = 0$, $x = 1$, $x = 3$

9. $f(x) = \sqrt{2x + 1}$, $y = 0$, $x = 1$, $x = 4$

10. $f(x) = \sqrt{4x + 2}$, $y = 0$, $x = 0$, $x = 2$

11. $f(x) = e^x$, $y = 0$, $x = 0$, $x = 2$

12. $f(x) = 2e^x$, $y = 0$, $x = -2$, $x = 1$

13. $f(x) = \frac{2}{\sqrt{x}}$, $y = 0$, $x = 1$, $x = 3$

14. $f(x) = \frac{2}{\sqrt{x + 2}}$, $y = 0$, $x = -1$, $x = 2$

15. $f(x) = x^2$, $y = 0$, $x = 1$, $x = 5$

16. $f(x) = \frac{x^2}{2}$, $y = 0$, $x = 0$, $x = 4$

17. $f(x) = 1 - x^2$, $y = 0$

18. $f(x) = 2 - x^2$, $y = 0$

The function defined by $y = \sqrt{r^2 - x^2}$ has as its graph a semicircle of radius r with center at $(0, 0)$ (see the figure). In Exercises 19–21, find the volume that results when each semicircle is rotated about the *x*-axis. (The result of Exercise 21 gives a formula for the volume of a sphere with radius r.)

19. $f(x) = \sqrt{1 - x^2}$ **20.** $f(x) = \sqrt{36 - x^2}$

21. $f(x) = \sqrt{r^2 - x^2}$

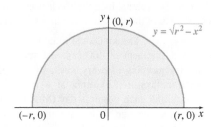

22. Find a formula for the volume of an ellipsoid. See Exercises 19–21 and the following figures.

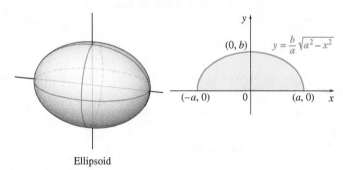

Ellipsoid

23. Use the methods of this section to find the volume of a cylinder with height h and radius r.

Find the average value of each function on the given interval.

24. $f(x) = 2 - 3x^2$; $[1, 3]$ 25. $f(x) = x^2 - 4$; $[0, 5]$

26. $f(x) = (2x - 1)^{1/2}$; $[1, 13]$

27. $f(x) = \sqrt{x + 1}$; $[3, 8]$ 28. $f(x) = e^{0.1x}$; $[0, 10]$

29. $f(x) = e^{x/7}$; $[0, 7]$ 30. $f(x) = x \ln x$; $[1, e]$

31. $f(x) = x^2 e^{2x}$; $[0, 2]$

In Exercises 32 and 33, use the integration feature on a graphing calculator to find the volume of the solid of revolution by rotating about the x-axis each region bounded by the given curves.

32. $f(x) = \dfrac{1}{4 + x^2}$, $y = 0$, $x = -2$, $x = 2$

33. $f(x) = e^{-x^2}$, $y = 0$, $x = -1$, $x = 1$

APPLICATIONS

Business and Economics

34. **Average Price** Otis Taylor plots the price per share of a stock that he owns as a function of time and finds that it can be approximated by the function

$$S(t) = t(25 - 5t) + 18,$$

where t is the time (in years) since the stock was purchased. Find the average price of the stock over the first five years.

35. **Average Price** A stock analyst plots the price per share of a certain common stock as a function of time and finds that it can be approximated by the function

$$S(t) = 37 + 6e^{-0.03t},$$

where t is the time (in years) since the stock was purchased. Find the average price of the stock over the first six years.

36. **Average Inventory** The Yasuko Okada Fragrance Company (YOFC) receives a shipment of 400 cases of specialty perfume early Monday morning of every week. YOFC sells the perfume to retail outlets in California at a rate of about 80 cases per day during each business day (Monday through Friday). What is the average daily inventory for YOFC? (*Hint:* Find a function that represents the inventory for any given business day and then integrate.)

37. **Average Inventory** The DeMarco Pasta Company receives 600 cases of imported San Marzano tomato sauce every 30 days. The number of cases of sauce on inventory t days after the shipment arrives is

$$N(t) = 600 - 20\sqrt{30t}.$$

Find the average daily inventory.

Life Sciences

38. **Blood Flow** The figure shows the blood flow in a small artery of the body. The flow of blood is *laminar* (in layers), with the velocity very low near the artery walls and highest in the center of the artery. In this model of blood flow, we calculate the total flow in the artery by thinking of the flow as being made up of many layers of concentric tubes sliding one on the other.

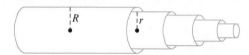

Suppose R is the radius of an artery and r is the distance from a given layer to the center. Then the velocity of blood in a given layer can be shown to equal

$$v(r) = k(R^2 - r^2),$$

where k is a numerical constant.

Since the area of a circle is $A = \pi r^2$, the change in the area of the cross section of one of the layers, corresponding to a small change in the radius, Δr, can be approximated by differentials. For $dr = \Delta r$, the differential of the area A is

$$dA = 2\pi r\, dr = 2\pi r\, \Delta r,$$

where Δr is the thickness of the layer. The total flow in the layer is defined to be the product of velocity and cross-section area, or

$$F(r) = 2\pi r k(R^2 - r^2)\Delta r.$$

a. Set up a definite integral to find the total flow in the artery.

b. Evaluate this definite integral.

39. **Drug Reaction** The intensity of the reaction to a certain drug, in appropriate units, is given by

$$R(t) = te^{-0.1t},$$

where t is time (in hours) after the drug is administered. Find the average intensity during the following hours.

a. Second hour

b. Twelfth hour

c. Twenty-fourth hour

40. **Bird Eggs** The average length and width of various bird eggs are given in the following table. *Source: NCTM.*

Bird Name	Length (cm)	Width (cm)
Canada goose	8.6	5.8
Robin	1.9	1.5
Turtledove	3.1	2.3
Hummingbird	1.0	1.0
Raven	5.0	3.3

a. Assume for simplicity that a bird's egg is roughly the shape of an ellipsoid. Use the result of Exercise 22 to estimate the volume of an egg of each bird.

   i. Canada goose

   ii. Robin

   iii. Turtledove

   iv. Hummingbird

   v. Raven

b. In Exercise 12 of Section 1.3, we showed that the average length (in centimeters) of an egg of width w cm is given by

$$l = 1.585w - 0.487.$$

Using this result and the ideas in part a, show that the average volume of an egg of width w centimeters is given by

$$V = \pi(1.585w^3 - 0.487w^2)/6.$$

Use this formula to calculate the average volume for the bird eggs in part a, and compare with your results from part a.

Social Sciences

41. **Production Rate** Suppose the number of items a new worker on an assembly line produces daily after t days on the job is given by

$$I(t) = 45 \ln(t + 1).$$

Find the average number of items produced daily by this employee after the following numbers of days.

   a. 5   **b.** 9   **c.** 30

42. **Typing Speed** The function $W(t) = -3.75t^2 + 30t + 40$ describes a typist's speed (in words per minute) over a time interval $[0, 5]$.

   a. Find $W(0)$.

   b. Find the maximum W value and the time t when it occurs.

   c. Find the average speed over $[0, 5]$.

Physical Sciences

43. **Earth's Volume** Most people assume that the Earth has a spherical shape. It is actually more of an ellipsoid shape, but not an exact ellipsoid, since there are numerous mountains and valleys. Researchers have found that a *datum*, or a reference ellipsoid, that is offset from the center of the Earth can be used to accurately map different regions. According to one datum, called the Geodetic Reference System 1980, this reference ellipsoid assumes an equatorial radius of 6,378,137 m and a polar radius of 6,356,752.3141 m. *Source: Geodesy Information System.* Use the result of Exercise 22 to estimate the volume of the Earth.

YOUR TURN ANSWERS

   1. $56\pi/15$ **2.** $73/18$

3 Continuous Money Flow

APPLY IT Given a changing rate of annual income and a certain rate of interest, how can we find the present value of the income?

We will answer this question in Example 2 using the concept of continuous money flow.

Consider the concepts of present value and future value when a lump sum of money is deposited in an account and allowed to accumulate interest. In some situations, however, money flows into and out of an account almost continuously over a period of time. Examples include income in a store, bank receipts and payments, and highway tolls. Although the flow of money in such cases is not exactly continuous, it can be treated as though it were continuous, with useful results.

EXAMPLE 1 Total Income

The income from a soda machine (in dollars per year) is growing exponentially. When the machine was first installed, it was producing income at a rate of \$500 per year. By the end of the first year, it was producing income at a rate of \$510.10 per year. Find the total income produced by the machine during its first 3 years of operation.

SOLUTION Let t be the time (in years) since the installation of the machine. The assumption of exponential growth, coupled with the initial value of 500, implies that the rate of change of income is of the form

$$f(t) = 500e^{kt},$$

where k is some constant. To find k, use the value at the end of the first year.

$$f(1) = 500e^{k(1)} = 510.10$$

$$e^k = 1.0202 \qquad \text{Divide by 500.}$$

$$k = \ln 1.0202 \qquad \text{Take ln of both sides.}$$

$$\approx 0.02$$

Therefore, we have

$$f(t) = 500e^{0.02t}.$$

Since the rate of change of incomes is given, the total income can be determined by using the definite integral.

$$\text{Total income} = \int_0^3 500e^{0.02t}\, dt$$

$$= \frac{500}{0.02} e^{0.02t} \Big|_0^3$$

$$= 25{,}000 e^{0.02t} \Big|_0^3 = 25{,}000(e^{0.06} - 1) \approx 1545.91$$

YOUR TURN 1 Find the total income over the first 2 years in Example 1 with the initial rate changed to $810 per year and the rate at the end of the first year changed to $797.94 per year.

Thus, the soda machine will produce $1545.91 total income in its first three years of operation.

TRY YOUR TURN 1

The money in Example 1 is not received as a one-time lump sum payment of $1545.91. Instead, it comes in on a regular basis, perhaps daily, weekly, or monthly. In discussions of such problems it is usually assumed that the income is received continuously over a period of time.

Total Money Flow

Let the continuous function $f(t)$ represent the rate of flow of money per unit of time. If t is in years and $f(t)$ is in dollars per year, the area under $f(t)$ between two points in time gives the total dollar flow over the given time interval.

The function $f(t) = 2000$, shown in Figure 9, represents a uniform rate of money flow of $2000 per year. The graph of this money flow is a horizontal line; the *total money flow* over a specified time T is given by the rectangular area below the graph of $f(t)$ and above the t-axis between $t = 0$ and $t = T$. For example, the total money flow over $T = 5$ years would be $2000(5) = 10{,}000$, or $10,000.

The area in the uniform rate example could be found by using an area formula from geometry. For a variable function like the function in Example 1, however, a definite integral is needed to find the total money flow over a specific time interval. For the function

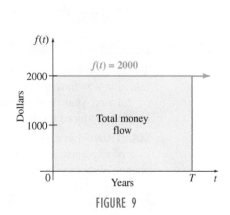

FIGURE 9

$f(t) = 2000e^{0.08t}$, for example, the total money flow over a 5-year period would be given by

$$\int_0^5 2000e^{0.08t} \, dt \approx 12{,}295.62,$$

or \$12,295.62. See Figure 10.

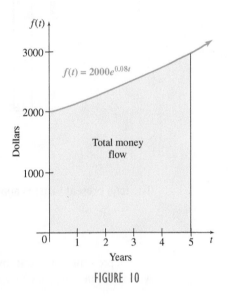

FIGURE 10

Total Money Flow

If $f(t)$ is the rate of money flow, then the **total money flow** over the time interval from $t = 0$ to $t = T$ is given by

$$\int_0^T f(t) \, dt.$$

This "total money flow" does not take into account the interest the money could earn after it is received. It is simply the total income.

Present Value of Money Flow

As mentioned earlier, an amount of money that can be deposited today at a specified interest rate to yield a given sum in the future is called the *present value* of this future sum. The future sum may be called the *future value* or *final amount*. To find the **present value of a continuous money flow** with interest compounded continuously, let $f(t)$ represent the rate of the continuous flow. In Figure 11 on the next page, the time axis from 0 to T is divided into n subintervals, each of width Δt. The amount of money that flows during any interval of time is given by the area between the t-axis and the graph of $f(t)$ over the specified time interval. The area of each subinterval is approximated by the area of a rectangle with height $f(t_i)$, where t_i is the left endpoint of the ith subinterval. The area of each rectangle is $f(t_i)\Delta t$, which (approximately) gives the amount of money flow over that subinterval.

Earlier, we saw that the present value P of an amount A compounded continuously for t years at a rate of interest r is $P = Ae^{-rt}$. Letting t_i represent the time and replacing A with $f(t_i)\Delta t$, the present value of the money flow over the ith subinterval is approximately equal to

$$P_i = [f(t_i)\Delta t]e^{-rt_i}.$$

93

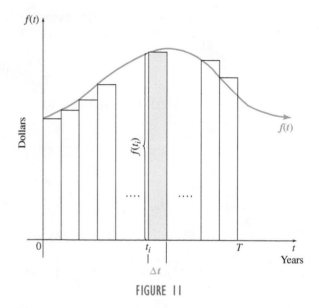

FIGURE 11

The total present value is approximately equal to the sum

$$\sum_{i=1}^{n} [f(t_i)\Delta t]e^{-rt_i}.$$

This approximation is improved as n increases; taking the limit of the sum as n increases without bound gives the present value

$$P = \lim_{n\to\infty} \sum_{i=1}^{n} [f(t_i)\Delta t]e^{-rt_i}.$$

This limit of a summation is given by the following definite integral.

Present Value of Money Flow

If $f(t)$ is the rate of continuous money flow at an interest rate r for T years, then the present value is

$$P = \int_0^T f(t)e^{-rt}\, dt.$$

To understand present value of money flow, consider an account that earns interest and has a continuous money flow. The present value of the money flow is the amount that would have to be deposited into a second account that has the same interest rate but does not have a continuous money flow, so the two accounts have the same amount of money after a specified time.

EXAMPLE 2   Present Value of Income

A company expects its rate of annual income during the next three years to be given by

$$f(t) = 75{,}000t, \quad 0 \le t \le 3.$$

What is the present value of this income over the 3-year period, assuming an annual interest rate of 8% compounded continuously?

APPLY IT   **SOLUTION**   Use the formula for present value, with $f(t) = 75{,}000t$, $T = 3$, and $r = 0.08$.

$$P = \int_0^3 75{,}000te^{-0.08t}\, dt = 75{,}000\int_0^3 te^{-0.08t}\, dt$$

Further Techniques and Applications of Integration

Using integration by parts, verify that

$$\int te^{-0.08t}\,dt = -12.5te^{-0.08t} - 156.25e^{-0.08t} + C.$$

Therefore,

$$
\begin{aligned}
75{,}000\int_0^3 te^{-0.08t}\,dt &= 75{,}000\left(-12.5te^{-0.08t} - 156.25e^{-0.08t}\right)\Big|_0^3 \\
&= 75{,}000\left[-12.5(3)e^{-0.08(3)} - 156.25e^{-0.08(3)} - (0 - 156.25)\right] \\
&\approx 75{,}000(-29.498545 - 122.910603 + 156.25) \\
&\approx 288{,}064,
\end{aligned}
$$

or about \$288,000. Notice that the actual income over the 3-year period is given by

$$\text{Total money flow} = \int_0^3 75{,}000t\,dt = \frac{75{,}000t^2}{2}\Big|_0^3 = 337{,}500,$$

or \$337,500. This means that it would take a lump-sum deposit of \$288,064 today paying a continuously compounded interest rate of 8% over a 3-year period to equal the total cash flow of \$337,500 with interest. This approach is used as a basis for determining insurance claims involving income considerations. **TRY YOUR TURN 2**

YOUR TURN 2 Find the present value of an income given by $f(t) = 50{,}000t$ over the next 5 years if the interest rate is 3.5%.

Accumulated Amount of Money Flow at Time T

To find the **accumulated amount of money flow** with interest at any time t, start with the formula $A = Pe^{rt}$, let $t = T$, and in place of P substitute the expression for present value of money flow. The result is the following formula.

Accumulated Amount of Money Flow at Time T
If $f(t)$ is the rate of money flow at an interest rate r at time t, the accumulated amount of money flow at time T is

$$A = e^{rT}\int_0^T f(t)e^{-rt}\,dt.$$

Here, the accumulated amount of money A represents the accumulated value or final amount of the money flow *including* interest received on the money after it comes in. (Recall, total money flow *does not* take the interest into account.)

It turns out that most money flows can be expressed as (or at least approximated by) exponential or polynomial functions. When these are multiplied by e^{-rt}, the result is a function that can be integrated. The next example illustrates uniform flow, where $f(t)$ is a constant function. (This is a special case of the polynomial function.)

EXAMPLE 3 **Accumulated Amount of Money Flow**

If money is flowing continuously at a constant rate of \$2000 per year over 5 years at 6% interest compounded continuously, find the following.

(a) The total money flow over the 5-year period

SOLUTION The total money flow is given by $\int_0^T f(t)\,dt$. Here $f(t) = 2000$ and $T = 5$.

$$\int_0^5 2000\,dt = 2000t\Big|_0^5 = 2000(5) = 10{,}000$$

The total money flow over the 5-year period is \$10,000.

Further Techniques and Applications of Integration

(b) The accumulated amount of money flow, compounded continuously, at time $T = 5$

SOLUTION At $T = 5$ with $r = 0.06$, the amount is

$$A = e^{rT} \int_0^T f(t)e^{-rt} \, dt = e^{(0.06)5} \int_0^5 (2000)e^{-0.06t} \, dt$$

$$= (e^{0.3})(2000) \int_0^5 e^{-0.06t} \, dt = e^{0.3}(2000)\left(\frac{1}{-0.06}\right)\left(e^{-0.06t}\Big|_0^5\right)$$

$$= \frac{2000e^{0.3}}{-0.06}(e^{-0.3} - 1) = \frac{2000}{-0.06}(1 - e^{0.3}) \qquad (e^{0.03})(e^{-0.03}) = 1$$

$$\approx 11{,}661.96,$$

or \$11,661.96. The answer to part (a), \$10,000, was the amount of money flow over the 5-year period. The \$11,661.96 gives that amount with interest compounded continuously over the 5-year period.

(c) The total interest earned

SOLUTION This is simply the accumulated amount of money flow minus the total amount of flow, or

$$\$11{,}661.96 - \$10{,}000.00 = \$1661.96.$$

(d) The present value of the amount with interest

SOLUTION Use $P = \int_0^T f(t)e^{-rt} \, dt$ with $f(t) = 2000$, $r = 0.06$, and $T = 5$.

$$P = \int_0^5 2000e^{-0.06t} \, dt = 2000\left(\frac{e^{-0.06t}}{-0.06}\right)\Big|_0^5$$

$$= \frac{2000}{-0.06}(e^{-0.3} - 1)$$

$$\approx 8639.39,$$

YOUR TURN 3 Find the accumulated amount of money flow for the income and interest rate in Your Turn 2 in this section.

The present value of the amount with interest in 5 years is \$8639.39, which can be checked by substituting \$11,661.96 for A in $A = Pe^{rt}$. The present value, P, could have been found by dividing the amount found in (b) by $e^{rT} = e^{0.3}$. Check that this would give the same result. TRY YOUR TURN 3

If the rate of money flow is increasing or decreasing exponentially, then $f(t) = Ce^{kt}$, where C is a constant that represents the initial amount and k is the (nominal) continuous rate of change, which may be positive or negative.

EXAMPLE 4 Accumulated Amount of Money Flow

A continuous money flow starts at a rate of \$1000 per year and increases exponentially at 2% per year.

(a) Find the accumulated amount of money flow at the end of 5 years at 10% interest compounded continuously.

SOLUTION Here $C = 1000$ and $k = 0.02$, so that $f(t) = 1000e^{0.02t}$. Using $r = 0.10$ and $T = 5$,

$$A = e^{(0.10)5} \int_0^5 1000e^{0.02t}e^{-0.10t} \, dt$$

$$= (e^{0.5})(1000) \int_0^5 e^{-0.08t} \, dt \qquad e^{0.02t} \cdot e^{-0.10t} = e^{-0.08t}$$

$$= 1000e^{0.5}\left(\frac{e^{-0.08t}}{-0.08}\right)\Big|_0^5$$

$$= \frac{1000e^{0.5}}{-0.08}(e^{-0.4} - 1) = \frac{1000}{-0.08}(e^{0.1} - e^{0.5}) \approx 6794.38,$$

or \$6794.38.

FOR REVIEW

In this example we use the following two rules for exponents.

1. $a^m \cdot a^n = a^{m+n}$

2. $a^0 = 1$

Further Techniques and Applications of Integration

(b) Find the present value at 5% interest compounded continuously.

SOLUTION Using $f(t) = 1000e^{0.02t}$ with $r = 0.05$ and $T = 5$ in the present value expression,

$$P = \int_0^5 1000e^{0.02t}e^{-0.05t}\,dt$$

$$= 1000\int_0^5 e^{-0.03t}\,dt = 1000\left(\frac{e^{-0.03t}}{-0.03}\Big|_0^5\right)$$

$$= \frac{1000}{-0.03}(e^{-0.15} - 1) \approx 4643.07,$$

or $4643.07.

If the rate of change of the continuous money flow is given by the polynomial function $f(t) = a_n t^n + a_{n-1}t^{n-1} + \cdots + a_0$, the expressions for present value and accumulated amount can be integrated using integration by parts.

EXAMPLE 5 **Present Value of Money Flow**

The rate of change of a continuous flow of money is given by

$$f(t) = 1000t^2 + 100t.$$

Find the present value of this money flow at the end of 10 years at 10% compounded continuously.

SOLUTION Evaluate

$$P = \int_0^{10} (1000t^2 + 100t)e^{-0.10t}\,dt.$$

Using integration by parts, verify that

$$\int (1000t^2 + 100t)e^{-0.10t}\,dt =$$

$$(-10,000t^2 - 1000t)e^{-0.1t} - (200,000t + 10,000)e^{-0.1t} - 2,000,000e^{-0.1t} + C.$$

Thus,

$$P = (-10,000t^2 - 1000t)e^{-0.1t} - (200,000t + 10,000)e^{-0.1t}$$

$$- 2,000,000e^{-0.1t}\Big|_0^{10}$$

$$= (-1,000,000 - 10,000)e^{-1} - (2,000,000 + 10,000)e^{-1}$$

$$- 2,000,000e^{-1} - (0 - 10,000 - 2,000,000)$$

$$\approx 163,245.21.$$

TRY YOUR TURN 4

YOUR TURN 4 Find the present value at the end of 8 years of the continuous flow of money given by $f(t) = 200t^2 + 100t + 50$ at 5% compounded continuously.

3 EXERCISES

Each of the functions in Exercises 1–14 represents the rate of flow of money in dollars per year. Assume a 10-year period at 8% compounded continuously and find the following: (a) the present value; (b) the accumulated amount of money flow at $t = 10$.

1. $f(t) = 1000$
2. $f(t) = 300$
3. $f(t) = 500$
4. $f(t) = 2000$
5. $f(t) = 400e^{0.03t}$
6. $f(t) = 800e^{0.05t}$
7. $f(t) = 5000e^{-0.01t}$
8. $f(t) = 1000e^{-0.02t}$
9. $f(t) = 25t$
10. $f(t) = 50t$
11. $f(t) = 0.01t + 100$
12. $f(t) = 0.05t + 500$
13. $f(t) = 1000t - 100t^2$
14. $f(t) = 2000t - 150t^2$

97

APPLICATIONS

Business and Economics

15. Accumulated Amount of Money Flow An investment is expected to yield a uniform continuous rate of money flow of $20,000 per year for 3 years. Find the accumulated amount at an interest rate of 4% compounded continuously.

16. Present Value A real estate investment is expected to produce a uniform continuous rate of money flow of $8000 per year for 6 years. Find the present value at the following rates, compounded continuously.

    a. 2%   **b.** 5%   **c.** 8%

17. Money Flow The rate of a continuous flow of money starts at $5000 and decreases exponentially at 1% per year for 8 years. Find the present value and final amount at an interest rate of 8% compounded continuously.

18. Money Flow The rate of a continuous money flow starts at $1000 and increases exponentially at 5% per year for 4 years. Find the present value and accumulated amount if interest earned is 3.5% compounded continuously.

19. Present Value A money market fund has a continuous flow of money at a rate of $f(t) = 1500 - 60t^2$, reaching 0 in 5 years. Find the present value of this flow if interest is 5% compounded continuously.

20. Accumulated Amount of Money Flow Find the amount of a continuous money flow in 3 years if the rate is given by $f(t) = 1000 - t^2$ and if interest is 5% compounded continuously.

YOUR TURN ANSWERS

  1. $1595.94   **2.** $556,653

  3. $663,111   **4.** $28,156.02

4   Improper Integrals

APPLY IT If we know the rate at which a pollutant is dumped into a stream, how can we compute the total amount released given that the rate of dumping is decreasing over time?

In this section we will learn how to answer questions such as this one, which is answered in Example 3.

Sometimes it is useful to be able to integrate a function over an infinite period of time. For example, we might want to find the total amount of income generated by an apartment building into the indefinite future or the total amount of pollution into a bay from a source that is continuing indefinitely. In this section we define integrals with one or more infinite limits of integration that can be used to solve such problems.

The graph in Figure 12(a) shows the area bounded by the curve $f(x) = x^{-3/2}$, the x-axis, and the vertical line $x = 1$. Think of the shaded region below the curve as extending indefinitely to the right. Does this shaded region have an area?

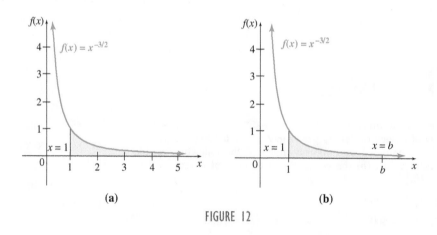

(a)   (b)

FIGURE 12

To see if the area of this region can be defined, introduce a vertical line at $x = b$, as shown in Figure 12(b). This vertical line gives a region with both upper and lower limits of integration. The area of this new region is given by the definite integral

$$\int_1^b x^{-3/2}\, dx.$$

By the Fundamental Theorem of Calculus,

$$\int_1^b x^{-3/2}\, dx = \left. \left(-2x^{-1/2} \right) \right|_1^b$$

$$= -2b^{-1/2} - \left(-2 \cdot 1^{-1/2} \right)$$

$$= -2b^{-1/2} + 2 = 2 - \frac{2}{b^{1/2}}.$$

FOR REVIEW

For any positive real number n,

$$\lim_{b \to \infty} \frac{1}{b^n} = 0.$$

Suppose we now let the vertical line $x = b$ in Figure 12(b) move farther to the right. That is, suppose $b \to \infty$. The expression $-2/b^{1/2}$ would then approach 0, and

$$\lim_{b \to \infty} \left(2 - \frac{2}{b^{1/2}} \right) = 2 - 0 = 2.$$

This limit is defined to be the *area* of the region shown in Figure 12(a), so that

$$\int_1^\infty x^{-3/2}\, dx = 2.$$

An integral of the form

$$\int_a^\infty f(x)\, dx, \qquad \int_{-\infty}^b f(x)\, dx, \qquad \text{or} \qquad \int_{-\infty}^\infty f(x)\, dx$$

is called an *improper integral*. These **improper integrals** are defined as follows.

Improper Integrals

If f is continuous on the indicated interval and if the indicated limits exist, then

$$\int_a^\infty f(x)\, dx = \lim_{b \to \infty} \int_a^b f(x)\, dx,$$

$$\int_{-\infty}^b f(x)\, dx = \lim_{a \to -\infty} \int_a^b f(x)\, dx,$$

$$\int_{-\infty}^\infty f(x)\, dx = \int_{-\infty}^c f(x)\, dx + \int_c^\infty f(x)\, dx,$$

for real numbers a, b, and c, where c is arbitrarily chosen.

If the expressions on the right side exist, the integrals are **convergent**; otherwise, they are **divergent**. A convergent integral has a value that is a real number. A divergent integral does not, often because the area under the curve is infinitely large.

EXAMPLE 1   Improper Integrals

Evaluate each integral.

(a) $\displaystyle \int_1^\infty \frac{dx}{x}$

SOLUTION   A graph of this region is shown in Figure 13. By the definition of an improper integral,

$$\int_1^\infty \frac{dx}{x} = \lim_{b \to \infty} \int_1^b \frac{dx}{x}.$$

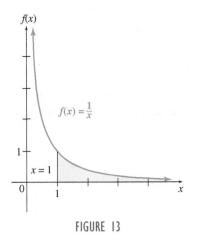

$f(x) = \dfrac{1}{x}$

$x = 1$

FIGURE 13

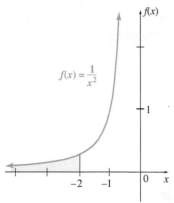

$f(x) = \dfrac{1}{x^2}$

FIGURE 14

YOUR TURN 1 Find each integral.

(a) $\displaystyle\int_8^\infty \frac{1}{x^{1/3}}\,dx$ (b) $\displaystyle\int_8^\infty \frac{1}{x^{4/3}}\,dx$

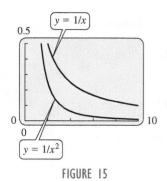

$y = 1/x$

0.5

0   10

0

$y = 1/x^2$

FIGURE 15

Find $\displaystyle\int_1^b \frac{dx}{x}$ by the Fundamental Theorem of Calculus.

$$\int_1^b \frac{dx}{x} = \ln|x|\Big|_1^b = \ln|b| - \ln|1| = \ln|b| - 0 = \ln|b|$$

As $b \to \infty$, $\ln|b| \to \infty$, so $\displaystyle\lim_{b \to \infty} \ln|b|$ does not exist. Since the limit does not exist, $\displaystyle\int_1^\infty \frac{dx}{x}$ is divergent.

(b) $\displaystyle\int_{-\infty}^{-2} \frac{1}{x^2}\,dx = \lim_{a \to -\infty} \int_a^{-2} \frac{1}{x^2}\,dx = \lim_{a \to -\infty}\left(\frac{-1}{x}\right)\Big|_a^{-2}$

$$= \lim_{a \to -\infty}\left(\frac{1}{2} + \frac{1}{a}\right) = \frac{1}{2}$$

A graph of this region is shown in Figure 14. Since the limit exists, this integral converges.   TRY YOUR TURN 1

It may seem puzzling that the areas under the curves $f(x) = 1/x^{3/2}$ and $f(x) = 1/x^2$ are finite, while $f(x) = 1/x$ has an infinite amount of area. At first glance the graphs of these functions appear similar. The difference is that although all three functions get small as x becomes infinitely large, $f(x) = 1/x$ does not become small enough fast enough. In the graphing calculator screen in Figure 15, notice how much faster $1/x^2$ becomes small compared with $1/x$.

CAUTION Since graphing calculators provide only approximations, using them to find improper integrals is tricky and requires skill and care. Although their approximations may be good in some cases, they are wrong in others, and they cannot tell us for certain that an improper integral does not exist. See Exercises 39–41.

EXAMPLE 2   **Improper Integral**

Find $\int_{-\infty}^{\infty} 4e^{-3x}\,dx$.

SOLUTION In the definition of an improper integral with limits of $-\infty$ and ∞, the value of c is arbitrary, so we'll choose the simple value $c = 0$. We can then write the integral as

$$\int_{-\infty}^{\infty} 4e^{-3x}\,dx = \int_{-\infty}^{0} 4e^{-3x}\,dx + \int_{0}^{\infty} 4e^{-3x}\,dx$$

and evaluate each of the two improper integrals on the right. If they both converge, the original integral will equal their sum. To show you all the details while maintaining the suspense, we will evaluate the second integral first.

By definition,

$$\int_0^\infty 4e^{-3x}\,dx = \lim_{b \to \infty} \int_0^b 4e^{-3x}\,dx = \lim_{b \to \infty}\left(\frac{-4}{3}e^{-3x}\right)\Big|_0^b$$

$$= \lim_{b \to \infty}\left(\frac{-4}{3e^{3b}} + \frac{4}{3}\right) = 0 + \frac{4}{3} = \frac{4}{3}.$$

Similarly, the second integral is evaluated as

$$\int_{-\infty}^{0} 4e^{-3x}\,dx = \lim_{b \to -\infty} \int_{b}^{0} 4e^{-3x}\,dx = \lim_{b \to -\infty} \left(\frac{-4}{3} e^{-3x} \right) \Big|_{b}^{0}$$

$$= \lim_{b \to -\infty} \left(-\frac{4}{3} + \frac{4}{3e^{3b}} \right) = \infty.$$

YOUR TURN 2

Find $\int_{0}^{\infty} 5e^{-2x}\,dx$.

Since one of the two improper integrals diverges, the original improper integral diverges. **TRY YOUR TURN 2**

The following examples describe applications of improper integrals.

EXAMPLE 3   Pollution

The rate at which a pollutant is being dumped into a stream at time t is given by $P_0 e^{-kt}$, where P_0 is the rate that the pollutant is initially released into the stream. Suppose $P_0 = 1000$ and $k = 0.06$. Find the total amount of the pollutant that will be released into the stream into the indefinite future.

APPLY IT **SOLUTION** Find

$$\int_{0}^{\infty} P_0 e^{-kt}\,dt = \int_{0}^{\infty} 1000e^{-0.06t}\,dt.$$

This integral is similar to one of the integrals used to solve Example 2 and may be evaluated by the same method.

$$\int_{0}^{\infty} 1000e^{-0.06t}\,dt = \lim_{b \to \infty} \int_{0}^{b} 1000e^{-0.06t}\,dt$$

$$= \lim_{b \to \infty} \left(\frac{1000}{-0.06} e^{-0.06t} \right) \Big|_{0}^{b}$$

$$= \lim_{b \to \infty} \left(\frac{1000}{-0.06 e^{0.06b}} - \frac{1000}{-0.06} e^{0} \right) = \frac{-1000}{-0.06} \approx 16{,}667$$

A total of approximately 16,667 units of the pollutant will be released over time.

The *capital value* of an asset is often defined as the present value of all future net earnings of the asset. In other words, suppose an asset provides a continuous money flow that is invested in an account earning a certain rate of interest. A lump sum is invested in a second account earning the same rate of interest, but with no money flow, so that as $t \to \infty$, the amounts in the two accounts approach each other. The lump sum necessary to make this happen is the capital value of the asset. If $R(t)$ gives the annual rate at which earnings are produced by an asset at time t, then the present value formula from Section 3 gives the **capital value** as

$$\int_{0}^{\infty} R(t)e^{-rt}\,dt,$$

where r is the annual rate of interest, compounded continuously.

EXAMPLE 4   Capital Value

Suppose income from a rental property is generated at the annual rate of $4000 per year. Find the capital value of this property at an interest rate of 10% compounded continuously.

SOLUTION   This is a continuous income stream with a rate of flow of $4000 per year, so $R(t) = 4000$. Also, $r = 0.10$ or 0.1. The capital value is given by

$$\int_0^\infty 4000e^{-0.1t}\, dt = \lim_{b\to\infty}\int_0^b 4000e^{-0.1t}\, dt$$

$$= \lim_{b\to\infty}\left(\frac{4000}{-0.1}e^{-0.1t}\right)\Bigg|_0^b$$

$$= \lim_{b\to\infty}\left(-40{,}000e^{-0.1b} + 40{,}000\right) = 40{,}000,$$

or $40,000.

4   EXERCISES

Determine whether each improper integral converges or diverges, and find the value of each that converges.

1. $\displaystyle\int_3^\infty \frac{1}{x^2}\, dx$

2. $\displaystyle\int_3^\infty \frac{1}{(x+1)^3}\, dx$

3. $\displaystyle\int_4^\infty \frac{2}{\sqrt{x}}\, dx$

4. $\displaystyle\int_{27}^\infty \frac{2}{\sqrt[3]{x}}\, dx$

5. $\displaystyle\int_{-\infty}^{-1} \frac{2}{x^3}\, dx$

6. $\displaystyle\int_{-\infty}^{-4} \frac{3}{x^4}\, dx$

7. $\displaystyle\int_1^\infty \frac{1}{x^{1.0001}}\, dx$

8. $\displaystyle\int_1^\infty \frac{1}{x^{0.999}}\, dx$

9. $\displaystyle\int_{-\infty}^{-10} x^{-2}\, dx$

10. $\displaystyle\int_{-\infty}^{-1} (x-2)^{-3}\, dx$

11. $\displaystyle\int_{-\infty}^{-1} x^{-8/3}\, dx$

12. $\displaystyle\int_{-\infty}^{-27} x^{-5/3}\, dx$

13. $\displaystyle\int_0^\infty 8e^{-8x}\, dx$

14. $\displaystyle\int_0^\infty 50e^{-50x}\, dx$

15. $\displaystyle\int_{-\infty}^0 1000e^x\, dx$

16. $\displaystyle\int_{-\infty}^0 5e^{60x}\, dx$

17. $\displaystyle\int_{-\infty}^{-1} \ln|x|\, dx$

18. $\displaystyle\int_1^\infty \ln|x|\, dx$

19. $\displaystyle\int_0^\infty \frac{dx}{(x+1)^2}$

20. $\displaystyle\int_0^\infty \frac{dx}{(4x+1)^3}$

21. $\displaystyle\int_{-\infty}^{-1} \frac{2x-1}{x^2-x}\, dx$

22. $\displaystyle\int_1^\infty \frac{4x+6}{x^2+3x}\, dx$

23. $\displaystyle\int_2^\infty \frac{1}{x\ln x}\, dx$

24. $\displaystyle\int_2^\infty \frac{1}{x(\ln x)^2}\, dx$

25. $\displaystyle\int_0^\infty xe^{4x}\, dx$

26. $\displaystyle\int_{-\infty}^0 xe^{0.2x}\, dx$ (*Hint:* Recall that $\lim_{x\to-\infty} xe^x = 0$.)

27. $\displaystyle\int_{-\infty}^\infty x^3e^{-x^4}\, dx$ (*Hint:* Recall that $\lim_{x\to\infty} x^n e^{-x} = 0$.)

28. $\displaystyle\int_{-\infty}^\infty e^{-|x|}\, dx$ (*Hint:* Recall that when $x < 0$, $|x| = -x$.)

29. $\displaystyle\int_{-\infty}^\infty \frac{x}{x^2+1}\, dx$

30. $\displaystyle\int_{-\infty}^\infty \frac{2x+4}{x^2+4x+5}\, dx$

⬤ Find the area between the graph of the given function and the *x*-axis over the given interval, if possible.

31. $f(x) = \dfrac{1}{x-1}$,   for $(-\infty, 0]$

32. $f(x) = e^{-x}$,   for $(-\infty, e]$

33. $f(x) = \dfrac{1}{(x-1)^2}$,   for $(-\infty, 0]$

34. $f(x) = \dfrac{3}{(x-1)^3}$,   for $(-\infty, 0]$

35. Find $\displaystyle\int_{-\infty}^\infty xe^{-x^2}\, dx$.

36. Find $\displaystyle\int_{-\infty}^\infty \frac{x}{(1+x^2)^2}\, dx$.

37. Show that $\displaystyle\int_1^\infty \frac{1}{x^p}\, dx$ converges if $p > 1$ and diverges if $p \le 1$.

38. Example 1(b) leads to a paradox. On the one hand, the unbounded region in that example has an area of $1/2$, so theoretically it could be colored with ink. On the other hand, the boundary of that region is infinite, so it cannot be drawn with a finite amount of ink. This seems impossible, because coloring the region automatically colors the boundary. Explain why it is possible to color the region.

39. Consider the functions $f(x) = 1/\sqrt{1+x^2}$ and $g(x) = 1/\sqrt{1+x^4}$.

   a. Use your calculator to approximate $\int_1^b f(x)\, dx$ for $b = 20, 50, 100, 1000,$ and $10{,}000$.

   b. Based on your answers from part a, would you guess that $\int_1^\infty f(x)\, dx$ is convergent or divergent?

c. Use your calculator to approximate $\int_1^b g(x)\,dx$ for $b = 20, 50, 100, 1000$, and $10,000$.

d. Based on your answers from part c, would you guess that $\int_1^\infty g(x)\,dx$ is convergent or divergent?

e. Show how the answer to parts b and d might be guessed by comparing the integrals with others whose convergence or divergence is known. (*Hint:* For large x, the difference between $1 + x^2$ and x^2 is relatively small.)

Note: The first integral is indeed divergent, and the second convergent, with an approximate value of 0.9270.

40. a. Use your calculator to approximate $\int_0^b e^{-x^2}\,dx$ for $b = 1$, $5, 10$, and 20.

b. Based on your answers to part a, does $\int_0^\infty e^{-x^2}\,dx$ appear to be convergent or divergent? If convergent, what seems to be its approximate value?

c. Explain why this integral should be convergent by comparing e^{-x^2} with e^{-x} for $x > 1$.

Note: The integral is convergent, with a value of $\sqrt{\pi}/2$.

41. a. Use your calculator to approximate $\int_0^b e^{-0.00001x}\,dx$ for $b = 10$, $50, 100$, and 1000.

b. Based on your answers to part a, does $\int_0^\infty e^{-0.00001x}\,dx$ appear to be convergent or divergent?

c. To what value does the integral actually converge?

APPLICATIONS

Business and Economics

Capital Value   Find the capital values of the properties in Exercises 42–43.

42. A castle for which annual rent of $225,000 will be paid in perpetuity; the interest rate is 6% compounded continuously

43. A fort on a strategic peninsula in the North Sea; the annual rent is $1,000,000, paid in perpetuity; the interest rate is 5% compounded continuously

44. Capital Value Find the capital value of an asset that generates $7200 yearly income if the interest rate is as follows.

a. 5% compounded continuously

b. 10% compounded continuously

45. Capital Value An investment produces a perpetual stream of income with a flow rate of

$$R(t) = 1200e^{0.03t}.$$

Find the capital value at an interest rate of 7% compounded continuously.

46. Capital Value Suppose income from an investment starts (at time 0) at $6000 a year and increases linearly and continuously at a rate of $200 a year. Find the capital value at an interest rate of 5% compounded continuously.

47. Scholarship The Drucker family wants to establish an ongoing scholarship award at a college. Each year in June $3000 will be awarded, starting 1 year from now. What amount must the Druckers provide the college, assuming funds will be invested at 10% compounded continuously?

Social Sciences

48. Drug Reaction The rate of reaction to a drug is given by

$$r'(t) = 2t^2 e^{-t},$$

where t is the number of hours since the drug was administered. Find the total reaction to the drug over all the time since it was administered, assuming this is an infinite time interval. (*Hint:* $\lim_{t \to \infty} t^k e^{-t} = 0$ for all real numbers k.)

49. Drug Epidemic In an epidemiological model used to study the spread of drug use, a single drug user is introduced into a population of N non-users. Under certain assumptions, the number of people expected to use drugs as a result of direct influence from each drug user is given by

$$S = N \int_0^\infty \frac{a(1 - e^{-kt})}{k} e^{-bt}\,dt,$$

where a, b, and k are constants. Find the value of S. *Source: Mathematical Biology.*

50. Present Value When harvesting a population, such as fish, the present value of the resource is given by

$$P = \int_0^\infty e^{-rt} n(t) y(t)\,dt,$$

where r is a discount factor, $n(t)$ is the net revenue at time t, and $y(t)$ is the harvesting effort. Suppose $y(t) = K$ and $n(t) = at + b$. Find the present value. *Source: Some Mathematical Questions in Biology.*

Physical Sciences

Radioactive Waste   Radioactive waste is entering the atmosphere over an area at a decreasing rate. Use the improper integral

$$\int_0^\infty P e^{-kt}\,dt$$

with $P = 50$ to find the total amount of the waste that will enter the atmosphere for each value of k.

51. $k = 0.06$

52. $k = 0.04$

YOUR TURN ANSWERS

1. (a) Divergent (b) 3/2   **2.** 5/2

CHAPTER REVIEW

SUMMARY

In this chapter, we introduced another technique of integration and some applications of integration. The technique is known as integration by parts, which is derived from the product rule for derivatives. We also developed definite integral formulas to calculate the volume of a solid of revolution and the average value of a function on some interval. We then used definite integrals to study continuous money flow. Finally, we learned how to evaluate improper integrals that have upper or lower limits of ∞ or $-\infty$.

Integration by Parts If u and v are differentiable functions, then

$$\int u\,dv = uv - \int v\,du.$$

Volume of a Solid of Revolution If $f(x)$ is nonnegative and R is the region between $f(x)$ and the x-axis from $x = a$ to $x = b$, the volume of the solid formed by rotating R about the x-axis is given by

$$V = \int_a^b \pi[f(x)]^2\,dx.$$

Average Value of a Function The average value of a function f on the interval $[a, b]$ is

$$\frac{1}{b-a}\int_a^b f(x)\,dx,$$

provided the indicated definite integral exists.

Total Money Flow If $f(t)$ is the rate of money flow, then the total money flow over the time interval from $t = 0$ to $t = T$ is given by

$$\int_0^T f(t)\,dt.$$

Present Value of Money Flow If $f(t)$ is the rate of continuous money flow at an interest rate r for T years, then the present value is

$$P = \int_0^T f(t)e^{-rt}\,dt.$$

Accumulated Amount of Money Flow at Time T If $f(t)$ is the rate of money flow at an interest rate r at time t, the accumulated amount of money flow at time T is

$$A = e^{rT}\int_0^T f(t)e^{-rt}\,dt.$$

Improper Integrals If f is continuous on the indicated interval and if the indicated limits exist, then

$$\int_a^\infty f(x)\,dx = \lim_{b\to\infty}\int_a^b f(x)\,dx,$$

$$\int_{-\infty}^b f(x)\,dx = \lim_{a\to-\infty}\int_a^b f(x)\,dx,$$

$$\int_{-\infty}^\infty f(x)\,dx = \int_{-\infty}^c f(x)\,dx + \int_c^\infty f(x)\,dx,$$

for real numbers a, b, and c, where c is arbitrarily chosen.

Capital Value If $R(t)$ gives the annual rate at which earnings are produced by an asset at time t, the capital value is given by

$$\int_0^\infty R(t)e^{-rt}\,dt,$$

where r is the annual rate of interest, compounded continuously.

KEY TERMS

1
integration by parts
column integration

2
solid of revolution
average value of a function

3
total money flow
  present value of continuous
  money flow
  accumulated amount of money
  flow

4
improper integral
convergent integral
divergent integral
capital value

REVIEW EXERCISES

CONCEPT CHECK

Determine whether each of the following statements is true or false, and explain why.

1. Integration by parts should be used to evaluate $\int_0^1 \frac{x^2}{x^3 + 1}\, dx$.

2. Integration by parts should be used to evaluate $\int_0^1 xe^{10x}\, dx$.

3. We would need to apply the method of integration by parts twice to determine

$$\int x^3 e^{-x^2}\, dx.$$

4. Integration by parts should be used to determine $\int \ln(4x)\, dx$.

5. The average value of the function $f(x) = 2x^2 + 3$ on $[1, 4]$ is given by

$$\frac{1}{3}\int_1^4 \pi(2x^2 + 3)^2\, dx.$$

6. The volume of the solid formed by revolving the function $f(x) = \sqrt{x^2 + 1}$ about the x-axis on the interval $[1, 2]$ is given by

$$\int_1^2 \pi\sqrt{x^2 + 1}\, dx.$$

7. The volume of the solid formed by revolving the function $f(x) = x + 4$ about the x-axis on the interval $[-4, 5]$ is given by

$$\int_{-4}^5 \pi(x + 4)^2\, dx.$$

8. If $f(t) = 1000e^{0.05t}$ represents the rate of flow of money for a vending machine over the first five years of income, then the total money flow for that time period is given by

$$\int_0^5 1000e^{0.05t}\, dt.$$

9. If a company expects an annual flow of money during the next five years to be $f(t) = 1000e^{0.05t}$, the present value of this income, assuming an annual interest rate of 4.5% compounded continuously is given by

$$\int_0^5 1000e^{0.005t}\, dt.$$

10. $\displaystyle\int_{-\infty}^{\infty} xe^{-2x}\, dx = \lim_{c\to\infty}\int_{-c}^c xe^{-2x}\, dx$

PRACTICE AND EXPLORATIONS

11. Describe the type of integral for which integration by parts is useful.

12. Compare finding the average value of a function with finding the average of n numbers.

13. What is an improper integral? Explain why improper integrals must be treated in a special way.

Find each integral, using techniques from this or the previous chapter.

14. $\displaystyle\int x(8 - x)^{3/2}\, dx$

15. $\displaystyle\int \frac{3x}{\sqrt{x - 2}}\, dx$

16. $\displaystyle\int xe^x\, dx$

17. $\displaystyle\int (3x + 6)e^{-3x}\, dx$

18. $\displaystyle\int \ln|4x + 5|\, dx$

19. $\displaystyle\int (x - 1)\ln|x|\, dx$

20. $\displaystyle\int \frac{x}{25 - 9x^2}\, dx$

21. $\displaystyle\int \frac{x}{\sqrt{16 + 8x^2}}\, dx$

22. $\displaystyle\int_1^e x^3 \ln x\, dx$

23. $\displaystyle\int_0^1 x^2 e^{x/2}\, dx$

24. Find the area between $y = (3 + x^2)e^{2x}$ and the x-axis from $x = 0$ to $x = 1$.

25. Find the area between $y = x^3(x^2 - 1)^{1/3}$ and the x-axis from $x = 1$ to $x = 3$.

Find the volume of the solid of revolution formed by rotating each bounded region about the x-axis.

26. $f(x) = 3x - 1, \quad y = 0, \quad x = 2$

27. $f(x) = \sqrt{x - 4}, \quad y = 0, \quad x = 13$

28. $f(x) = e^{-x}, \quad y = 0, \quad x = -2, \quad x = 1$

29. $f(x) = \dfrac{1}{\sqrt{x - 1}}, \quad y = 0, \quad x = 2, \quad x = 4$

30. $f(x) = 4 - x^2, \quad y = 0, \quad x = -1, \quad x = 1$

31. $f(x) = \dfrac{x^2}{4}, \quad y = 0, \quad x = 4$

32. A frustum is what remains of a cone when the top is cut off by a plane parallel to the base. Suppose a right circular frustum (that is, one formed from a right circular cone) has a base with radius r, a top with radius $r/2$, and a height h. (See the figure below.) Find the volume of this frustum by rotating about the x-axis the region below the line segment from $(0, r)$ to $(h, r/2)$.

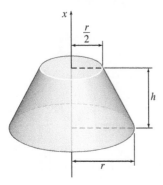

33. How is the average value of a function found?

34. Find the average value of $f(x) = \sqrt{x + 1}$ over the interval $[0, 8]$.

35. Find the average value of $f(x) = 7x^2(x^3 + 1)^6$ over the interval $[0, 2]$.

Find the value of each integral that converges.

36. $\displaystyle\int_{10}^{\infty} x^{-1}\, dx$

37. $\displaystyle\int_{-\infty}^{-5} x^{-2}\, dx$

38. $\displaystyle\int_{0}^{\infty} \frac{dx}{(3x + 1)^2}$

39. $\displaystyle\int_{1}^{\infty} 6e^{-x}\, dx$

40. $\displaystyle\int_{-\infty}^{0} \frac{x}{x^2 + 3}\, dx$

41. $\displaystyle\int_{4}^{\infty} \ln(5x)\, dx$

Find the area between the graph of each function and the x-axis over the given interval, if possible.

42. $f(x) = \dfrac{5}{(x - 2)^2}$, for $(-\infty, 1]$

43. $f(x) = 3e^{-x}$, for $[0, \infty)$

44. How is the present value of money flow found? The accumulated amount of money flow?

APPLICATIONS

Business and Economics

45. Total Revenue The rate of change of revenue from the sale of x toaster ovens is

$$R'(x) = x(x - 50)^{1/2}.$$

Find the total revenue from the sale of the 50th to the 75th ovens.

Present Value of Money Flow **Each function in Exercises 46–49 represents the rate of flow of money (in dollars per year) over the given time period, compounded continuously at the given annual interest rate. Find the present value in each case.**

46. $f(t) = 5000$, 8 years, 9%

47. $f(t) = 25{,}000$, 12 years, 10%

48. $f(t) = 150e^{0.04t}$, 5 years, 6%

49. $f(t) = 15t$, 18 months, 8%

Accumulated Amount of Money Flow at Time T **Assume that each function gives the rate of flow of money in dollars per year over the given period, with continuous compounding at the given annual interest rate. Find the accumulated amount of money flow at the end of the time period.**

50. $f(t) = 1000$, 5 years, 6%

51. $f(t) = 500e^{-0.04t}$, 8 years, 10%

52. $f(t) = 20t$, 6 years, 4%

53. $f(t) = 1000 + 200t$, 10 years, 9%

54. Money Flow An investment scheme is expected to produce a continuous flow of money, starting at $1000 and increasing exponentially at 5% a year for 7 years. Find the present value at an interest rate of 11% compounded continuously.

55. Money Flow The proceeds from the sale of a building will yield a uniform continuous flow of $10,000 a year for 10 years. Find the final amount at an interest rate of 10.5% compounded continuously.

56. Capital Value Find the capital value of an office building for which annual rent of $50,000 will be paid in perpetuity, if the interest rate is 9%.

Life Sciences

57. Drug Reaction The reaction rate to a new drug t hours after the drug is administered is

$$r'(t) = 0.5te^{-t}.$$

Find the total reaction over the first 5 hours.

58. Oil Leak Pollution An oil leak from an uncapped well is polluting a bay at a rate of $f(t) = 125e^{-0.025t}$ gallons per year. Use an improper integral to find the total amount of oil that will enter the bay, assuming the well is never capped.

Physical Sciences

59. Average Temperatures Suppose the temperature (degrees F) in a river at a point x meters downstream from a factory that is discharging hot water into the river is given by

$$T(x) = 160 - 0.05x^2.$$

Find the average temperature over each interval.

a. $[0, 10]$ **b.** $[10, 40]$ **c.** $[0, 40]$

ESTIMATING LEARNING CURVES IN MANUFACTURING WITH INTEGRALS

Recall how the trapezoidal rule uses sums of areas of polygons to approximate the area under a smooth curve that is a definite integral. In this Extended Application we look at the reverse process, using an integral to estimate a sum, in the context of estimating production costs.

As a manufacturer produces more units of a new product, the individual units generally become cheaper to produce, because with experience, production workers gain skill and speed, and managers spot opportunities for improved efficiency. This decline in unit costs is often called an *experience curve* or *learning curve*. This curve is important when a manufacturer negotiates a contract with a buyer.

Here's an example, based on an actual contract that came before the Armed Services Board of Contract Appeals. *Source: Armed Services Board of Contract Appeals*. The Navy asked the ITT Defense Communications Division to bid on the manufacture of several different kinds of mobile telephone switchboards, including 280 of the model called the SB 3865. ITT figured that the cost of making a single SB 3865 was around $300,000. But they couldn't submit a bid of $300,000 × 280 or $84 million, because multiple units should have a lower unit price. So ITT used a learning curve to estimate an average unit cost of $135,300 for all 280 switchboards and submitted a bid of $135,300 × 280 or $37.9 million.

The contract gave the Navy an option to purchase 280 SB units over three years, but in fact it bought fewer. Suppose the Navy bought 140 SBs. Should it pay half of the original price of $37.9 million? No: ITT's bid was based on the efficiencies of a 280-unit run, so 140 units should be repriced to yield *more* than half the full price. A repricing clause in the contract specified that a learning curve would be used to reprice partial orders, and when the Navy ordered less than the full amount, ITT invoked this clause to reprice the switchboards. The question in dispute at the hearing was which learning curve to use.

There are two common learning curve models. The *unit learning curve* model assumes that each time the number of units doubles, say from n to $2n$, the cost of producing the last unit is some constant fraction r of the cost for the nth unit. Usually the fraction r is given as a percent. If $r = 90\%$ (typical for big pieces of hardware), then the contract would refer to a "90% learning curve." The *cumulative learning curve* model assumes that when the number of units doubles, the *average cost* of producing all $2n$ units is some constant fraction of the *average cost* of the first n units. The Navy's contract with ITT didn't specify which model was to be used—it just referred to "a 90% learning curve." The government used the unit model and ITT used the cumulative average model, and ITT calculated a fair price millions of dollars higher than the government's price!

In practice, ITT used a calculator program to make its estimate, and the government used printed tables, but both the program and the tables were derived using calculus. To see how the computation works, we'll derive the government's unit learning curve.

Each unit has a different cost, with the first unit being the most expensive and the 280th unit the least expensive. So the cost of the nth unit, call it $C(n)$, is a function of n. To find a fair price for n units we'll add up all the unit prices. That is, we will compute $C(1) + C(2) + \cdots + C(n-1) + C(n)$. Before we can do that, we need a formula for $C(n)$ in terms of n, but all we know about $C(n)$ is that

$$C(2n) = r \cdot C(n)$$

for *every* n, with $r = 0.90$. This sort of equation is called a *functional equation:* It relates two different values of the function without giving an explicit formula for the function. In Exercise 3 you'll see how you might discover a solution to this functional equation, but here we'll just give the result:

$$C(n) = C(1) \cdot n^b, \text{ where } b = \frac{\ln r}{\ln 2} \approx -0.152.$$

Thus, to find the price for making 280 units, we need to add up all the values of $C(1) \cdot n^b$ as n ranges from 1 to 280. There's just one problem: We don't know $C(1)$! The only numbers that ITT gave were the *average* cost per unit for 280 units, namely $135,300, and the total price of $37.9 million. But if we write out the formula for the 280-unit price in terms of $C(1)$, we can figure out $C(1)$ by dividing. Here's how it works.

The cost C is a function of an integer variable n, since the contractor can't deliver fractional units of the hardware. But the function $C(x) = C(1) \cdot x^{-0.152}$ is a perfectly good function of the real variable x, and the sum of the first 280 values of $C(n)$ should be close to $\int_1^{280} C(x)\, dx = C(1) \cdot \int_1^{280} x^{-0.152}\, dx$. In Exercise 4 you'll see how to derive the following improved estimate:

$$C(1)\left(\int_1^{281} x^{-0.152}\, dx + \frac{1 - 281^{-0.152}}{2} \right).$$

The integrand is a power function, so you know how to evaluate the integral exactly.

$$\int_1^{281} x^{-0.152}\, dx = \frac{1}{0.848} x^{0.848} \Big|_1^{281} = \frac{1}{0.848}\left(281^{0.848} - 1^{0.848}\right)$$

Thus, the sum is approximately

$$C(1)\left[\frac{1}{0.848}\left(281^{0.848} - 1^{0.848}\right) + \frac{1 - 281^{-0.152}}{2} \right] \approx C(1) \cdot 139.75.$$

Since ITT's price for 280 units was $37.9 million,

$$C(1) = \frac{\$37,900,000}{139.75} \approx \$271,000.$$

Now that we know $C(1)$, we can reprice an order of 140 units by adding up the first 140 values of $C(n)$. An estimate exactly like the one above tells us that according to the government's model, a fair price for 140 units is about $21 million. As we expected, this is more than half the 280-unit price, in fact about $2 million more.

EXERCISES

1. According to the formula for $C(n)$, what is the unit price of the 280th unit, to the nearest thousand dollars?

2. Suppose that instead of using natural logarithms to compute b, we use logarithms with a base of 10 and define $b = (\log r)/(\log 2)$. Does this change the value of b?

3. All power functions satisfy an equation similar to our functional equation: If $f(x) = ax^b$, then $f(2x) = a(2x)^b = a2^b \cdot x^b = 2^b \cdot f(x)$. How can you choose a and b to make $C(x) = ax^b$ a solution to the functional equation $C(2n) = r \cdot C(n)$?

4. Figure 16 indicates how you could use the integral

$$\int_1^5 \frac{1}{x}\,dx + \frac{1 - \dfrac{1}{5}}{2} \text{ as an estimate for the sum } 1 + \frac{1}{2} + \frac{1}{3} + \frac{1}{4}.$$

The graph shows the function $y = \dfrac{1}{x}$.

a. Write a justification for the integral estimate. (Your argument will also justify the integral estimate for the $C(n)$ sum.) Based on your explanation, does the integral expression overestimate the sum?

b. You know how to integrate the function $1/x$. Compute the integral estimate and the actual value. What is the percentage error in the estimate?

5. Go to the website WolframAlpha.com and enter: "integrate." Follow the instructions and use them along with the improved estimate to verify the fair price for 140 units of about $21 million given in the text. Then enter "sum" into Wolfram Alpha and follow the instructions to verify the fair price by summing the first 140 values of $C(n)$. Discuss how the solution compares with the solutions provided by the integration and summation features on a graphing calculator, as well as the solution provided by adding up the values using a spreadsheet.

DIRECTIONS FOR GROUP PROJECT

Suppose that you and three other students have an internship with a manufacturing company that is submitting a bid to make several thousand units of some highly technical equipment. The one problem with the bid is that the number of units that will be purchased is only an estimate and that the actual number needed may greatly vary from the estimate. Using the information given above, prepare a presentation for an internal sales meeting that will describe the case listed above and its applications to the bid at hand. Make your presentation realistic in the sense that the product you are manufacturing should have a name, average price, and so on. Then show how integrals can be used to estimate learning curves in this situation and produce a pricing structure for the bid. Presentation software, such as Microsoft PowerPoint, should be used.

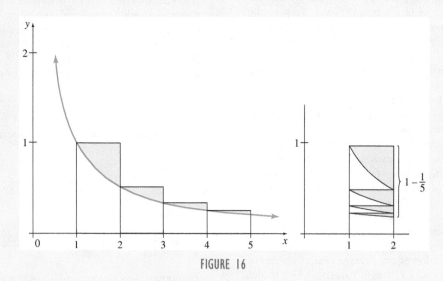

FIGURE 16

ANSWERS TO SELECTED EXERCISES

Exercises 1

For exercises . . .	1–4,36,40,41,43,44	5,6,35,39,42	7–10,20–22	13–19	23–28
Refer to example . . .	1,3	2	4	1–3	5

1. $xe^x - e^x + C$ **3.** $(-x/2 + 23/16)\,e^{-8x} + C$ **5.** $(x^2 \ln x)/2 - x^2/4 + C$ **7.** $-5e^{-1} + 3 \approx 1.161$
9. $26 \ln 3 - 8 \approx 20.56$ **11.** $e^4 + e^2 \approx 61.99$ **13.** $x^2e^{2x}/2 - xe^{2x}/2 + e^{2x}/4 + C$
15. $(2/7)(x + 4)^{7/2} - (16/5)(x + 4)^{5/2} + (32/3)(x + 4)^{3/2} + C$ or $(2/3)x^2(x + 4)^{3/2} - (8/15)x(x + 4)^{5/2} + (16/105)(x + 4)^{7/2} + C$
17. $(4x^2 + 10x) \ln 5x - 2x^2 - 10x + C$ **19.** $(-e^2/4)(3e^2 + 1) \approx -42.80$ **21.** $2\sqrt{3} - 10/3 \approx 0.1308$
23. $16 \ln |x + \sqrt{x^2 + 16}| + C$ **25.** $-(3/11) \ln |(11 + \sqrt{121 - x^2})/x| + C$ **27.** $-1/(4x + 6) - (1/6) \ln |x/(4x + 6)| + C$
31. -18 **33.** 15 **37. a.** $(2/3)x(x + 1)^{3/2} - (4/15)(x + 1)^{5/2} + C$ **b.** $(2/5)(x + 1)^{5/2} - (2/3)(x + 1)^{3/2} + C$
39. $(169/2) \ln 13 - 42 \approx \$174.74$ **41.** $15e^6 + 3 \approx 6054$ **43.** About 219 kJ

Exercises 2

For exercises . . .	1–23,32,33,40,43	24–31,34–37,39,41,42	38
Refer to example . . .	1–3	4	Derivation of volume formula

1. 9π **3.** $364\pi/3$ **5.** $386\pi/27$ **7.** $15\pi/2$ **9.** 18π **11.** $\pi(e^4 - 1)/2 \approx 84.19$ **13.** $4\pi \ln 3 \approx 13.81$ **15.** $3124\pi/5$
17. $16\pi/15$ **19.** $4\pi/3$ **21.** $4\pi r^3/3$ **23.** $\pi r^2 h$ **25.** $13/3 \approx 4.333$ **27.** $38/15 \approx 2.533$ **29.** $e - 1 \approx 1.718$
31. $(5e^4 - 1)/8 \approx 34.00$ **33.** 3.758 **35.** $\$42.49$ **37.** 200 cases **39. a.** $110e^{-0.1} - 120e^{-0.2} \approx 1.284$
b. $210e^{-1.1} - 220e^{-1.2} \approx 3.640$ **c.** $330e^{-2.3} - 340e^{-2.4} \approx 2.241$ **41. a.** $9(6 \ln 6 - 5) \approx 51.76$ **b.** $5(10 \ln 10 - 9) \approx 70.13$
c. $3(31 \ln 31 - 30)/2 \approx 114.7$ **43.** $1.083 \times 10^{21} \, \mathrm{m}^3$

Exercises 3

For exercises . . .	1(a)–8(a),16	1(b)–8(b),15,17,18	9–14,19,20
Refer to example . . .	2	3,4	5

1. a. $\$6883.39$ **b.** $\$15,319.26$ **3. a.** $\$3441.69$ **b.** $\$7659.63$ **5. a.** $\$3147.75$ **b.** $\$7005.46$ **7. a.** $\$32,968.35$
b. $\$73,372.42$ **9. a.** $\$746.91$ **b.** $\$1662.27$ **11. a.** $\$688.64$ **b.** $\$1532.59$ **13. a.** $\$11,351.78$ **b.** $\$25,263.84$
15. $\$63,748.43$ **17.** $\$28,513.76, \$54,075.81$ **19.** $\$4560.94$

Exercises 4

For exercises . . .	1–26,31–34,37	27–30,35,36	42–47,50	48,49,51,52
Refer to example . . .	1	2	4	3

1. $1/3$ **3.** Divergent **5.** -1 **7.** $10,000$ **9.** $1/10$
11. $3/5$ **13.** 1 **15.** 1000 **17.** Divergent **19.** 1 **21.** Divergent
23. Divergent **25.** Divergent **27.** 0 **29.** Divergent **31.** Divergent **33.** 1 **35.** 0 **39. a.** $2.808, 3.724, 4.417, 6.720, 9.022$
b. Divergent **c.** $0.8770, 0.9070, 0.9170, 0.9260, 0.9269$ **d.** Convergent **41. a.** $9.9995, 49.9875, 99.9500, 995.0166$
b. Divergent **c.** $100,000$ **43.** $\$20,000,000$ **45.** $\$30,000$ **47.** $\$30,000$ **49.** $Na/[b(b + k)]$ **51.** About 833.3

Chapter Review Exercises

For exercises . . .	1–4,14–25	5–7,26–35,59	8,9,44–55,57	10,36–43,56,58
Refer to section . . .	1	2	3	4

1. False **2.** True **3.** False **4.** True
5. False **6.** False **7.** True **8.** True
9. True **10.** False
15. $6x(x - 2)^{1/2} - 4(x - 2)^{3/2} + C$ **17.** $-(x + 2)e^{-3x} - (1/3)e^{-3x} + C$ **19.** $(x^2/2 - x) \ln |x| - x^2/4 + x + C$
21. $(1/8)\sqrt{16 + 8x^2} + C$ **23.** $10e^{1/2} - 16 \approx 0.4872$ **25.** $234/7 \approx 33.43$ **27.** $81\pi/2 \approx 127.2$ **29.** $\pi \ln 3 \approx 3.451$
31. $64\pi/5 \approx 40.21$ **35.** $2,391,484/3$ **37.** $1/5$ **39.** $6/e \approx 2.207$ **41.** Divergent **43.** 3 **45.** $16,250/3 \approx \$5416.67$
47. $\$174,701.45$ **49.** $\$15.58$ **51.** $\$5354.97$ **53.** $\$30,035.17$ **55.** $\$176,919.15$ **57.** 0.4798
59. a. $158.3°$ **b.** $125°$ **c.** $133.3°$

SAMPLE SOURCES

Section 1

1. Exercise 38 from Sam Northshield, Plattsburgh State University.
2. Exercise 43 from Reed, George and James Hill, "Measuring the Thermic Effect of Food," *American Journal of Clinical Nutrition*, Vol. 63, 1996, pp. 164–169.
3. Exercise 44 from Hungate, R. E., "The Rumen Microbial Ecosystem," *Annual Review of Ecology and Systematics*, Vol. 6, 1975, pp. 39–66.

Section 2

1. Exercise 40 from http://www.nctm.org/wlme/wlme6/five.htm.
2. Exercise 43 from http://www.nctm.org/eresources/view_article.asp?article_id=6219&page=5.

Section 4

1. Exercise 49 from Murray, J. D., *Mathematical Biology*, Springer-Verlag, 1989, p. 642, 648.
2. Exercise 50 from Ludwig, Donald, "An Unusual Free Boundary Problem from the Theory of Optimal Harvesting," in *Lectures on Mathematics in the Life Sciences, Vol. 12: Some Mathematical Questions in Biology*, American Mathematical Society, 1979, pp. 173–209.

Extended Application

1. For a report on this case, see ASBCA No. 44791, 1994. For an introduction to learning curves see Heizer, Jay and Barry Render, *Operations Management*, Prentice-Hall, 2001, or Argote, Linda and Dennis Epple, "Learning Curves in Manufacturing," *Science*, Feb. 23, 1990.

CREDITS

Exercise 38: Professor Sam Northshield

Multivariable Calculus

Safe diving requires an understanding of how the increased pressure below the surface affects the body's intake of nitrogen. An exercise in Section 2 of this chapter investigates a formula for nitrogen pressure as a function of two variables, depth and dive time. Partial derivatives tell us how this function behaves when one variable is held constant as the other changes. Dive tables based on the formula help divers to choose a safe time for a given depth, or a safe depth for a given time.

Specta/ Shutterstock

From Chapter 9 of *Calculus with Applications*. Tenth Edition. Margaret L. Lial, Raymond N. Greenwell, Nathan P. Ritchey.

Thus far your study of calculus may have been limited to functions of one variable. There are other phenomena that require more than one variable to adequately model the situation. For example, the price of an electronics device depends on how long it has been on the market, the number of competing devices, labor costs, demand, and many other factors. In this case, the price is a function of more than one variable. To analyze and better understand situations like this, we will extend the ideas of calculus, including differentiation and integration, to functions of more than one variable.

1 Functions of Several Variables

APPLY IT How are the amounts of labor and capital needed to produce a certain number of items related?
We will study this question in Example 8 using a production function that depends on the two independent variables of labor and capital.

If a company produces x items at a cost of \$10 per item, then the total cost $C(x)$ of producing the items is given by

$$C(x) = 10x.$$

The cost is a function of one independent variable, the number of items produced. If the company produces two products, with x of one product at a cost of \$10 each, and y of another product at a cost of \$15 each, then the total cost to the firm is a function of *two* independent variables, x and y. By generalizing $f(x)$ notation, the total cost can be written as $C(x, y)$, where

$$C(x, y) = 10x + 15y.$$

When $x = 5$ and $y = 12$ the total cost is written $C(5, 12)$, with

$$C(5, 12) = 10 \cdot 5 + 15 \cdot 12 = 230.$$

A general definition follows.

Function of Two or More Variables

The expression $z = f(x, y)$ is a **function of two variables** if a unique value of z is obtained from each ordered pair of real numbers (x, y). The variables x and y are **independent variables**, and z is the **dependent variable**. The set of all ordered pairs of real numbers (x, y) such that $f(x, y)$ exists is the **domain** of f; the set of all values of $f(x, y)$ is the **range**. Similar definitions could be given for functions of three, four, or more independent variables.

EXAMPLE 1   Evaluating Functions

Let $f(x, y) = 4x^2 + 2xy + 3/y$ and find the following.

(a) $f(-1, 3)$

SOLUTION   Replace x with -1 and y with 3.

$$f(-1, 3) = 4(-1)^2 + 2(-1)(3) + \frac{3}{3} = 4 - 6 + 1 = -1$$

(b) $f(2, 0)$

SOLUTION Because of the quotient $3/y$, it is not possible to replace y with 0, so $f(2, 0)$ is undefined. By inspection, we see that the domain of the function is the set of all (x, y) such that $y \neq 0$.

(c) $\dfrac{f(x + h, y) - f(x, y)}{h}$

SOLUTION Calculate as follows:

$$\frac{f(x + h, y) - f(x, y)}{h} = \frac{4(x + h)^2 + 2(x + h)y + 3/y - [4x^2 + 2xy + 3/y]}{h}$$

$$= \frac{4x^2 + 8xh + 4h^2 + 2xy + 2hy + 3/y - 4x^2 - 2xy - 3/y}{h}$$

$$= \frac{8xh + 4h^2 + 2hy}{h} \qquad \text{Simplify the numerator.}$$

$$= \frac{h(8x + 4h + 2y)}{h} \qquad \text{Factor } h \text{ from the numerator.}$$

$$= 8x + 4h + 2y. \qquad \text{TRY YOUR TURN 1}$$

YOUR TURN 1 For the function in Example 1, find $f(2, 3)$.

EXAMPLE 2 Volume of a Can

Let r and h represent the radius and height of a can in cm. The volume of the can is then a function of the two variables r and h given by

$$V(r, h) = \pi r^2 h.$$

Find $V(3, 11)$.

SOLUTION Replace r with 3 and h with 11 to get

$$V(3, 11) = \pi \cdot 3^2 \cdot 11 = 99\pi \approx 311 \text{ cm}^3.$$

This says that a can with radius 3 cm and height 11 cm has a volume of approximately 311 cm³.

EXAMPLE 3 Evaluating a Function

Let $f(x, y, z) = 4xz - 3x^2y + 2z^2$. Find $f(2, -3, 1)$.

SOLUTION Replace x with 2, y with -3, and z with 1.

$$f(2, -3, 1) = 4(2)(1) - 3(2)^2(-3) + 2(1)^2 = 8 + 36 + 2 = 46$$

TRY YOUR TURN 2

YOUR TURN 2 For the function in Example 3, find $f(1, 2, 3)$.

Graphing Functions of Two Independent Variables

Functions of one independent variable are graphed by using an x-axis and a y-axis to locate points in a plane. The plane determined by the x- and y-axes is called the *xy-plane*. A third axis is needed to graph functions of two independent variables—the z-axis, which goes through the origin in the *xy-plane* and is perpendicular to both the x-axis and the y-axis.

Figure 1 shows one possible way to draw the three axes. In Figure 1, the *yz-plane* is in the plane of the page, with the x-axis perpendicular to the plane of the page.

Just as we graphed ordered pairs earlier we can now graph **ordered triples** of the form (x, y, z). For example, to locate the point corresponding to the ordered triple $(2, -4, 3)$, start at the origin and go 2 units along the positive x-axis. Then go 4 units in a negative direction (to the left) parallel to the y-axis. Finally, go up 3 units parallel to the z-axis. The point representing $(2, -4, 3)$ is shown in Figure 1, together with several other points. The region of three-dimensional space where all coordinates are positive is called the **first octant**.

In Chapter 1 we saw that the graph of $ax + by = c$ (where a and b are not both 0) is a straight line. This result generalizes to three dimensions.

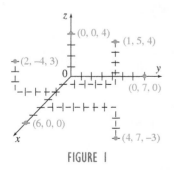

FIGURE 1

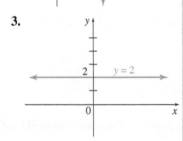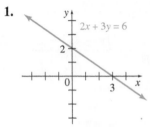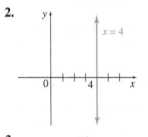
YOUR TURN 3 Graph $x + 2y + 3z = 12$ in the first octant.

Plane

The graph of

$$ax + by + cz = d$$

is a **plane** if a, b, and c are not all 0.

EXAMPLE 4 **Graphing a Plane**

Graph $2x + y + z = 6$.

SOLUTION The graph of this equation is a plane. Earlier, we graphed straight lines by finding x- and y-intercepts. A similar idea helps in graphing a plane. To find the x-intercept, which is the point where the graph crosses the x-axis, let $y = 0$ and $z = 0$.

$$2x + 0 + 0 = 6$$
$$x = 3$$

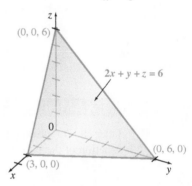

FIGURE 2

The point $(3, 0, 0)$ is on the graph. Letting $x = 0$ and $z = 0$ gives the point $(0, 6, 0)$, while $x = 0$ and $y = 0$ lead to $(0, 0, 6)$. The plane through these three points includes the triangular surface shown in Figure 2. This surface is the first-octant part of the plane that is the graph of $2x + y + z = 6$. The plane does not stop at the axes but extends without bound.

TRY YOUR TURN 3

EXAMPLE 5 **Graphing a Plane**

Graph $x + z = 6$.

SOLUTION To find the x-intercept, let $y = 0$ and $z = 0$, giving $(6, 0, 0)$. If $x = 0$ and $y = 0$, we get the point $(0, 0, 6)$. Because there is no y in the equation $x + z = 6$, there can be no y-intercept. A plane that has no y-intercept is parallel to the y-axis. The first-octant portion of the graph of $x + z = 6$ is shown in Figure 3.

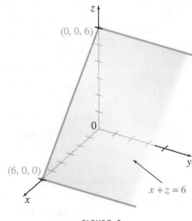

FIGURE 3

EXAMPLE 6 Graphing Planes

Graph each equation in the first octant.

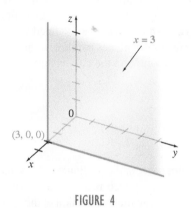

(a) $x = 3$

SOLUTION This graph, which goes through $(3, 0, 0)$, can have no y-intercept and no z-intercept. It is, therefore, a plane parallel to the y-axis and the z-axis and, therefore, to the yz-plane. The first-octant portion of the graph is shown in Figure 4.

(b) $y = 4$

SOLUTION This graph goes through $(0, 4, 0)$ and is parallel to the xz-plane. The first-octant portion of the graph is shown in Figure 5.

(c) $z = 1$

SOLUTION The graph is a plane parallel to the xy-plane, passing through $(0, 0, 1)$. Its first-octant portion is shown in Figure 6.

FIGURE 4

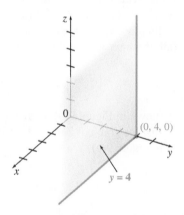

FIGURE 5

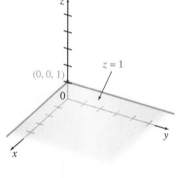

FIGURE 6

The graph of a function of one variable, $y = f(x)$, is a curve in the plane. If x_0 is in the domain of f, the point $(x_0, f(x_0))$ on the graph lies directly above or below the number x_0 on the x-axis, as shown in Figure 7.

The graph of a function of two variables, $z = f(x, y)$, is a **surface** in three-dimensional space. If (x_0, y_0) is in the domain of f, the point $(x_0, y_0, f(x_0, y_0))$ lies directly above or below the point (x_0, y_0) in the xy-plane, as shown in Figure 8.

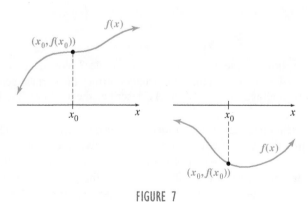

FIGURE 7

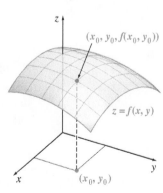

FIGURE 8

Although computer software is available for drawing the graphs of functions of two independent variables, you can often get a good picture of the graph without it by finding various **traces**—the curves that result when a surface is cut by a plane. The **xy-trace** is the intersection of the surface with the xy-plane. The **yz-trace** and **xz-trace** are defined similarly. You can also determine the intersection of the surface with planes parallel to the xy-plane. Such planes are of the form $z = k$, where k is a constant, and the curves that result when they cut the surface are called **level curves**.

EXAMPLE 7 Graphing a Function

Graph $z = x^2 + y^2$.

SOLUTION The yz-plane is the plane in which every point has a first coordinate of 0, so its equation is $x = 0$. When $x = 0$, the equation becomes $z = y^2$, which is the equation of a parabola in the yz-plane, as shown in Figure 9(a). Similarly, to find the intersection of the surface with the xz-plane (whose equation is $y = 0$), let $y = 0$ in the equation. It then becomes $z = x^2$, which is the equation of a parabola in the xz-plane, as shown in Figure 9(a). The xy-trace (the intersection of the surface with the plane $z = 0$) is the single point $(0, 0, 0)$ because $x^2 + y^2$ is equal to 0 only when $x = 0$ and $y = 0$.

Next, we find the level curves by intersecting the surface with the planes $z = 1$, $z = 2$, $z = 3$, etc. (all of which are parallel to the xy-plane). In each case, the result is a circle:

$$x^2 + y^2 = 1, \qquad x^2 + y^2 = 2, \qquad x^2 + y^2 = 3,$$

and so on, as shown in Figure 9(b). Drawing the traces and level curves on the same set of axes suggests that the graph of $z = x^2 + y^2$ is the bowl-shaped figure, called a **paraboloid**, that is shown in Figure 9(c).

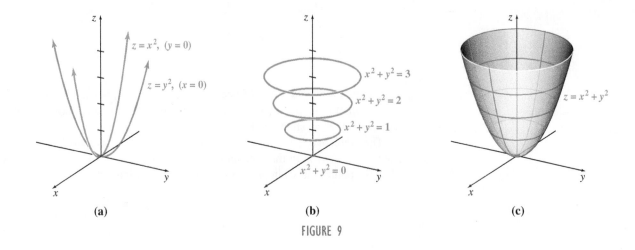

(a)   (b)   (c)

FIGURE 9

Figure 10 shows the level curves from Example 7 plotted in the xy-plane. The picture be thought of as a topographical map that describes the surface generated by $z = x^2 + y^2$, just as the topographical map in Figure 11 describes the surface of the land in a part of New York state.

One application of level curves occurs in economics with production functions. A **production function** $z = f(x, y)$ is a function that gives the quantity z of an item produced as a function of x and y, where x is the amount of labor and y is the amount of capital (in appropriate units) needed to produce z units. If the production function has the special form $z = P(x, y) = Ax^a y^{1-a}$, where A is a constant and $0 < a < 1$, the function is called

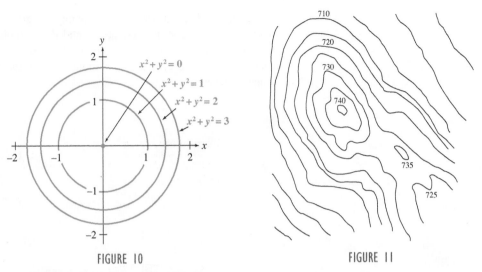

FIGURE 10   FIGURE 11

a **Cobb-Douglas production function**. This function was developed in 1928 by economist Paul H. Douglas (1892–1976), who later became a senator for the state of Illinois, and mathematician Charles W. Cobb. For production functions, level curves are used to indicate combinations of the values of x and y that produce the same value of production z.

EXAMPLE 8   Cobb-Douglas Production Function

Find the level curve at a production of 100 items for the Cobb-Douglas production function $z = x^{2/3}y^{1/3}$.

APPLY IT

YOUR TURN 4 Find the level curve at a production of 27 items in the form $y = f(x)$ for the Cobb-Douglas production function $z = x^{1/4}y^{3/4}$.

SOLUTION   Let $z = 100$ to get

$$100 = x^{2/3}y^{1/3}$$
$$\frac{100}{x^{2/3}} = y^{1/3}.$$

Now cube both sides to express y as a function of x.

$$y = \frac{100^3}{x^2} = \frac{1,000,000}{x^2}$$

TRY YOUR TURN 4

The level curve of height 100 found in Example 8 is shown graphed in three dimensions in Figure 12(a) and on the familiar xy-plane in Figure 12(b). The points of the graph correspond to those values of x and y that lead to production of 100 items.

The curve in Figure 12 is called an *isoquant,* for *iso* (equal) and *quant* (amount). In Example 8, the "amounts" all "equal" 100.

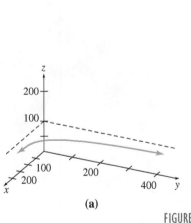

(a)

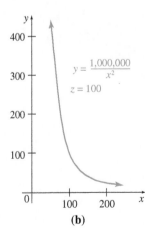

$$y = \frac{1,000,000}{x^2}$$
$$z = 100$$

(b)

FIGURE 12

Because of the difficulty of drawing the graphs of more complicated functions, we merely list some common equations and their graphs. We encourage you to explore why these graphs look the way they do by studying their traces, level curves, and axis intercepts. These graphs were drawn by computer, a very useful method of depicting three-dimensional surfaces.

Paraboloid, $z = x^2 + y^2$

xy-trace: point
yz-trace: parabola
xz-trace: parabola

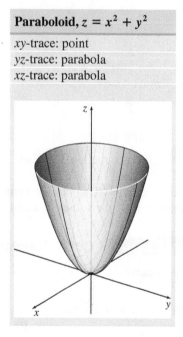

Ellipsoid, $\dfrac{x^2}{a^2} + \dfrac{y^2}{b^2} + \dfrac{z^2}{c^2} = 1$

xy-trace: ellipse
yz-trace: ellipse
xz-trace: ellipse

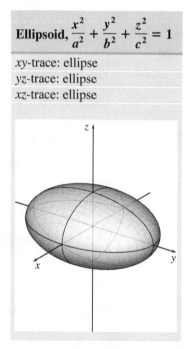

Hyperbolic Paraboloid, $z = x^2 - y^2$
(sometimes called a *saddle*)

xy-trace: two intersecting lines
yz-trace: parabola
xz-trace: parabola

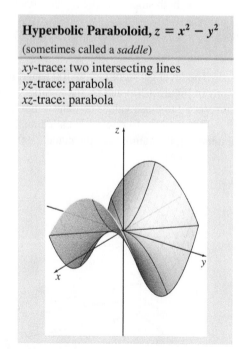

Hyperboloid of Two Sheets,
$-x^2 - y^2 + z^2 = 1$

xy-trace: none
yz-trace: hyperbola
xz-trace: hyperbola

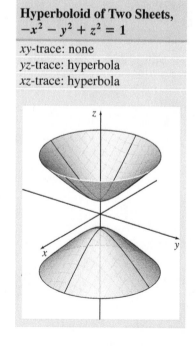

Notice that not all the graphs correspond to functions of two variables. In the ellipsoid, for example, if x and y are both 0, then z can equal c or $-c$, whereas a function can take on only one value. We can, however, interpret the graph as a **level surface** for a function of three variables. Let

$$w(x, y, z) = \frac{x^2}{a^2} + \frac{y^2}{b^2} + \frac{z^2}{c^2}.$$

Then $w = 1$ produces the level surface of the ellipsoid shown, just as $z = c$ gives level curves for the function $z = f(x, y)$.

Another way to draw the graph of a function of two variables is with a graphing calculator. Figure 13 shows the graph of $z = x^2 + y^2$ generated by a TI-89. Figure 14 shows the same graph drawn by the computer program Maple™.

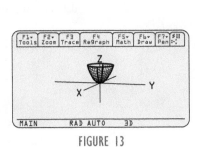

FIGURE 13

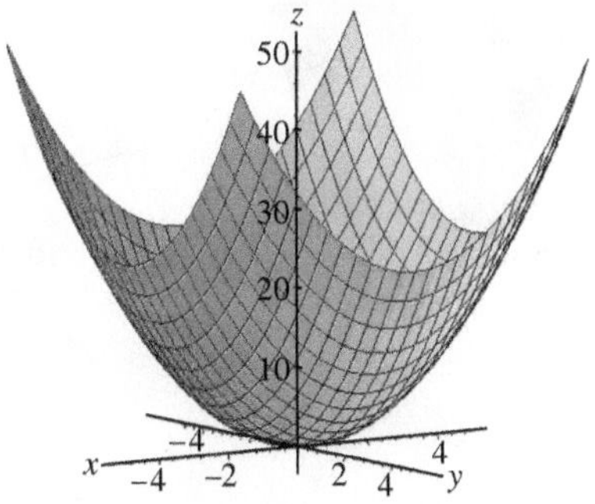

FIGURE 14

EXERCISES

1. Let $f(x, y) = 2x - 3y + 5$. Find the following.

   a. $f(2, -1)$ b. $f(-4, 1)$ c. $f(-2, -3)$ d. $f(0, 8)$

2. Let $g(x, y) = x^2 - 2xy + y^3$. Find the following.

   a. $g(-2, 4)$ b. $g(-1, -2)$ c. $g(-2, 3)$ d. $g(5, 1)$

3. Let $h(x, y) = \sqrt{x^2 + 2y^2}$. Find the following.

   a. $h(5, 3)$ b. $h(2, 4)$ c. $h(-1, -3)$ d. $h(-3, -1)$

4. Let $f(x, y) = \dfrac{\sqrt{9x + 5y}}{\log x}$. Find the following.

   a. $f(10, 2)$ b. $f(100, 1)$

   c. $f(1000, 0)$ d. $f\left(\dfrac{1}{10}, 5\right)$

Graph the first-octant portion of each plane.

5. $x + y + z = 9$ 6. $x + y + z = 15$

7. $2x + 3y + 4z = 12$ 8. $4x + 2y + 3z = 24$

9. $x + y = 4$ 10. $y + z = 5$

11. $x = 5$ 12. $z = 4$

Graph the level curves in the first quadrant of the xy-plane for the following functions at heights of $z = 0$, $z = 2$, and $z = 4$.

13. $3x + 2y + z = 24$ 14. $3x + y + 2z = 8$

15. $y^2 - x = -z$ 16. $2y - \dfrac{x^2}{3} = z$

17. Discuss how a function of three variables in the form $w = f(x, y, z)$ might be graphed.

18. Suppose the graph of a plane $ax + by + cz = d$ has a portion in the first octant. What can be said about a, b, c, and d?

19. In the chapter on Nonlinear Functions, the vertical line test was presented, which tells whether a graph is the graph of a function. Does this test apply to functions of two variables? Explain.

20. A graph that was not shown in this section is the *hyperboloid of one sheet*, described by the equation $x^2 + y^2 - z^2 = 1$. Describe it as completely as you can.

Match each equation in Exercises 21–26 with its graph in a–f on the next page

21. $z = x^2 + y^2$ 22. $z^2 - y^2 - x^2 = 1$

119

23. $x^2 - y^2 = z$

24. $z = y^2 - x^2$

25. $\dfrac{x^2}{16} + \dfrac{y^2}{25} + \dfrac{z^2}{4} = 1$

26. $z = 5(x^2 + y^2)^{-1/2}$

a.

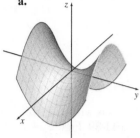

b.

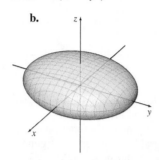

c.

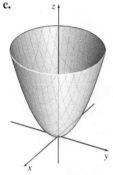

d.

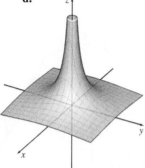

e.

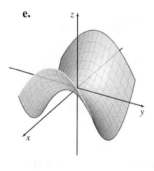

f.

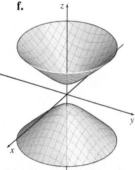

27. Let $f(x, y) = 4x^2 - 2y^2$, and find the following.

a. $\dfrac{f(x + h, y) - f(x, y)}{h}$

b. $\dfrac{f(x, y + h) - f(x, y)}{h}$

c. $\lim\limits_{h \to 0} \dfrac{f(x + h, y) - f(x, y)}{h}$

d. $\lim\limits_{h \to 0} \dfrac{f(x, y + h) - f(x, y)}{h}$

28. Let $f(x, y) = 5x^3 + 3y^2$, and find the following.

a. $\dfrac{f(x + h, y) - f(x, y)}{h}$

b. $\dfrac{f(x, y + h) - f(x, y)}{h}$

c. $\lim\limits_{h \to 0} \dfrac{f(x + h, y) - f(x, y)}{h}$

d. $\lim\limits_{h \to 0} \dfrac{f(x, y + h) - f(x, y)}{h}$

29. Let $f(x, y) = xye^{x^2 + y^2}$. Use a graphing calculator or spreadsheet to find each of the following and give a geometric interpretation of the results. (*Hint:* First factor e^2 from the limit and then evaluate the quotient at smaller and smaller values of h.)

a. $\lim\limits_{h \to 0} \dfrac{f(1 + h, 1) - f(1, 1)}{h}$

b. $\lim\limits_{h \to 0} \dfrac{f(1, 1 + h) - f(1, 1)}{h}$

30. The following table provides values of the function $f(x, y)$. However, because of potential errors in measurement, the functional values may be slightly inaccurate. Using the statistical package included with a graphing calculator or spreadsheet and critical thinking skills, find the function $f(x, y) = a + bx + cy$ that best estimates the table where a, b, and c are integers. (*Hint:* Do a linear regression on each column with the value of y fixed and then use these four regression equations to determine the coefficient c.)

x \ y	0	1	2	3
0	4.02	7.04	9.98	13.00
1	6.01	9.06	11.98	14.96
2	7.99	10.95	14.02	17.09
3	9.99	13.01	16.01	19.02

APPLICATIONS

Business and Economics

31. Production Production of a digital camera is given by

$$P(x, y) = 100\left(\frac{3}{5}x^{-2/5} + \frac{2}{5}y^{-2/5}\right)^{-5},$$

where x is the amount of labor in work-hours and y is the amount of capital. Find the following.

a. What is the production when 32 work-hours and 1 unit of capital are provided?

b. Find the production when 1 work-hour and 32 units of capital are provided.

c. If 32 work-hours and 243 units of capital are used, what is the production output?

Individual Retirement Accounts The multiplier function

$$M = \frac{(1 + i)^n(1 - t) + t}{[1 + (1 - t)i]^n}$$

compares the growth of an Individual Retirement Account (IRA) with the growth of the same deposit in a regular savings account. The function M depends on the three variables n, i, and t, where n represents the number of years an amount is left at interest, i represents the interest rate in both types of accounts, and t represents the income tax rate. Values of $M > 1$ indicate that the IRA grows faster than the savings account. Let $M = f(n, i, t)$ and find the following.

32. Find the multiplier when funds are left for 25 years at 5% interest and the income tax rate is 33%. Which account grows faster?

33. What is the multiplier when money is invested for 40 years at 6% interest and the income tax rate is 28%? Which account grows faster?

Production **Find the level curve at a production of 500 for the production functions in Exercises 34 and 35. Graph each level curve in the xy-plane.**

34. In their original paper, Cobb and Douglas estimated the production function for the United States to be $z = 1.01x^{3/4}y^{1/4}$, where x represents the amount of labor and y the amount of capital. *Source: American Economic Review*.

35. A study of the connection between immigration and the fiscal problems associated with the aging of the baby boom generation considered a production function of the form $z = x^{0.6}y^{0.4}$, where x represents the amount of labor and y the amount of capital. *Source: Journal of Political Economy*.

36. Production For the function in Exercise 34, what is the effect on z of doubling x? Of doubling y? Of doubling both?

37. Cost If labor (x) costs $250 per unit, materials (y) cost $150 per unit, and capital (z) costs $75 per unit, write a function for total cost.

Life Sciences

38. Heat Loss The rate of heat loss (in watts) in harbor seal pups has been approximated by

$$H(m,T,A) = \frac{15.2m^{0.67}(T - A)}{10.23 \ln m - 10.74},$$

where m is the body mass of the pup (in kg), and T and A are the body core temperature and ambient water temperature, respectively (in °C). Find the heat loss for the following data. *Source: Functional Ecology*.

a. Body mass = 21 kg; body core temperature = 36°C; ambient water temperature = 4°C

b. Body mass = 29 kg; body core temperature = 38°C; ambient water temperature = 16°C

39. Body Surface Area The surface area of a human (in square meters) has been approximated by

$$A = 0.024265h^{0.3964}m^{0.5378},$$

where h is the height (in cm) and m is the mass (in kg). Find A for the following data. *Source: The Journal of Pediatrics*.

a. Height, 178 cm; mass, 72 kg

b. Height, 140 cm; mass, 65 kg

c. Height, 160 cm; mass, 70 kg

d. Using your mass and height, find your own surface area.

40. Dinosaur Running An article entitled "How Dinosaurs Ran" explains that the locomotion of different sized animals can be compared when they have the same Froude number, defined as

$$F = \frac{v^2}{gl},$$

where v is the velocity, g is the acceleration of gravity $(9.81$ m per sec$^2)$, and l is the leg length (in meters). *Source: Scientific American*.

a. One result described in the article is that different animals change from a trot to a gallop at the same Froude number, roughly 2.56. Find the velocity at which this change occurs for a ferret, with a leg length of 0.09 m, and a rhinoceros, with a leg length of 1.2 m.

b. Ancient footprints in Texas of a sauropod, a large herbivorous dinosaur, are roughly 1 m in diameter, corresponding to a leg length of roughly 4 m. By comparing the stride divided by the leg length with that of various modern creatures, it can be determined that the Froude number for these dinosaurs is roughly 0.025. How fast were the sauropods traveling?

41. Pollution Intolerance According to research at the Great Swamp in New York, the percentage of fish that are intolerant to pollution can be estimated by the function

$$P(W, R, A) = 48 - 2.43W - 1.81R - 1.22A,$$

where W is the percentage of wetland, R is the percentage of residential area, and A is the percentage of agricultural area surrounding the swamp. *Source: Northeastern Naturalist*.

a. Use this function to estimate the percentage of fish that will be intolerant to pollution if 5 percent of the land is classified as wetland, 15 percent is classified as residential, and 0 percent is classified as agricultural. (*Note*: The land can also be classified as forest land.)

b. What is the maximum percentage of fish that will be intolerant to pollution?

c. Develop two scenarios that will drive the percentage of fish that are intolerant to pollution to zero.

d. Which variable has the greatest influence on P?

42. Dengue Fever In tropical regions, dengue fever is a significant health problem that affects nearly 100 million people each year. Using data collected from the 2002 dengue epidemic in Colima, Mexico, researchers have estimated that the incidence I (number of new cases in a given year) of dengue can be predicted by the following function.

$$I(p, a, m, n, e) = (25.54 + 0.04p - 7.92a + 2.62m + 4.46n + 0.15e)^2,$$

where p is the precipitation (mm), a is the mean temperature (°C), m is the maximum temperature (°C), n is the minimum temperature (°C), and e is the evaporation (mm). *Source: Journal of Environmental Health*.

a. Estimate the incidence of a dengue fever outbreak for a region with 80 mm of rainfall, average temperature of 23°C, maximum temperature of 34°C, minimum temperature of 16°C, and evaporation of 50 mm.

b. Which variable has a negative influence on the incidence of dengue? Describe this influence and what can be inferred mathematically about the biology of the fever.

43. Deer-Vehicle Accidents Using data collected by the U.S. Forest Service, the annual number of deer-vehicle accidents for any given county in Ohio can be estimated by the function

$$A(L, T, U, C) = 53.02 + 0.383L + 0.0015T + 0.0028U$$
$$- 0.0003C,$$

where A is the estimated number of accidents, L is the road length (in kilometers), T is the total county land area (in hundred-acres (Ha)), U is the urban land area (in hundred-acres), and C is the number of hundred-acres of crop land. *Source: Ohio Journal of Science.*

a. Use this formula to estimate the number of deer-vehicle accidents for Mahoning County, where $L = 266$ km, $T = 107,484$ Ha, $U = 31,697$ Ha, and $C = 24,870$ Ha. The actual value was 396.

b. Given the magnitude and nature of the input numbers, which of the variables have the greatest potential to influence the number of deer-vehicle accidents? Explain your answer.

44. Deer Harvest Using data collected by the U.S. Forest Service, the annual number of deer that are harvested for any given county in Ohio can be estimated by the function

$$N(R, C) = 329.32 + 0.0377R - 0.0171C,$$

where N is the estimated number of harvested deer, R is the rural land area (in hundred-acres), and C is the number of hundred-acres of crop land. *Source: Ohio Journal of Science.*

a. Use this formula to estimate the number of harvested deer for Tuscarawas County, where $R = 141,319$ Ha and $C = 37,960$ Ha. The actual value was 4925 deer harvested.

b. Sketch the graph of this function in the first octant.

45. Agriculture Pregnant sows tethered in stalls often show high levels of repetitive behavior, such as bar biting and chain chewing, indicating chronic stress. Researchers from Great Britain have developed a function that estimates the relationship between repetitive behavior, the behavior of sows in adjacent stalls, and food allowances such that

$$\ln(T) = 5.49 - 3.00 \ln(F) + 0.18 \ln(C),$$

where T is the percent of time spent in repetitive behavior, F is the amount of food given to the sow (in kilograms per day), and C is the percent of time that neighboring sows spent bar biting and chain chewing. *Source: Applied Animal Behaviour Science.*

a. Solve the above expression for T.

b. Find and interpret T when $F = 2$ and $C = 40$.

General Interest

46. Postage Rates Extra postage is charged for parcels sent by U.S. mail that are more than 84 in. in length and girth combined. (Girth is the distance around the parcel perpendicular to its length. See the figure.) Express the combined length and girth as a function of L, W, and H.

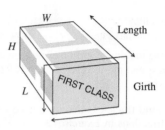

47. Required Material Refer to the figure for Exercise 46. Assume L, W, and H are in feet. Write a function in terms of L, W, and H that gives the total area of the material required to build the box.

48. Elliptical Templates The holes cut in a roof for vent pipes require elliptical templates. A formula for determining the length of the major axis of the ellipse is given by

$$L = f(H, D) = \sqrt{H^2 + D^2},$$

where D is the (outside) diameter of the pipe and H is the "rise" of the roof per D units of "run"; that is, the slope of the roof is H/D. (See the figure below.) The width of the ellipse (minor axis) equals D. Find the length and width of the ellipse required to produce a hole for a vent pipe with a diameter of 3.75 in. in roofs with the following slopes.

a. $3/4$ **b.** $2/5$

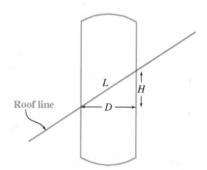

YOUR TURN ANSWERS

1. 29

2. 24

3.

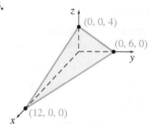

4. $y = 81/x^{1/3}$.

2 Partial Derivatives

APPLY IT   What is the change in productivity if labor is increased by one work-hour? What if capital is increased by one unit?

We will answer this question in Example 5 using the concept of partial derivatives.

Earlier, we found that the derivative dy/dx gives the rate of change of y with respect to x. In this section, we show how derivatives are found and interpreted for multivariable functions.

A small firm makes only two products, radios and CD players. The profits of the firm are given by

$$P(x, y) = 40x^2 - 10xy + 5y^2 - 80,$$

where x is the number of radios sold and y is the number of CD players sold. How will a change in x or y affect P?

Suppose that sales of radios have been steady at 10 units; only the sales of CD players vary. The management would like to find the marginal profit with respect to y, the number of CD players sold. Recall that marginal profit is given by the derivative of the profit function. Here, x is fixed at 10. Using this information, we begin by finding a new function, $f(y) = P(10, y)$. Let $x = 10$ to get

$$f(y) = P(10, y) = 40(10)^2 - 10(10)y + 5y^2 - 80$$
$$= 3920 - 100y + 5y^2.$$

The function $f(y)$ shows the profit from the sale of y CD players, assuming that x is fixed at 10 units. Find the derivative df/dy to get the marginal profit with respect to y.

$$\frac{df}{dy} = -100 + 10y$$

In this example, the derivative of the function $f(y)$ was taken with respect to y only; we assumed that x was fixed. To generalize, let $z = f(x, y)$. An intuitive definition of the *partial derivatives* of f with respect to x and y follows.

Partial Derivatives (Informal Definition)

The **partial derivative of f with respect to x** is the derivative of f obtained by treating x as a variable and y as a constant.

The **partial derivative of f with respect to y** is the derivative of f obtained by treating y as a variable and x as a constant.

The symbols $f_x(x, y)$ (no prime is used), $\partial z/\partial x$, z_x, and $\partial f/\partial x$ are used to represent the partial derivative of $z = f(x, y)$ with respect to x, with similar symbols used for the partial derivative with respect to y.

Generalizing from the definition of the derivative given earlier, partial derivatives of a function $z = f(x, y)$ are formally defined as follows.

Partial Derivatives (Formal Definition)

Let $z = f(x, y)$ be a function of two independent variables. Let all indicated limits exist. Then the partial derivative of f with respect to x is

$$f_x(x, y) = \frac{\partial f}{\partial x} = \lim_{h \to 0} \frac{f(x + h, y) - f(x, y)}{h},$$

and the partial derivative of f with respect to y is

$$f_y(x, y) = \frac{\partial f}{\partial y} = \lim_{h \to 0} \frac{f(x, y + h) - f(x, y)}{h}.$$

If the indicated limits do not exist, then the partial derivatives do not exist.

Similar definitions could be given for functions of more than two independent variables.

EXAMPLE 1 Partial Derivatives

Let $f(x, y) = 4x^2 - 9xy + 6y^3$. Find $f_x(x, y)$ and $f_y(x, y)$.

SOLUTION To find $f_x(x, y)$, treat y as a constant and x as a variable. The derivative of the first term, $4x^2$, is $8x$. In the second term, $-9xy$, the constant coefficient of x is $-9y$, so the derivative with x as the variable is $-9y$. The derivative of $6y^3$ is zero, since we are treating y as a constant. Thus,

$$f_x(x, y) = 8x - 9y.$$

Now, to find $f_y(x, y)$, treat y as a variable and x as a constant. Since x is a constant, the derivative of $4x^2$ is zero. In the second term, the coefficient of y is $-9x$ and the derivative of $-9xy$ is $-9x$. The derivative of the third term is $18y^2$. Thus,

$$f_y(x, y) = -9x + 18y^2. \qquad \text{TRY YOUR TURN 1}$$

YOUR TURN 1 Let $f(x,y) = 2x^2y^3 + 6x^5y^4$. Find $f_x(x,y)$ and $f_y(x,y)$.

The next example shows how the chain rule can be used to find partial derivatives.

EXAMPLE 2 Partial Derivatives

Let $f(x, y) = \ln |x^2 + 3y|$. Find $f_x(x, y)$ and $f_y(x, y)$.

SOLUTION Recall the formula for the derivative of a natural logarithm function. If $g(x) = \ln |x|$, then $g'(x) = 1/x$. Using this formula and the chain rule,

$$f_x(x, y) = \frac{1}{x^2 + 3y} \cdot \frac{\partial}{\partial x}(x^2 + 3y) = \frac{1}{x^2 + 3y} \cdot 2x = \frac{2x}{x^2 + 3y},$$

and

$$f_y(x, y) = \frac{1}{x^2 + 3y} \cdot \frac{\partial}{\partial y}(x^2 + 3y) = \frac{1}{x^2 + 3y} \cdot 3 = \frac{3}{x^2 + 3y}.$$

TRY YOUR TURN 2

YOUR TURN 2 Let $f(x,y) = e^{3x^2y}$. Find $f_x(x,y)$ and $f_y(x,y)$.

The notation

$$f_x(a, b) \quad \text{or} \quad \frac{\partial f}{\partial y}(a, b)$$

represents the value of the partial derivative when $x = a$ and $y = b$, as shown in the next example.

EXAMPLE 3 Evaluating Partial Derivatives

Let $f(x, y) = 2x^2 + 9xy^3 + 8y + 5$. Find the following.

(a) $f_x(-1, 2)$

SOLUTION First, find $f_x(x, y)$ by holding y constant.

$$f_x(x, y) = 4x + 9y^3$$

Now let $x = -1$ and $y = 2$.

$$f_x(-1, 2) = 4(-1) + 9(2)^3 = -4 + 72 = 68$$

(b) $\dfrac{\partial f}{\partial y}(-4, -3)$

SOLUTION Since $\partial f/\partial y = 27xy^2 + 8$,

$$\frac{\partial f}{\partial y}(-4, -3) = 27(-4)(-3)^2 + 8 = 27(-36) + 8 = -964.$$

(c) All values of x and y such that both $f_x(x, y) = 0$ and $f_y(x, y) = 0$. (The importance of such points will be shown in the next section.)

SOLUTION From parts (a) and (b),

$$f_x(x, y) = 4x + 9y^3 = 0 \quad \text{and} \quad f_y(x, y) = 27xy^2 + 8 = 0.$$

Solving the first equation for x yields $x = -9y^3/4$. Substituting this into the second equation yields

$$27\left(\frac{-9y^3}{4}\right)y^2 + 8 = 0$$

$$\frac{-243y^5}{4} + 8 = 0$$

$$\frac{-243y^5}{4} = -8$$

$$y^5 = \frac{32}{243}$$

$$y = \frac{2}{3}. \qquad \text{Take the fifth root of both sides.}$$

Substituting $y = 2/3$ yields $x = -9y^3/4 = -9(2/3)^3/4 = -2/3$. Thus, $f_x(x, y) = 0$ and $f_y(x, y) = 0$ when $x = -2/3$ and $y = 2/3$.

(d) $f_x(x, y)$ using the formal definition of the partial derivative.

SOLUTION Calculate as follows:

$$\frac{f(x+h, y) - f(x, y)}{h} = \frac{2(x+h)^2 + 9(x+h)y^3 + 8y + 5 - (2x^2 + 9xy^3 + 8y + 5)}{h}$$

$$= \frac{2x^2 + 4xh + 2h^2 + 9xy^3 + 9hy^3 + 8y + 5 - 2x^2 - 9xy^3 - 8y - 5}{h}$$

$$= \frac{4xh + 2h^2 + 9hy^3}{h} \qquad \text{Simplify the numerator.}$$

$$= \frac{h(4x + 2h + 9y^3)}{h} \qquad \text{Factor } h \text{ from the numerator.}$$

$$= 4x + 2h + 9y^3.$$

Now take the limit as h goes to 0. Thus,

$$f_x(x, y) = \lim_{h \to 0} \frac{f(x + h, y) - f(x, y)}{h} = \lim_{h \to 0}(4x + 2h + 9y^3)$$

$$= 4x + 9y^3,$$

YOUR TURN 3 Let $f(x,y) = xye^{x^2+y^3}$. Find $f_x(2,1)$ and $f_y(2,1)$.

the same answer we found in part (a).

TRY YOUR TURN 3

In some cases, the difference quotient may not simplify as easily as it did in Example 3(d). In such cases, the derivative may be approximated by putting a small value for h into $[f(x + h) - f(x)]/h$. In Example 3(d), with $x = -1$ and $y = 2$, the values $h = 10^{-4}$ and 10^{-5} give approximations for $f_x(-1, 2)$ as 68.0002 and 68.00002, respectively, compared with the exact value of 68 found in Example 3(a).

The derivative of a function of one variable can be interpreted as the slope of the tangent line to the graph at that point. With some modification, the same is true of partial derivatives of functions of two variables. At a point on the graph of a function of two variables, $z = f(x, y)$, there may be many tangent lines, all of which lie in the same tangent plane, as shown in Figure 15.

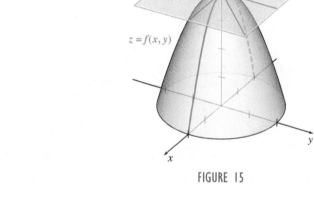

FIGURE 15

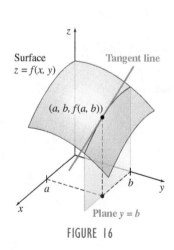

FIGURE 16

In any particular direction, however, there will be only one tangent line. We use partial derivatives to find the slope of the tangent lines in the x- and y-directions as follows.

Figure 16 shows a surface $z = f(x, y)$ and a plane that is parallel to the xz-plane. The equation of the plane is $y = b$. (This corresponds to holding y fixed.) Since $y = b$ for points on the plane, any point on the curve that represents the intersection of the plane and the surface must have the form $(x, y, z) = (x, b, f(x, b))$. Thus, this curve can be described as $z = f(x, b)$. Since b is constant, $z = f(x, b)$ is a function of one variable. When the derivative of $z = f(x, b)$ is evaluated at $x = a$, it gives the slope of the line tangent to this curve at the point $(a, b, f(a, b))$, as shown in Figure 16. Thus, the partial derivative of f with respect to x, $f_x(a, b)$, gives the rate of change of the surface $z = f(x, y)$ in the x-direction at the point $(a, b, f(a, b))$. In the same way, the partial derivative with respect to y will give the slope of the line tangent to the surface in the y-direction at the point $(a, b, f(a, b))$.

Rate of Change

The derivative of $y = f(x)$ gives the rate of change of y with respect to x. In the same way, if $z = f(x, y)$, then $f_x(x, y)$ gives the rate of change of z with respect to x, if y is held constant.

EXAMPLE 4   Water Temperature

Suppose that the temperature of the water at the point on a river where a nuclear power plant discharges its hot waste water is approximated by

$$T(x, y) = 2x + 5y + xy - 40,$$

where x represents the temperature of the river water (in degrees Celsius) before it reaches the power plant and y is the number of megawatts (in hundreds) of electricity being produced by the plant.

(a) Find and interpret $T_x(9, 5)$.

SOLUTION   First, find the partial derivative $T_x(x, y)$.

$$T_x(x, y) = 2 + y$$

This partial derivative gives the rate of change of T with respect to x. Replacing x with 9 and y with 5 gives

$$T_x(9, 5) = 2 + 5 = 7.$$

Just as marginal cost is the approximate cost of one more item, this result, 7, is the approximate change in temperature of the output water if input water temperature changes by 1 degree, from $x = 9$ to $x = 9 + 1 = 10$, while y remains constant at 5 (500 megawatts of electricity produced).

(b) Find and interpret $T_y(9, 5)$.

SOLUTION   The partial derivative $T_y(x, y)$ is

$$T_y(x, y) = 5 + x.$$

This partial derivative gives the rate of change of T with respect to y as

$$T_y(9, 5) = 5 + 9 = 14.$$

This result, 14, is the approximate change in temperature resulting from a 1-unit increase in production of electricity from $y = 5$ to $y = 5 + 1 = 6$ (from 500 to 600 megawatts), while the input water temperature x remains constant at 9°C.

As mentioned in the previous section, if $P(x, y)$ gives the output P produced by x units of labor and y units of capital, $P(x, y)$ is a production function. The partial derivatives of this production function have practical implications. For example, $\partial P/\partial x$ gives the marginal productivity of labor. This represents the rate at which the output is changing with respect to labor for a fixed capital investment. That is, if the capital investment is held constant and labor is increased by 1 work-hour, $\partial P/\partial x$ will yield the approximate change in the production level. Likewise, $\partial P/\partial y$ gives the marginal productivity of capital, which represents the rate at which the output is changing with respect to a one-unit change in capital for a fixed labor value. So if the labor force is held constant and the capital investment is increased by 1 unit, $\partial P/\partial y$ will approximate the corresponding change in the production level.

EXAMPLE 5   Production Function

A company that manufactures computers has determined that its production function is given by

$$P(x, y) = 0.1xy^2 \ln(2x + 3y + 2),$$

where x is the size of the labor force (measured in work-hours per week) and y is the amount of capital (measured in units of $1000) invested. Find the marginal productivity of labor and capital when $x = 50$ and $y = 20$, and interpret the results.

APPLY IT

SOLUTION The marginal productivity of labor is found by taking the derivative of P with respect to x.

$$\frac{\partial P}{\partial x} = 0.1\left[\frac{xy^2}{2x + 3y + 2} \cdot 2 + y^2 \ln(2x + 3y + 2)\right] \quad \text{Use the product and chain rules.}$$

$$\frac{\partial P}{\partial x}(50,20) = 0.1\left[\frac{50(20)^2}{2(50) + 3(20) + 2} \cdot 2 + 20^2 \ln(2(50) + 3(20) + 2)\right] \approx 228$$

Thus, if the capital investment is held constant at $20,000 and labor is increased from 50 to 51 work-hours per week, production will increase by about 228 units. In the same way, the marginal productivity of capital is $\partial P/\partial y$.

$$\frac{\partial P}{\partial y} = 0.1\left[\frac{xy^2}{2x + 3y + 2} \cdot 3 + 2xy \ln(2x + 3y + 2)\right] \quad \text{Use the product and chain rules.}$$

$$\frac{\partial P}{\partial y}(50,20) = 0.1\left[\frac{50(20)^2}{2(50) + 3(20) + 2} \cdot 3 + 2(50)(20)\ln(2(50) + 3(20) + 2)\right] \approx 1055$$

If work-hours are held constant at 50 hours per week and the capital investment is increased from $20,000 to $21,000, production will increase by about 1055 units.

Second-Order Partial Derivatives

The second derivative of a function of one variable is very useful in determining relative maxima and minima. **Second-order partial derivatives** (partial derivatives of a partial derivative) are used in a similar way for functions of two or more variables. The situation is somewhat more complicated, however, with more independent variables. For example, $f(x, y) = 4x + x^2y + 2y$ has two first-order partial derivatives,

$$f_x(x, y) = 4 + 2xy \qquad \text{and} \qquad f_y(x, y) = x^2 + 2.$$

Since each of these has two partial derivatives, one with respect to y and one with respect to x, there are *four* second-order partial derivatives of function f. The notations for these four second-order partial derivatives are given below.

Second-Order Partial Derivatives

For a function $z = f(x, y)$, if the indicated partial derivative exists, then

$$\frac{\partial}{\partial x}\left(\frac{\partial z}{\partial x}\right) = \frac{\partial^2 z}{\partial x^2} = f_{xx}(x,y) = z_{xx} \qquad \frac{\partial}{\partial y}\left(\frac{\partial z}{\partial y}\right) = \frac{\partial^2 z}{\partial y^2} = f_{yy}(x,y) = z_{yy}$$

$$\frac{\partial}{\partial y}\left(\frac{\partial z}{\partial x}\right) = \frac{\partial^2 z}{\partial y \partial x} = f_{xy}(x,y) = z_{xy} \qquad \frac{\partial}{\partial x}\left(\frac{\partial z}{\partial y}\right) = \frac{\partial^2 z}{\partial x \partial y} = f_{yx}(x,y) = z_{yx}$$

NOTE For most functions found in applications and for all of the functions in this book, the second-order partial derivatives $f_{xy}(x, y)$ and $f_{yx}(x, y)$ are equal. This is always true when $f_{xy}(x, y)$ and $f_{yx}(x, y)$ are continuous. Therefore, it is not necessary to be particular about the order in which these derivatives are found.

EXAMPLE 6 Second-Order Partial Derivatives

Find all second-order partial derivatives for

$$f(x, y) = -4x^3 - 3x^2y^3 + 2y^2.$$

SOLUTION   First find $f_x(x, y)$ and $f_y(x, y)$.

$$f_x(x, y) = -12x^2 - 6xy^3 \quad \text{and} \quad f_y(x, y) = -9x^2y^2 + 4y$$

To find $f_{xx}(x, y)$, take the partial derivative of $f_x(x, y)$ with respect to x.

$$f_{xx}(x, y) = -24x - 6y^3$$

Take the partial derivative of $f_y(x, y)$ with respect to y; this gives f_{yy}.

$$f_{yy}(x, y) = -18x^2y + 4$$

Find $f_{xy}(x, y)$ by starting with $f_x(x, y)$, then taking the partial derivative of $f_x(x, y)$ with respect to y.

$$f_{xy}(x, y) = -18xy^2$$

YOUR TURN 4 Let
$f(x, y) = x^2e^{7y} + x^4y^5$. Find all
second partial derivatives.

Finally, find $f_{yx}(x, y)$ by starting with $f_y(x, y)$; take its partial derivative with respect to x.

$$f_{yx}(x, y) = -18xy^2$$

TRY YOUR TURN 4

EXAMPLE 7 Second-Order Partial Derivatives

Let $f(x, y) = 2e^x - 8x^3y^2$. Find all second-order partial derivatives.

SOLUTION   Here $f_x(x, y) = 2e^x - 24x^2y^2$ and $f_y(x, y) = -16x^3y$. (Recall: If $g(x) = e^x$, then $g'(x) = e^x$.) Now find the second-order partial derivatives.

$$f_{xx}(x, y) = 2e^x - 48xy^2 \qquad f_{xy}(x, y) = -48x^2y$$
$$f_{yy}(x, y) = -16x^3 \qquad f_{yx}(x, y) = -48x^2y$$

Partial derivatives of functions with more than two independent variables are found in a similar manner. For instance, to find $f_z(x, y, z)$ for $f(x, y, z)$, hold x and y constant and differentiate with respect to z.

EXAMPLE 8 Second-Order Partial Derivatives

Let $f(x, y, z) = 2x^2yz^2 + 3xy^2 - 4yz$. Find $f_x(x, y, z)$, $f_y(x, y, z)$, $f_{xz}(x, y, z)$, and $f_{yz}(x, y, z)$.

SOLUTION
$$f_x(x, y, z) = 4xyz^2 + 3y^2$$
$$f_y(x, y, z) = 2x^2z^2 + 6xy - 4z$$

To find $f_{xz}(x, y, z)$, differentiate $f_x(x, y, z)$ with respect to z.

$$f_{xz}(x, y, z) = 8xyz$$

Differentiate $f_y(x, y, z)$ with respect to z to get $f_{yz}(x, y, z)$.

$$f_{yz}(x, y, z) = 4x^2z - 4$$

2 EXERCISES

1. Let $z = f(x, y) = 6x^2 - 4xy + 9y^2$. Find the following using the formal definition of the partial derivative.

a. $\dfrac{\partial z}{\partial x}$ **b.** $\dfrac{\partial z}{\partial y}$ **c.** $\dfrac{\partial f}{\partial x}(2, 3)$ **d.** $f_y(1, -2)$

2. Let $z = g(x, y) = 8x + 6x^2y + 2y^2$. Find the following using the formal definition of the partial derivative.

a. $\dfrac{\partial g}{\partial x}$ **b.** $\dfrac{\partial g}{\partial y}$ **c.** $\dfrac{\partial z}{\partial y}(-3, 0)$ **d.** $g_x(2, 1)$

In Exercises 3–20, find $f_x(x, y)$ and $f_y(x, y)$. Then find $f_x(2, -1)$ and $f_y(-4, 3)$. Leave the answers in terms of e in Exercises 7–10, 15–16, and 19–20.

3. $f(x, y) = -4xy + 6y^3 + 5$ **4.** $f(x, y) = 9x^2y^2 - 4y^2$

5. $f(x, y) = 5x^2y^3$ **6.** $f(x, y) = -3x^4y^3 + 10$

7. $f(x, y) = e^{x+y}$ **8.** $f(x, y) = 4e^{3x+2y}$

9. $f(x, y) = -6e^{4x-3y}$ **10.** $f(x, y) = 8e^{7x-y}$

11. $f(x, y) = \dfrac{x^2 + y^3}{x^3 - y^2}$ **12.** $f(x, y) = \dfrac{3x^2y^3}{x^2 + y^2}$

13. $f(x, y) = \ln|1 + 5x^3y^2|$ **14.** $f(x, y) = \ln|4x^4 - 2x^2y^2|$

15. $f(x, y) = xe^{x^2y}$ **16.** $f(x, y) = y^2e^{x+3y}$

17. $f(x, y) = \sqrt{x^4 + 3xy + y^4 + 10}$

18. $f(x, y) = (7x^2 + 18xy^2 + y^3)^{1/3}$

19. $f(x, y) = \dfrac{3x^2y}{e^{xy} + 2}$

20. $f(x, y) = (7e^{x+2y} + 4)(e^{x^2} + y^2 + 2)$

Find all second-order partial derivatives for the following.

21. $f(x, y) = 4x^2y^2 - 16x^2 + 4y$

22. $g(x, y) = 5x^4y^2 + 12y^3 - 9x$

23. $R(x, y) = 4x^2 - 5xy^3 + 12y^2x^2$

24. $h(x, y) = 30y + 5x^2y + 12xy^2$

25. $r(x, y) = \dfrac{6y}{x + y}$ **26.** $k(x, y) = \dfrac{-7x}{2x + 3y}$

27. $z = 9ye^x$ **28.** $z = -6xe^y$

29. $r = \ln|x + y|$ **30.** $k = \ln|5x - 7y|$

31. $z = x \ln|xy|$ **32.** $z = (y + 1) \ln|x^3y|$

For the functions defined as follows, find all values of x and y such that both $f_x(x, y) = 0$ and $f_y(x, y) = 0$.

33. $f(x, y) = 6x^2 + 6y^2 + 6xy + 36x - 5$

34. $f(x, y) = 50 + 4x - 5y + x^2 + y^2 + xy$

35. $f(x, y) = 9xy - x^3 - y^3 - 6$

36. $f(x, y) = 2200 + 27x^3 + 72xy + 8y^2$

Find $f_x(x, y, z)$, $f_y(x, y, z)$, $f_z(x, y, z)$, and $f_{yz}(x, y, z)$ for the following.

37. $f(x, y, z) = x^4 + 2yz^2 + z^4$

38. $f(x, y, z) = 6x^3 - x^2y^2 + y^5$

39. $f(x, y, z) = \dfrac{6x - 5y}{4z + 5}$

40. $f(x, y, z) = \dfrac{2x^2 + xy}{yz - 2}$

41. $f(x, y, z) = \ln|x^2 - 5xz^2 + y^4|$

42. $f(x, y, z) = \ln|8xy + 5yz - x^3|$

In Exercises 43 and 44, approximate the indicated derivative for each function by using the definition of the derivative with small values of h.

43. $f(x, y) = (x + y/2)^{x+y/2}$

a. $f_x(1, 2)$ **b.** $f_y(1, 2)$

44. $f(x, y) = (x + y^2)^{2x+y}$

a. $f_x(2, 1)$ **b.** $f_y(2, 1)$

APPLICATIONS

Business and Economics

45. Manufacturing Cost Suppose that the manufacturing cost of a personal digital assistant (PDA) is approximated by

$$M(x, y) = 45x^2 + 40y^2 - 20xy + 50,$$

where x is the cost of electronic chips and y is the cost of labor. Find the following.

a. $M_y(4, 2)$ **b.** $M_x(3, 6)$ **c.** $(\partial M/\partial x)(2, 5)$

d. $(\partial M/\partial y)(6, 7)$

46. Revenue The revenue from the sale of x units of a sedative and y units of an antibiotic is given by

$$R(x, y) = 5x^2 + 9y^2 - 4xy.$$

Suppose 9 units of sedative and 5 units of antibiotic are sold.

a. What is the approximate effect on revenue if 10 units of sedative and 5 units of antibiotic are sold?

b. What is the approximate effect on revenue if the amount of antibiotic sold is increased to 6 units, while sedative sales remain constant?

47. Sales A car dealership estimates that the total weekly sales of its most popular model is a function of the car's list price, p, and the interest rate in percent, i, offered by the manufacturer. The approximate weekly sales are given by

$$f(p, i) = 99p - 0.5pi - 0.0025p^2.$$

a. Find the weekly sales if the average list price is $19,400 and the manufacturer is offering an 8% interest rate.

b. Find and interpret $f_p(p, i)$ and $f_i(p, i)$.

c. What would be the effect on weekly sales if the price is $19,400 and interest rates rise from 8% to 9%?

48. Marginal Productivity Suppose the production function of a company is given by

$$P(x, y) = 250\sqrt{x^2 + y^2},$$

where x represents units of labor and y represents units of capital. Find the following when 6 units of labor and 8 units of capital are used.

a. The marginal productivity of labor

b. The marginal productivity of capital

49. Marginal Productivity A manufacturer estimates that production (in hundreds of units) is a function of the amounts x and y of labor and capital used, as follows.

$$f(x, y) = \left(\frac{1}{4}x^{-1/4} + \frac{3}{4}y^{-1/4}\right)^{-4}$$

a. Find the number of units produced when 16 units of labor and 81 units of capital are utilized.

b. Find and interpret $f_x(16, 81)$ and $f_y(16, 81)$.

c. What would be the approximate effect on production of increasing labor by 1 unit from 16 units of labor with 81 units of capital?

50. Marginal Productivity The production function z for the United States was once estimated as

$$z = x^{0.7}y^{0.3},$$

where x stands for the amount of labor and y the amount of capital. Find the marginal productivity of labor and of capital.

51. Marginal Productivity A similar production function for Canada is

$$z = x^{0.4}y^{0.6},$$

with x, y, and z as in Exercise 50. Find the marginal productivity of labor and of capital.

52. Marginal Productivity A manufacturer of automobile batteries estimates that his total production (in thousands of units) is given by

$$f(x, y) = 3x^{1/3}y^{2/3},$$

where x is the number of units of labor and y is the number of units of capital utilized.

a. Find and interpret $f_x(64, 125)$ and $f_y(64, 125)$ if the current level of production uses 64 units of labor and 125 units of capital.

b. Use your answer from part a to calculate the approximate effect on production of increasing labor to 65 units while holding capital at the current level.

c. Suppose that sales have been good and management wants to increase either capital or labor by 1 unit. Which option would result in a larger increase in production?

Life Sciences

53. Calorie Expenditure The average energy expended for an animal to walk or run 1 km can be estimated by the function

$$f(m, v) = 25.92m^{0.68} + \frac{3.62m^{0.75}}{v},$$

where $f(m, v)$ is the energy used (in kcal per hour), m is the mass (in g), and v is the speed of movement (in km per hour) of the animal. *Source: Wildlife Feeding and Nutrition.*

a. Find $f(300, 10)$.

b. Find $f_m(300, 10)$ and interpret.

c. If a mouse could run at the same speed that an elephant walks, which animal would expend more energy? How can partial derivatives be used to explore this question?

54. Heat Loss The rate of heat loss (in watts) in harbor seal pups has been approximated by

$$H(m, T, A) = \frac{15.2m^{0.67}(T - A)}{10.23 \ln m - 10.74},$$

where m is the body mass of the pup (in kg), and T and A are the body core temperature and ambient water temperature, respectively (in °C). Find the approximate change in heat loss under the following conditions. *Source: Functional Ecology.*

a. The body core temperature increases from 37°C to 38°, while the ambient water temperature remains at 8°C and the body mass remains at 24 kg.

b. The ambient water temperature increases from 10°C to 11°, while the body core temperature remains at 37°C and the body mass remains at 26 kg.

55. Body Surface Area The surface area of a human (in square meters) has been approximated by

$$A = 0.024265h^{0.3964}m^{0.5378},$$

where h is the height (in cm) and m is the mass (in kg). *Source: The Journal of Pediatrics.*

a. Find the approximate change in surface area when the mass changes from 72 kg to 73 kg, while the height remains at 180 cm.

b. Find the approximate change in surface area when the height changes from 160 cm to 161 cm, while the mass remains at 70 kg.

56. Blood Flow According to the Fick Principle, the quantity of blood pumped through the lungs depends on the following variables (in milliliters):

b = quantity of oxygen used by the body in one minute

a = quantity of oxygen per liter of blood that has just gone through the lungs

v = quantity of oxygen per liter of blood that is about to enter the lungs

In one minute,

Amount of oxygen used = Amount of oxygen per liter
× Liters of blood pumped.

If C is the number of liters of blood pumped through the lungs in one minute, then

$$b = (a - v) \cdot C \quad \text{or} \quad C = \frac{b}{a - v}.$$

Source: Anaesthesia UK.

a. Find the number of liters of blood pumped through the lungs in one minute if $a = 160$, $b = 200$, and $v = 125$.

b. Find the approximate change in C when a changes from 160 to 161, $b = 200$, and $v = 125$.

c. Find the approximate change in C when $a = 160$, b changes from 200 to 201, and $v = 125$.

d. Find the approximate change in C when $a = 160$, $b = 200$, and v changes from 125 to 126.

e. A change of 1 unit in which quantity of oxygen produces the greatest change in the liters of blood pumped?

57. Health A weight-loss counselor has prepared a program of diet and exercise for a client. If the client sticks to the program, the weight loss that can be expected (in pounds per week) is given by

$$\text{Weight loss} = f(n, c) = \frac{1}{8}n^2 - \frac{1}{5}c + \frac{1937}{8},$$

where c is the average daily calorie intake for the week and n is the number of 40-minute aerobic workouts per week.

a. How many pounds can the client expect to lose by eating an average of 1200 cal per day and participating in four 40-minute workouts in a week?

b. Find and interpret $\partial f / \partial n$.

c. The client currently averages 1100 cal per day and does three 40-minute workouts each week. What would be the approximate impact on weekly weight loss of adding a fourth workout per week?

58. Health The body mass index is a number that can be calculated for any individual as follows: Multiply a person's weight by 703 and divide by the person's height squared. That is,

$$B = \frac{703w}{h^2},$$

where w is in pounds and h is in inches. The National Heart, Lung and Blood Institute uses the body mass index to determine whether a person is "overweight" ($25 \leq B < 30$) or "obese" ($B \geq 30$). *Source: The National Institutes of Health.*

a. Calculate the body mass index for Miami Dolphins offensive tackle Jake Long, who weighs 317 lb and is 6′7″ tall.

b. Calculate $\dfrac{\partial B}{\partial w}$ and $\dfrac{\partial B}{\partial h}$ and interpret.

c. Using the fact that 1 in. = 0.0254 m and 1 lb. = 0.4536 kg. transform this formula to handle metric units.

59. Drug Reaction The reaction to x units of a drug t hours after it was administered is given by

$$R(x, t) = x^2(a - x)t^2e^{-t},$$

for $0 \leq x \leq a$ (where a is a constant). Find the following.

a. $\dfrac{\partial R}{\partial x}$ **b.** $\dfrac{\partial R}{\partial t}$ **c.** $\dfrac{\partial^2 R}{\partial x^2}$ **d.** $\dfrac{\partial^2 R}{\partial x \partial t}$

e. Interpret your answers to parts a and b.

60. Scuba Diving In 1908, J. Haldane constructed diving tables that provide a relationship between the water pressure on body tissues for various water depths and dive times. The tables were successfully used by divers to virtually eliminate decompression sickness. The pressure in atmospheres for a no-stop dive is given by the following formula:*

$$p(l, t) = 1 + \frac{l}{33}(1 - 2^{-t/5}),$$

where t is in minutes, l is in feet, and p is in atmospheres (atm). *Source: The UMAP Journal.*

a. Find the pressure at 33 ft for a 10-minute dive.

b. Find $p_l(33, 10)$ and $p_t(33, 10)$ and interpret. (*Hint:* $D_t(a^t) = \ln(a)a^t$.)

c. Haldane estimated that decompression sickness for no-stop dives could be avoided if the diver's tissue pressure did not exceed 2.15 atm. Find the maximum amount of time that a diver could stay down (time includes going down and coming back up) if he or she wants to dive to a depth of 66 ft.

61. Wind Chill In 1941, explorers Paul Siple and Charles Passel discovered that the amount of heat lost when an object is exposed to cold air depends on both the temperature of the air and the velocity of the wind. They developed the *Wind Chill Index* as a way to measure the danger of frostbite while doing outdoor activities. The wind chill can be calculated as follows:

$$W(V, T) = 91.4 - \frac{(10.45 + 6.69\sqrt{V} - 0.447V)(91.4 - T)}{22}$$

where V is the wind speed in miles per hour and T is the temperature in Fahrenheit for wind speeds between 4 and 45 mph. *Source: The UMAP Journal.*

a. Find the wind chill for a wind speed of 20 mph and 10°F.

b. If a weather report indicates that the wind chill is −25°F and the actual outdoor temperature is 5°F, use a graphing calculator to find the corresponding wind speed to the nearest mile per hour.

c. Find $W_V(20, 10)$ and $W_T(20, 10)$ and interpret.

d. Using the table command on a graphing calculator or a spreadsheet, develop a wind chill chart for various wind speeds and temperatures.

62. Heat Index The chart on the next page shows the heat index, which combines the effects of temperature with humidity to give a measure of the apparent temperature, or how hot it feels to

*These estimates are conservative. Please consult modern dive tables before making a dive.

the body. *Source: The Weather Channel*. For example, when the outside temperature is 90°F and the relative humidity is 40%, then the apparent temperature is approximately 93°F. Let $I = f(T, H)$ give the heat index, I, as a function of the temperature T (in degrees Fahrenheit) and the percent humidity H. Estimate the following.

a. $f(90, 30)$ **b.** $f(90, 75)$ **c.** $f(80, 75)$

Heat Index

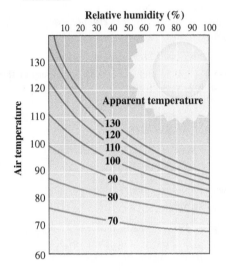

Estimate the following by approximating the partial derivative using a value of $h = 5$ in the difference quotient.

d. $f_T(90, 30)$ **e.** $f_H(90, 30)$ **f.** $f_T(90, 75)$

g. $f_H(90, 75)$

h. Describe in words what your answers in parts d–g mean.

63. Breath Volume The table at the bottom of this page accompanies the Voldyne® 5000 Volumetric Exerciser. The table gives the typical lung capacity (in milliliters) for women of various ages and heights. Based on the chart, it is possible to conclude that the partial derivative of the lung capacity with respect to age and with respect to height has constant values. What are those values?

Social Sciences

64. Education A developmental mathematics instructor at a large university has determined that a student's probability of success in the university's pass/fail remedial algebra course is a function of s, n, and a, where s is the student's score on the departmental placement exam, n is the number of semesters of mathematics passed in high school, and a is the student's mathematics SAT score. She estimates that p, the probability of passing the course (in percent), will be

$$p = f(s, n, a) = 0.05a + 6(sn)^{1/2}$$

for $200 \leq a \leq 800$, $0 \leq s \leq 10$, and $0 \leq n \leq 8$. Assuming that the above model has some merit, find the following.

a. If a student scores 6 on the placement exam, has taken 4 semesters of high school math, and has an SAT score of 460, what is the probability of passing the course?

b. Find p for a student with 5 semesters of high school mathematics, a placement score of 4, and an SAT score of 300.

c. Find and interpret $f_n(4, 5, 480)$ and $f_a(4, 5, 480)$.

Physical Sciences

65. Gravitational Attraction The gravitational attraction F on a body a distance r from the center of Earth, where r is greater than the radius of Earth, is a function of its mass m and the distance r as follows:

$$F = \frac{mgR^2}{r^2},$$

Height (in.)	58"	60"	62"	64"	66"	68"	70"	72"	74"
20	1900	2100	2300	2500	2700	2900	3100	3300	3500
A 25	1850	2050	2250	2450	2650	2850	3050	3250	3450
G 30	1800	2000	2200	2400	2600	2800	3000	3200	3400
E 35	1750	1950	2150	2350	2550	2750	2950	3150	3350
40	1700	1900	2100	2300	2500	2700	2900	3100	3300
I 45	1650	1850	2050	2250	2450	2650	2850	3050	3250
N 50	1600	1800	2000	2200	2400	2600	2800	3000	3200
55	1550	1750	1950	2150	2350	2550	2750	2950	3150
Y 60	1500	1700	1900	2100	2300	2500	2700	2900	3100
E 65	1450	1650	1850	2050	2250	2450	2650	2850	3050
A 70	1400	1600	1800	2000	2200	2400	2600	2800	3000
R 75	1350	1550	1750	1950	2150	2350	2550	2750	2950
S 80	1300	1500	1700	1900	2100	2300	2500	2700	2900

where R is the radius of Earth and g is the force of gravity—about 32 feet per second per second (ft per sec^2).

a. Find and interpret F_m and F_r.

b. Show that $F_m > 0$ and $F_r < 0$. Why is this reasonable?

66. Velocity In 1931, Albert Einstein developed the following formula for the sum of two velocities, x and y:

$$w(x, y) = \frac{x + y}{1 + \dfrac{xy}{c^2}},$$

where x and y are in miles per second and c represents the speed of light, 186,282 miles per second. *Source: The Mathematics Teacher.*

a. Suppose that, relative to a stationary observer, a new super space shuttle is capable of traveling at 50,000 miles per second and that, while traveling at this speed, it launches a rocket that travels at 150,000 miles per second. How fast is the rocket traveling relative to the stationary observer?

b. What is the instantaneous rate of change of w with respect to the speed of the space shuttle, x, when the space shuttle is traveling at 50,000 miles per second and the rocket is traveling at 150,000 miles per second?

c. Hypothetically, if a person is driving at the speed of light, c, and she turns on the headlights, what is the velocity of the light coming from the headlights relative to a stationary observer?

67. Movement Time Fitts' law is used to estimate the amount of time it takes for a person, using his or her arm, to pick up a light object, move it, and then place it in a designated target area. Mathematically, Fitts' law for a particular individual is given by

$$T(s, w) = 105 + 265 \log_2\left(\frac{2s}{w}\right),$$

where s is the distance (in feet) the object is moved, w is the width of the area in which the object is being placed, and T is the time (in msec). *Source: Human Factors in Engineering Design.*

a. Calculate $T(3, 0.5)$.

b. Find $T_s(3, 0.5)$ and $T_w(3, 0.5)$ and interpret these values. (*Hint:* $\log_2 x = \ln x / \ln 2$.)

YOUR TURN ANSWERS

1. $f_x(x, y) = 4xy^3 + 30x^4y^4$; $f_y(x, y) = 6x^2y^2 + 24x^5y^3$
2. $f_x(x, y) = 6xye^{3x^2y}$; $f_y(x, y) = 3x^2e^{3x^2y}$
3. $9e^5, 8e^5$
4. $f_{xx}(x, y) = 2e^{7y} + 12x^2y^5$;
   $f_{yy}(x, y) = 49x^2e^{7y} + 20x^4y^3$;
   $f_{xy}(x, y) = f_{yx}(x, y) = 14xe^{7y} + 20x^3y^4$

3 Maxima and Minima

APPLY IT What amounts of sugar and flavoring produce the minimum cost per batch of a soft drink? What is the minimum cost?

In this section we will learn how to answer questions such as this one, which is answered in Example 4.

FOR REVIEW
It may be helpful to review relative extrema at this point.

One of the most important applications of calculus is finding maxima and minima of functions. Earlier, we studied this idea extensively for functions of a single independent variable; now we will see that extrema can be found for functions of two variables. In particular, an extension of the second derivative test can be defined and used to identify maxima or minima. We begin with the definitions of relative maxima and minima.

Relative Maxima and Minima

Let (a, b) be the center of a circular region contained in the xy-plane. Then, for a function $z = f(x, y)$ defined for every (x, y) in the region, $f(a, b)$ is a **relative (or local) maximum** if

$$f(a, b) \geq f(x, y)$$

for all points (x, y) in the circular region, and $f(a, b)$ is a **relative (or local) minimum** if

$$f(a, b) \leq f(x, y)$$

for all points (x, y) in the circular region.

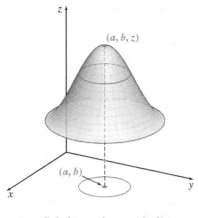

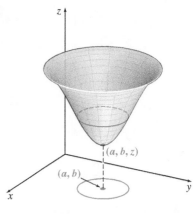

Relative maximum at (a, b)

FIGURE 17

Relative minimum at (a, b)

FIGURE 18

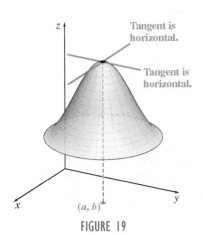

Tangent is horizontal.

Tangent is horizontal.

FIGURE 19

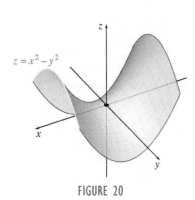

$z = x^2 - y^2$

FIGURE 20

As before, the word *extremum* is used for either a relative maximum or a relative minimum. Examples of a relative maximum and a relative minimum are given in Figures 17 and 18.

NOTE   When functions of a single variable were discussed, a distinction was made between relative extrema and absolute extrema. The methods for finding absolute extrema are quite involved for functions of two variables, so we will discuss only relative extrema here. In many practical applications the relative extrema coincide with the absolute extrema. In this brief discussion of extrema for multivariable functions, we omit cases where an extremum occurs on a boundary of the domain.

As suggested by Figure 19, at a relative maximum the tangent line parallel to the xz-plane has a slope of 0, as does the tangent line parallel to the yz-plane. (Notice the similarity to functions of one variable.) That is, if the function $z = f(x, y)$ has a relative extremum at (a, b), then $f_x(a, b) = 0$ and $f_y(a, b) = 0$, as stated in the next theorem.

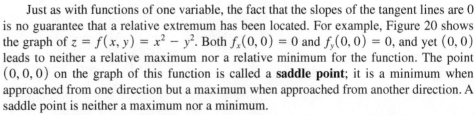

Location of Extrema

Let a function $z = f(x, y)$ have a relative maximum or relative minimum at the point (a, b). Let $f_x(a, b)$ and $f_y(a, b)$ both exist. Then

$$f_x(a, b) = 0 \qquad \text{and} \qquad f_y(a, b) = 0.$$

Just as with functions of one variable, the fact that the slopes of the tangent lines are 0 is no guarantee that a relative extremum has been located. For example, Figure 20 shows the graph of $z = f(x, y) = x^2 - y^2$. Both $f_x(0, 0) = 0$ and $f_y(0, 0) = 0$, and yet $(0, 0)$ leads to neither a relative maximum nor a relative minimum for the function. The point $(0, 0, 0)$ on the graph of this function is called a **saddle point**; it is a minimum when approached from one direction but a maximum when approached from another direction. A saddle point is neither a maximum nor a minimum.

The theorem on location of extrema suggests a useful strategy for finding extrema. First, locate all points (a, b) where $f_x(a, b) = 0$ and $f_y(a, b) = 0$. Then test each of these points separately, using the test given after the next example. For a function $f(x, y)$, the points (a, b) such that $f_x(a, b) = 0$ and $f_y(a, b) = 0$ are called **critical points**.

NOTE   When we discussed functions of a single variable, we allowed critical points to include points from the domain where the derivative does not exist. For functions of more than one variable, to avoid complications, we will only consider cases in which the function is differentiable.

Multivariable Calculus

EXAMPLE 1 Critical Points

Find all critical points for

$$f(x, y) = 6x^2 + 6y^2 + 6xy + 36x - 5.$$

SOLUTION Find all points (a, b) such that $f_x(a, b) = 0$ and $f_y(a, b) = 0$. Here

$$f_x(x, y) = 12x + 6y + 36 \quad \text{and} \quad f_y(x, y) = 12y + 6x.$$

Set each of these two partial derivatives equal to 0.

$$12x + 6y + 36 = 0 \quad \text{and} \quad 12y + 6x = 0$$

These two equations make up a system of linear equations. We can use the substitution method to solve this system. First, rewrite $12y + 6x = 0$ as follows:

$$12y + 6x = 0$$
$$6x = -12y$$
$$x = -2y.$$

Now substitute $-2y$ for x in the other equation and solve for y.

$$12x + 6y + 36 = 0$$
$$12(-2y) + 6y + 36 = 0$$
$$-24y + 6y + 36 = 0$$
$$-18y + 36 = 0$$
$$-18y = -36$$
$$y = 2$$

YOUR TURN 1 Find all critical points for $f(x,y) = 4x^3 + 3xy + 4y^3$.

From the equation $x = -2y$, $x = -2(2) = -4$. The solution of the system of equations is $(-4, 2)$. Since this is the only solution of the system, $(-4, 2)$ is the only critical point for the given function. By the theorem above, if the function has a relative extremum, it will occur at $(-4, 2)$.   **TRY YOUR TURN 1**

The results of the next theorem can be used to decide whether $(-4, 2)$ in Example 1 leads to a relative maximum, a relative minimum, or neither.

Test for Relative Extrema

For a function $z = f(x, y)$, let f_{xx}, f_{yy}, and f_{xy} all exist in a circular region contained in the xy-plane with center (a, b). Further, let

$$f_x(a, b) = 0 \quad \text{and} \quad f_y(a, b) = 0.$$

Define the number D, known as **the discriminant**, by

$$D = f_{xx}(a, b) \cdot f_{yy}(a, b) - [f_{xy}(a, b)]^2.$$

Then
a. $f(a, b)$ is a relative maximum if $D > 0$ and $f_{xx}(a, b) < 0$;
b. $f(a, b)$ is a relative minimum if $D > 0$ and $f_{xx}(a, b) > 0$;
c. $f(a, b)$ is a saddle point (neither a maximum nor a minimum) if $D < 0$;
d. if $D = 0$, the test gives no information.

This test is comparable to the second derivative test for extrema of functions of one independent variable. The following table summarizes the conclusions of the theorem.

	$f_{xx}(a, b) < 0$	$f_{xx}(a, b) > 0$
$D > 0$	Relative maximum	Relative minimum
$D = 0$	No information	
$D < 0$	Saddle point	

Notice that in parts a and b of the test for relative extrema, it is only necessary to test the second partial $f_{xx}(a, b)$ and not $f_{yy}(a, b)$. This is because if $D > 0$, $f_{xx}(a, b)$ and $f_{yy}(a, b)$ must have the same sign.

EXAMPLE 2   Relative Extrema

The previous example showed that the only critical point for the function

$$f(x, y) = 6x^2 + 6y^2 + 6xy + 36x - 5$$

is $(-4, 2)$. Does $(-4, 2)$ lead to a relative maximum, a relative minimum, or neither?

SOLUTION   Find out by using the test above. From Example 1,

$$f_x(-4, 2) = 0 \quad \text{and} \quad f_y(-4, 2) = 0.$$

Now find the various second partial derivatives used in finding D. From $f_x(x, y) = 12x + 6y + 36$ and $f_y(x, y) = 12y + 6x$,

$$f_{xx}(x, y) = 12, \quad f_{yy}(x, y) = 12, \quad \text{and} \quad f_{xy}(x, y) = 6.$$

(If these second-order partial derivatives had not all been constants, they would have had to be evaluated at the point $(-4, 2)$.) Now

$$D = f_{xx}(-4, 2) \cdot f_{yy}(-4, 2) - [f_{xy}(-4, 2)]^2 = 12 \cdot 12 - 6^2 = 108.$$

Since $D > 0$ and $f_{xx}(-4, 2) = 12 > 0$, part b of the theorem applies, showing that $f(x, y) = 6x^2 + 6y^2 + 6xy + 36x - 5$ has a relative minimum at $(-4, 2)$. This relative minimum is $f(-4, 2) = -77$. A graph of this surface drawn by the computer program Maple™ is shown in Figure 21.

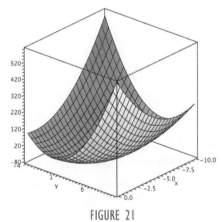

FIGURE 21

EXAMPLE 3   Saddle Point

Find all points where the function

$$f(x, y) = 9xy - x^3 - y^3 - 6$$

has any relative maxima or relative minima.

SOLUTION   First find any critical points. Here

$$f_x(x, y) = 9y - 3x^2 \quad \text{and} \quad f_y(x, y) = 9x - 3y^2.$$

Set each of these partial derivatives equal to 0.

$$
\begin{array}{ll}
f_x(x, y) = 0 & f_y(x, y) = 0 \\
9y - 3x^2 = 0 & 9x - 3y^2 = 0 \\
9y = 3x^2 & 9x = 3y^2 \\
3y = x^2 & 3x = y^2
\end{array}
$$

The substitution method can be used again to solve the system of equations

$$3y = x^2$$
$$3x = y^2.$$

The first equation, $3y = x^2$, can be rewritten as $y = x^2/3$. Substitute this into the second equation to get

$$3x = y^2 = \left(\frac{x^2}{3}\right)^2 = \frac{x^4}{9}.$$

Solve this equation as follows.

$$
\begin{array}{ll}
27x = x^4 & \text{Multiply both sides by 9.} \\
x^4 - 27x = 0 & \\
x(x^3 - 27) = 0 & \text{Factor.} \\
x = 0 \quad \text{or} \quad x^3 - 27 = 0 & \text{Set each factor equal to 0.} \\
x = 0 \quad \text{or} \quad x^3 = 27 & \\
x = 0 \quad \text{or} \quad x = 3 & \text{Take the cube root on both sides.}
\end{array}
$$

Use these values of x, along with the equation $3y = x^2$, rewritten as $y = x^2/3$, to find y. If $x = 0$, $y = 0^2/3 = 0$. If $x = 3$, $y = 3^2/3 = 3$. The critical points are $(0, 0)$ and $(3, 3)$. To identify any extrema, use the test. Here

$$f_{xx}(x, y) = -6x, \qquad f_{yy}(x, y) = -6y, \qquad \text{and} \qquad f_{xy}(x, y) = 9.$$

Test each of the possible critical points.

For $(0, 0)$:	For $(3, 3)$:
$f_{xx}(0, 0) = -6(0) = 0$	$f_{xx}(3, 3) = -6(3) = -18$
$f_{yy}(0, 0) = -6(0) = 0$	$f_{yy}(3, 3) = -6(3) = -18$
$f_{xy}(0, 0) = 9$	$f_{xy}(3, 3) = 9$
$D = 0 \cdot 0 - 9^2 = -81.$	$D = -18(-18) - 9^2 = 243.$
Since $D < 0$, there is a saddle point at $(0, 0)$.	Here $D > 0$ and $f_{xx}(3, 3) = -18 < 0$; there is a relative maximum at $(3, 3)$.

Notice that these values are in accordance with the graph generated by the computer program Maple™ shown in Figure 22.

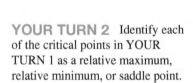

FIGURE 22

YOUR TURN 2 Identify each of the critical points in YOUR TURN 1 as a relative maximum, relative minimum, or saddle point.

TRY YOUR TURN 2

EXAMPLE 4 **Production Costs**

A company is developing a new soft drink. The cost in dollars to produce a batch of the drink is approximated by

$$C(x, y) = 2200 + 27x^3 - 72xy + 8y^2,$$

where x is the number of kilograms of sugar per batch and y is the number of grams of flavoring per batch. Find the amounts of sugar and flavoring that result in the minimum cost per batch. What is the minimum cost?

APPLY IT **SOLUTION**

Method 1
Calculating by Hand

Start with the following partial derivatives.

$$C_x(x, y) = 81x^2 - 72y \qquad \text{and} \qquad C_y(x, y) = -72x + 16y$$

Set each of these equal to 0 and solve for y.

$$
\begin{array}{ll}
81x^2 - 72y = 0 & -72x + 16y = 0 \\
-72y = -81x^2 & 16y = 72x \\
y = \frac{9}{8}x^2 & y = \frac{9}{2}x
\end{array}
$$

Since $(9/8)x^2$ and $(9/2)x$ both equal y, they are equal to each other. Set them equal, and solve the resulting equation for x.

$$\frac{9}{8}x^2 = \frac{9}{2}x$$

$$9x^2 = 36x$$

$$9x^2 - 36x = 0 \qquad \text{Subtract } 36x \text{ from both sides.}$$

$$9x(x - 4) = 0 \qquad \text{Factor.}$$

$$9x = 0 \quad \text{or} \quad x - 4 = 0 \qquad \text{Set each factor equal to } 0.$$

The equation $9x = 0$ leads to $x = 0$ and $y = 0$, which cannot be a minimizer of $C(x, y)$ since, for example, $C(1, 1) < C(0, 0)$. This fact can also be verified by the test for relative extrema. Substitute $x = 4$, the solution of $x - 4 = 0$, into $y = (9/2)x$ to find y.

$$y = \frac{9}{2}x = \frac{9}{2}(4) = 18$$

Now check to see whether the critical point $(4, 18)$ leads to a relative minimum. Here

$$C_{xx}(x, y) = 162x, \quad C_{yy}(x, y) = 16, \quad \text{and} \quad C_{xy}(x, y) = -72.$$

For $(4, 18)$,

$$C_{xx}(4, 18) = 162(4) = 648, \quad C_{yy}(4, 18) = 16, \quad \text{and} \quad C_{xy}(4, 18) = -72,$$

so that

$$D = (648)(16) - (-72)^2 = 5184.$$

Since $D > 0$ and $C_{xx}(4, 18) > 0$, the cost at $(4, 18)$ is a minimum.

To find the minimum cost, go back to the cost function and evaluate $C(4, 18)$.

$$C(x, y) = 2200 + 27x^3 - 72xy + 8y^2$$
$$C(4, 18) = 2200 + 27(4)^3 - 72(4)(18) + 8(18)^2 = 1336$$

The minimum cost for a batch of soft drink is $1336.00. A graph of this surface drawn by the computer program Maple™ is shown in Figure 23.

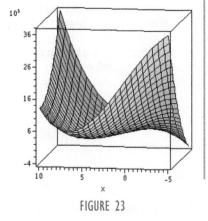

FIGURE 23

**Method 2
Spreadsheets**

Finding the maximum or minimum of a function of one or more variables can be done using a spreadsheet. The Solver included with Excel is located in the Tools menu and requires that cells be identified ahead of time for each variable in the problem. (On some versions of Excel, the Solver must be installed from an outside source.) It also requires that another cell be identified where the function, in terms of the variable cells, is placed. For example, to solve the above problem, we could identify cells A1 and B1 to represent the variables x and y, respectively. The Solver requires that we place a guess for the answer in these cells. Thus, our initial value or guess will be to place the number 5 in each of these cells. An expression for the function must be placed in another cell, with x and y replaced by A1 and B1. If we choose cell A3 to represent the function, in cell A3 we would type "$= 2200 + 27*A1^3 - 72*A1*B1 + 8*B1^2$."

We now click on the Tools menu and choose Solver. This solver will attempt to find a solution that either maximizes or minimizes the value of cell A3. Figure 24 illustrates the Solver box and the items placed in it.

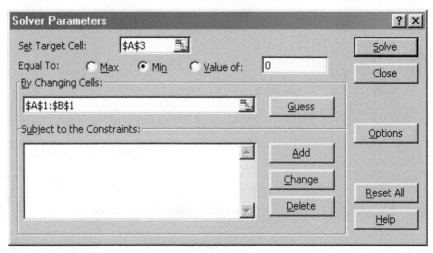

FIGURE 24

To obtain a solution, click on Solve. The rounded solution $x = 4$ and $y = 18$ is located in cells A1 and B1. The minimum cost $C(4, 18) = 1336$ is located in cell A3.

CAUTION One must be careful when using Solver because it will not find a maximizer or minimizer of a function if the initial guess is the exact place in which a saddle point occurs. For example, in the problem above, if our initial guess was $(0, 0)$, the Solver would have returned the value of $(0, 0)$ as the place where a minimum occurs. But $(0, 0)$ is a saddle point. Thus, it is always a good idea to run the Solver for two different initial values and compare the solutions.

3   EXERCISES

Find all points where the functions have any relative extrema. Identify any saddle points.

1. $f(x, y) = xy + y - 2x$

2. $f(x, y) = 3xy + 6y - 5x$

3. $f(x, y) = 3x^2 - 4xy + 2y^2 + 6x - 10$

4. $f(x, y) = x^2 + xy + y^2 - 6x - 3$

5. $f(x, y) = x^2 - xy + y^2 + 2x + 2y + 6$

6. $f(x, y) = 2x^2 + 3xy + 2y^2 - 5x + 5y$

7. $f(x, y) = x^2 + 3xy + 3y^2 - 6x + 3y$

8. $f(x, y) = 5xy - 7x^2 - y^2 + 3x - 6y - 4$

9. $f(x, y) = 4xy - 10x^2 - 4y^2 + 8x + 8y + 9$

10. $f(x, y) = 4y^2 + 2xy + 6x + 4y - 8$

11. $f(x, y) = x^2 + xy - 2x - 2y + 2$

12. $f(x, y) = x^2 + xy + y^2 - 3x - 5$

13. $f(x, y) = 3x^2 + 2y^3 - 18xy + 42$

14. $f(x, y) = 7x^3 + 3y^2 - 126xy - 63$

15. $f(x, y) = x^2 + 4y^3 - 6xy - 1$

16. $f(x, y) = 3x^2 + 7y^3 - 42xy + 5$

17. $f(x, y) = e^{x(y+1)}$

18. $f(x, y) = y^2 + 2e^x$

19. Describe the procedure for finding critical points of a function in two independent variables.

20. How are second-order partial derivatives used in finding extrema?

Figures a–f show the graphs of the functions defined in Exercises 21–26. Find all relative extrema for each function, and then match the equation to its graph.

21. $z = -3xy + x^3 - y^3 + \dfrac{1}{8}$

22. $z = \dfrac{3}{2}y - \dfrac{1}{2}y^3 - x^2y + \dfrac{1}{16}$

23. $z = y^4 - 2y^2 + x^2 - \dfrac{17}{16}$

24. $z = -2x^3 - 3y^4 + 6xy^2 + \dfrac{1}{16}$

25. $z = -x^4 + y^4 + 2x^2 - 2y^2 + \dfrac{1}{16}$

26. $z = -y^4 + 4xy - 2x^2 + \dfrac{1}{16}$

a.

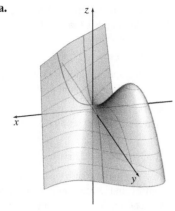

b.

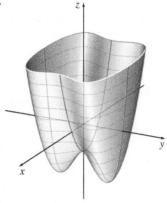

c.

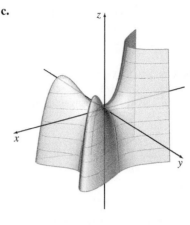

d.

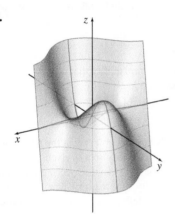

e.

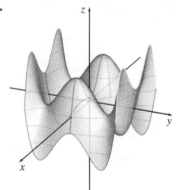

f.

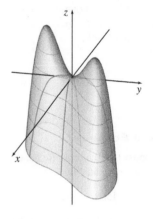

27. Show that $f(x, y) = 1 - x^4 - y^4$ has a relative maximum, even though D in the theorem is 0.

28. Show that $D = 0$ for $f(x, y) = x^3 + (x - y)^2$ and that the function has no relative extrema.

29. A friend taking calculus is puzzled. She remembers that for a function of one variable, if the first derivative is zero at a point and the second derivative is positive, then there must be a relative minimum at the point. She doesn't understand why that isn't true for a function of two variables—that is, why $f_x(x, y) = 0$ and $f_{xx}(x, y) > 0$ doesn't guarantee a relative minimum. Provide an explanation.

30. Let $f(x, y) = y^2 - 2x^2y + 4x^3 + 20x^2$. The only critical points are $(-2, 4)$, $(0, 0)$, and $(5, 25)$. Which of the following correctly describes the behavior of f at these points? *Source: Society of Actuaries.*

a. $(-2, 4)$:   local (relative) minimum
$(0, 0)$:   local (relative) minimum
$(5, 25)$:   local (relative) maximum

b. $(-2, 4)$:   local (relative) minimum
$(0, 0)$:   local (relative) maximum
$(5, 25)$:   local (relative) maximum

c. $(-2, 4)$:   neither a local (relative) minimum nor a local (relative) maximum
$(0, 0)$:   local (relative) maximum
$(5, 25)$:   local (relative) minimum

d. $(-2, 4)$:   local (relative) maximum
$(0, 0)$:   neither a local (relative) minimum nor a local (relative) maximum
$(5, 25)$:   local (relative) minimum

e. $(-2, 4)$:   neither a local (relative) minimum nor a local (relative) maximum
$(0, 0)$:   local (relative) minimum
$(5, 25)$:   neither a local (relative) minimum nor a local (relative) maximum

31. Consider the function $f(x, y) = x^2(y + 1)^2 + k(x + 1)^2y^2$.

a. For what values of k is the point $(x, y) = (0, 0)$ a critical point?

b. For what values of k is the point $(x, y) = (0, 0)$ a relative minimum of the function?

32. We find the least squares line through a set of n points (x_1, y_1), $(x_2, y_2), \ldots, (x_n, y_n)$ by choosing the slope of the line

m and the y-intercept b to minimize the quantity

$$S(m, b) = \sum (mx + b - y)^2,$$

where the summation symbol Σ means that we sum over all the data points. Minimize S by setting $S_m(m, b) = 0$ and $S_b(m, b) = 0$, and then rearrange the results to derive the equations

$$\left(\sum x\right)b + \left(\sum x^2\right)m = \sum xy$$
$$nb + \left(\sum x\right)m = \sum y.$$

33. Suppose a function $z = f(x, y)$ satisfies the criteria for the test for relative extrema at a point (a, b), and $f_{xx}(a, b) > 0$, while $f_{yy}(a, b) < 0$. What does this tell you about $f(a, b)$? Based on the sign of $f_{xx}(a, b)$ and $f_{yy}(a, b)$, why does this seem intuitively plausible?

APPLICATIONS

Business and Economics

34. Profit Suppose that the profit (in hundreds of dollars) of a certain firm is approximated by

$$P(x, y) = 1500 + 36x - 1.5x^2 + 120y - 2y^2,$$

where x is the cost of a unit of labor and y is the cost of a unit of goods. Find values of x and y that maximize profit. Find the maximum profit.

35. Labor Costs Suppose the labor cost (in dollars) for manufacturing a precision camera can be approximated by

$$L(x, y) = \frac{3}{2}x^2 + y^2 - 2x - 2y - 2xy + 68,$$

where x is the number of hours required by a skilled craftsperson and y is the number of hours required by a semiskilled person. Find values of x and y that minimize the labor cost. Find the minimum labor cost.

36. Cost The total cost (in dollars) to produce x units of electrical tape and y units of packing tape is given by

$$C(x, y) = 2x^2 + 2y^2 - 3xy + 4x - 94y + 4200.$$

Find the number of units of each kind of tape that should be produced so that the total cost is a minimum. Find the minimum total cost.

37. Revenue The total revenue (in hundreds of dollars) from the sale of x spas and y solar heaters is approximated by

$$R(x, y) = 15 + 169x + 182y - 5x^2 - 7y^2 - 7xy.$$

Find the number of each that should be sold to produce maximum revenue. Find the maximum revenue.

38. Profit The profit (in thousands of dollars) that Aunt Mildred's Metalworks earns from producing x tons of steel and y tons of aluminum can be approximated by

$$P(x, y) = 36xy - x^3 - 8y^3.$$

Find the amounts of steel and aluminum that maximize the profit, and find the value of the maximum profit.

39. Time The time (in hours) that a branch of Amalgamated Entities needs to spend to meet the quota set by the main office can be approximated by

$$T(x, y) = x^4 + 16y^4 - 32xy + 40,$$

where x represents how many thousands of dollars the factory spends on quality control and y represents how many thousands of dollars they spend on consulting. Find the amount of money they should spend on quality control and on consulting to minimize the time spent, and find the minimum number of hours.

Social Sciences

40. Political Science The probability that a three-person jury will make a correct decision is given by

$$P(\alpha, r, s) = \alpha[3r^2(1 - r) + r^3]$$
$$+ (1 - \alpha)[3s^2(1 - s) + s^3],$$

where $0 < \alpha < 1$ is the probability that the person is guilty of the crime, r is the probability that a given jury member will vote "guilty" when the defendant is indeed guilty of the crime, and s is the probability that a given jury member will vote "innocent" when the defendant is indeed innocent. *Source: Frontiers of Economics.*

a. Calculate $P(0.9, 0.5, 0.6)$ and $P(0.1, 0.8, 0.4)$ and interpret your answers.

b. Using common sense and without using calculus, what value of r and s would maximize the jury's probability of making the correct verdict? Do these values depend on α in this problem? Should they? What is the maximum probability?

c. Verify your answer for part b using calculus. (*Hint:* There are two critical points. Argue that the maximum value occurs at one of these points.)

Physical Sciences

41. Computer Chips The table on the following page illustrates the dramatic increase in the number of transistors in personal computers since 1985.

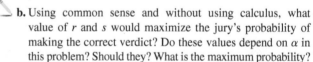

a. To fit the data to a function of the form $y = ab^t$, where t is the number of years since 1985 and y is the number of transistors (in millions), we could take natural logarithms of both sides of the equation to get $\ln y = \ln a + t \ln b$. We could then let $w = \ln y$, $r = \ln a$, and $s = \ln b$ to form $w = r + st$. Using linear regression, find values for r and s that will fit the data. Then find the function $y = ab^t$. (*Hint:* Take the natural logarithm of the values in the transistors column and then use linear regression to find values of r and s that fit the data. Once you know r and s, you can determine the values of a and b by calculating $a = e^r$ and $b = e^s$.)

Year (since 1985)	Chip	Transistors (in millions)
0	386	0.275
4	486	1.2
8	Pentium	3.1
12	Pentium II	7.5
14	Pentium III	9.5
15	Pentium 4	42
20	Pentium D	291
22	Penryn	820
24	Nehalem	1900

b. Use the solver capability of a spreadsheet to find a function of the form $y = ab^t$ that fits the data above. (*Hint:* Using the ideas from part a, find values for a and b that minimize the function

$$
\begin{aligned}
f(a, b) = \ & [\ln(0.275) - 0 \ln b - \ln a]^2 \\
& + [\ln(1.2) - 4 \ln b - \ln a]^2 \\
& + [\ln(3.1) - 8 \ln b - \ln a]^2 \\
& + [\ln(7.5) - 12 \ln b - \ln a]^2 \\
& + [\ln(9.5) - 14 \ln b - \ln a]^2 \\
& + [\ln(42) - 15 \ln b - \ln a]^2 \\
& + [\ln(291) - 20 \ln b - \ln a]^2 \\
& + [\ln(820) - 22 \ln b - \ln a]^2 \\
& + [\ln(1900) - 24 \ln b - \ln a]^2.)
\end{aligned}
$$

c. Compare your answer to this problem with one found with a graphing calculator.

General Interest

42. **Food Frying** The process of frying food changes its quality, texture, and color. According to research done at the University of Saskatchewan, the total change in color E (which is measured in the form of energy as kJ/mol) of blanched potato strips can be estimated by the function

$$E(t, T) = 436.16 - 10.57t - 5.46T - 0.02t^2 + 0.02T^2 + 0.08Tt,$$

where T is the temperature (in °C) and t is the frying time (in min). *Source: Critical Reviews in Food Science and Nutrition.*

a. What is the value of E prior to cooking? (Assume that $T = 0$.)

b. Use this function to estimate the total change in color of a potato strip that has been cooked for 10 minutes at 180°C.

c. Determine the critical point of this function and determine if a maximum, minimum, or saddle point occurs at that point. Describe what may be happening at this point.

YOUR TURN ANSWERS

1. $(0, 0)$ and $(-1/4, -1/4)$

2. Saddle point at $(0, 0)$; relative maximum at $(-1/4, -1/4)$

4 Lagrange Multipliers

APPLY IT What dimensions for a new building will maximize the floor space at a fixed cost?

Using Lagrange multipliers, we will answer this question in Example 2.

It is sometimes possible to express problems involving two variables as equivalent problems requiring only a single variable. This method works well, provided that it is possible to use algebra to express the one variable in terms of the other. It is not always possible to do this, however, and most real applications require more than two variables and one or more additional restrictions, called **constraints**.

An approach that works well when there is a constraint in the problem uses an additional variable, called the **Lagrange multiplier**. For example, in the opening question, suppose a builder wants to maximize the floor space in a new building while keeping the costs fixed at \$500,000. The building will be 40 ft high, with a rectangular floor plan and three stories. The costs, which depend on the dimensions of the rectangular floor plan, are given by

$$\text{Costs} = xy + 20y + 20x + 474{,}000,$$

where x is the width and y the length of the rectangle. Thus, the builder wishes to maximize the area $A(x, y) = xy$ and satisfy the condition

$$xy + 20y + 20x + 474{,}000 = 500{,}000.$$

In addition to maximizing area, then, the builder must keep costs at (or below) $500,000. We will see how to solve this problem in Example 2 of this section.

Problems with constraints are often solved by the method of Lagrange multipliers, named for the French mathematician Joseph Louis Lagrange (1736–1813). The method of Lagrange multipliers is used for problems of the form:

$$\text{Find the relative extrema for } z = f(x, y),$$

$$\text{subject to } g(x, y) = 0.$$

We state the method only for functions of two independent variables, but it is valid for any number of variables.

Lagrange Multipliers

All relative extrema of the function $z = f(x, y)$, subject to a constraint $g(x, y) = 0$, will be found among those points (x, y) for which there exists a value of λ such that

$$F_x(x, y, \lambda) = 0, \qquad F_y(x, y, \lambda) = 0, \qquad F_\lambda(x, y, \lambda) = 0,$$

where

$$F(x, y, \lambda) = f(x, y) - \lambda \cdot g(x, y),$$

and all indicated partial derivatives exist.

In the theorem, the function $F(x, y, \lambda) = f(x, y) - \lambda \cdot g(x, y)$ is called the Lagrange function; λ, the Greek letter *lambda*, is the *Lagrange multiplier*.

CAUTION | If the constraint is not of the form $g(x, y) = 0$, it must be put in that form before using the method of Lagrange multipliers. For example, if the constraint is $x^2 + y^3 = 5$, subtract 5 from both sides to get $g(x, y) = x^2 + y^3 - 5 = 0$.

EXAMPLE 1   Lagrange Multipliers

Find the minimum value of

$$f(x, y) = 5x^2 + 6y^2 - xy,$$

subject to the constraint $x + 2y = 24$.

SOLUTION   Go through the following steps.

Step 1 Rewrite the constraint in the form $g(x, y) = 0$.

In this example, the constraint $x + 2y = 24$ becomes

$$x + 2y - 24 = 0,$$

with

$$g(x, y) = x + 2y - 24.$$

Step 2 Form the Lagrange function $F(x, y, \lambda)$, the difference of the function $f(x, y)$ and the product of λ and $g(x, y)$.

Here,

$$\begin{aligned} F(x, y, \lambda) &= f(x, y) - \lambda \cdot g(x, y) \\ &= 5x^2 + 6y^2 - xy - \lambda(x + 2y - 24) \\ &= 5x^2 + 6y^2 - xy - \lambda x - 2\lambda y + 24\lambda. \end{aligned}$$

Step 3 Find $F_x(x, y, \lambda)$, $F_y(x, y, \lambda)$, and $F_\lambda(x, y, \lambda)$.

$$F_x(x, y, \lambda) = 10x - y - \lambda$$
$$F_y(x, y, \lambda) = 12y - x - 2\lambda$$
$$F_\lambda(x, y, \lambda) = -x - 2y + 24$$

Step 4 Form the system of equations $F_x(x, y, \lambda) = 0$, $F_y(x, y, \lambda) = 0$, and $F_\lambda(x, y, \lambda) = 0$.

$$10x - y - \lambda = 0 \qquad \text{(1)}$$
$$12y - x - 2\lambda = 0 \qquad \text{(2)}$$
$$-x - 2y + 24 = 0 \qquad \text{(3)}$$

Step 5 Solve the system of equations from Step 4 for x, y, and λ.

One way to solve this system is to begin by solving each of the first two equations for λ, then set the two results equal and simplify, as follows.

$$10x - y - \lambda = 0 \qquad \text{becomes} \qquad \lambda = 10x - y$$

$$12y - x - 2\lambda = 0 \qquad \text{becomes} \qquad \lambda = \frac{-x + 12y}{2}$$

$$10x - y = \frac{-x + 12y}{2} \qquad \text{Set the expressions for } \lambda \text{ equal.}$$

$$20x - 2y = -x + 12y$$

$$21x = 14y$$

$$x = \frac{14y}{21} = \frac{2y}{3}$$

Now substitute $2y/3$ for x in Equation (3).

$$-x - 2y + 24 = 0$$

$$-\frac{2y}{3} - 2y + 24 = 0 \qquad \text{Let } x = \frac{2y}{3}.$$

$$2y + 6y - 72 = 0 \qquad \text{Multiply by } -3.$$

$$8y = 72$$

$$y = \frac{72}{8} = 9$$

Since $x = 2y/3$ and $y = 9$, $x = 6$. It is not necessary to find the value of λ.

Thus, if $f(x, y) = 5x^2 + 6y^2 - xy$ has a minimum value subject to the constraint $x + 2y = 24$, it is at the point $(6, 9)$. The value of $f(6, 9)$ is 612.

We need to convince ourselves that $f(6, 9) = 612$ is indeed a minimum for the function. How can we tell that it is not a maximum? The second derivative test from the previous section does not apply to the solutions found by Lagrange multipliers. (See Exercise 21.) We could gain some insight by trying a point very close to $(6, 9)$ that also satisfies the constraint $x + 2y = 24$. For example, let $y = 9.1$, so $x = 24 - 2y = 24 - 2(9.1) = 5.8$. Then $f(5.8, 9.1) = 5(5.8)^2 + 6(9.1)^2 - (5.8)(9.1) = 612.28$, which is greater than 612. Because a nearby point has a value larger than 612, the value 612 is probably not a maximum. Another method would be to use a computer to sketch the graph of the function and see that it has a minimum but not a maximum. In practical problems, such as Example 2, it is often obvious whether a function has a minimum or a maximum. **TRY YOUR TURN 1**

YOUR TURN 1 Find the minimum value of $f(x, y) = x^2 + 2x + 9y^2 + 3y + 6xy$ subject to the constraint $2x + 3y = 12$.

NOTE   In Example 1, we solved the system of equations by solving each equation with λ in it for λ. We then set these expressions for λ equal and solved for one of the original variables. This is a good general approach to use in solving these systems of equations, since we are usually not interested in the value of λ.

CAUTION   Lagrange multipliers give only the relative extrema, not the absolute extrema. In many applications, the relative extrema will be the absolute extrema, but this is not guaranteed. In some cases in which the method of Lagrange multipliers finds a solution, there may not even be any absolute extrema. For example, see Exercises 18 and 19 at the end of this section.

Before looking at applications of Lagrange multipliers, let us summarize the steps involved in solving a problem by this method.

Using Lagrange Multipliers

1. Write the constraint in the form $g(x, y) = 0$.
2. Form the Lagrange function

$$F(x, y, \lambda) = f(x, y) - \lambda \cdot g(x, y).$$

3. Find $F_x(x, y, \lambda)$, $F_y(x, y, \lambda)$, and $F_\lambda(x, y, \lambda)$.
4. Form the system of equations

$$F_x(x, y, \lambda) = 0, \qquad F_y(x, y, \lambda) = 0, \qquad F_\lambda(x, y, \lambda) = 0.$$

5. Solve the system in Step 4; the relative extrema for f are among the solutions of the system.

The proof of this method is complicated and is not given here, but we can explain why the method is plausible. Consider the curve formed by points in the xy-plane that satisfy $F_\lambda(x, y, \lambda) = -g(x, y) = 0$ (or just $g(x, y) = 0$). Figure 25 shows how such a curve might look. Crossing this region are curves $f(x, y) = k$ for various values of k. Notice that at the points where the curve $f(x, y) = k$ is tangent to the curve $g(x, y) = 0$, the largest and smallest meaningful values of f occur. It can be shown that this is equivalent to $f_x(x, y) = \lambda g_x(x, y)$ and $f_y(x, y) = \lambda g_y(x, y)$ for some constant λ. In Exercise 20, you are asked to show that this is equivalent to the system of equations found in Step 4 above.

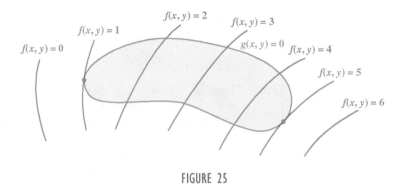

FIGURE 25

Lagrange multipliers are widely used in economics, where a frequent goal is to maximize a utility function, which measures how well consumption satisfies the consumers' desires, subject to constraints on income or time.

EXAMPLE 2 Lagrange Multipliers

Complete the solution of the problem given in the introduction to this section. Maximize the area, $A(x, y) = xy$, subject to the cost constraint

$$xy + 20y + 20x + 474{,}000 = 500{,}000.$$

APPLY IT **SOLUTION** Go through the five steps presented earlier.

Step 1 $g(x, y) = xy + 20y + 20x - 26{,}000 = 0$

Step 2 $F(x, y, \lambda) = xy - \lambda(xy + 20y + 20x - 26{,}000)$

Step 3 $F_x(x, y, \lambda) = y - \lambda y - 20\lambda$

$F_y(x, y, \lambda) = x - \lambda x - 20\lambda$

$F_\lambda(x, y, \lambda) = -xy - 20y - 20x + 26{,}000$

Step 4 $y - \lambda y - 20\lambda = 0$ (4)

$x - \lambda x - 20\lambda = 0$ (5)

$-xy - 20y - 20x + 26{,}000 = 0$ (6)

Step 5 Solving Equations (4) and (5) for λ gives

$$\lambda = \frac{y}{y + 20} \quad \text{and} \quad \lambda = \frac{x}{x + 20}$$

$$\frac{y}{y + 20} = \frac{x}{x + 20}$$

$$y(x + 20) = x(y + 20)$$

$$xy + 20y = xy + 20x$$

$$x = y.$$

Now substitute y for x in Equation (6) to get

$$-y^2 - 20y - 20y + 26{,}000 = 0$$

$$-y^2 - 40y + 26{,}000 = 0.$$

Use the quadratic formula to find $y \approx -182.5$ or $y \approx 142.5$. We eliminate the negative value because length cannot be negative. Since $x = y$, we know that $x \approx 142.5$.

The maximum area of $(142.5)^2 \approx 20{,}306 \text{ ft}^2$ will be achieved if the floor plan is a square with a side of 142.5 ft. You can verify that this answer is a maximum using the method at the end of Example 1.

As mentioned earlier, the method of Lagrange multipliers works for more than two independent variables. The next example shows how to find extrema for a function of three independent variables.

EXAMPLE 3 Volume of a Box

Find the dimensions of the closed rectangular box of maximum volume that can be produced from 6 ft^2 of material.

Method 1
Lagrange Multipliers **SOLUTION** We are able to solve problems such as this by adding an extra constraint, such as requiring the bottom of the box to be square. Here we have no such constraint. Let x, y, and z represent the dimensions of the box, as shown in Figure 26. The volume of the box is given by

$$f(x, y, z) = xyz.$$

FIGURE 26

As shown in Figure 26, the total amount of material required for the two ends of the box is $2xy$, the total needed for the sides is $2xz$, and the total needed for the top and bottom is $2yz$. Since 6 ft^2 of material is available,

$$2xy + 2xz + 2yz = 6 \quad \text{or} \quad xy + xz + yz = 3.$$

In summary, $f(x, y, z) = xyz$ is to be maximized subject to the constraint $xy + xz + yz = 3$. Go through the steps that were given.

Step 1 $g(x, y, z) = xy + xz + yz - 3 = 0$

Step 2 $F(x, y, z, \lambda) = xyz - \lambda(xy + xz + yz - 3)$

Step 3 $F_x(x, y, z, \lambda) = yz - \lambda y - \lambda z$
$F_y(x, y, z, \lambda) = xz - \lambda x - \lambda z$
$F_z(x, y, z, \lambda) = xy - \lambda x - \lambda y$
$F_\lambda(x, y, z, \lambda) = -xy - xz - yz + 3$

Step 4 $yz - \lambda y - \lambda z = 0$
$xz - \lambda x - \lambda z = 0$
$xy - \lambda x - \lambda y = 0$
$-xy - xz - yz + 3 = 0$

Step 5 Solve each of the first three equations for λ. You should get

$$\lambda = \frac{yz}{y + z}, \qquad \lambda = \frac{xz}{x + z}, \qquad \text{and} \qquad \lambda = \frac{xy}{x + y}.$$

Set these expressions for λ equal, and simplify as follows. Notice in the second and last steps that since none of the dimensions of the box can be 0, we can divide both sides of each equation by x or z.

$$\frac{yz}{y + z} = \frac{xz}{x + z} \qquad \text{and} \qquad \frac{xz}{x + z} = \frac{xy}{x + y}$$

$$\frac{y}{y + z} = \frac{x}{x + z} \qquad\qquad \frac{z}{x + z} = \frac{y}{x + y}$$

$$xy + yz = xy + xz \qquad\qquad zx + zy = yx + yz$$

$$yz = xz \qquad\qquad\qquad zx = yx$$

$$y = x \qquad\qquad\qquad\qquad z = y$$

(Setting the first and third expressions equal gives no additional information.) Thus $x = y = z$. From the fourth equation in Step 4, with $x = y$ and $z = y$,

$$-xy - xz - yz + 3 = 0$$
$$-y^2 - y^2 - y^2 + 3 = 0$$
$$-3y^2 = -3$$
$$y^2 = 1$$
$$y = \pm 1.$$

The negative solution is not applicable, so the solution of the system of equations is $x = 1, y = 1, z = 1$. In other words, the box with maximum volume under the constraint is a cube that measures 1 ft on each side. As in the previous examples, verify that this is a maximum.

Method 2
Spreadsheets

Finding extrema of a constrained function of one or more variables can be done using a spreadsheet. In addition to the requirements stated in the last section, the constraint must also be input into the Excel Solver. To do this, we need to input the left-hand or variable part of the constraint into a designated cell. If A5 is the designated cell, then in cell A5 we would type "=A1*B1 + A1*C1 + B1*C1."

We now click on the Tools menu and choose Solver. This solver will attempt to find a solution that either maximizes or minimizes the value of cell A3, depending on which option we choose. Figure 27 illustrates the Solver box and the items placed in it.

To obtain a solution, click on Solve. The solution $x = 1$ and $y = 1$ and $z = 1$ is located in cells A1, B1, and C1, respectively. The maximum volume $f(1, 1, 1) = 1$ is located in cell A3.

YOUR TURN 2 Solve Example 3 with the box changed so that the front and the top are missing.

TRY YOUR TURN 2

CAUTION One must be careful when using Solver because the solution may depend on the initial value. Thus, it is always a good idea to run the Solver for two different initial values and compare the solutions.

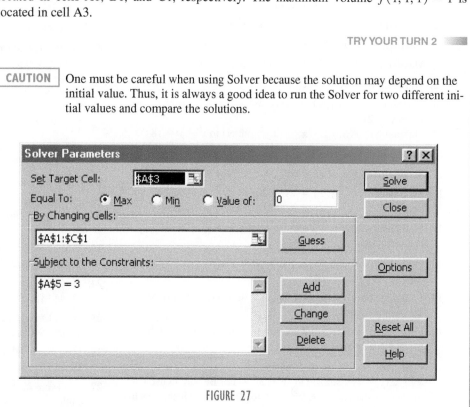

FIGURE 27

Utility Functions

A **utility function** of two variables is a function $z = f(x, y)$ in which x and y give the quantity of items that a consumer might value, such as cereal and milk, and z is a measure of the value that the consumer places on the combination of items represented by the point (x, y). (Naturally, this definition can be extended to any number of variables, but for simplicity we will restrict this discussion to two variables.) For example, if $z = f(x, y) = x^2y^4$, where x represents the number of quarts of milk and y represents the number of pounds of cereal, then 4 quarts of milk and 3 pounds of cereal has a utility of $4^2 \cdot 3^4 = 1296$. The consumer would value this combination as much as 36 quarts of milk and 1 pound of cereal, since this combination also has a utility of $36^2 \cdot 1^4 = 1296$, but less so than 3 quarts of milk and 4 pounds of cereal, which has a utility of $3^2 \cdot 4^4 = 2304$. The set of points $c = f(x, y)$ form an **indifference curve**, since the consumer considers all points on this curve to be equally desirable.

Now suppose a quart of milk costs \$2 and a pound of cereal costs \$3, so that the combination of milk and cereal represented by the point (x, y) costs $2x + 3y$. Suppose further that the consumer has \$90 to spend. A natural question would be how much of each quantity to buy to maximize the consumer's utility. In other words, the consumer wishes to maximize $f(x, y) = x^2y^4$ subject to the constraint that $2x + 3y = 90$, or $g(x, y) = 2x + 3y - 90 = 0$. This is exactly the type of problem that Lagrange multipliers were designed to solve. Use Lagrange multipliers to verify that the function $f(x, y) = x^2y^4$ subject to the constraint $g(x, y) = 2x + 3y - 90 = 0$ has a maximum value of 36,000,000 when $x = 15$ and $y = 20$, so the consumer should purchase 15 quarts of milk and 20 pounds of cereal.

4   EXERCISES

Find the relative maxima or minima in Exercises 1–10.

1. Maximum of $f(x, y) = 4xy$, subject to $x + y = 16$

2. Maximum of $f(x, y) = 2xy + 4$, subject to $x + y = 20$

3. Maximum of $f(x, y) = xy^2$, subject to $x + 2y = 15$

4. Maximum of $f(x, y) = 8x^2y$, subject to $3x - y = 9$

5. Minimum of $f(x, y) = x^2 + 2y^2 - xy$, subject to $x + y = 8$

6. Minimum of $f(x, y) = 3x^2 + 4y^2 - xy - 2$, subject to $2x + y = 21$

7. Maximum of $f(x, y) = x^2 - 10y^2$, subject to $x - y = 18$

8. Maximum of $f(x, y) = 12xy - x^2 - 3y^2$, subject to $x + y = 16$

9. Maximum of $f(x, y, z) = xyz^2$, subject to $x + y + z = 6$

10. Maximum of $f(x, y, z) = xy + 2xz + 2yz$, subject to $xyz = 32$

11. Find positive numbers x and y such that $x + y = 24$ and $3xy^2$ is maximized.

12. Find positive numbers x and y such that $x + y = 48$ and $5x^2y + 10$ is maximized.

13. Find three positive numbers whose sum is 90 and whose product is a maximum.

14. Find three positive numbers whose sum is 240 and whose product is a maximum.

15. Find the maximum and minimum values of $f(x,y) = x^3 + 2xy + 4y^2$ subject to $x + 2y = 12$. Be sure to use the method at the end of Example 1 to determine whether each solution is a maximum or a minimum.

16. Explain the difference between the two methods we used in Sections 3 and 4 to solve extrema problems.

17. Why is it unnecessary to find the value of λ when using the method explained in this section?

18. Show that the function $f(x, y) = xy^2$ in Exercise 3, subject to $x + 2y = 15$, does not have an absolute minimum or maximum. (*Hint*: Solve the constraint for x and substitute into f.)

19. Show that the function $f(x, y) = 8x^2y$ in Exercise 4, subject to $3x - y = 9$, does not have an absolute minimum or maximum. (*Hint*: Solve the constraint for y and substitute into f.)

20. Show that the three equations in Step 4 of the box "Using Lagrange Multipliers" are equivalent to the three equations

$$f_x(x, y) = \lambda g_x(x, y), \quad f_y(x, y) = \lambda g_y(x, y), \quad g(x, y) = 0.$$

21. Consider the problem of minimizing $f(x,y) = x^2 + 2x + 9y^2 + 4y + 8xy$ subject to $x + y = 1$.

    a. Find the solution using the method of Lagrange multipliers.

    b. Experiment with points very near the point from part a to convince yourself that the point from part a actually gives a minimum. (*Hint:* See the last paragraph of Example 1.)

    c. Solve $x + y = 1$ for y and substitute the expression for y into $f(x,y)$. Then explain why the resulting expression in x has a minimum but no maximum.

    d. Suppose you erroneously applied the method of finding the discriminant D from the previous section to determine whether the point found in part a is a minimum. What does the test erroneously tell you about the point?

22. Discuss the advantages and disadvantages of the method of Lagrange multipliers compared with solving the equation $g(x, y) = 0$ for y (or x), substituting that expression into f and then minimizing or maximizing f as a function of one variable. You might want to try some examples both ways and consider what happens when there are more than two variables.

APPLICATIONS

Business and Economics

Utility Maximize each of the following utility functions, with the cost of each commodity and total amount available to spend given.

23. $f(x,y) = xy^2$, cost of a unit of x is \$1, cost of a unit of y is \$2, and \$60 is available.

24. $f(x,y) = x^2y^3$, cost of a unit of x is \$2, cost of a unit of y is \$1, and \$80 is available.

25. $f(x,y) = x^4y^2$, cost of a unit of x is \$2, cost of a unit of y is \$4, and \$60 is available.

26. $f(x,y) = x^3y^4$, cost of a unit of x is \$3, cost of a unit of y is \$3, and \$42 is available.

27. **Maximum Area for Fixed Expenditure** Because of terrain difficulties, two sides of a fence can be built for \$6 per ft, while the other two sides cost \$4 per ft. (See the sketch.) Find the field of maximum area that can be enclosed for \$1200.

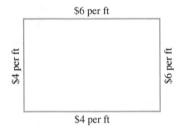

28. **Maximum Area for Fixed Expenditure** To enclose a yard, a fence is built against a large building, so that fencing material is used only on three sides. Material for the ends costs \$15 per ft; material for the side opposite the building costs \$25 per ft. Find the dimensions of the yard of maximum area that can be enclosed for \$2400.

29. **Cost** The total cost to produce x large jewelry-making kits and y small ones is given by

$$C(x, y) = 2x^2 + 6y^2 + 4xy + 10.$$

If a total of ten kits must be made, how should production be allocated so that total cost is minimized?

30. Profit The profit from the sale of x units of radiators for automobiles and y units of radiators for generators is given by

$$P(x, y) = -x^2 - y^2 + 4x + 8y.$$

Find values of x and y that lead to a maximum profit if the firm must produce a total of 6 units of radiators.

31. Production A manufacturing firm estimates that its total production of automobile batteries in thousands of units is

$$f(x, y) = 3x^{1/3}y^{2/3},$$

where x is the number of units of labor and y is the number of units of capital utilized. Labor costs are \$80 per unit, and capital costs are \$150 per unit. How many units each of labor and capital will maximize production, if the firm can spend \$40,000 for these costs?

32. Production For another product, the manufacturing firm in Exercise 31 estimates that production is a function of labor x and capital y as follows:

$$f(x, y) = 12x^{3/4}y^{1/4}.$$

If \$25,200 is available for labor and capital, and if the firm's costs are \$100 and \$180 per unit, respectively, how many units of labor and capital will give maximum production?

33. Area A farmer has 500 m of fencing. Find the dimensions of the rectangular field of maximum area that can be enclosed by this amount of fencing.

34. Area Find the area of the largest rectangular field that can be enclosed with 600 m of fencing. Assume that no fencing is needed along one side of the field.

35. Surface Area A cylindrical can is to be made that will hold 250π in^3 of candy. Find the dimensions of the can with minimum surface area.

36. Surface Area An ordinary 12-oz beer or soda pop can holds about 25 in^3. Find the dimensions of a can with minimum surface area. Measure a can and see how close its dimensions are to the results you found.

37. Volume A rectangular box with no top is to be built from 500 m^2 of material. Find the dimensions of such a box that will enclose the maximum volume.

38. Surface Area A 1-lb soda cracker box has a volume of 185 in^3. The end of the box is square. Find the dimensions of such a box that has minimum surface area.

39. Cost A rectangular closed box is to be built at minimum cost to hold 125 m^3. Since the cost will depend on the surface area, find the dimensions that will minimize the surface area of the box.

40. Cost Find the dimensions that will minimize the surface area (and hence the cost) of a rectangular fish aquarium, open on top, with a volume of 32 ft^3.

41. Container Construction A company needs to construct a box with an open top that will be used to transport 400 yd^3 of material, in several trips, from one place to another. Two of the sides and bottom of the box can be made of a free, lightweight material, but only 4 yd^2 of the material is available. Because of the nature of the material to be transported, the two ends of the box must be made from a heavyweight material that costs \$20 per yd^2. Each trip costs 10 cents. *Source: Geometric Programming*.

a. Let x, y, and z denote the length, width, and height of the box, respectively. If we want to use all of the free material, show that the total cost in dollars is given by the function

$$f(x, y, z) = \frac{40}{xyz} + 40yz,$$

subject to the constraint $2xz + xy = 4$.

b. Use the Solver feature on a spreadsheet to find the dimensions of the box that minimize the transportation cost, subject to the constraint.

Social Sciences

42. Political Science The probability that the majority of a three-person jury will convict a guilty person is given by the formula:

$$P(r, s, t) = rs(1 - t) + (1 - r)st + r(1 - s)t + rst$$

subject to the constraint that

$$r + s + t = \alpha,$$

where r, s, and t represent each of the three jury members' probability of reaching a guilty verdict and α is some fixed constant that is generally less than or equal to the number of jurors. *Source: Mathematical Social Sciences*.

a. Form the Lagrange function.

b. Find the values of r, s, and t that maximize the probability of convicting a guilty person when $\alpha = 0.75$.

c. Find the values of r, s, and t that maximize the probability of convicting a guilty person when $\alpha = 3$.

YOUR TURN ANSWERS

1. $f(12, -4) = 12$

2. The box should be 2 ft wide and 1 ft high and long.

5 Total Differentials and Approximations

APPLY IT How do errors in measuring the length and radius of a blood vessel affect the calculation of its volume?

In Example 3 in this section, we will see how to answer this question using a total differential.

In the second section of this chapter we used partial derivatives to find the marginal productivity of labor and of capital for a production function. The marginal productivity approximates the change of production for a 1-unit change in labor or capital. To estimate

Multivariable Calculus

the change in productivity for a small change in both labor and capital, we can extend the concept of differential, introduced in an earlier chapter for functions of one variable, to the concept of *total differential.*

> ### Total Differential for Two Variables
> Let $z = f(x, y)$ be a function of x and y. Let dx and dy be real numbers. Then the **total differential** of z is
>
> $$dz = f_x(x,y) \cdot dx + f_y(x,y) \cdot dy.$$
>
> (Sometimes dz is written df.)

Recall that the differential for a function of one variable $y = f(x)$ is used to approximate the function by its tangent line. This works because a differentiable function appears very much like a line when viewed closely. Similarly, the differential for a function of two variables $z = f(x, y)$ is used to approximate a function by its tangent plane. A differentiable function of two variables looks like a plane when viewed closely, which is why the earth looks flat when you are standing on it.

FOR REVIEW

Recall that the differerential of a function defined by $y = f(x)$ is

$$dy = f'(x) \cdot dx,$$

where dx, the differential of x, is any real number (usually small). The differential dy is often a good approximation of Δy, where $\Delta y = f(x + \Delta x) - f(x)$ and $\Delta x = dx$.

EXAMPLE 1 Total Differentials

Consider the function $z = f(x, y) = 9x^3 - 8x^2y + 4y^3$.

(a) Find dz.

SOLUTION First find $f_x(x, y)$ and $f_y(x, y)$.

$$f_x(x, y) = 27x^2 - 16xy \quad \text{and} \quad f_y(x, y) = -8x^2 + 12y^2$$

By the definition,

$$dz = (27x^2 - 16xy)\, dx + (-8x^2 + 12y^2)\, dy.$$

(b) Evaluate dz when $x = 1$, $y = 3$, $dx = 0.01$, and $dy = -0.02$.

SOLUTION Putting these values into the result from part (a) gives

$$dz = [27(1)^2 - 16(1)(3)](0.01) + [-8(1)^2 + 12(3)^2](-0.02)$$
$$= (-21)(0.01) + (100)(-0.02)$$
$$= -2.21.$$

YOUR TURN 1 For the function $f(x,y) = 3x^2y^4 + 6\sqrt{x^2 - 7y^2}$, find (a) dz, and (b) the value of dz when $x = 4$, $y = 1$, $dx = 0.02$, and $dy = -0.03$.

This result indicates that an increase of 0.01 in x and a decrease of 0.02 in y, when $x = 1$ and $y = 3$, will produce an approximate *decrease* of 2.21 in $f(x, y)$.

TRY YOUR TURN 1

Approximations
Recall that with a function of one variable, $y = f(x)$, the differential dy approximates the change in y, Δy, corresponding to a change in x, Δx or dx. The approximation for a function of two variables is similar.

> ### Approximations
> For small values of dx and dy,
>
> $$dz \approx \Delta z,$$
>
> where $\Delta z = f(x + dx, y + dy) - f(x, y).$

EXAMPLE 2 Approximations

Approximate $\sqrt{2.98^2 + 4.01^2}$.

SOLUTION Notice that $2.98 \approx 3$ and $4.01 \approx 4$, and we know that $\sqrt{3^2 + 4^2} = \sqrt{25} = 5$. We, therefore, let $f(x, y) = \sqrt{x^2 + y^2}$, $x = 3$, $dx = -0.02$, $y = 4$, and $dy = 0.01$. We then use dz to approximate $\Delta z = \sqrt{2.98^2 + 4.01^2} - \sqrt{3^2 + 4^2}$.

$$
\begin{aligned}
dz &= f_x(x, y) \cdot dx + f_y(x, y) \cdot dy \\
&= \left(\frac{1}{2\sqrt{x^2 + y^2}} \cdot 2x \right) dx + \left(\frac{1}{2\sqrt{x^2 + y^2}} \cdot 2y \right) dy \\
&= \left(\frac{x}{\sqrt{x^2 + y^2}} \right) dx + \left(\frac{y}{\sqrt{x^2 + y^2}} \right) dy \\
&= \frac{3}{5}(-0.02) + \frac{4}{5}(0.01) \\
&= -0.004
\end{aligned}
$$

YOUR TURN 2

Approximate $\sqrt{5.03^2 + 11.99^2}$.

Thus, $\sqrt{2.98^2 + 4.01^2} \approx 5 + (-0.004) = 4.996$. A calculator gives $\sqrt{2.98^2 + 4.01^2} \approx 4.996048$. The error is approximately 0.000048.   **TRY YOUR TURN 2**

For small values of dx and dy, the values of Δz and dz are approximately equal. Since $\Delta z = f(x + dx, y + dy) - f(x, y)$,

$$f(x + dx, y + dy) = f(x, y) + \Delta z$$

or

$$f(x + dx, y + dy) \approx f(x, y) + dz.$$

Replacing dz with the expression for the total differential gives the following result.

Approximations by Differentials

For a function f having all indicated partial derivatives, and for small values of dx and dy,

$$f(x + dx, y + dy) \approx f(x, y) + dz,$$

or

$$f(x + dx, y + dy) \approx f(x, y) + f_x(x, y) \cdot dx + f_y(x, y) \cdot dy.$$

The idea of a total differential can be extended to include functions of three or more independent variables.

Total Differential for Three Variables

If $w = f(x, y, z)$, then the total differential dw is

$$dw = f_x(x, y, z)\, dx + f_y(x, y, z)\, dy + f_z(x, y, z)\, dz,$$

provided all indicated partial derivatives exist.

EXAMPLE 3 Blood Vessels

A short length of blood vessel is in the shape of a right circular cylinder (see Figure 28).

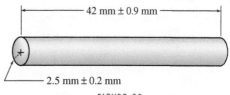

FIGURE 28

(a) The length of the vessel is measured as 42 mm, and the radius is measured as 2.5 mm. Suppose the maximum error in the measurement of the length is 0.9 mm, with an error of no more than 0.2 mm in the measurement of the radius. Find the maximum possible error in calculating the volume of the blood vessel.

APPLY IT

SOLUTION The volume of a right circular cylinder is given by $V = \pi r^2 h$. To approximate the error in the volume, find the total differential, dV.

$$dV = (2\pi rh) \cdot dr + (\pi r^2) \cdot dh$$

Here, $r = 2.5$, $h = 42$, $dr = 0.2$, and $dh = 0.9$. Substitution gives

$$dV = [(2\pi)(2.5)(42)](0.2) + [\pi(2.5)^2](0.9) \approx 149.6.$$

The maximum possible error in calculating the volume is approximately 149.6 mm³.

(b) Suppose that the errors in measuring the radius and length of the vessel are at most 1% and 3%, respectively. Estimate the maximum percent error in calculating the volume.

SOLUTION To find the percent error, calculate dV/V.

$$\frac{dV}{V} = \frac{(2\pi rh)dr + (\pi r^2)dh}{\pi r^2 h} = 2\frac{dr}{r} + \frac{dh}{h}$$

YOUR TURN 3 In Example 3, estimate the maximum percent error in calculating the volume if the errors in measuring the radius and length of the vessel are at most 4% and 2%, respectively.

Because $dr/r = 0.01$ and $dh/h = 0.03$,

$$\frac{dV}{V} = 2(0.01) + 0.03 = 0.05.$$

The maximum percent error in calculating the volume is approximately 5%.

TRY YOUR TURN 3

EXAMPLE 4 Volume of a Can of Beer

The formula for the volume of a cylinder given in Example 3 also applies to cans of beer, for which $r \approx 1.5$ in. and $h \approx 5$ in. How sensitive is the volume to changes in the radius compared with changes in the height?

SOLUTION Using the formula for dV from the previous example with $r = 1.5$ and $h = 5$ gives

$$dV = (2\pi)(1.5)(5)dr + \pi(1.5)^2 dh = \pi(15dr + 2.25dh).$$

The factor of 15 in front of dr in this equation, compared with the factor of 2.25 in front of dh, shows that a small change in the radius has almost 7 times the effect on the volume as a small change in the height. One author argues that this is the reason that beer cans are so tall and thin. *Source: The College Mathematics Journal.* The brewers can reduce the radius by a tiny amount and compensate by making the can taller. The resulting can appears larger in volume than the shorter, wider can. (Others have argued that a shorter, wider can does not fit as easily in the hand.)

5 EXERCISES

Evaluate dz using the given information.

1. $z = 2x^2 + 4xy + y^2$; $x = 5, y = -1, dx = 0.03, dy = -0.02$

2. $z = 5x^3 + 2xy^2 - 4y$; $x = 1, y = 3, dx = 0.01, dy = 0.02$

3. $z = \dfrac{y^2 + 3x}{y^2 - x}$; $x = 4, y = -4, dx = 0.01, dy = 0.03$

4. $z = \ln(x^2 + y^2)$; $x = 2, y = 3, dx = 0.02, dy = -0.03$

Evaluate dw using the given information.

5. $w = \dfrac{5x^2 + y^2}{z + 1}$; $x = -2, y = 1, z = 1, dx = 0.02, dy = -0.03, dz = 0.02$

6. $w = x \ln(yz) - y \ln\dfrac{x}{z}$; $x = 2, y = 1, z = 4, dx = 0.03, dy = 0.02, dz = -0.01$

Use the total differential to approximate each quantity. Then use a calculator to approximate the quantity, and give the absolute value of the difference in the two results to 4 decimal places.

7. $\sqrt{8.05^2 + 5.97^2}$

8. $\sqrt{4.96^2 + 12.06^2}$

9. $(1.92^2 + 2.1^2)^{1/3}$

10. $(2.93^2 - 0.94^2)^{1/3}$

11. $1.03e^{0.04}$

12. $0.98e^{-0.04}$

13. $0.99 \ln 0.98$

14. $2.03 \ln 1.02$

APPLICATIONS

Business and Economics

15. Manufacturing Approximate the volume of aluminum needed for a beverage can of radius 2.5 cm and height 14 cm. Assume the walls of the can are 0.08 cm thick.

16. Manufacturing Approximate the volume of material needed to make a water tumbler of diameter 3 cm and height 9 cm. Assume the walls of the tumbler are 0.2 cm thick.

17. Volume of a Coating An industrial coating 0.1 in. thick is applied to all sides of a box of dimensions 10 in. by 9 in. by 18 in. Estimate the volume of the coating used.

18. Manufacturing Cost The manufacturing cost of a smart-phone is approximated by

$$M(x, y) = 45x^2 + 40y^2 - 20xy + 50,$$

where x is the cost of the parts and y is the cost of labor. Right now, the company spends $8 on parts and $14 on labor. Use differentials to approximate the change in cost if the company spends $8.25 on parts and $13.75 on labor.

19. Production The production function for one country is

$$z = x^{0.65}y^{0.35},$$

where x stands for units of labor and y for units of capital. At present, 50 units of labor and 29 units of capital are available. Use differentials to estimate the change in production if the number of units of labor is increased to 52 and capital is decreased to 27 units.

20. Production The production function for another country is

$$z = x^{0.8}y^{0.2},$$

where x stands for units of labor and y for units of capital. At present, 20 units of labor and 18 units of capital are being provided. Use differentials to estimate the change in production if an additional unit of labor is provided and if capital is decreased to 16 units.

Life Sciences

21. Bone Preservative Volume A piece of bone in the shape of a right circular cylinder is 7 cm long and has a radius of 1.4 cm. It is coated with a layer of preservative 0.09 cm thick. Estimate the volume of preservative used.

22. Blood Vessel Volume A portion of a blood vessel is measured as having length 7.9 cm and radius 0.8 cm. If each measurement could be off by as much as 0.15 cm, estimate the maximum possible error in calculating the volume of the vessel.

23. Blood Volume In Exercise 56 of Section 2 in this chapter, we found that the number of liters of blood pumped through the lungs in one minute is given by

$$C = \frac{b}{a - v}.$$

Suppose $a = 160$, $b = 200$, and $v = 125$. Estimate the change in C if a becomes 145, b becomes 190, and v changes to 130.

24. Heat Loss In Exercise 54 of Section 2 of this chapter, we found that the rate of heat loss (in watts) in harbor seal pups could be approximated by

$$H(m, T, A) = \frac{15.2m^{0.67}(T - A)}{10.23 \ln m - 10.74},$$

where m is the body mass of the pup (in kg), and T and A are the body core temperature and ambient water temperature, respectively (in °C). Suppose m is 25 kg, T is 36.0°, and A is 12.0°C. Approximate the change in H if m changes to 26 kg, T to 36.5°, and A to 10.0°C.

25. Dialysis A model that estimates the concentration of urea in the body for a particular dialysis patient, following a dialysis session, is given by

$$C(t, g) = 0.6(0.96)^{(210t/1500) - 1}$$
$$+ \frac{gt}{126t - 900}[1 - (0.96)^{(210t/1500) - 1}],$$

where t represents the number of minutes of the dialysis session and g represents the rate at which the body generates urea in mg per minute. *Source: Clinical Dialysis.*

a. Find $C(180, 8)$.

b. Using the total differential, estimate the urea concentration if the dialysis session of part a was cut short by 10 minutes and the urea generation rate was 9 mg per minute. Compare this with the actual concentration. (*Hint:* First, replace the variable g with the number 8, thus reducing the function to one variable. Then use your graphing calculator to calculate the partial derivative $C_t(180, 8)$. A similar procedure can be done for $C_g(180, 8)$.)

26. Horn Volume The volume of the horns from bighorn sheep was estimated by researchers using the equation

$$V = \frac{h\pi}{3}(r_1^2 + r_1 r_2 + r_2^2),$$

where h is the length of a horn segment (in centimeters) and r_1 and r_2 are the radii of the two ends of the horn segment (in centimeters). *Source: Conservation Biology.*

a. Determine the volume of a segment of horn that is 40 cm long with radii of 5 cm and 3 cm, respectively.

b. Use the total differential to estimate the volume of the segment of horn if the horn segment from part a was actually 42 cm long with radii of 5.1 cm and 2.9 cm, respectively. Compare this with the actual volume.

27. Eastern Hemlock Ring shake, which is the separation of the wood between growth rings, is a serious problem in hemlock trees. Researchers have developed the following function that estimates the probability P that a given hemlock tree has ring shake.

$$P(A, B, D) = \frac{1}{1 + e^{3.68 - 0.016A - 0.77B - 0.12D}},$$

where A is the age of the tree (yr), B is 1 if bird pecking is present and 0 otherwise, and D is the diameter (in.) of the tree at breast height. *Source: Forest Products Journal.*

a. Estimate the probability that a 150-year-old tree, with bird pecking present and a breast height diameter of 20 in., will have ring shake.

b. Estimate the probability that a 150-year-old tree, with no presence of bird pecking and a breast height diameter of 20 in., will have ring shake.

c. Develop a statement about what can be said about the influence that the three variables have on the probability of ring shake.

d. Using the total differential, estimate the probability if the actual age of the tree was 160 years and the diameter at breast height was 25 in. Assume that no bird pecking was present. Compare your answer to the actual value. (*Hint:* Assume that $B = 0$ and exclude that variable from your calculations.)

e. Comment on the practicality of using differentials in part d.

Physical Sciences

28. Swimming The amount of time in seconds it takes for a swimmer to hear a single, hand-held, starting signal is given by the formula

$$t(x, y, p, C) = \frac{\sqrt{x^2 + (y - p)^2}}{331.45 + 0.6C},$$

where (x, y) is the location of the starter (in meters), $(0, p)$ is the location of the swimmer (in meters), and C is the air temperature (in degrees Celsius). *Source: COMAP.* Assume that the starter is located at the point $(x, y) = (5, -2)$. See the diagram.

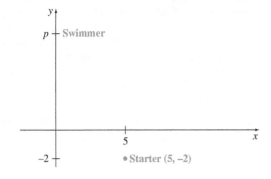

a. Calculate $t(5, -2, 20, 20)$ and $t(5, -2, 10, 20)$. Could the difference in time change the outcome of a race?

b. Calculate the total differential for t if the starter remains stationary, the swimmer moves from 20 m to 20.5 m away from the starter in the y direction, and the temperature decreases from 20°C to 15°C. Interpret your answer.

General Interest

29. Estimating Area The height of a triangle is measured as 37.5 cm, with the base measured as 15.8 cm. The measurement of the height can be off by as much as 0.8 cm and that of the base by no more than 1.1 cm. Estimate the maximum possible error in calculating the area of the triangle.

30. Estimating Volume The height of a cone is measured as 9.3 cm and the radius as 3.2 cm. Each measurement could be off by as much as 0.1 cm. Estimate the maximum possible error in calculating the volume of the cone.

31. Estimating Volume Suppose that in measuring the length, width, and height of a box, there is a maximum 1% error in each measurement. Estimate the maximum error in calculating the volume of the box.

32. Estimating Volume Suppose there is a maximum error of $a\%$ in measuring the radius of a cone and a maximum error of $b\%$ in measuring the height. Estimate the maximum percent error in calculating the volume of the cone, and compare this value with the maximum percent error in calculating the volume of a cylinder.

33. Ice Cream Cone An ice cream cone has a radius of approximately 1 in. and a height of approximately 4 in. By what factor does a change in the radius affect the volume compared with a change in the height?

34. Hose A hose has a radius of approximately 0.5 in. and a length of approximately 20 ft. By what factor does a change in the radius affect the volume compared with a change in the length?

YOUR TURN ANSWERS

1. (a) $dz = (6xy^4 + 6x/\sqrt{x^2 - 7y^2})dx + (12x^2y^3 - 42y/\sqrt{x^2 - 7y^2})dy$ **(b)** -4.7

2. 13.0023   **3.** 10%

6   Double Integrals

APPLY IT   How can we find the volume of a bottle with curved sides?

We will answer this question in Example 6 using a double integral, the key idea in this section.

In an earlier chapter, we saw how integrals of functions with one variable may be used to find area. In this section, this idea is extended and used to find volume. We found partial derivatives of functions of two or more variables at the beginning of this chapter by holding constant all variables except one. A similar process is used in this section to find antiderivatives of functions of two or more variables. For example, in

$$\int (5x^3y^4 - 6x^2y + 2)\, dy$$

the notation dy indicates integration with respect to y, so we treat y as the variable and x as a constant. Using the rules for antiderivatives gives

$$\int (5x^3y^4 - 6x^2y + 2)\, dy = x^3y^5 - 3x^2y^2 + 2y + C(x).$$

The constant C used earlier must be replaced with $C(x)$ to show that the "constant of integration" here can be any function involving only the variable x. Just as before, check this work by taking the derivative (actually the partial derivative) of the answer:

$$\frac{\partial}{\partial y}[x^3y^5 - 3x^2y^2 + 2y + C(x)] = 5x^3y^4 - 6x^2y + 2 + 0,$$

which shows that the antiderivative is correct.

We can use this antiderivative to evaluate a definite integral.

EXAMPLE 1 Definite Integral

Evaluate $\int_1^2 (5x^3y^4 - 6x^2y + 2)\, dy$.

SOLUTION

$$\int_1^2 (5x^3y^4 - 6x^2y + 2)\, dy = \left[x^3y^5 - 3x^2y^2 + 2y + C(x)\right]\Big|_1^2 \quad \text{Use the indefinite integral previously found.}$$

$$= x^3 2^5 - 3x^2 2^2 + 2\cdot 2 + C(x)$$
$$\quad - [x^3 1^5 - 3x^2 1^2 + 2\cdot 1 + C(x)]$$
$$= 32x^3 - 12x^2 + 4 + C(x)$$
$$\quad - [x^3 - 3x^2 + 2 + C(x)]$$
$$= 31x^3 - 9x^2 + 2 \quad \text{Simplify.}$$

YOUR TURN 1 Evaluate $\int_1^3 (6x^2y^2 + 4xy + 8x^3 + 10y^4 + 3)\,dy$.

In the second step, we substituted $y = 2$ and $y = 1$ and subtracted, according to the Fundamental Theorem of Calculus. Notice that $C(x)$ does not appear in the final answer, just as the constant does not appear in a regular definite integral. Therefore, from now on we will not include $C(x)$ when we find the antiderivative for a definite integral with respect to y.

TRY YOUR TURN 1

By integrating the result from Example 1 with respect to x, we can evaluate a double integral.

EXAMPLE 2 Definite Integral

Evaluate $\int_0^3 \left[\int_1^2 (5x^3y^4 - 6x^2y + 2)\, dy\right] dx$.

SOLUTION

$$\int_0^3 \left[\int_1^2 (5x^3y^4 - 6x^2y + 2)\, dy\right] dx = \int_0^3 [31x^3 - 9x^2 + 2]\,dx \quad \text{Use the result from Example 1.}$$

$$= \frac{31}{4}x^4 - 3x^3 + 2x\Big|_0^3 \quad \text{Use the Fundamental Theorem of Calculus.}$$

$$= \frac{31}{4}\cdot 3^4 - 3\cdot 3^3 + 2\cdot 3 - \left(\frac{31}{4}\cdot 0^4 - 3\cdot 0^3 + 2\cdot 0\right)$$

$$= \frac{2211}{4}$$

We can integrate the inner integral with respect to y and the outer integral with respect to x, as in Example 2, or in the reverse order. The next example shows the same integral done both ways.

EXAMPLE 3 Definite Integrals

Evaluate each integral.

(a) $\displaystyle \int_1^2 \left[\int_3^5 (6xy^2 + 12x^2y + 4y)\, dx \right] dy$

SOLUTION

$$\int_1^2 \left[\int_3^5 (6xy^2 + 12x^2y + 4y)\, dx \right] dy = \int_1^2 \left[(3x^2y^2 + 4x^3y + 4xy) \Big|_3^5 \right] dy \quad \text{Integrate with respect to } x.$$

$$= \int_1^2 [(3 \cdot 5^2 \cdot y^2 + 4 \cdot 5^3 \cdot y + 4 \cdot 5 \cdot y)$$
$$- (3 \cdot 3^2 \cdot y^2 + 4 \cdot 3^3 \cdot y + 4 \cdot 3 \cdot y)]\, dy$$

$$= \int_1^2 [(75y^2 + 500y + 20y)$$
$$- (27y^2 + 108y + 12y)]\, dy$$

$$= \int_1^2 (48y^2 + 400y)\, dy$$

$$= (16y^3 + 200y^2) \Big|_1^2 \quad \text{Integrate with respect to } y.$$

$$= 16 \cdot 2^3 + 200 \cdot 2^2 - (16 \cdot 1^3 + 200 \cdot 1^2)$$

$$= 128 + 800 - (16 + 200)$$

$$= 712.$$

(b) $\displaystyle \int_3^5 \left[\int_1^2 (6xy^2 + 12x^2y + 4y)\, dy \right] dx$

SOLUTION (This is the same integrand with the same limits of integration as in part (a), but the order of integration is reversed.)

$$\int_3^5 \left[\int_1^2 (6xy^2 + 12x^2y + 4y)\, dy \right] dx = \int_3^5 \left[(2xy^3 + 6x^2y^2 + 2y^2) \Big|_1^2 \right] dx \quad \text{Integrate with respect to } y.$$

$$= \int_3^5 [(2x \cdot 2^3 + 6x^2 \cdot 2^2 + 2 \cdot 2^2)$$
$$- (2x \cdot 1^3 \cdot + 6x^2 \cdot 1^2 + 2 \cdot 1^2)]\, dx$$

$$= \int_3^5 [(16x + 24x^2 + 8)$$
$$- (2x + 6x^2 + 2)]\, dx$$

$$= \int_3^5 (14x + 18x^2 + 6)\, dx \quad \text{Integrate with respect to } x.$$

$$= (7x^2 + 6x^3 + 6x) \Big|_3^5$$

$$= 7 \cdot 5^2 + 6 \cdot 5^3 + 6 \cdot 5 - (7 \cdot 3^2 + 6 \cdot 3^3 + 6 \cdot 3)$$

$$= 175 + 750 + 30 - (63 + 162 + 18) = 712$$

TRY YOUR TURN 2

YOUR TURN 2 Evaluate $\displaystyle \int_0^2 \left[\int_1^3 (6x^2y^2 + 4xy + 8x^3 + 10y^4 + 3)\, dy \right] dx$, and then integrate with the order of integration changed.

NOTE In the second step of Example 3 (a), it might help you avoid confusion as to whether to put the limits of 3 and 5 into x or y by writing the integral as

$$\int_1^2 \left[(3x^2y^2 + 4x^3y + 4xy) \Big|_{x=3}^{x=5} \right] dy$$

The brackets we have used for the inner integral in Example 3 are not essential because the order of integration is indicated by the order of $dx\,dy$ or $dy\,dx$. For example, if the integral is written as

$$\int_1^2 \int_3^5 (6xy^2 + 12x^2y + 4y) \, dx \, dy,$$

we first integrate with respect to x, letting x vary from 3 to 5, and then with respect to y, letting y vary from 1 to 2, as in Example 3(a).

The answers in the two parts of Example 3 are equal. It can be proved that for a large class of functions, including most functions that occur in applications, the following equation holds true.

Fubini's Theorem

$$\int_a^b \int_c^d f(x,y) \, dy \, dx = \int_c^d \int_a^b f(x,y) \, dx \, dy$$

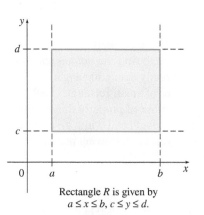

Rectangle R is given by
$a \le x \le b,\ c \le y \le d.$

FIGURE 29

Either of these integrals is called an **iterated integral** since it is evaluated by integrating twice, first using one variable and then using the other. The fact that the iterated integrals above are equal makes it possible to define a *double integral*. First, the set of points (x, y), with $a \le x \le b$ and $c \le y \le d$, defines a rectangular region R in the plane, as shown in Figure 29. Then, the *double integral over R* is defined as follows.

Double Integral

The **double integral** of $f(x, y)$ over a rectangular region R is written

$$\iint_R f(x,y) \, dy \, dx \qquad \text{or} \qquad \iint_R f(x,y) \, dx \, dy,$$

and equals either

$$\int_a^b \int_c^d f(x,y) \, dy \, dx \qquad \text{or} \qquad \int_c^d \int_a^b f(x,y) \, dx \, dy.$$

Extending earlier definitions, $f(x, y)$ is the **integrand** and R is the **region of integration**.

EXAMPLE 4 Double Integrals

Find $\displaystyle\iint_R \frac{3\sqrt{x} \cdot y}{y^2 + 1} \, dx \, dy$ over the rectangular region R defined by $0 \le x \le 4$ and $0 \le y \le 2$.

SOLUTION Integrate first with respect to x; then integrate the result with respect to y.

$$\iint_R \frac{3\sqrt{x} \cdot y}{y^2 + 1} \, dx \, dy = \int_0^2 \int_0^4 \frac{3\sqrt{x} \cdot y}{y^2 + 1} \, dx \, dy$$

$$= \int_0^2 \frac{2x^{3/2} \cdot y}{y^2 + 1} \bigg|_0^4 \, dy \qquad \text{Use the power rule with } x^{1/2}.$$

$$= \int_0^2 \left(\frac{2(4)^{3/2} \cdot y}{y^2 + 1} - \frac{2(0)^{3/2} \cdot y}{y^2 + 1} \right) dy$$

$$= 8 \int_0^2 \frac{2y}{y^2 + 1} \, dy \qquad \text{Factor out } 4^{3/2} = 8.$$

$$= 8 \int_1^5 \frac{du}{u} \qquad \text{Let } u = y^2 + 1. \text{ Change limits of integration.}$$

$$= 8 \ln u \big|_1^5$$

$$= 8 \ln 5 - 8 \ln 1 = 8 \ln 5$$

As a check, integrate with respect to y first. The answer should be the same.

TRY YOUR TURN 3

YOUR TURN 3 Find

$$\iint_R \frac{1}{\sqrt{x + y + 3}} \, dx \, dy$$

over the rectangular region R defined by $0 \leq x \leq 5$ and $1 \leq y \leq 6$.

Volume

As shown earlier, the definite integral $\int_a^b f(x) \, dx$ can be used to find the area under a curve. In a similar manner, double integrals are used to find the *volume under a surface*. Figure 30 shows that portion of a surface $f(x, y)$ directly over a rectangle R in the xy-plane. Just as areas were approximated by a large number of small rectangles, volume could be approximated by adding the volumes of a large number of properly drawn small boxes. The height of a typical box would be $f(x, y)$ with the length and width given by dx and dy. The formula for the volume of a box would then suggest the following result.

> ### Volume
>
> Let $z = f(x, y)$ be a function that is never negative on the rectangular region R defined by $a \leq x \leq b$, $c \leq y \leq d$. The volume of the solid under the graph of f and over the region R is
>
> $$\iint_R f(x, y) \, dx \, dy.$$

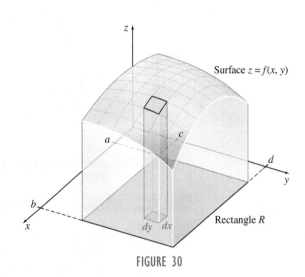

Surface $z = f(x, y)$

Rectangle R

FIGURE 30

EXAMPLE 5   Volume

Find the volume under the surface $z = x^2 + y^2$ shown in Figure 31.

SOLUTION   By the equation just given, the volume is

$$\iint\limits_{R} f(x, y) \, dx \, dy,$$

where $f(x, y) = x^2 + y^2$ and R is the region $0 \leq x \leq 4$, $0 \leq y \leq 4$. By definition,

$$\iint\limits_{R} f(x, y) \, dx \, dy = \int_0^4 \int_0^4 (x^2 + y^2) \, dx \, dy$$

$$= \int_0^4 \left(\frac{1}{3}x^3 + xy^2 \right) \bigg|_0^4 dy$$

$$= \int_0^4 \left(\frac{64}{3} + 4y^2 \right) dy = \left(\frac{64}{3}y + \frac{4}{3}y^3 \right) \bigg|_0^4$$

$$= \frac{64}{3} \cdot 4 + \frac{4}{3} \cdot 4^3 - 0 = \frac{512}{3}.$$

TRY YOUR TURN 4

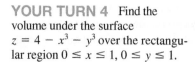

YOUR TURN 4   Find the volume under the surface $z = 4 - x^3 - y^3$ over the rectangular region $0 \leq x \leq 1$, $0 \leq y \leq 1$.

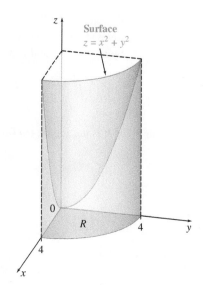

FIGURE 31

EXAMPLE 6   Perfume Bottle

A product design consultant for a cosmetics company has been asked to design a bottle for the company's newest perfume. The thickness of the glass is to vary so that the outside of the bottle has straight sides and the inside has curved sides, with flat ends shaped like parabolas on the 4-cm sides, as shown in Figure 32. Before presenting the design to management, the consultant needs to make a reasonably accurate estimate of the amount each bottle will hold. If the base of the bottle is to be 4 cm by 3 cm, and if a cross section of its interior is to be a parabola of the form $z = -y^2 + 4y$, what is its internal volume?

FIGURE 32

161

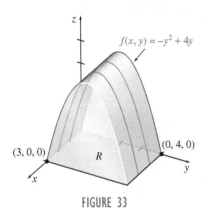

APPLY IT

FIGURE 33

SOLUTION The interior of the bottle can be graphed in three-dimensional space, as shown in Figure 33, where $z = 0$ corresponds to the base of the bottle. Its volume is simply the volume above the region R in the xy-plane and below the graph of $f(x, y) = -y^2 + 4y$. This volume is given by the double integral

$$\int_0^3 \int_0^4 (-y^2 + 4y)\, dy\, dx = \int_0^3 \left(\frac{-y^3}{3} + \frac{4y^2}{2} \right)\Big|_0^4 dx$$

$$= \int_0^3 \left(\frac{-64}{3} + 32 - 0 \right) dx$$

$$= \frac{32}{3} x \Big|_0^3$$

$$= 32 - 0 = 32.$$

The bottle holds 32 cm³.

Double Integrals Over Other Regions

In this section, we found double integrals over rectangular regions by evaluating iterated integrals with constant limits of integration. We can also evaluate iterated integrals with *variable* limits of integration. (Notice in the following examples that the variable limits always go on the *inner* integral sign.)

The use of variable limits of integration permits evaluation of double integrals over the types of regions shown in Figure 34. Double integrals over more complicated regions are discussed in more advanced texts. Integration over regions such as those in Figure 34 is done with the results of the following theorem.

Double Integrals Over Variable Regions

Let $z = f(x, y)$ be a function of two variables. If R is the region (in Figure 34(a)) defined by $a \le x \le b$ and $g(x) \le y \le h(x)$, then

$$\iint_R f(x, y)\, dy\, dx = \int_a^b \left[\int_{g(x)}^{h(x)} f(x, y)\, dy \right] dx.$$

If R is the region (in Figure 34(b)) defined by $g(y) \le x \le h(y)$ and $c \le y \le d$, then

$$\iint_R f(x, y)\, dx\, dy = \int_c^d \left[\int_{g(y)}^{h(y)} f(x, y)\, dx \right] dy.$$

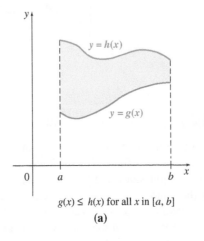

$g(x) \le h(x)$ for all x in $[a, b]$

(a)

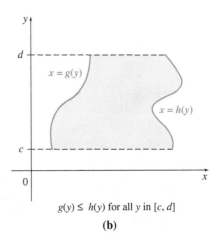

$g(y) \le h(y)$ for all y in $[c, d]$

(b)

FIGURE 34

EXAMPLE 7 Double Integrals

Evaluate $\displaystyle\int_1^2 \int_y^{y^2} xy \, dx \, dy$.

SOLUTION   The region of integration is shown in Figure 35. Integrate first with respect to x, then with respect to y.

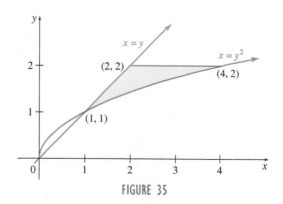

FIGURE 35

$$\int_1^2 \int_y^{y^2} xy \, dx \, dy = \int_1^2 \left(\int_y^{y^2} xy \, dx \right) dy = \int_1^2 \left(\frac{1}{2} x^2 y \right)\bigg|_y^{y^2} dy$$

Replace x first with y^2 and then with y, and subtract.

$$\int_1^2 \int_y^{y^2} xy \, dx \, dy = \int_1^2 \left[\frac{1}{2}(y^2)^2 y - \frac{1}{2}(y)^2 y \right] dy$$

$$= \int_1^2 \left(\frac{1}{2} y^5 - \frac{1}{2} y^3 \right) dy = \left(\frac{1}{12} y^6 - \frac{1}{8} y^4 \right)\bigg|_1^2$$

$$= \left(\frac{1}{12} \cdot 2^6 - \frac{1}{8} \cdot 2^4 \right) - \left(\frac{1}{12} \cdot 1^6 - \frac{1}{8} \cdot 1^4 \right)$$

$$= \frac{64}{12} - \frac{16}{8} - \frac{1}{12} + \frac{1}{8} = \frac{27}{8}$$

YOUR TURN 5 Find $\displaystyle\iint_R (x^3 + 4y) \, dy \, dx$ over the region bounded by $y = 4x$ and $y = x^3$ for $0 \le x \le 2$.

TRY YOUR TURN 5

EXAMPLE 8 Double Integrals

Let R be the shaded region in Figure 36, and evaluate

$$\iint_R (x + 2y) \, dy \, dx.$$

SOLUTION   Region R is bounded by $h(x) = 2x$ and $g(x) = x^2$, with $0 \le x \le 2$. By the first result in the previous theorem,

$$\iint_R (x + 2y) \, dy \, dx = \int_0^2 \int_{x^2}^{2x} (x + 2y) \, dy \, dx$$

$$= \int_0^2 (xy + y^2)\bigg|_{x^2}^{2x} dx$$

$$= \int_0^2 [x(2x) + (2x)^2 - [x \cdot x^2 + (x^2)^2]] \, dx$$

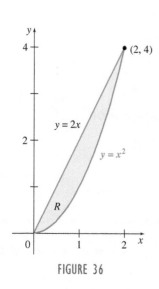

FIGURE 36

163

$$= \int_0^2 [2x^2 + 4x^2 - (x^3 + x^4)] \, dx$$

$$= \int_0^2 (6x^2 - x^3 - x^4) \, dx$$

$$= \left(2x^3 - \frac{1}{4}x^4 - \frac{1}{5}x^5 \right)\Big|_0^2$$

$$= 2 \cdot 2^3 - \frac{1}{4} \cdot 2^4 - \frac{1}{5} \cdot 2^5 - 0$$

$$= 16 - 4 - \frac{32}{5} = \frac{28}{5}.$$

Interchanging Limits of Integration

Sometimes it is easier to integrate first with respect to x and then y, while with other integrals the reverse process is easier. The limits of integration can be reversed whenever the region R is like the region in Figure 36, which has the property that it can be viewed as either type of region shown in Figure 34. In practice, this means that all boundaries can be written in terms of y as a function of x, or by solving for x as a function of y.

For instance, in Example 8, the same result would be found if we evaluated the double integral first with respect to x and then with respect to y. In that case, we would need to define the equations of the boundaries in terms of y rather than x, so R would be defined by $y/2 \le x \le \sqrt{y}, 0 \le y \le 4$. The resulting integral is

$$\int_0^4 \int_{y/2}^{\sqrt{y}} (x + 2y) \, dx \, dy = \int_0^4 \left(\frac{x^2}{2} + 2xy \right)\Big|_{y/2}^{\sqrt{y}} dy$$

$$= \int_0^4 \left[\left(\frac{y}{2} + 2y\sqrt{y} \right) - \left(\frac{y^2}{8} + 2\left(\frac{y}{2}\right)y \right) \right] dy$$

$$= \int_0^4 \left(\frac{y}{2} + 2y^{3/2} - \frac{9}{8}y^2 \right) dy$$

$$= \left(\frac{y^2}{4} + \frac{4}{5}y^{5/2} - \frac{3}{8}y^3 \right)\Big|_0^4$$

$$= 4 + \frac{4}{5} \cdot 4^{5/2} - 24$$

$$= \frac{28}{5}.$$

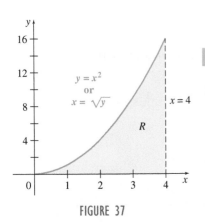

FIGURE 37

EXAMPLE 9 **Interchanging Limits of Integration**

Evaluate

$$\int_0^{16} \int_{\sqrt{y}}^4 \sqrt{x^3 + 4} \, dx \, dy.$$

SOLUTION Notice that it is impossible to first integrate this function with respect to x. Thus, we attempt to interchange the limits of integration.

For this integral, region R is given by $\sqrt{y} \le x \le 4, 0 \le y \le 16$. A graph of R is shown in Figure 37.

The same region R can be written in an alternate way. As Figure 37 shows, one boundary of R is $x = \sqrt{y}$. Solving for y gives $y = x^2$. Also, Figure 37 shows that $0 \le x \le 4$. Since R can be written as $0 \le y \le x^2$, $0 \le x \le 4$, the double integral above can be written

$$\int_0^4 \int_0^{x^2} \sqrt{x^3 + 4} \, dy \, dx = \int_0^4 y \sqrt{x^3 + 4} \Big|_0^{x^2} dx$$

$$= \int_0^4 x^2 \sqrt{x^3 + 4} \, dx$$

$$= \frac{1}{3} \int_0^4 3x^2 \sqrt{x^3 + 4} \, dx \qquad \text{Let } u = x^3 + 4. \text{ Change limits of integration.}$$

$$= \frac{1}{3} \int_4^{68} u^{1/2} du$$

$$= \frac{2}{9} u^{3/2} \Big|_4^{68}$$

$$= \frac{2}{9} [68^{3/2} - 4^{3/2}]$$

$$\approx 122.83.$$

CAUTION Fubini's Theorem cannot be used to interchange the order of integration when the limits contain variables, as in Example 9. Notice in Example 9 that after the order of integration was changed, the new limits were completely different. It would be a serious error to rewrite the integral in Example 9 as

$$\int_{\sqrt{y}}^4 \int_0^{16} \sqrt{x^3 + 4} \, dy \, dx.$$

6 EXERCISES

Evaluate each integral.

1. $\displaystyle\int_0^5 (x^4 y + y) \, dx$

2. $\displaystyle\int_1^2 (xy^3 - x) \, dy$

3. $\displaystyle\int_4^5 x\sqrt{x^2 + 3y} \, dy$

4. $\displaystyle\int_3^6 x\sqrt{x^2 + 3y} \, dx$

5. $\displaystyle\int_4^9 \frac{3 + 5y}{\sqrt{x}} \, dx$

6. $\displaystyle\int_2^7 \frac{3 + 5y}{\sqrt{x}} \, dy$

7. $\displaystyle\int_2^6 e^{2x + 3y} \, dx$

8. $\displaystyle\int_{-1}^1 e^{2x + 3y} \, dy$

9. $\displaystyle\int_0^3 ye^{4x + y^2} \, dy$

10. $\displaystyle\int_1^5 ye^{4x + y^2} \, dx$

Evaluate each iterated integral. (Many of these use results from Exercises 1–10.)

11. $\displaystyle\int_1^2 \int_0^5 (x^4 y + y) \, dx \, dy$

12. $\displaystyle\int_0^3 \int_1^2 (xy^3 - x) \, dy \, dx$

13. $\displaystyle\int_0^1 \int_3^6 x\sqrt{x^2 + 3y} \, dx \, dy$

14. $\displaystyle\int_0^3 \int_4^5 x\sqrt{x^2 + 3y} \, dy \, dx$

15. $\displaystyle\int_1^2 \int_4^9 \frac{3 + 5y}{\sqrt{x}} \, dx \, dy$

16. $\displaystyle\int_{16}^{25} \int_2^7 \frac{3 + 5y}{\sqrt{x}} \, dy \, dx$

17. $\displaystyle\int_1^3 \int_1^3 \frac{1}{xy} \, dy \, dx$

18. $\displaystyle\int_1^5 \int_2^4 \frac{1}{y} \, dx \, dy$

19. $\displaystyle\int_2^4 \int_3^5 \left(\frac{x}{y} + \frac{y}{3}\right) dx \, dy$

20. $\displaystyle\int_3^4 \int_1^2 \left(\frac{6x}{5} + \frac{y}{x}\right) dx \, dy$

Find each double integral over the rectangular region R with the given boundaries.

21. $\displaystyle\iint_R (3x^2 + 4y) \, dx \, dy; \quad 0 \le x \le 3, 1 \le y \le 4$

22. $\displaystyle\iint_R (x^2 + 4y^3) \, dy \, dx; \quad 1 \le x \le 2, 0 \le y \le 3$

23. $\displaystyle\iint_R \sqrt{x + y} \, dy \, dx; \quad 1 \le x \le 3, 0 \le y \le 1$

24. $\displaystyle\iint_R x^2 \sqrt{x^3 + 2y} \, dx \, dy; \quad 0 \le x \le 2, 0 \le y \le 3$

25. $\displaystyle\iint_R \frac{3}{(x + y)^2} \, dy \, dx; \quad 2 \le x \le 4, 1 \le y \le 6$

26. $\displaystyle\iint\limits_{R} \frac{y}{\sqrt{2x + 5y^2}}\, dx\, dy;\quad 0 \le x \le 2, 1 \le y \le 3$

27. $\displaystyle\iint\limits_{R} ye^{x+y^2}\, dx\, dy;\quad 2 \le x \le 3, 0 \le y \le 2$

28. $\displaystyle\iint\limits_{R} x^2 e^{x^3 + 2y}\, dx\, dy;\quad 1 \le x \le 2, 1 \le y \le 3$

Find the volume under the given surface $z = f(x, y)$ and above the rectangle with the given boundaries.

29. $z = 8x + 4y + 10;\quad -1 \le x \le 1, 0 \le y \le 3$

30. $z = 3x + 10y + 20;\quad 0 \le x \le 3, -2 \le y \le 1$

31. $z = x^2;\quad 0 \le x \le 2, 0 \le y \le 5$

32. $z = \sqrt{y};\quad 0 \le x \le 4, 0 \le y \le 9$

33. $z = x\sqrt{x^2 + y};\quad 0 \le x \le 1, 0 \le y \le 1$

34. $z = yx\sqrt{x^2 + y^2};\quad 0 \le x \le 4, 0 \le y \le 1$

35. $z = \dfrac{xy}{(x^2 + y^2)^2};\quad 1 \le x \le 2, 1 \le y \le 4$

36. $z = e^{x+y};\quad 0 \le x \le 1, 0 \le y \le 1$

Although it is often true that a double integral can be evaluated by using either dx or dy first, sometimes one choice over the other makes the work easier. Evaluate the double integrals in Exercises 37 and 38 in the easiest way possible.

37. $\displaystyle\iint\limits_{R} xe^{xy}\, dx\, dy;\quad 0 \le x \le 2, 0 \le y \le 1$

38. $\displaystyle\iint\limits_{R} 2x^3 e^{x^2 y}\, dx\, dy;\quad 0 \le x \le 1, 0 \le y \le 1$

Evaluate each double integral.

39. $\displaystyle\int_{2}^{4}\int_{2}^{x^2} (x^2 + y^2)\, dy\, dx$

40. $\displaystyle\int_{0}^{2}\int_{0}^{3y} (x^2 + y)\, dx\, dy$

41. $\displaystyle\int_{0}^{4}\int_{0}^{x} \sqrt{xy}\, dy\, dx$

42. $\displaystyle\int_{1}^{4}\int_{0}^{x} \sqrt{x + y}\, dy\, dx$

43. $\displaystyle\int_{2}^{6}\int_{2y}^{4y} \frac{1}{x}\, dx\, dy$

44. $\displaystyle\int_{1}^{4}\int_{x}^{x^2} \frac{1}{y}\, dy\, dx$

45. $\displaystyle\int_{0}^{4}\int_{1}^{e^x} \frac{x}{y}\, dy\, dx$

46. $\displaystyle\int_{0}^{1}\int_{2x}^{4x} e^{x+y}\, dy\, dx$

Use the region R with the indicated boundaries to evaluate each double integral.

47. $\displaystyle\iint\limits_{R} (5x + 8y)\, dy\, dx;\quad 1 \le x \le 3, 0 \le y \le x - 1$

48. $\displaystyle\iint\limits_{R} (2x + 6y)\, dy\, dx;\quad 2 \le x \le 4, 2 \le y \le 3x$

49. $\displaystyle\iint\limits_{R} (4 - 4x^2)\, dy\, dx;\quad 0 \le x \le 1, 0 \le y \le 2 - 2x$

50. $\displaystyle\iint\limits_{R} \frac{1}{x}\, dy\, dx;\quad 1 \le x \le 2, 0 \le y \le x - 1$

51. $\displaystyle\iint\limits_{R} e^{x/y^2}\, dx\, dy;\quad 1 \le y \le 2, 0 \le x \le y^2$

52. $\displaystyle\iint\limits_{R} (x^2 - y)\, dy\, dx;\quad -1 \le x \le 1, -x^2 \le y \le x^2$

53. $\displaystyle\iint\limits_{R} x^3 y\, dy\, dx;\quad R \text{ bounded by } y = x^2, y = 2x$

54. $\displaystyle\iint\limits_{R} x^2 y^2\, dx\, dy;\quad R \text{ bounded by } y = x, y = 2x, x = 1$

55. $\displaystyle\iint\limits_{R} \frac{1}{y}\, dy\, dx;\quad R \text{ bounded by } y = x, y = \frac{1}{x}, x = 2$

56. $\displaystyle\iint\limits_{R} e^{2y/x}\, dy\, dx;\quad R \text{ bounded by } y = x^2, y = 0, x = 2$

Evaluate each double integral. If the function seems too difficult to integrate, try interchanging the limits of integration, as in Exercises 37 and 38.

57. $\displaystyle\int_{0}^{\ln 2}\int_{e^y}^{2} \frac{1}{\ln x}\, dx\, dy$

58. $\displaystyle\int_{0}^{2}\int_{y/2}^{1} e^{x^2}\, dx\, dy$

59. Recall from the Volume and Average Value section in the previous chapter that volume could be found with a single integral. In this section volume is found using a double integral. Explain when volume can be found with a single integral and when a double integral is needed.

60. Give an example of a region that cannot be expressed by either of the forms shown in Figure 34. (One example is the disk with a hole in the middle between the graphs of $x^2 + y^2 = 1$ and $x^2 + y^2 = 2$ in Figure 10.)

The idea of the average value of a function, discussed earlier for functions of the form $y = f(x)$, can be extended to functions of more than one independent variable. For a function $z = f(x, y)$, the average value of f over a region R is defined as

$$\frac{1}{A}\iint\limits_{R} f(x, y)\, dx\, dy,$$

where A is the area of the region R. Find the average value for each function over the regions R having the given boundaries.

61. $f(x, y) = 6xy + 2x;\quad 2 \le x \le 5, 1 \le y \le 3$

62. $f(x, y) = x^2 + y^2;\quad 0 \le x \le 2, 0 \le y \le 3$

63. $f(x, y) = e^{-5y + 3x};\quad 0 \le x \le 2, 0 \le y \le 2$

64. $f(x, y) = e^{2x+y};\quad 1 \le x \le 2, 2 \le y \le 3$

APPLICATIONS

Business and Economics

65. Packaging The manufacturer of a fruit juice drink has decided to try innovative packaging in order to revitalize sagging sales. The fruit juice drink is to be packaged in containers in the shape of tetrahedra in which three edges are perpendicular, as shown in the figure on the next page. Two of the perpendicular edges will be 3 in. long, and the third edge will be 6 in. long. Find the volume of the container. (*Hint:* The equation of the plane shown in the figure is $z = f(x, y) = 6 - 2x - 2y$.)

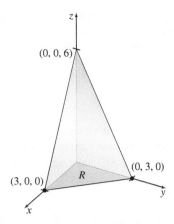

66. Average Cost A company's total cost for operating its two warehouses is

$$C(x, y) = \frac{1}{9}x^2 + 2x + y^2 + 5y + 100$$

dollars, where x represents the number of units stored at the first warehouse and y represents the number of units stored at the second. Find the average cost to store a unit if the first warehouse has between 40 and 80 units, and the second has between 30 and 70 units. (*Hint:* Refer to Exercises 61–64.)

67. Average Production A production function is given by

$$P(x, y) = 500x^{0.2}y^{0.8},$$

where x is the number of units of labor and y is the number of units of capital. Find the average production level if x varies from 10 to 50 and y from 20 to 40. (*Hint:* Refer to Exercises 61–64.)

68. Average Profit The profit (in dollars) from selling x units of one product and y units of a second product is

$$P = -(x - 100)^2 - (y - 50)^2 + 2000.$$

The weekly sales for the first product vary from 100 units to 150 units, and the weekly sales for the second product vary from 40 units to 80 units. Estimate average weekly profit for these two products. (*Hint:* Refer to Exercises 61–64.)

69. Average Revenue A company sells two products. The demand functions of the products are given by

$$q_1 = 300 - 2p_1 \quad \text{and} \quad q_2 = 500 - 1.2p_2,$$

where q_1 units of the first product are demanded at price p_1 and q_2 units of the second product are demanded at price p_2. The total revenue will be given by

$$R = q_1p_1 + q_2p_2.$$

Find the average revenue if the price p_1 varies from \$25 to \$50 and the price p_2 varies from \$50 to \$75. (*Hint:* Refer to Exercises 61–64.)

70. Time In an exercise earlier in this chapter, we saw that the time (in hours) that a branch of Amalgamated Entities needs to spend to meet the quota set by the main office can be approximated by

$$T(x, y) = x^4 + 16y^4 - 32xy + 40,$$

where x represents how many thousands of dollars the factory spends on quality control and y represents how many thousands of dollars they spend on consulting. Find the average time if the amount spent on quality control varies from \$0 to \$4000 and the amount spent on consulting varies from \$0 to \$2000. (*Hint:* Refer to Exercises 61–64.)

71. Profit In an exercise earlier in this chapter, we saw that the profit (in thousands of dollars) that Aunt Mildred's Metalworks earns from producing x tons of steel and y tons of aluminum can be approximated by

$$P(x, y) = 36xy - x^3 - 8y^3.$$

Find the average profit if the amount of steel produced varies from 0 to 8 tons, and the amount of aluminum produced varies from 0 to 4 tons. (*Hint:* Refer to Exercises 61–64.)

YOUR TURN ANSWERS

1. $52x^2 + 16x + 16x^3 + 490$ **2.** $3644/3$

3. $(56\sqrt{14} - 184)/3$ **4.** $7/2$ **5.** $5888/105$

CHAPTER REVIEW

SUMMARY

In this chapter, we extended our study of calculus to include functions of several variables. We saw that it is possible to produce three-dimensional graphs of functions of two variables and that the process is greatly enhanced using level curves. Level curves are formed by determining the values of x and y that produce a particular functional value. We also saw the graphs of several surfaces, including the

- paraboloid, whose equation is $z = x^2 + y^2$,
- ellipsoid, whose general equation is $\dfrac{x^2}{a^2} + \dfrac{y^2}{b^2} + \dfrac{z^2}{c^2} = 1$,
- hyperbolic paraboloid, whose equation is $z = x^2 - y^2$, and
- hyperboloid of two sheets, whose equation is $-x^2 - y^2 + z^2 = 1$.

Level curves are also important in economics and are used to indicate combinations of the values of x and y that produce the same value of production z. This procedure was used to analyze the Cobb-Douglas production function, which has the general form

$$z = P(x, y) = Ax^a y^{1-a}, \text{ where } A \text{ is constant and } 0 < a < 1.$$

Partial derivatives are the extension of the concept of differentiation with respect to one of the variables while the other variables are held constant. Partial derivatives were used to identify extrema of a function of several variables. In particular, we identified all points where the partial with respect to x and the partial with respect to y are both zero, which we called critical points. We then classified each critical point as a relative maximum, a relative minimum, or a saddle point. Recall that a saddle point is a minimum when approached from one direction but a maximum when approached from another direction. We introduced the method of Lagrange multipliers to determine extrema in problems with constraints. Differentials, introduced earlier for functions of one variable, were generalized to define the total differential. We saw that total differentials can be used to approximate the value of a function using its tangent plane. We concluded the chapter by introducing double integrals, which are simply two iterated integrals, one for each variable. Double integrals were then used to find volume.

Function of Two Variables The expression $z = f(x, y)$ is a function of two variables if a unique value of z is obtained from each ordered pair of real numbers (x, y). The variables x and y are independent variables, and z is the dependent variable. The set of all ordered pairs of real numbers (x, y) such that $f(x, y)$ exists is the domain of f; the set of all values of $f(x, y)$ is the range.

Plane The graph of $ax + by + cz = d$ is a plane if a, b, and c are not all 0.

Partial Derivatives (Informal Definition) The partial derivative of f with respect to x is the derivative of f obtained by treating x as a variable and y as a constant.

The partial derivative of f with respect to y is the derivative of f obtained by treating y as a variable and x as a constant.

Partial Derivatives (Formal Definition) Let $z = f(x, y)$ be a function of two independent variables. Let all indicated limits exist. Then the partial derivative of f with respect to x is

$$f_x(x, y) = \frac{\partial f}{\partial x} = \lim_{h \to 0} \frac{f(x + h, y) - f(x, y)}{h},$$

and the partial derivative of f with respect to y is

$$f_y(x, y) = \frac{\partial f}{\partial y} = \lim_{h \to 0} \frac{f(x, y + h) - f(x, y)}{h}.$$

If the indicated limits do not exist, then the partial derivatives do not exist.

Second-Order Partial Derivatives For a function $z = f(x, y)$, if the partial derivative exists, then

$$\frac{\partial}{\partial x}\left(\frac{\partial z}{\partial x}\right) = \frac{\partial^2 z}{\partial x^2} = f_{xx}(x, y) = z_{xx} \qquad \frac{\partial}{\partial y}\left(\frac{\partial z}{\partial y}\right) = \frac{\partial^2 z}{\partial y^2} = f_{yy}(x, y) = z_{yy}$$

$$\frac{\partial}{\partial y}\left(\frac{\partial z}{\partial x}\right) = \frac{\partial^2 z}{\partial y \partial x} = f_{xy}(x, y) = z_{xy} \qquad \frac{\partial}{\partial x}\left(\frac{\partial z}{\partial y}\right) = \frac{\partial^2 z}{\partial x \partial y} = f_{yx}(x, y) = z_{yx}$$

Relative Extrema Let (a, b) be the center of a circular region contained in the xy-plane. Then, for a function $z = f(x, y)$ defined for every (x, y) in the region, $f(a, b)$ is a relative maximum if

$$f(a, b) \geq f(x, y)$$

for all points (x, y) in the circular region, and $f(a, b)$ is a relative minimum if

$$f(a, b) \leq f(x, y)$$

for all points (x, y) in the circular region.

Location of Extrema Let a function $z = f(x, y)$ have a relative maximum or relative minimum at the point (a, b). Let $f_x(a, b)$ and $f_y(a, b)$ both exist. Then

$$f_x(a, b) = 0 \text{ and } f_y(a, b) = 0.$$

Test for Relative Extrema For a function $z = f(x, y)$, let f_{xx}, f_{yy}, and f_{xy} all exist in a circular region contained in the xy-plane with center (a, b). Further, let

$$f_x(a, b) = 0 \text{ and } f_y(a, b) = 0.$$

Define D, known as the discriminant, by

$$D = f_{xx}(a, b) \cdot f_{yy}(a, b) - [f_{xy}(a, b)]^2.$$

Then

a. $f(a, b)$ is a relative maximum if $D > 0$ and $f_{xx}(a, b) < 0$;
b. $f(a, b)$ is a relative minimum if $D > 0$ and $f_{xx}(a, b) > 0$;
c. $f(a, b)$ is a saddle point (neither a maximum nor a minimum) if $D < 0$;
d. if $D = 0$, the test gives no information.

Lagrange Multipliers All relative extrema of the function $z = f(x, y)$, subject to the constraint $g(x, y) = 0$, will be found among those points (x, y) for which there exists a value of λ such that
$$F_x(x, y, \lambda) = 0, F_y(x, y, \lambda) = 0, \text{ and } F_\lambda(x, y, \lambda) = 0,$$
where
$$F(x, y, \lambda) = f(x, y) - \lambda \cdot g(x, y),$$
and all indicated partial derivatives exist.

Using Lagrange Multipliers
1. Write the constraint in the form $g(x, y) = 0$.
2. Form the Lagrange function
$$F(x, y, \lambda) = f(x, y) - \lambda \cdot g(x, y).$$
3. Find $F_x(x, y, \lambda)$, $F_y(x, y, \lambda)$, and $F_\lambda(x, y, \lambda)$.
4. Form the system of equations
$$F_x(x, y, \lambda) = 0, F_y(x, y, \lambda) = 0, \text{ and } F_\lambda(x, y, \lambda) = 0.$$
5. Solve the system in Step 4; the relative extrema for f are among the solutions of the system.

Total Differential for Two Variables Let $z = f(x, y)$ be a function of x and y. Let dx and dy be real numbers. Then the total differential of z is
$$dz = f_x(x, y) \cdot dx + f_y(x, y) \cdot dy.$$
(Sometimes dz is written df.)

Approximations For small values of dx and dy,
$$dz \approx \Delta z$$
where $\Delta z = f(x + dx, y + dy) - f(x, y)$.

Approximations by Differentials For a function f having all indicated partial derivatives, and for small values of dx and dy,
$$f(x + dx, y + dy) \approx f(x, y) + dz,$$
or
$$f(x + dx, y + dy) \approx f(x, y) + f_x(x, y) \cdot dx + f_y(x, y) \cdot dy.$$

Total Differential for Three Variables If $w = f(x, y, z)$, then the total differential dw is
$$dw = f_x(x, y, z) \cdot dx + f_y(x, y, z) \cdot dy + f_z(x, y, z) \cdot dz,$$
provided all indicated partial derivatives exist.

Double Integral The double integral of $f(x, y)$ over a rectangular region R defined by $a \le x \le b, c \le y \le d$ is written
$$\iint\limits_R f(x, y) \, dy \, dx \text{ or } \iint\limits_R f(x, y) \, dx \, dy,$$
and equals either
$$\int_a^b \int_c^d f(x, y) \, dy \, dx \text{ or } \int_c^d \int_a^b f(x, y) \, dx \, dy.$$

Volume Let $z = f(x, y)$ be a function that is never negative on the rectangular region R defined by $a \le x \le b, c \le y \le d$. The volume of the solid under the graph of f and over the region R is
$$\iint\limits_R f(x, y) \, dy \, dx.$$

Double Integrals over Variable Regions Let $z = f(x, y)$ be a function of two variables. If R is the region defined by $a \le x \le b$ and $g(x) \le y \le h(x)$, then
$$\iint\limits_R f(x, y) \, dy \, dx = \int_a^b \left[\int_{g(x)}^{h(x)} f(x, y) \, dy \right] dx.$$

If R is the region defined by $g(y) \le x \le h(y)$ and $c \le y \le d$, then
$$\iint\limits_R f(x, y) \, dx \, dy = \int_c^d \left[\int_{g(y)}^{h(y)} f(x, y) \, dx \right] dy.$$

KEY TERMS

1
function of two variables
independent variable
dependent variable
domain
range
ordered triple
first octant
plane
surface
trace
level curves

paraboloid
production function
Cobb-Douglas production
   function
level surface
ellipsoid
hyperbolic paraboloid
hyperboloid of two sheets

2
partial derivative
second-order partial derivative

3
relative maximum
relative minimum
saddle point
critical point
discriminant

4
constraints
Lagrange multiplier
utility function
indifference curve

5
total differential
6
Fubini's Theorem
iterated integral
double integral
integrand
region of integration

REVIEW EXERCISES

CONCEPT CHECK

Determine whether each of the following statements is true or false, and explain why.

1. The graph of $6x - 2y + 7z = 14$ is a plane.

2. The graph of $2x + 4y = 10$ is a plane that is parallel to the z-axis.

3. A level curve for a paraboloid could be a single point.

4. If the partial derivatives with respect to x and y at some point are both 0, the tangent plane to the function at that point is horizontal.

5. If $f(x, y) = 3x^2 + 2xy + y^2$, then $f(x + h, y) = 3(x + h)^2 + 2xy + h + y^2$.

6. For a function $z = f(x, y)$, suppose that the point (a, b) has been identified such that $f_x(a, b) = f_y(a, b) = 0$. We can conclude that a relative maximum or a relative minimum must exist at (a, b).

7. A saddle point can be a relative maximum or a relative minimum.

8. A function of two variables may have both a relative maximum and an absolute maximum at the same point.

9. The method of Lagrange multipliers tells us whether a point identified by the method is a maximum or minimum.

10. $\int_2^4 \int_1^5 (3x + 4y) \, dy \, dx = \int_2^4 \int_1^5 (3x + 4y) \, dx \, dy$

11. $\int_0^1 \int_{-2}^2 xe^y \, dy \, dx = \int_{-2}^2 \int_0^1 xe^y \, dx \, dy$

12. $\int_0^4 \int_1^x (x + xy^2) \, dy \, dx = \int_1^x \int_0^4 (x + xy^2) \, dx \, dy$

PRACTICE AND EXPLORATIONS

13. Describe in words how to take a partial derivative.

14. Describe what a partial derivative means geometrically.

15. Describe what a total differential is and how it is useful.

16. Suppose you are walking through the region of New York state shown in the topographical map in Figure 11 in the first section of this chapter. Assume you are heading north, toward the top of the map, over the western side of the mountain at the left, but not directly over the peak. Explain why you reach your highest point when you are going in the same direction as a contour line. Explain how this relates to Lagrange multipliers. (*Hint:* See Figure 25.)

Find $f(-1, 2)$ and $f(6, -3)$ for the following.

17. $f(x, y) = -4x^2 + 6xy - 3$

18. $f(x, y) = 2x^2y^2 - 7x + 4y$

19. $f(x, y) = \dfrac{x - 2y}{x + 5y}$

20. $f(x, y) = \dfrac{\sqrt{x^2 + y^2}}{x - y}$

Graph the first-octant portion of each plane.

21. $x + y + z = 4$ **22.** $x + 2y + 6z = 6$

23. $5x + 2y = 10$ **24.** $4x + 3z = 12$

25. $x = 3$ **26.** $y = 4$

27. Let $z = f(x, y) = 3x^3 + 4x^2y - 2y^2$. Find the following.

    a. $\dfrac{\partial z}{\partial x}$ **b.** $\dfrac{\partial z}{\partial y}(-1, 4)$ **c.** $f_{xy}(2, -1)$

28. Let $z = f(x, y) = \dfrac{x + y^2}{x - y^2}$. Find the following.

    a. $\dfrac{\partial z}{\partial y}$ **b.** $\dfrac{\partial z}{\partial x}(0, 2)$ **c.** $f_{xx}(-1, 0)$

Find $f_x(x, y)$ and $f_y(x, y)$.

29. $f(x, y) = 6x^2y^3 - 4y$ **30.** $f(x, y) = 5x^4y^3 - 6x^5y$

31. $f(x, y) = \sqrt{4x^2 + y^2}$ **32.** $f(x, y) = \dfrac{2x + 5y^2}{3x^2 + y^2}$

33. $f(x, y) = x^3e^{3y}$ **34.** $f(x, y) = (y - 2)^2e^{x + 2y}$

35. $f(x, y) = \ln|2x^2 + y^2|$ **36.** $f(x, y) = \ln|2 - x^2y^3|$

Find $f_{xx}(x, y)$ and $f_{xy}(x, y)$.

37. $f(x, y) = 5x^3y - 6xy^2$

38. $f(x, y) = -3x^2y^3 + x^3y$

39. $f(x, y) = \dfrac{3x}{2x - y}$

40. $f(x, y) = \dfrac{3x + y}{x - 1}$

41. $f(x, y) = 4x^2e^{2y}$

42. $f(x, y) = ye^{x^2}$

43. $f(x, y) = \ln|2 - x^2y|$

44. $f(x, y) = \ln|1 + 3xy^2|$

Find all points where the functions defined below have any relative extrema. Find any saddle points.

45. $z = 2x^2 - 3y^2 + 12y$

46. $z = x^2 + y^2 + 9x - 8y + 1$

47. $f(x, y) = x^2 + 3xy - 7x + 5y^2 - 16y$

48. $z = x^3 - 8y^2 + 6xy + 4$

49. $z = \dfrac{1}{2}x^2 + \dfrac{1}{2}y^2 + 2xy - 5x - 7y + 10$

50. $f(x, y) = 2x^2 + 4xy + 4y^2 - 3x + 5y - 15$

51. $z = x^3 + y^3 + 2xy - 4x - 3y - 2$

52. $f(x, y) = 7x^2 + y^2 - 3x + 6y - 5xy$

53. Describe the different types of points that might occur when $f_x(x, y) = f_y(x, y) = 0$.

Use Lagrange multipliers to find the extrema of the functions defined in Exercises 54 and 55.

54. $f(x, y) = x^2y$; $x + y = 4$

55. $f(x, y) = x^2 + y^2$; $x = y - 6$

56. Find positive numbers x and y, whose sum is 80, such that x^2y is maximized.

57. Find positive numbers x and y, whose sum is 75, such that xy^2 is maximized.

58. Notice in the previous two exercises that we specified that x and y must be positive numbers. Does a maximum exist without this requirement? Explain why or why not.

Evaluate dz using the given information.

59. $z = 6x^2 - 7y^2 + 4xy$; $x = 3, y = -1, dx = 0.03, dy = 0.01$

60. $z = \dfrac{x + 5y}{x - 2y}$; $x = 1, y = -2, dx = -0.04, dy = 0.02$

Use the total differential to approximate each quantity. Then use a calculator to approximate the quantity, and give the absolute value of the difference in the two results to 4 decimal places.

61. $\sqrt{5.1^2 + 12.05^2}$

62. $\sqrt{4.06}\, e^{0.04}$

Evaluate the following.

63. $\displaystyle\int_1^4 \dfrac{4y - 3}{\sqrt{x}}\, dx$

64. $\displaystyle\int_1^5 e^{3x + 5y}\, dx$

65. $\displaystyle\int_0^5 \dfrac{6x}{\sqrt{4x^2 + 2y^2}}\, dx$

66. $\displaystyle\int_1^3 \dfrac{y^2}{\sqrt{7x + 11y^3}}\, dy$

Evaluate each iterated integral.

67. $\displaystyle\int_0^2 \int_0^4 (x^2y^2 + 5x)\, dx\, dy$

68. $\displaystyle\int_0^3 \int_0^5 (2x + 6y + y^2)\, dy\, dx$

69. $\displaystyle\int_3^4 \int_2^5 \sqrt{6x + 3y}\, dx\, dy$

70. $\displaystyle\int_1^2 \int_3^5 e^{2x - 7y}\, dx\, dy$

71. $\displaystyle\int_2^4 \int_2^4 \dfrac{1}{y}\, dx\, dy$

72. $\displaystyle\int_1^2 \int_1^2 \dfrac{1}{x}\, dx\, dy$

Find each double integral over the region R with boundaries as indicated.

73. $\displaystyle\iint_R (x^2 + 2y^2)\, dx\, dy;$ $0 \le x \le 5, 0 \le y \le 2$

74. $\displaystyle\iint_R \sqrt{2x + y}\, dx\, dy;$ $1 \le x \le 3, 2 \le y \le 5$

75. $\displaystyle\iint_R \sqrt{y + x}\, dx\, dy;$ $0 \le x \le 7, 1 \le y \le 9$

76. $\displaystyle\iint_R ye^{y^2 + x}\, dx\, dy;$ $0 \le x \le 1, 0 \le y \le 1$

Find the volume under the given surface $z = f(x, y)$ and above the given rectangle.

77. $z = x + 8y + 4$; $0 \le x \le 3, 1 \le y \le 2$

78. $z = x^2 + y^2$; $3 \le x \le 5, 2 \le y \le 4$

Evaluate each double integral. If the function seems too difficult to integrate, try interchanging the limits of integration.

79. $\displaystyle\int_0^1 \int_0^{2x} xy\, dy\, dx$

80. $\displaystyle\int_1^2 \int_2^{2x^2} y\, dy\, dx$

81. $\displaystyle\int_0^1 \int_{x^2}^x x^3y\, dy\, dx$

82. $\displaystyle\int_0^1 \int_y^{\sqrt{y}} x\, dx\, dy$

83. $\displaystyle\int_0^2 \int_{x/2}^1 \dfrac{1}{y^2 + 1}\, dy\, dx$

84. $\displaystyle\int_0^8 \int_{x/2}^4 \sqrt{y^2 + 4}\, dy\, dx$

Use the region R, with boundaries as indicated, to evaluate the given double integral.

85. $\displaystyle\iint_R (2x + 3y)\, dx\, dy;$ $0 \le y \le 1, y \le x \le 2 - y$

86. $\displaystyle\iint_R (2 - x^2 - y^2)\, dy\, dx;$ $0 \le x \le 1, x^2 \le y \le x$

APPLICATIONS

Business and Economics

87. Charge for Auto Painting The charge (in dollars) for painting a sports car is given by

$$C(x, y) = 4x^2 + 5y^2 - 4xy + \sqrt{x},$$

where x is the number of hours of labor needed and y is the number of gallons of paint and sealant used. Find the following.

a. The charge for 10 hours and 5 gal of paint and sealant

b. The charge for 15 hours and 10 gal of paint and sealant

c. The charge for 20 hours and 20 gal of paint and sealant

88. Manufacturing Costs The manufacturing cost (in dollars) for a certain computer is given by

$$c(x, y) = 2x + y^2 + 4xy + 25,$$

where x is the memory capacity of the computer in gigabytes (GB) and y is the number of hours of labor required. For 640 GB and 6 hours of labor, find the following.

a. The approximate change in cost for an additional 1 GB of memory

b. The approximate change in cost for an additional hour of labor

89. Productivity The production function z for one country is

$$z = x^{0.7}y^{0.3},$$

where x represents the amount of labor and y the amount of capital. Find the marginal productivity of the following.

a. Labor   **b.** Capital

90. Cost The cost (in dollars) to manufacture x solar cells and y solar collectors is

$$c(x, y) = x^2 + 5y^2 + 4xy - 70x - 164y + 1800.$$

a. Find values of x and y that produce minimum total cost.

b. Find the minimum total cost.

Utility Maximize each of the following utility functions, with the cost of each commodity and total amount available to spend given.

91. $f(x, y) = xy^3$, cost of a unit of x is \$2, cost of a unit of y is \$4, and \$80 is available.

92. $f(x, y) = x^5y^2$, cost of a unit of x is \$10, cost of a unit of y is \$6, and \$42 is available.

93. Cost The cost (in dollars) to produce x satellite receiving dishes and y transmitters is given by

$$C(x, y) = 100 \ln(x^2 + y) + e^{xy/20}.$$

Production schedules now call for 15 receiving dishes and 9 transmitters. Use differentials to approximate the change in costs if 1 more dish and 1 fewer transmitter are made.

94. Production Materials Approximate the volume of material needed to manufacture a cone of radius 2 cm, height 8 cm, and wall thickness 0.21 cm.

95. Production Materials A sphere of radius 2 ft is to receive an insulating coating 1 in. thick. Approximate the volume of the coating needed.

96. Production Error The height of a sample cone from a production line is measured as 11.4 cm, while the radius is measured as 2.9 cm. Each of these measurements could be off by 0.2 cm. Approximate the maximum possible error in the volume of the cone.

97. Profit The total profit from 1 acre of a certain crop depends on the amount spent on fertilizer, x, and on hybrid seed, y, according to the model

$$P(x, y) = 0.01(-x^2 + 3xy + 160x - 5y^2 + 200y + 2600).$$

The budget for fertilizer and seed is limited to \$280.

a. Use the budget constraint to express one variable in terms of the other. Then substitute into the profit function to get a function with one independent variable. Use the method shown in Chapter 6 on Applications of the Derivative to find the amounts spent on fertilizer and seed that will maximize profit. What is the maximum profit per acre? (*Hint:* Throughout this exercise you may ignore the coefficient of 0.01 until you need to find the maximum profit.)

b. Find the amounts spent on fertilizer and seed that will maximize profit using the first method shown in this chapter. (*Hint:* You will not need to use the budget constraint.)

c. Use the Lagrange multiplier method to solve the original problem.

d. Look for the relationships among these methods.

Life Sciences

98. Blood Vessel Volume A length of blood vessel is measured as 2.7 cm, with the radius measured as 0.7 cm. If each of these measurements could be off by 0.1 cm, estimate the maximum possible error in the volume of the vessel.

99. Total Body Water Accurate prediction of total body water is critical in determining adequate dialysis doses for patients with renal disease. For African American males, total body water can be estimated by the function

$$T(A, M, S) = -18.37 - 0.09A + 0.34M + 0.25S,$$

where T is the total body water (in liters), A is age (in years), M is mass (in kilograms), and S is height (in centimeters). *Source: Kidney International.*

a. Find $T(65, 85, 180)$.

b. Find and interpret $T_A(A, M, S)$, $T_M(A, M, S)$, and $T_S(A, M, S)$.

100. Brown Trout Researchers from New Zealand have determined that the length of a brown trout depends on both its mass and age and that the length can be estimated by

$$L(m, t) = (0.00082t + 0.0955)e^{(\ln m + 10.49)/2.842},$$

where $L(m, t)$ is the length of the trout (in centimeters), m is the mass of the trout (in grams), and t is the age of the trout (in years). *Source: Transactions of the American Fisheries Society.*

a. Find $L(450, 4)$.

b. Find $L_m(450, 7)$ and $L_t(450, 7)$ and interpret.

101. Survival Curves The following figure shows survival curves (percent surviving as a function of age) for people in the United States in 1900 and 2000. *Source: National Vital Statistics Report.* Let $f(x, y)$ give the proportion surviving at age x in year y. Use the graph to estimate the following. Interpret each answer in words.

a. $f(60, 1900)$ **b.** $f(70, 2000)$

c. $f_x(60, 1900)$ **d.** $f_x(70, 2000)$

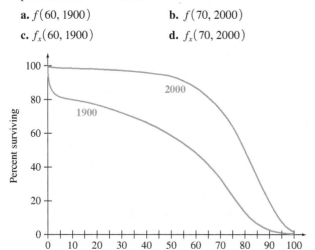

General Interest

102. Area The bottom of a planter is to be made in the shape of an isosceles triangle, with the two equal sides 3 ft long and the third side 2 ft long. The area of an isosceles triangle with two equal sides of length a and third side of length b is

$$f(a, b) = \frac{1}{4}b\sqrt{4a^2 - b^2}.$$

a. Find the area of the bottom of the planter.

b. The manufacturer is considering changing the shape so that the third side is 2.5 ft long. What would be the approximate effect on the area?

103. Surface Area A closed box with square ends must have a volume of 125 in³. Use Lagrange multipliers to find the dimensions of such a box that has minimum surface area.

104. Area Use Lagrange multipliers to find the maximum rectangular area that can be enclosed with 400 ft of fencing, if no fencing is needed along one side.

EXTENDED APPLICATION

USING MULTIVARIABLE FITTING TO CREATE A RESPONSE SURFACE DESIGN

Suppose you are designing a flavored drink with orange and banana flavors. You want to find the ideal concentrations of orange and banana flavoring agents, but since the concentrations could range from 0% to 100%, you can't try every possibility. A common design technique in the food industry is to make up several test drinks using different combinations of flavorings and have them rated for taste appeal by a panel of tasters. Such ratings are called *hedonic responses* and are often recorded on a 10-point scale from 0 (worst) to 9 (best). One combination will most likely get the highest average score, but since you have only tried a few of the infinite number of flavor combinations, the winning combination on the taste test might be far from the mix that would be the most popular in the market. How can you use the information from your test to locate the best point on the *flavor plane*?

One approach to this problem uses *response surfaces*, three-dimensional surfaces that approximate the data points from your flavor test.* For your test, you might choose mixtures that are spread out over the flavor plane. For example, you could combine low, medium, and high orange with low, medium, and high banana to get 9 different flavors. If you had 15 tasters and used intensities of 20, 50, and 80 for each fruit, the test data might look like the table.

Average Hedonic Scores ($n = 15$) Banana Intensity (0 to 100)				
		20	50	80
Orange	20	3.2	4.9	2.8
Intensity	50	6.0	7.2	5.1
0 to 100	80	4.5	5.5	4.8

For example, the table shows that the drink with orange intensity 20 and banana intensity 80 got an average flavor rating of 2.8 from the test panel (they didn't like it).

Your test results are points in space, where you can think of the x-axis as the orange axis, the y-axis as banana, and the z-axis as taste score. A three-dimensional bar chart is a common way of displaying data of this kind. Figure 38 on the next page is a bar chart of the flavor test results.

Looking at the bar chart, we can guess that the best flavor mix will be somewhere near the middle. We'd like to "drape" a smooth surface over the bars and see where that surface has a maximum. But as with any sample, our tasters are not perfectly representative

*For a brief introduction to response surfaces, see Devore, Jay L. and Nicholas R. Farnum, *Applied Statistics for Engineers and Scientists*, Duxbury, 2004.

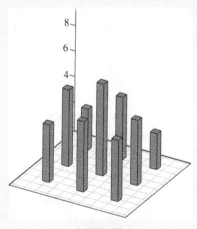

FIGURE 38

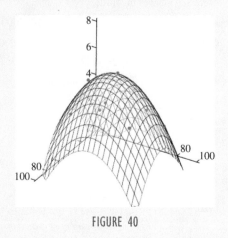

FIGURE 40

of the whole population: Our test results give the general shape of the true population response, but each bar includes an error that results from our small sample size. The solution is to fit a *smooth* surface to the data points.

A simple type of function for modeling such data sets is a quadratic function. You've seen many quadratic functions of two variables in the examples and exercises for this chapter, and you know that they can have maxima, minima, and saddle points. We don't know in advance which quadratic shape will give us the best fit, so we'll use the most general quadratic,

$$G(x, y) = Ax^2 + By^2 + Cxy + Dx + Ey + F.$$

Our job is to find the six coefficients, A through F, that give the best fit to our nine data points. As with the least squares line formula you used in Section 1.3, there are formulas for these six coefficients. Most statistical software packages will generate them directly from your data set, and here is the best-fitting quadratic found by one such program:

$$G(x, y) = -0.00202x^2 - 0.00163y^2 + 0.000194xy$$
$$+ 0.21380x + 0.14768y - 2.36204.$$

In this case the response surface shows how the dependent variable, taste rating, *responds* to the two independent variables, orange and banana intensity. Figures 39 and 40 are two views of

the surface together with the data: a surface superimposed on the bar chart, and the same surface with the data shown as points in space.

In research papers, response surface models are often reported using level curves. A contour map for the surface we have found looks like Figure 41, with orange increasing from left to right and banana from bottom to top.

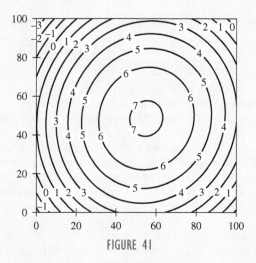

FIGURE 41

It's quite easy to estimate the location of the maximum by marking a point in the middle of the central ellipse and finding its coordinates on the two axes (try it!). You can also use the techniques you learned in the section on Maxima and Minima, computing partial derivatives of G with respect to x and y and solving the resulting linear system. The numbers are awkward, but with some help from a calculator you'll find that the maximum occurs at approximately $(55.3, 48.6)$. So the quadratic model predicts that the most popular drink will have an orange concentration of 55.3 and a banana concentration of 48.6. The model also predicts the public's flavor rating for this drink: We would expect it to be $G(55.3, 48.6)$, which turns

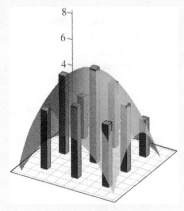

FIGURE 39

out to be about 7.14. When food technologists design a new food, this kind of modeling is often a first step. The next step might be to make a new set of test drinks with concentrations clustered around the point $(55.3, 48.6)$, and use further tests to explore this region of the "flavor plane" in greater detail.

Response surfaces are also helpful for constrained optimization. In the section on Lagrange Multipliers, you saw how Lagrange multipliers could solve problems of the form:

> Find the relative extrema for $z = f(x, y)$,
> subject to the constraint $g(x, y) = 0$.

Sometimes the constraints have a different form: You may have *several* dependent variables that respond to the same inputs, and the design goal is to keep each variable *within a given range*. Here's an example based on the data in U.S. Patent No. 4,276,316, which is titled *Process for Treating Nuts*. **Source: United States Patent and Trademark Office**. The patent granted to researcher Shri C. Sharma and assigned to CPC International, Inc. covers a method for preparing nuts for blanching (that is, having their skins removed). The patent summary reads in part:

> *The nuts are heated with a gas at a temperature of 125° to 175°C for 30 to 180 seconds and then immediately cooled to below 35°C within 5 minutes prior to blanching. This provides improved blanching, sorting and other steps in a process for producing products ranging from nuts per se to peanut butters or spreads.*

In support of the effectiveness of the method, the patent offers data that describe the effects of nine different combinations of air temperature and treatment time on three variables of interest for blanched peanuts: blanching efficiency, roasted peanut flavor, and overall flavor. Efficiency is given in percent, and the two hedonic variables were rated by tasters on a scale of 0 to 9.

The time variable has been converted into a natural logarithm because treatment time effects typically scale with the log of the time. The problem is now to pick a temperature and time range that give the optimum combination of efficiency, roasted flavor, and overall flavor. Each of these three dependent variables responds to the inputs in a different way, and the patent documentation includes quadratic response surfaces for each variable. The lighter shading in Figures 42–44 indicates higher values, which are more

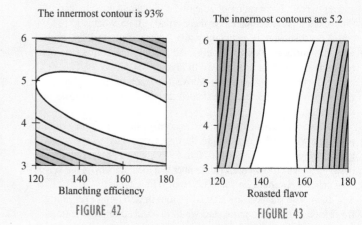

The innermost contour is 93%

FIGURE 42
Blanching efficiency

The innermost contours are 5.2

FIGURE 43
Roasted flavor

The "pointed" contours are 5.5

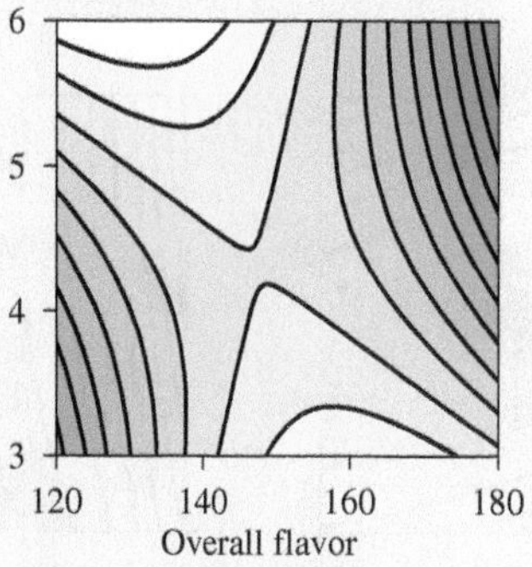

FIGURE 44
Overall flavor

Air Temperature, °C	Treatment Time, Seconds	Log of Treatment Time	Blanching Efficiency	Roasted Peanut Flavor	Overall Flavor
138	45	3.807	93.18	4.94	5.51
160	120	4.787	94.99	5.24	5.37
149	75	4.317	98.43	5.27	5.10
138	120	4.787	96.42	5.05	5.71
160	45	3.807	96.48	5.17	5.62
127	75	4.317	93.56	4.64	5.04
149	180	5.193	94.99	5.24	5.37
149	30	3.401	87.30	5.43	5.44
171	45	3.807	94.40	4.37	5.18

desirable. Temperature is plotted across the bottom, and the log of treatment time increases from bottom to top.

Sometimes process designers faced with this kind of problem will combine the dependent variables into a single function by taking a weighted average of their values, and then use a single response surface to optimize this function. Here we look at a different scenario. Suppose we set the following process goals: We want blanching efficiency of at least 93%, a roasted flavor rating of at least 5.2, and an overall flavor rating of at least 5.5. Is there a combination of time and temperature that meets these criteria? If so, what is it?

The first step is to identify the "successful" area on each response surface, which we can do by shading the corresponding region in the contour plot, shown in Figures 45–47.

Now the strategy is clear: We want to stack the three plots on top of each other and see if the shaded regions overlap. Figure 48 is the result.

So we can see that there are two regions on the temperature–time plane that will work. For example, the upper area of overlap suggests a processing temperature of 140°C to 150°C, with a processing time between 90 and 150 seconds (remember that the numbers on the vertical axis are *natural logarithms* of the time in seconds).

Response surfaces are a standard tool in designing everything from food to machine parts, and we have touched on only a small part of the theory here. Frequently a process depends on more than two independent variables. For example, a soft-drink formula might include three flavorings, an acidifying agent, and a sweetener. The response "surface" now lives in six dimensions and we can no longer draw nice pictures, but the same multivariable mathematics that generated our quadratic response surfaces will lead us to the optimal combination of variables.

EXERCISES

1. The general quadratic function of two variables has six terms. How many terms are in the general cubic function of two variables?

2. Use the contour plot of orange-banana flavor to estimate the "flavor coordinates" of the best-tasting drink.

3. Find the maximum on the flavor response surface by finding the critical point of the function $G(x, y)$.

4. Without shading or numbers on the contours, how would you know that the point you found in Exercises 2 and 3 represents the best flavor rather than the worst flavor? (*Hint:* Compute the discriminant D as described in the section on Maxima and Minima.)

5. Our best drink has a predicted flavor rating of 7.14, but one of our test drinks got a *higher* rating, 7.2. What's going on?

6. Blanching efficiency has a maximum near the center of the temperature–time plane. What is going on near the center of the plane for the roasted flavor and overall flavor response surfaces? Within the domain plotted, where does overall flavor reach a maximum?

7. In the overall flavor contour plot, if we move one contour toward higher flavor from the "pointed" 5.5 contours, we find curved contours that represent an overall flavor rating of about 5.6. If instead of requiring an overall flavor rating of 5.5 we decided to require a rating of 5.6, what would happen to our process design?

8. Use the last figure to describe the other region in the temperature–time plane that delivers a successful process for preparing nuts for blanching.

9. At the website WolframAlpha.com, you can enter "maximize" followed by an expression $f(x, y)$, such as $4 - x^2 - y^2$, and you will be told the maximum value of the expression, as well as the point where the maximum occurs. You will also be shown a graph of the surface $z = f(x, y)$ and a contour plot. Try this for the function $G(x, y)$ given in this Extended Application, and compare with your answers to Exercises 2 and 3.

DIRECTIONS FOR GROUP PROJECT

Perform an experiment that is similar to the flavored drink example from the text on some other product. For example, you could perform an experiment where you develop hedonic responses for various levels of salt and butter on popcorn. Using technology, to the extent that it is available to you, carry out the analysis of your experiment to determine an optimal mixture of each ingredient.

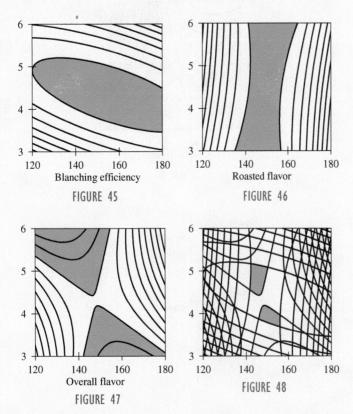

FIGURE 45 — Blanching efficiency

FIGURE 46 — Roasted flavor

FIGURE 47 — Overall flavor

FIGURE 48

ANSWERS TO SELECTED EXERCISES

Exercises 1

For exercises . . .	1–4,27,28,32, 33,38–45,48	5–12	13–16	21–26	23–28	31,34–36
Refer to example . . .	1–3	4–6	7,8	material after Example 8	5	8

1. a. 12 **b.** -6 **c.** 10 **d.** -19 **3. a.** $\sqrt{43}$ **b.** 6 **c.** $\sqrt{19}$ **d.** $\sqrt{11}$

5.
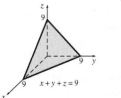

7.
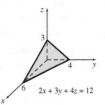

9.
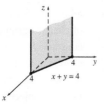

11.
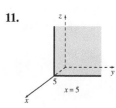

13.
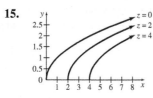

15.

21. c **23.** e **25.** b **27. a.** $8x + 4h$ **b.** $-4y - 2h$ **c.** $8x$ **d.** $-4y$ **29. a.** $3e^2$; slope of tangent line in the direction of x at $(1, 1)$ **b.** $3e^2$; slope of tangent line in the direction of y at $(1, 1)$ **31. a.** 1987 (rounded) **b.** 595 (rounded) **c.** 359,768 (rounded) **33.** 1.416; the IRA account grows faster.

35. $y = 500^{5/2}/x^{3/2} \approx 5{,}590{,}170/x^{3/2}$

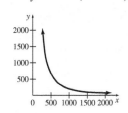

37. $C(x, y, z) = 250x + 150y + 75z$ **39. a.** 1.89 m² **b.** 1.62 m² **c.** 1.78 m²
41. a. 8.7% **b.** 48% **c.** Multiple solutions: $W = 19.75, R = 0, A = 0$ or $W = 10, R = 10, A = 4.59$ **d.** Wetland percentage **43. a.** 397 accidents
45. a. $T = 242.257\,C^{0.18}/F^3$ **b.** 58.82; a tethered sow spends nearly 59% of the time doing repetitive behavior when she is fed 2 kg of food a day and neighboring sows spend 40% of the time doing repetitive behavior. **47.** $g(L, W, H) = 2LW + 2WH + 2LH$ ft²

Exercises 2

For exercises . . .	1,2,33–36,43,44	3–20	21–32	37–42	45–47,53–67	48–52
Refer to example . . .	3	1–3	6,7	8	4	5

1. a. $12x - 4y$ **b.** $-4x + 18y$ **c.** 12 **d.** -40 **3.** $f_x(x, y) = -4y$; $f_y(x, y) = -4x + 18y^2$; 4; 178 **5.** $f_x(x, y) = 10xy^3$; $f_y(x, y) = 15x^2y^2$; -20; 2160 **7.** $f_x(x, y) = e^{x+y}$; $f_y(x, y) = e^{x+y}$; e^1 or e; e^{-1} or $1/e$ **9.** $f_x(x, y) = -24e^{4x-3y}$; $f_y(x, y) = 18e^{4x-3y}$; $-24e^{11}$; $18e^{-25}$ **11.** $f_x(x, y) = (-x^4 - 2xy^2 - 3x^2y^3)/(x^3 - y^2)^2$; $f_y(x, y) = (3x^3y^2 - y^4 + 2x^2y)/(x^3 - y^2)^2$; $-8/49$; $-1713/5329$
13. $f_x(x, y) = 15x^2y^2/(1 + 5x^3y^2)$; $f_y(x, y) = 10x^3y/(1 + 5x^3y^2)$; 60/41; 1920/2879 **15.** $f_x(x, y) = e^{x^2y}(2x^2y + 1)$; $f_y(x, y) = x^3e^{x^2y}$; $-7e^{-4}$; $-64e^{48}$ **17.** $f_x(x, y) = (1/2)(4x^3 + 3y)/(x^4 + 3xy + y^4 + 10)^{1/2}$; $f_y(x, y) = (1/2)(3x + 4y^3)/(x^4 + 3xy + y^4 + 10)^{1/2}$; $29/(2\sqrt{21})$; $48/\sqrt{311}$
19. $f_x(x, y) = [6xy(e^{xy} + 2) - 3x^2y^2e^{xy}]/(e^{xy} + 2)^2$; $f_y(x, y) = [3x^2(e^{xy} + 2) - 3x^3ye^{xy}]/(e^{xy} + 2)^2$; $-24(e^{-2} + 1)/(e^{-2} + 2)^2$; $(624e^{-12} + 96)/(e^{-12} + 2)^2$ **21.** $f_{xx}(x, y) = 8y^2 - 32$; $f_{yy}(x, y) = 8x^2$; $f_{xy}(x, y) = f_{yx}(x, y) = 16xy$
23. $R_{xx}(x, y) = 8 + 24y^2$; $R_{yy}(x, y) = -30xy + 24x^2$; $R_{xy}(x, y) = R_{yx}(x, y) = -15y^2 + 48xy$
25. $r_{xx}(x, y) = 12y/(x + y)^3$; $r_{yy}(x, y) = -12x/(x + y)^3$; $r_{xy}(x, y) = r_{yx}(x, y) = (6y - 6x)/(x + y)^3$
27. $z_{xx} = 9ye^x$; $z_{yy} = 0$; $z_{xy} = z_{yx} = 9e^x$ **29.** $r_{xx} = -1/(x + y)^2$; $r_{yy} = -1/(x + y)^2$; $r_{xy} = r_{yx} = -1/(x + y)^2$
31. $z_{xx} = 1/x$; $z_{yy} = -x/y^2$; $z_{xy} = z_{yx} = 1/y$ **33.** $x = -4, y = 2$ **35.** $x = 0, y = 0$; or $x = 3, y = 3$ **37.** $f_x(x, y, z) = 4x^3$; $f_y(x, y, z) = 2z^2$; $f_z(x, y, z) = 4yz + 4z^3$; $f_{yz}(x, y, z) = 4z$ **39.** $f_x(x, y, z) = 6/(4z + 5)$; $f_y(x, y, z) = -5/(4z + 5)$; $f_z(x, y, z) = -4(6x - 5y)/(4z + 5)^2$; $f_{yz}(x, y, z) = 20/(4z + 5)^2$ **41.** $f_x(x, y, z) = (2x - 5z^2)/(x^2 - 5xz^2 + y^4)$; $f_y(x, y, z) = 4y^3/(x^2 - 5xz^2 + y^4)$; $f_z(x, y, z) = -10xz/(x^2 - 5xz^2 + y^4)$; $f_{yz}(x, y, z) = 40xy^3z/(x^2 - 5xz^2 + y^4)^2$
43. a. 6.773 **b.** 3.386 **45. a.** 80 **b.** 150 **c.** 80 **d.** 440 **47. a.** $902,100 **b.** $f_p(p, i) = 99 - 0.5i - 0.005p$; $f_i(p, i) = -0.5p$; the rate at which weekly sales are changing per unit of change in price when the interest rate remains constant $(f_p(p, i))$ or per unit change in interest rate when the price remains constant $(f_i(p, i))$ **c.** A weekly sales decrease of $9700 **49. a.** 50.57 hundred units
b. $f_x(16, 81) = 1.053$ hundred units and is the rate at which production is changing when labor changes by 1 unit (from 16 to 17) and capital remains constant; $f_y(16, 81) = 0.4162$ hundred units and is the rate at which production is changing when capital changes by 1 unit (from 81 to 82) and labor remains constant. **c.** Production would increase by approximately 105 units. **51.** $0.4x^{-0.6}y^{0.6}$; $0.6x^{0.4}y^{-0.4}$

53. a. 1279 kcal per hr **b.** 2.906 kcal per hr per g; the instantaneous rate of change of energy usage for a 300-kg animal traveling at 10 km per hr is about 2.9 kcal per hr per g. **55. a.** 0.0142 m² **b.** 0.00442 m² **57. a.** 4.125 lb **b.** $\partial f / \partial n = n/4$; the rate of change of weight loss per unit change in workouts **c.** An additional loss of 3/4 lb **59. a.** $(2ax - 3x^2)t^2e^{-t}$
b. $x^2(a - x)(2t - t^2)e^{-t}$ **c.** $(2a - 6x)t^2e^{-t}$ **d.** $(2ax - 3x^2)(2t - t^2)e^{-t}$ **e.** $\partial R/\partial x$ gives the rate of change of the reaction per unit of change in the amount of drug administered. $\partial R/\partial t$ gives the rate of change of the reaction for a 1-hour change in the time after the drug is administered. **61. a.** $-24.9°F$ **b.** 15 mph **c.** $W_V(20, 10) = -1.114$; while holding the temperature fixed at 10°F, the wind chill decreases approximately 1.1°F when the wind velocity increases by 1 mph; $W_T(20, 10) = 1.429$; while holding the wind velocity fixed at 20 mph, the wind chill increases approximately 1.429°F if the actual temperature increases from 10°F to 11°F.
d. Sample table

T\W	5	10	15	20
30	27	16	9	4
20	16	3	-5	-11
10	6	-9	-18	-25
0	-5	-21	-32	-39

63. -10 ml per year, 100 ml per in. **65. a.** $F_m = gR^2/r^2$; the rate of change in force per unit change in mass while the distance is held constant; $F_r = -2mgR^2/r^3$; the rate of change in force per unit change in distance while the mass is held constant
67. a. 1055 **b.** $T_s(3, 0.5) = 127.4$ msec per ft. If the distance to move an object increases from 3 ft to 4 ft, while keeping w fixed at 0.5, the approximate increase in movement time is 127.4 msec.

$T_w(3, 0.5) = -764.6$ msec per ft. If the width of the target area increases by 1 ft, while keeping s fixed at 3 ft, the approximate decrease in movement time is 764.6 msec.

Exercises 3

For exercises . . .	1–18,21–28	34–40,42
Refer to example . . .	1–3	4

1. Saddle point at $(-1, 2)$ **3.** Relative minimum at $(-3, -3)$
5. Relative minimum at $(-2, -2)$ **7.** Relative minimum at $(15, -8)$ **9.** Relative maximum at $(2/3, 4/3)$ **11.** Saddle point at $(2, -2)$ **13.** Saddle point at $(0, 0)$; relative minimum at $(27, 9)$ **15.** Saddle point at $(0, 0)$; relative minimum at $(9/2, 3/2)$
17. Saddle point at $(0, -1)$ **21.** Relative maximum of 9/8 at $(-1, 1)$; saddle point at $(0, 0)$; a **23.** Relative minima of $-33/16$ at $(0, 1)$ and at $(0, -1)$; saddle point at $(0, 0)$; b **25.** Relative maxima of 17/16 at $(1, 0)$ and $(-1, 0)$; relative minima of $-15/16$ at $(0, 1)$ and $(0, -1)$; saddle points at $(0, 0)$, $(-1, 1)$, $(1, -1)$, $(1, 1)$, and $(-1, -1)$; e **31. a.** all values of k **b.** $k \geq 0$
35. Minimum cost of $59 when $x = 4, y = 5$ **37.** Sell 12 spas and 7 solar heaters for a maximum revenue of $166,600.
39. $2000 on quality control and $1000 on consulting, for a minimum time of 8 hours
41. a. $r = -1.722, s = 0.3652, y = 0.1787(1.441)^t$ **b.** Same as a **c.** Same as a

Exercises 4

For exercises . . .	1–8,11,12,15,21	9,10,13,14,37–42	23–26	27–36
Refer to example . . .	1	3	material after Example 3	2

1. $f(8, 8) = 256$ **3.** $f(5, 5) = 125$ **5.** $f(5, 3) = 28$ **7.** $f(20, 2) = 360$ **9.** $f(3/2, 3/2, 3) = 81/4 = 20.25$
11. $x = 8, y = 16$ **13.** 30, 30, 30 **15.** Minimum value of 128 at $(2, 5)$, maximum value of 160 at $(-2, 7)$
21. a. Minimum value of -5 at $(3, -2)$. **d.** $(3, -2)$ is a saddle point. **23.** Purchase 20 units of x and 20 units of y for a maximum utility of 8000. **25.** Purchase 20 units of x and 5 units of y for a maximum utility of 4,000,000.
27. 60 feet by 60 feet **29.** 10 large kits and no small kits **31.** 167 units of labor and 178 units of capital **33.** 125 m by 125 m **35.** Radius = 5 in.; height = 10 in. **37.** 12.91 m by 12.91 m by 6.455 m **39.** 5 m by 5 m by 5 m
41. b. 2 yd by 1 yd by 1/2 yd

Exercises 5

For exercises . . .	1–6,18–20,23–28	7–14	15–17,21,22,29–32	33,34
Refer to example . . .	1	2	3	4

1. 0.12 **3.** 0.0311 **5.** -0.335
7. 10.022; 10.0221; 0.0001 **9.** 2.0067; 2.0080; 0.0013 **11.** 1.07; 1.0720; 0.0020 **13.** -0.02; -0.0200; 0 **15.** 20.73 cm³
17. 86.4 in³ **19.** 0.07694 unit **21.** 6.65 cm³ **23.** 2.98 liters **25. a.** 0.2649 **b.** Actual 0.2817; approximation 0.2816
27. a. 87% **b.** 75% **d.** 89%; 87% **29.** 26.945 cm² **31.** 3% **33.** 8

Exercises 6

For exercises . . .	1–10	11–20	21–28,61–64,66–71	29–38,65	39–46	47–56	57,58
Refer to example . . .	1	2,3	4	5,6	7	8	9

1. $630y$ **3.** $(2x/9)[(x^2 + 15)^{3/2} - (x^2 + 12)^{3/2}]$ **5.** $6 + 10y$ **7.** $(1/2)(e^{12+3y} - e^{4+3y})$ **9.** $(1/2)(e^{4x+9} - e^{4x})$ **11.** 945
13. $(2/45)(39^{5/2} - 12^{5/2} - 7533)$ **15.** 21 **17.** $(\ln 3)^2$ **19.** $8 \ln 2 + 4$ **21.** 171 **23.** $(4/15)(33 - 2^{5/2} - 3^{5/2})$
25. $-3 \ln(3/4)$ or $3 \ln(4/3)$ **27.** $(1/2)(e^7 - e^6 - e^3 + e^2)$ **29.** 96 **31.** 40/3 **33.** $(2/15)(2^{5/2} - 2)$
35. $(1/4) \ln(17/8)$ **37.** $e^2 - 3$ **39.** 97,632/105 **41.** 128/9 **43.** $\ln 16$ or $4 \ln 2$ **45.** 64/3 **47.** 34 **49.** 10/3
51. $7(e - 1)/3$ **53.** 16/3 **55.** $4 \ln 2 - 2$ **57.** 1 **61.** 49 **63.** $(e^6 + e^{-10} - e^{-4} - 1)/60$ **65.** 9 in³ **67.** 14,753 units
69. $34,833 **71.** $32,000

Chapter Review Exercises

For exercises . . .	1–5,17–26,87	6,13,14,27–44, 89,98–101	7,8,45–53,90, 103,104	9,54–57, 91,92	10–12,67–86, 100	15,59–66,88, 93–96,98
Refer to section . . .	1	2	3	4	6	5

1. True **2.** True **3.** True **4.** True **5.** False **6.** False **7.** False **8.** True **9.** False **10.** False **11.** True **12.** False
17. -19; -255 **19.** $-5/9$; $-4/3$ **21.**

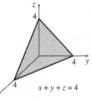

23.

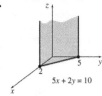

25.

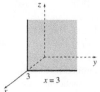

27. a. $9x^2 + 8xy$ **b.** -12 **c.** 16 **29.**
$f_x(x, y) = 12xy^3$; $f_y(x, y) = 18x^2y^2 - 4$ **31.** $f_x(x, y) = 4x/(4x^2 + y^2)^{1/2}$;
$f_y(x, y) = y/(4x^2 + y^2)^{1/2}$ **33.** $f_x(x, y) = 3x^2e^{3y}$; $f_y(x, y) = 3x^3e^{3y}$ **35.** $f_x(x, y) = 4x/(2x^2 + y^2)$; $f_y(x, y) = 2y/(2x^2 + y^2)$
37. $f_{xx}(x, y) = 30xy$; $f_{xy}(x, y) = 15x^2 - 12y$ **39.** $f_{xx}(x, y) = 12y/(2x - y)^3$; $f_{xy}(x, y) = (-6x - 3y)/(2x - y)^3$
41. $f_{xx}(x, y) = 8e^{2y}$; $f_{xy}(x, y) = 16xe^{2y}$ **43.** $f_{xx}(x, y) = (-2x^2y^2 - 4y)/(2 - x^2y)^2$; $f_{xy}(x, y) = -4x/(2 - x^2y)^2$
45. Saddle point at $(0, 2)$ **47.** Relative minimum at $(2, 1)$ **49.** Saddle point at $(3, 1)$ **51.** Saddle point at $(-1/3, 11/6)$;
relative minimum at $(1, 1/2)$ **55.** Minimum of 18 at $(-3, 3)$ **57.** $x = 25$, $y = 50$ **59.** 1.22 **61.** 13.0846; 13.0848; 0.0002
63. $8y - 6$ **65.** $(3/2)[(100 + 2y^2)^{1/2} - (2y^2)^{1/2}]$ **67.** $1232/9$ **69.** $(2/135)[(42)^{5/2} - (24)^{5/2} - (39)^{5/2} + (21)^{5/2}]$
71. $2 \ln 2$ or $\ln 4$ **73.** 110 **75.** $(4/15)(782 - 8^{5/2})$ **77.** $105/2$ **79.** $1/2$ **81.** $1/48$ **83.** $\ln 2$ **85.** 3
87. a. $\$(325 + \sqrt{10}) \approx \$328.16$ **b.** $\$(800 + \sqrt{15}) \approx \$803.87$ **c.** $\$(2000 + \sqrt{20}) \approx \$2004.47$ **89. a.** $0.7y^{0.3}/x^{0.3}$
b. $0.3x^{0.7}/y^{0.7}$ **91.** Purchase 10 units of x and 15 units of y for a maximum utility of 33,750. **93.** Decrease by $\$243.82$
95. 4.19 ft^3 **97. a.** $\$200$ spent on fertilizer and $\$80$ spent on seed will produce a maximum profit of $\$266$ per acre.
b. Same as a. **c.** Same as a **99. a.** 49.68 liters **b.** -0.09, the approximate change in total body water if age is increased by 1
yr and mass and height are held constant is -0.09 liters; 0.34, the approximate change in total body water if mass is increased by 1
kg and age and height are held constant is 0.34 liters; 0.25, the approximate change in total body water if height is increased by 1
cm and age and mass are held constant is 0.25 liters. **101. a.** 50; in 1900, 50% of those born 60 years earlier are still alive.
b. 75; in 2000, 75% of those born 70 years earlier are still alive. **c.** -1.25; in 1900, the percent of those born 60 years earlier
who are still alive was dropping at a rate of 1.25 percent per additional year of life. **d.** -2; in 2000, the percent of those
born 70 years earlier who are still alive was dropping at a rate of 2 percent per additional year of life. **103.** 5 in. by 5 in. by 5 in.

SAMPLE SOURCES

Section 1

1. Exercise 34 from Cobb, Charles W. and Paul H. Douglas, "A Theory of Production," *American Economic Review*, Vol. 18, No. 1, Supplement, March 1928, pp. 139–165.
2. Exercise 35 from Storesletten, Kjetil, "Sustaining Fiscal Policy Thorough Immigration," *Journal of Political Economy*, Vol. 108, No. 2, April 2000, pp. 300–323.
3. Exercise 38 from Harding, K. C. et al., "Mass-Dependent Energetics and Survival in Harbour Seal Pups," *Functional Ecology*, Vol. 19, No.1, Feb., 2005, pp. 129–135.
4. Exercise 39 from Haycock G.B., G.J. Schwartz, and D.H. Wisotsky, "Geometric Method for Measuring Body Surface Area: A Height Weight Formula Validated in Infants, Children and Adults," *The Journal of Pediatrics*, Vol. 93, No.1, 1978, pp. 62–66.
5. Exercise 40 from Alexander, R. McNeill, "How Dinosaurs Ran," *Scientific American*, Vol. 264, April 1991, p. 4.
6. Exercise 41 from Van Holt, T., D. Murphy, and L. Chapman, "Local and Landscape Predictors of Fish-assemblage Characteristics in the Great Swamp, New York," *Northeastern Naturalist*, Vol. 12, No. 3, 2006, pp. 353–374.
7. Exercise 42 from Chowell, F. and F. Sanchez, "Climate-based Descriptive Models of Dengue Fever: The 2002 Epidemic in Colima, Mexico," *Journal of Environmental Health*, Vol. 68, No. 10, June 2006, pp. 40–44.
8. Exercises 43 and 44 from Iverson, Aaron and Louis Iverson, "Spatial and Temporal Trends of Deer Harvest and Deer-Vehicle Accidents in Ohio," *Ohio Journal of Science*, 99, 1999, pp. 84–94.
9. Exercise 45 from Appleby, M., A. Lawrence, and A. Illius, "Influence of Neighbours on Stereotypic Behaviour of Tethered Sows," *Applied Animal Behaviour Science*, Vol. 24, 1989, pp. 137–146.

Section 2

1. Exercise 53 from Robbins, C., *Wildlife Feeding and Nutrition*, New York: Academic Press, 1983, p. 114.
2. Exercise 54 from Harding, K. C. et al., "Mass-Dependent Energetics and Survival in Harbour Seal Pups," *Functional Ecology*, Vol. 19, No. 1, Feb., 2005, pp. 129–135.
3. Exercise 55 from Haycock G.B., G.J. Schwartz, and D.H. Wisotsky, "Geometric Method for Measuring Body Surface Area: A Height Weight Formula Validated in Infants, Children and Adults," *The Journal of Pediatrics*, Vol. 93, No.1, 1978, pp. 62–66.

4. Exercise 56 from http://www.anaesthesiauk.com/article.aspx?articleid=251.
5. Exercise 58 from http://www.win.niddk.nih.gov/publications/tools.htm.
6. Exercise 60 from Westbrook, David, "The Mathematics of Scuba Diving," *The UMAP Journal*, Vol. 18, No. 2, 1997, pp. 2–19.
7. Exercise 61 from Bosch, William and L. Cobb, "Windchill," *The UMAP Journal*, Vol. 13, No. 3, 1990, pp. 481–489.
8. Exercise 62 from www.weather.com (May 9, 2000).
9. Exercise 66 from Fiore, Greg, "An Out-of-Math Experience: Einstein, Relativity, and the Developmental Mathematics Student," *Mathematics Teacher*, Vol. 93, No. 3, 2000, pp. 194–199.
10. Exercise 67 from Sanders, Mark and Ernest McCormick, *Human Factors in Engineering Design*, 7th ed., New York: McGraw-Hill, 1993, pp. 290–291.

Section 3

1. Exercise 32 from Problem 35 from May 2003 Course 1 Examination of the *Education and Examination Committee of the Society of Actuaries*. Reprinted by permission of the Society of Actuaries.
2. Exercise 40 from Grofman, Bernard, "A Preliminary Model of Jury Decision Making as a Function of Jury Size, Effective Jury Decision Rule, and Mean Juror Judgmental Competence," *Frontiers of Economics*, Vol. 3, 1980, pp. 98–110.
3. Exercise 41 from http://www.intel.com/technology/mooreslaw/.
4. Exercise 42 from Hindra, F. and Oon-Doo Baik, "Kinetics of Quality Changes During Food Frying," *Critical Reviews in Food Science and Nutrition*, Vol. 46, 2006, pp. 239–258.

Section 4

1. Exercise 41 from Duffin, R., E. Peterson, and C. Zener, *Geometric Programming: Theory and Application*, New York: Wiley, 1967. Copyright © 1967 John Wiley & Sons, Inc.
2. Exercise 42 from Owen, Guillermo et al., "Proving a Distribution-Free Generalization of the Condorcet Jury Theorem," *Mathematical Social Sciences*, Vol. 17, 1989, pp. 1–16.

Section 5

1. From Colley, Susan Jane, "Calculus in the Brewery," *The College Mathematics Journal*, Vol. 25, No. 3, May 1994, p. 227.
2. Exercise 25 from Gotch, Frank, "Clinical Dialysis: Kinetic Modeling in Hemodialysis," *Clinical Dialysis*, 3rd ed., Norwalk: Appleton & Lange, 1995, pp. 156–186.
3. Exercise 26 from Fitzsimmons, N., S. Buskirk, and M. Smith, "Population History, Genetic Variability, and Horn Growth in Bighorn Sheep," *Conservation Biology*, Vol. 9, No. 2, April 1995, pp. 314–323.
4. Exercise 27 from Brown, J. P. and P. E. Sendak, "Association of Ring Shake in Eastern Hemlock with Tree Attributes," *Forest Products Journal*, Vol. 56, No. 10, October 2006, pp. 31–36.
5. Exercise 28 from Walker, Anita, "Mathematics Makes a Splash: Evaluating Hand Timing Systems," *The HiMAP Pull-Out Section*, Spring 1992, COMAP.

Review Exercises

1. Exercise 99 from Chumlea, W., S. Guo, C. Zellar et al., "Total Body Water Reference Values and Prediction Equations for Adults," *Kidney International*, Vol. 59, 2001, pp. 2250–2258.
2. Exercise 100 from Hayes, J., J. Stark, and K. Shearer, "Development and Test of a Whole-Lifetime Foraging and Bio-energetics Growth Model for Drift-Feeding Brown Trout," *Transactions of the American Fisheries Society*, Vol. 129, 2000, pp. 315–332.
3. Exercise 101 from *National Vital Statistics Reports*, Vol. 51, No. 3, December 19, 2002.

Extended Application

1. From www.uspto.gov/patents. You can locate patents by number or carry out a text search of the full patent database.

CREDITS

Differential Equations

When these sky divers open their parachutes, their speed will decrease until air resistance exactly balances the force of gravity. An exercise at the end of this chapter explores solutions to the differential equation that describes free fall with air resistance. The limiting speed with an open parachute is on the order of 10 miles per hour, slow enough for a safe landing.

Joggie Botma/ Shutterstock

From Chapter 10 of *Calculus with Applications*. Tenth Edition. Margaret L. Lial, Raymond N. Greenwell, Nathan P. Ritchey. Copyright © 2012 by Pearson Education, Inc. All rights reserved.

S uppose that an economist wants to develop an equation that will forecast interest rates. By studying data on previous changes in interest rates, she hopes to find a relationship between the level of interest rates and their rate of change. A function giving the rate of change of interest rates would be the derivative of the function describing the level of interest rates. A **differential equation** is an equation that involves an unknown function $y = f(x)$ and a finite number of its derivatives. Solving the differential equation for y would give the unknown function to be used for forecasting interest rates.

Differential equations have been important in the study of physical science and engineering since the eighteenth century. More recently, differential equations have become useful in the social sciences, life sciences, and economics for solving problems about population growth, ecological balance, and interest rates. In this chapter, we will introduce some methods for solving differential equations and give examples of their applications.

1 Solutions of Elementary and Separable Differential Equations

APPLY IT   How can we predict the future population of a flock of mountain goats?
Using differential equations, we will answer this question in Example 6.

Usually a solution of an equation is a *number*. A solution of a differential equation, however, is a *function* that satisfies the equation.

EXAMPLE 1   Solving a Differential Equation

Find all solutions of the differential equation

$$\frac{dy}{dx} = 3x^2 - 2x. \tag{1}$$

SOLUTION   To say that a function $y(x)$ is a solution of Equation (1) simply means that the derivative of the function y is $3x^2 - 2x$. This is the same as saying that y is an antiderivative of $3x^2 - 2x$, or

$$y = \int (3x^2 - 2x)\, dx = x^3 - x^2 + C. \tag{2}$$

YOUR TURN 1   Find all solutions of the differential equation $\frac{dy}{dx} = 12x^5 + \sqrt{x} + e^{5x}.$

We can verify that the function given by Equation (2) is a solution by taking its derivative. The result is the differential equation (1).   **TRY YOUR TURN 1**

-FOR REVIEW-
Review finding antiderivatives.

Each different value of C in Equation (2) leads to a different solution of Equation (1), showing that a differential equation can have an infinite number of solutions. Equation (2) is the **general solution** of the differential equation (1). Some of the solutions of Equation (1) are graphed in Figure 1.

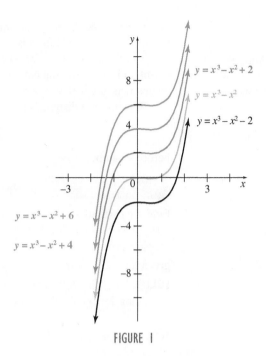

FIGURE 1

The simplest kind of differential equation has the form

$$\frac{dy}{dx} = g(x).$$

Since Equation (1) has this form, the solution of Equation (1) suggests the following generalization.

General Solution of $\dfrac{dy}{dx} = g(x)$

The general solution of the differential equation $\dfrac{dy}{dx} = g(x)$ is

$$y = \int g(x)\, dx.$$

EXAMPLE 2 Population

The population P of a flock of birds is growing exponentially so that

$$\frac{dP}{dt} = 20e^{0.05t},$$

where t is time in years. Find P in terms of t if there were 20 birds in the flock initially.

SOLUTION To solve the differential equation, first determine the antiderivative of $20e^{0.05t}$, that is,

$$P = \int 20e^{0.05t}\, dt = \frac{20}{0.05}e^{0.05t} + C = 400e^{0.05t} + C.$$

Initially, there were 20 birds, so $P = 20$ at time $t = 0$. We can substitute this information into the equation to determine the value of C that satisfies this condition.

$$20 = 400e^0 + C$$
$$-380 = C$$

Therefore, $P = 400e^{0.05t} - 380$. Verify that P is a solution to the differential equation by taking its derivative. The result should be the original differential equation.

In Example 2, the given information was used to produce a solution with a specific value of C. Such a solution is called a **particular solution** of the differential equation. The given information, $P = 20$ when $t = 0$, is called an **initial condition**. An **initial value problem** is a differential equation with a value of y given at $x = x_0$ (or $t = t_0$ in this case), where x_0 is any real number.

Sometimes a differential equation must be rewritten in the form

$$\frac{dy}{dx} = g(x)$$

before it can be solved.

EXAMPLE 3 Initial Value Problem

Find the particular solution of

$$\frac{dy}{dx} - 2x = \frac{2x}{\sqrt{x^2 + 3}},$$

given that $y(1) = 8$.

SOLUTION This differential equation is not in the proper form, but we can easily fix this by adding $2x$ to both sides of the equation. That is,

$$\frac{dy}{dx} = 2x + \frac{2x}{\sqrt{x^2 + 3}}.$$

To find the general solution, integrate this expression, using the substitution $u = x^2 + 3$ in the second term.

$$y = \int \left(2x + \frac{2x}{\sqrt{x^2 + 3}}\right) dx$$

$$= x^2 + \int \frac{1}{\sqrt{u}} du \qquad du = 2x\,dx$$

$$= x^2 + 2\sqrt{u} + C \qquad \text{Use the power rule with } n = -1/2.$$

$$= x^2 + 2\sqrt{x^2 + 3} + C$$

Now use the initial condition to find the value of C. Substituting 8 for y and 1 for x gives

$$8 = 1^2 + 2\sqrt{1^2 + 3} + C$$
$$8 = 5 + C$$
$$C = 3.$$

YOUR TURN 2 Find the particular solution of $\frac{dy}{dx} - 12x^3 = 6x^2$, given that $y(2) = 60$.

The particular solution is $y = x^2 + 2\sqrt{x^2 + 3} + 3$. Verify that $y(1) = 8$ and that differentiating y leads to the original differential equation. **TRY YOUR TURN 2**

So far in this section, we have used a method that is essentially the same as that used in the section on antiderivatives, when we first started the topic of integration. But not all differential equations can be solved so easily. For example, if interest on an investment is compounded continuously, then the investment grows at a rate proportional to the amount of money present. If A is the amount in an account at time t, then for some constant k, the differential equation

$$\frac{dA}{dt} = kA \qquad (3)$$

gives the rate of growth of A with respect to t. This differential equation is different from those discussed previously, which had the form

$$\frac{dy}{dx} = g(x).$$

CAUTION Since the right-hand side of Equation (3) is a function of A, rather than a function of t, it would be completely invalid to simply integrate both sides as we did before. The previous method only works when the side opposite the derivative is simply a function of the independent variable.

Equation (3) is an example of a more general differential equation we will now learn to solve; namely, those that can be written in the form

$$\frac{dy}{dx} = \frac{p(x)}{q(y)}.$$

Suppose we think of dy/dx as a fraction dy over dx. This is incorrect, of course; the derivative is actually the limit of a small change in y over a small change in x, but the notation is chosen so that this interpretation gives a correct answer, as we shall see. Multiply on both sides by $q(y)\, dx$ to get

$$q(y)\, dy = p(x)\, dx.$$

In this form all terms involving y (including dy) are on one side of the equation and all terms involving x (and dx) are on the other side. A differential equation that can be put into this form is said to be *separable*, since the variables x and y can be separated. After separation, a **separable differential equation** may be solved by integrating each side with respect to the variable given. This method is known as **separation of variables**.

$$\int q(y)\, dy = \int p(x)\, dx$$

$$Q(y) = P(x) + C,$$

where P and Q are antiderivatives of p and q. (We don't need a constant of integration on the left side of the equation; it can be combined with the constant of integration on the right side as C.) To show that this answer is correct, differentiate implicitly with respect to x.

$$Q'(y)\frac{dy}{dx} = P'(x) \qquad \text{Use the chain rule on the left side.}$$

$$q(y)\frac{dy}{dx} = p(x) \qquad \begin{array}{l}q(y) \text{ is the derivative of } Q(y) \text{ and}\\ p(x) \text{ is the derivative of } P(x).\end{array}$$

$$\frac{dy}{dx} = \frac{p(x)}{q(y)}$$

This last equation is the one we set out to solve.

EXAMPLE 4 Separation of Variables

Find the general solution of

$$y\frac{dy}{dx} = x^2.$$

SOLUTION Begin by separating the variables to get

$$y\, dy = x^2\, dx.$$

The general solution is found by determining the antiderivatives of each side.

$$\int y\, dy = \int x^2\, dx$$

$$\frac{y^2}{2} = \frac{x^3}{3} + C$$

$$y^2 = \frac{2}{3}x^3 + 2C$$

$$y^2 = \frac{2}{3}x^3 + K$$

YOUR TURN 3 Find the general solution of $\dfrac{dy}{dx} = \dfrac{x^2 + 1}{xy^2}$.

The constant K was substituted for $2C$ in the last step. The solution is left in implicit form, not solved explicitly for y. In general, we will use C for the arbitrary constant, so that our final answer would be written as $y^2 = (2/3)x^3 + C$. It would also be nice to solve for y by taking the square root of both sides, but since we don't know anything about the sign of y, we don't know whether the solution is $y = \sqrt{(2/3)x^3 + C}$ or $y = -\sqrt{(2/3)x^3 + C}$. If y were raised to the third power, we could solve for y by taking the cube root of both sides, since the cube root is unique.   **TRY YOUR TURN 3**

EXAMPLE 5   Separation of Variables

Find the general solution of the differential equation for interest compounded continuously,

$$\frac{dA}{dt} = kA.$$

SOLUTION   Separating variables leads to

$$\frac{1}{A}\,dA = k\,dt.$$

To solve this equation, determine the antiderivative of each side.

$$\int \frac{1}{A}\,dA = \int k\,dt$$
$$\ln|A| = kt + C$$

(Here A represents a nonnegative quantity, so the absolute value is unnecessary, but we wish to show how to solve equations for which this may not be true.) Use the definition of logarithm to write the equation in exponential form as

$$|A| = e^{kt+C} = e^{kt}e^{C}. \qquad \text{Use the property } e^{m+n} = e^{m}e^{n}.$$

Finally, use the definition of absolute value to get

$$A = e^{kt}e^{C} \quad \text{or} \quad A = -e^{kt}e^{C}.$$

Because e^{C} and $-e^{C}$ are constants, replace them with the constant M, which may be any nonzero real number. (We use M rather than K because we already have a constant k in this example. We could also relabel M as C, as we did in Example 4.) The resulting equation,

$$A = Me^{kt},$$

not only describes interest compounded continuously but also defines an exponential growth or decay function.

FOR REVIEW

The amount of money in an account with interest compounded continuously is given by

$$A = Pe^{rt},$$

where P is the initial amount in the account, r is the annual interest rate, and t is the time in years. Observe that this is the same as the equation for the amount of money in an account derived here, where P and r have been replaced with M and k, respectively.

CAUTION   Notice that $y = 0$ is also a solution to the differential equation in Example 5, but after we divide by A (which is not possible if $A = 0$) and integrate, the resulting equation $|A| = e^{kt+C}$ does not allow y to equal 0. In this example, the lost solution can be recovered in the final answer if we allow M to equal 0, a value that was previously excluded. When dividing by an expression in separation of variables, look for solutions that would make this expression 0 and may be lost.

Recall that equations of the form $A = Me^{kt}$ arise in situations where the rate of change of a quantity is proportional to the amount present at time t, which is precisely what the differential equation (3) describes. The constant k is called the **growth constant**, while M represents the amount present at time $t = 0$. A positive value of k indicates growth, while a negative value of k indicates decay. The equation was often written in the form $y = y_0 e^{kt}$.

As a model of population growth, the equation $y = Me^{kt}$ is not realistic over the long run for most populations. As shown by graphs of functions of the form $y = Me^{kt}$, with both M and k positive, growth would be unbounded. Additional factors, such as space restrictions or a limited amount of food, tend to inhibit growth of populations as time goes on. In an alternative model that assumes a maximum population of size N, the rate of growth of a population is proportional to how close the population is to that maximum, that is, to the difference between N and y. These assumptions lead to the differential equation

$$\frac{dy}{dt} = k(N - y),$$

whose solution is a limited growth function.

EXAMPLE 6 Population

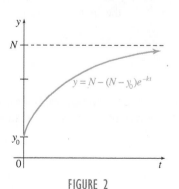

Randal Sedler/ Shutterstock

A certain nature reserve can support no more than 4000 mountain goats. Assume that the rate of growth is proportional to how close the population is to this maximum, with a growth rate of 20 percent. There are currently 1000 goats in the area.

(a) Solve the general limited growth differential equation, and then write a function describing the goat population at time t.

SOLUTION To solve the equation

$$\frac{dy}{dt} = k(N - y),$$

first separate the variables.

$$\frac{dy}{N - y} = k\, dt$$

$$\int \frac{dy}{N - y} = \int k\, dt \qquad \text{Integrate both sides.}$$

$$-\ln(N - y) = kt + C \qquad \text{We assume the population is less than } N, \text{ so } N - y > 0.$$

$$\ln(N - y) = -kt - C$$

$$N - y = e^{-kt - C} \qquad \text{Apply the function } e^x \text{ to both sides.}$$

$$N - y = e^{-kt}e^{-C} \qquad \text{Use the property } e^{m+n} = e^m e^n.$$

$$y = N - e^{-kt}e^{-C} \qquad \text{Solve for } y.$$

$$y = N - Me^{-kt} \qquad \text{Relabel the constant } e^{-C} \text{ as } M.$$

Now apply the initial condition that $y(0) = y_0$.

$$y_0 = N - Me^{-k \cdot 0} = N - M \qquad e^0 = 1$$

$$M = N - y_0 \qquad \text{Solve for } M.$$

Substituting this value of M into the previous solution gives

$$y = N - (N - y_0)e^{-kt}.$$

The graph of this function is shown in Figure 2.

For the goat problem, the maximum population is $N = 4000$, the initial population is $y_0 = 1000$, and the growth rate constant is 20%, or $k = 0.2$. Therefore,

$$y = 4000 - (4000 - 1000)e^{-0.2t} = 4000 - 3000e^{-0.2t}.$$

$$y = N - (N - y_0)e^{-kt}$$

FIGURE 2

(b) What will the goat population be in 5 years?

SOLUTION In 5 years, the population will be

$$y = 4000 - 3000e^{-(0.2)(5)} = 4000 - 3000e^{-1}$$
$$\approx 4000 - 1103.6 = 2896.4,$$

or about 2900 goats.

TRY YOUR TURN 4

APPLY IT

YOUR TURN 4 In Example 6, find the goat population in 5 years if the reserve can support 6000 goats, the growth rate is 15%, and there are currently 1200 goats in the area.

Logistic Growth

Let y be the size of a certain population at time t. In the standard model for unlimited growth given by Equation (3), the rate of growth is proportional to the current population size. The constant k, the growth rate constant, is the difference between the birth and death rates of the population. The unlimited growth model predicts that the population's growth rate is a constant, k.

Growth usually is not unlimited, however, and the population's growth rate is usually not constant because the population is limited by environmental factors to a maximum size N, called the **carrying capacity** of the environment for the species. In the limited growth model already given,

$$\frac{dy}{dt} = k(N - y),$$

the rate of growth is proportional to the remaining room for growth, $N - y$.

In the **logistic growth model**

$$\frac{dy}{dt} = k\left(1 - \frac{y}{N}\right)y \tag{4}$$

the rate of growth is proportional to both the current population size y and a factor $(1 - y/N)$ that is equal to the remaining room for growth, $N - y$, divided by N. Equation (4) is called the **logistic equation**. Notice that $(1 - y/N) \to 1$ as $y \to 0$, and the differential equation can be approximated as

$$\frac{dy}{dt} = k\left(1 - \frac{y}{N}\right)y \approx k(1)y = ky.$$

In other words, when y is small, the growth of the population behaves as if it were unlimited. On the other hand, $(1 - y/N) \to 0$ as $y \to N$, so

$$\frac{dy}{dt} = k\left(1 - \frac{y}{N}\right)y \approx k(0)y = 0.$$

That is, population growth levels off as y nears the maximum population N. Thus, the logistic Equation (4) is the unlimited growth Equation (3) with a damping factor $(1 - y/N)$ to account for limiting environmental factors when y nears N. Let y_0 denote the initial population size. Under the assumption $0 < y < N$, the general solution of Equation (4) is

$$y = \frac{N}{1 + be^{-kt}}, \tag{5}$$

where $b = (N - y_0)/y_0$ (see Exercise 31). This solution, called a **logistic curve**, is shown in Figure 3. You may know this function in terms of derivatives of exponential functions in the form

$$G(t) = \frac{m}{1 + \left(\frac{m}{G_0}\right)e^{-kmt}},$$

where m is the limiting value of the population, G_0 is the initial number present, and k is a positive constant.

As expected, the logistic curve begins exponentially and subsequently levels off. Another important feature is the point of inflection $((\ln b)/k, N/2)$, where dy/dx is a maximum (see Exercise 33). Notice that the point of inflection is when the population is half of the carrying capacity and that at this point, the population is increasing most rapidly.

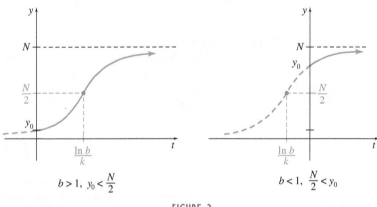

FIGURE 3

Logistic equations arise frequently in the study of populations. In about 1840 the Belgian sociologist P. F. Verhulst fitted a logistic curve to U.S. census figures and made predictions about the population that were subsequently proved to be quite accurate. American biologist Raymond Pearl (circa 1920) found that the growth of a population of fruit flies in a limited space could be modeled by the logistic equation

$$\frac{dy}{dt} = 0.2y - \frac{0.2}{1035}y^2.$$

TECHNOLOGY NOTE | Some calculators can fit a logistic curve to a set of data points. For example, the TI-84 Plus has this capability, listed as `Logistic` in the STAT CALC menu, along with other types of regression. See Exercises 40, 47, 48, and 52.

Logistic growth is an example of how a model is modified over time as new insights occur. The model for population growth changed from the early exponential curve $y = Me^{kt}$ to the logistic curve

$$y = \frac{N}{1 + be^{-kt}}.$$

Many other quantities besides population grow logistically. That is, their initial rate of growth is slow, but as time progresses, their rate of growth increases to a maximum value and subsequently begins to decline and to approach zero.

EXAMPLE 7 **Logistic Curve**

Rapid technological advancements in the last 20 years have made many products obsolete practically overnight. J. C. Fisher and R. H. Pry successfully described the phenomenon of a technically superior new product replacing another product by the logistic equation

$$\frac{dz}{dt} = k(1 - z)z, \qquad \qquad \text{(6)}$$

where z is the market share of the new product and $1 - z$ is the market share of the other product. *Source: Technological Forecasting and Social Change*. The new product will initially have little or no market share; that is, $z_0 \approx 0$. Thus, the constant b in Equation (5) will have to be determined in a different way. Let t_0 be the time at which $z = 1/2$. Under the assumption $0 < z < 1$, the general solution of Equation (6) is

$$z = \frac{1}{1 + be^{-kt}}, \tag{7}$$

where $b = e^{kt_0}$ (see Exercise 32).

TECHNOLOGY NOTE

Fisher and Pry applied their model to the fraction of fabric consumed in the United States that was synthetic. Their data is shown in the table below. At the time of the study, natural fabrics in clothing were being replaced with synthetic fabric. Using the logistic regression function on a TI-84 Plus calculator, with t as the number of years since 1930, the best logistic function to fit this data can be shown to be

$$z = \frac{1.293}{1 + 21.80e^{-0.06751t}}.$$

A graph of the data and this function is shown in Figure 4(a). Although the data fits the function well, this function is not of the form studied by Fisher and Pry because it has a numerator of 1.293, rather than 1. This function predicts that the percentage of fabric that is synthetic approaches 129%! A more appropriate function can be found by rewriting Equation (7) as

$$be^{-kt} = \frac{1}{z} - 1,$$

and then finding the best fit exponential function to the points $(t, 1/z - 1)$. This leads to the equation

$$z = \frac{1}{1 + 18.93(0.92703)^t} = \frac{1}{1 + 18.93e^{(\ln 0.92703)t}} = \frac{1}{1 + 18.93e^{-0.07577t}}.$$

As Figure 4(b) shows, this more realistic model also fits the data well. The dangers of extrapolating beyond the data are illustrated by this equation's prediction that 95.8% of fabrics in the United States would be synthetic by 2010. In fact, cotton is still more popular than synthetic fabrics. *Source: Fabrics Manufacturers*.

Synthetic Fabric as Percent of U.S. Consumption								
Year	1930	1935	1940	1945	1950	1955	1960	1965	1967
Fraction synthetic	0.044	0.079	0.10	0.14	0.22	0.28	0.29	0.43	0.47

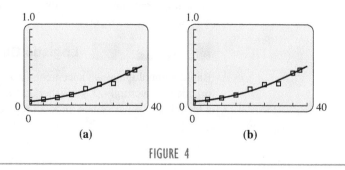

(a) (b)

FIGURE 4

EXERCISES

Find the general solution for each differential equation. Verify that each solution satisfies the original differential equation.

1. $\dfrac{dy}{dx} = -4x + 6x^2$

2. $\dfrac{dy}{dx} = 4e^{-3x}$

3. $4x^3 - 2\dfrac{dy}{dx} = 0$

4. $3x^2 - 3\dfrac{dy}{dx} = 2$

5. $y\dfrac{dy}{dx} = x^2$

6. $y\dfrac{dy}{dx} = x^2 - x$

7. $\dfrac{dy}{dx} = 2xy$

8. $\dfrac{dy}{dx} = x^2 y$

9. $\dfrac{dy}{dx} = 3x^2 y - 2xy$

10. $(y^2 - y)\dfrac{dy}{dx} = x$

11. $\dfrac{dy}{dx} = \dfrac{y}{x}, \; x > 0$

12. $\dfrac{dy}{dx} = \dfrac{y}{x^2}$

13. $\dfrac{dy}{dx} = \dfrac{y^2 + 6}{2y}$

14. $\dfrac{dy}{dx} = \dfrac{e^{y^2}}{y}$

15. $\dfrac{dy}{dx} = y^2 e^{2x}$

16. $\dfrac{dy}{dx} = \dfrac{e^x}{e^y}$

Find the particular solution for each initial value problem.

17. $\dfrac{dy}{dx} + 3x^2 = 2x; \quad y(0) = 5$

18. $\dfrac{dy}{dx} = 4x^3 - 3x^2 + x; \quad y(1) = 0$

19. $2\dfrac{dy}{dx} = 4xe^{-x}; \quad y(0) = 42$

20. $x\dfrac{dy}{dx} = x^2 e^{3x}; \quad y(0) = \dfrac{8}{9}$

21. $\dfrac{dy}{dx} = \dfrac{x^3}{y}; \quad y(0) = 5$

22. $x^2\dfrac{dy}{dx} - y\sqrt{x} = 0; \quad y(1) = e^{-2}$

23. $(2x + 3)y = \dfrac{dy}{dx}; \quad y(0) = 1$

24. $\dfrac{dy}{dx} = \dfrac{x^2 + 5}{2y - 1}; \quad y(0) = 11$

25. $\dfrac{dy}{dx} = \dfrac{2x + 1}{y - 3}; \quad y(0) = 4$

26. $x^2\dfrac{dy}{dx} = y; \quad y(1) = -1$

27. $\dfrac{dy}{dx} = \dfrac{y^2}{x}; \quad y(e) = 3$

28. $\dfrac{dy}{dx} = x^{1/2} y^2; \quad y(4) = 9$

29. $\dfrac{dy}{dx} = (y - 1)^2 e^{x-1}; \quad y(1) = 2$

30. $\dfrac{dy}{dx} = (x + 2)^2 e^y; \quad y(1) = 0$

31. a. Solve the logistic Equation (4) in this section by observing that
$$\frac{1}{y} + \frac{1}{N - y} = \frac{N}{(N - y)y}.$$

b. Assume $0 < y < N$. Verify that $b = (N - y_0)/y_0$ in Equation (5), where y_0 is the initial population size.

c. Assume $0 < N < y$ for all y. Verify that $b = (y_0 - N)/y_0$.

32. Suppose that $0 < z < 1$ for all z. Solve the logistic Equation (6) as in Exercise 31. Verify that $b = e^{kx_0}$, where x_0 is the time at which $z = 1/2$.

33. Suppose that $0 < y_0 < N$. Let $b = (N - y_0)/y_0$, and let $y(x) = N/(1 + be^{-kx})$ for all x. Show the following.

a. $0 < y(x) < N$ for all x.

b. The lines $y = 0$ and $y = N$ are horizontal asymptotes of the graph.

c. $y(x)$ is an increasing function.

d. $((\ln b)/k, N/2)$ is a point of inflection of the graph.

e. dy/dx is a maximum at $x_0 = (\ln b)/k$.

34. Suppose that $0 < N < y_0$. Let $b = (y_0 - N)/y_0$ and let
$$y(x) = \frac{N}{1 - be^{-kx}} \quad \text{for all } x \neq \frac{\ln b}{k}.$$

See the figure. Show the following.

a. $0 < b < 1$

b. The lines $y = 0$ and $y = N$ are horizontal asymptotes of the graph.

c. The line $x = (\ln b)/k$ is a vertical asymptote of the graph.

d. $y(x)$ is decreasing on $((\ln b)/k, \infty)$ and on $(-\infty, (\ln b)/k)$.

e. $y(x)$ is concave upward on $((\ln b)/k, \infty)$ and concave downward on $(-\infty, (\ln b)/k)$.

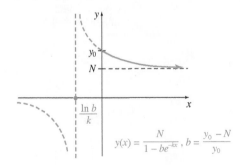

APPLICATIONS

Business and Economics

35. Profit The marginal profit of a certain company is given by
$$\frac{dy}{dx} = \frac{100}{32 - 4x},$$
where x represents the amount of money (in thousands of dollars) that the company spends on advertising. Find the profit for each advertising expenditure if the profit is $1000 when nothing is spent on advertising.

a. $3000

b. $5000

c. Can advertising expenditures ever reach $8000 according to this model? Explain why or why not.

36. Sales Decline Sales (in thousands) of a certain product are declining at a rate proportional to the amount of sales, with a decay constant of 15% per year.

a. Write a differential equation to express the rate of sales decline.

b. Find a general solution to the equation in part a.

c. How much time will pass before sales become 25% of their original value?

37. Inflation If inflation grows continuously at a rate of 5% per year, how long will it take for $1 to lose half its value?

Elasticity of Demand **Given that elasticity of demand is defined as**

$$E = -\frac{p}{q} \cdot \frac{dq}{dp},$$

for demand q and price p. Find the general demand equation $q = f(p)$ for each elasticity function. (Hint: Set each elasticity function equal to $-\frac{p}{q} \cdot \frac{dq}{dp}$, then solve for q. Write the constant of integration as $\ln C$ in Exercise 39.)

38. $E = \dfrac{4p^2}{q^2}$ **39.** $E = 2$

40. Internet Usage During the early days of the Internet, growth in the number of users worldwide could be approximated by an exponential function. The following table gives the number of worldwide users of the Internet. *Source: Internet World Stats.*

Year	Number of Users (in millions)
1995	16
1996	36
1997	70
1998	147
1999	248
2000	361
2001	513
2002	587
2003	719
2004	817
2005	1018
2006	1093
2007	1319
2008	1574
2009	1802

Use a calculator with exponential and logistic regression capabilities to complete the following.

a. Letting t represent the years since 1990, plot the number of worldwide users of the Internet on the y-axis against the year on the t-axis. Discuss the shape of the graph.

b. Use the exponential regression function on your calculator to determine the exponential equation that best fits the data. Plot the exponential equation on the same graph as the data points. Discuss the appropriateness of fitting an exponential function to these data.

c. Use the logistic regression function on your calculator to determine the logistic equation that best fits the data. Plot the logistic equation on the same graph. Discuss the appropriateness of fitting a logistic function to these data. Which graph better fits the data?

d. Assuming that the logistic function found in part c continues to be accurate, what seems to be the limiting size of the number of worldwide Internet users?

41. Life Insurance A life insurance company invests $5000 in a bank account in order to fund a death benefit of $20,000. Growth in the investment over time can be modeled by the differential equation

$$\frac{dA}{dt} = Ai$$

where i is the interest rate and $A(t)$ is the amount invested at time t (in years). Calculate the interest rate that the investment must earn in order for the company to fund the death benefit in 24 years. Choose one of the following. *Source: Society of Actuaries.*

a. $\dfrac{-\ln 2}{12}$ **b.** $\dfrac{-\ln 2}{24}$ **c.** $\dfrac{\ln 2}{24}$ **d.** $\dfrac{\ln 2}{12}$ **e.** $\dfrac{\ln 2}{6}$

Life Sciences

42. Tracer Dye The amount of a tracer dye injected into the bloodstream decreases exponentially, with a decay constant of 3% per minute. If 6 cc are present initially, how many cubic centimeters are present after 10 minutes? (Here k will be negative.)

43. Soil Moisture The evapotranspiration index I is a measure of soil moisture. An article on 10- to 14-year-old heath vegetation described the rate of change of I with respect to W, the amount of water available, by the equation

$$\frac{dI}{dW} = 0.088(2.4 - I).$$

Source: Australian Journal of Botany.

a. According to the article, I has a value of 1 when $W = 0$. Solve the initial value problem.

b. What happens to I as W becomes larger and larger?

44. Fish Population An isolated fish population is limited to 4000 by the amount of food available. If there are now 320 fish and the population is growing with a growth constant of 2% a year, find the expected population at the end of 10 years.

Dieting **A person's weight depends both on the daily rate of energy intake, say C calories per day, and on the daily rate of energy consumption, typically between 15 and 20 calories per pound per day. Using an average value of 17.5 calories per pound per day, a person weighing w pounds uses $17.5w$ calories per day. If $C = 17.5w$, then weight remains constant, and weight gain or loss occurs according to whether C is greater or less than $17.5w$. Source: The College Mathematics Journal.**

45. To determine how fast a change in weight will occur, the most plausible assumption is that dw/dt is proportional to the net excess (or deficit) $C - 17.5w$ in the number of calories per day.

a. Assume C is constant and write a differential equation to express this relationship. Use k to represent the constant of proportionality. What does C being constant imply?

b. The units of dw/dt are pounds per day, and the units of $C - 17.5w$ are calories per day. What units must k have?

c. Use the fact that 3500 calories is equivalent to 1 lb to rewrite the differential equation in part a.

d. Solve the differential equation.

e. Let w_0 represent the initial weight and use it to express the coefficient of $e^{-0.005t}$ in terms of w_0 and C.

46. (Refer to Exercise 45.) Suppose someone initially weighing 180 lb adopts a diet of 2500 calories per day.

a. Write the weight function for this individual.

b. Graph the weight function on the window $[0, 300]$ by $[120, 200]$. What is the asymptote? This value of w is the equilibrium weight w_{eq}. According to the model, can a person ever achieve this weight?

c. How long will it take a dieter to reach a weight just 2 lb more than w_{eq}?

47. H1N1 Virus The cumulative number of deaths worldwide due to the H1N1 virus, or swine flu, at various days into the epidemic are listed below, where April 21, 2009 was day 1. *Source: BBC.*

Day	Deaths	Day	Deaths
14	27	148	3696
28	74	163	4334
43	114	182	4804
57	164	206	6704
71	315	221	8450
84	580	234	9797
99	1049	266	14,024
117	2074	274	14,378
132	2967		

Use a calculator with logistic regression capability to complete the following.

a. Plot the number of deaths y against the number of days t. Discuss the appropriateness of fitting a logistic function to this data.

b. Use the logistic regression function on your calculator to determine the logistic equation that best fits the data.

c. Plot the logistic regression function from part b on the same graph as the data points. Discuss how well the logistic equation fits the data.

d. Assuming the logistic equation found in part b continues to be accurate, what seems to be the limiting size of the number of deaths due to this outbreak of the H1N1 virus?

e. Discuss whether a logistic model is more appropriate than an exponential model for estimating the number of deaths due to the H1N1 virus.

48. Population Growth The following table gives the historic and projected populations (in millions) of China and India. *Source: United Nations.*

Year	China	India
1950	545	372
1960	646	448
1970	816	553
1980	981	693
1990	1142	862
2000	1267	1043
2010	1354	1214
2020	1431	1367
2030	1462	1485
2040	1455	1565
2050	1417	1614

Use a calculator with logistic regression capability to complete the following.

a. Letting t represent the years since 1950, plot the Chinese population on the y-axis against the year on the t-axis. Discuss the appropriateness of fitting a logistic function to these data.

b. Use the logistic regression function on your calculator to determine the logistic equation that best fits the data. Plot the logistic function on the same graph as the data points. Discuss how well the logistic function fits the data.

c. Assuming the logistic equation found in part b continues to be accurate, what seems to be the limiting size of the Chinese population?

d. Repeat parts a–c using the population for India.

49. U.S. Hispanic Population A recent report by the U.S. Census Bureau predicts that the U.S. Hispanic population will increase from 35.6 million in 2000 to 102.6 million in 2050. *Source: U.S. Census Bureau.* Assuming the unlimited growth model $dy/dt = ky$ fits this population growth, express the population y as a function of the year t. Let 2000 correspond to $t = 0$.

50. U.S. Asian Population (Refer to Exercise 49.) The report also predicted that the U.S. Asian population would increase from 10.7 million in 2000 to 33.4 million in 2050. *Source: U.S. Census Bureau.* Repeat Exercise 49 using this data.

51. Spread of a Rumor Suppose the rate at which a rumor spreads—that is, the number of people who have heard the rumor over a period of time—increases with the number of people who have heard it. If y is the number of people who have heard the rumor, then

$$\frac{dy}{dt} = ky,$$

where t is the time in days.

a. If y is 1 when $t = 0$, and y is 5 when $t = 2$, find k.

Using the value of k from part a, find y for each time.

b. $t = 3$ **c.** $t = 5$ **d.** $t = 10$

52. World Population The following table gives the population of the world at various times over the last two centuries, plus projections for this century. *Source: The New York Times*.

Year	Population (billions)
1804	1
1927	2
1960	3
1974	4
1987	5
1999	6
2011	7
2025	8
2041	9
2071	10

Use a calculator with logistic regression capability to complete the following.

a. Use the logistic regression function on your calculator to determine the logistic equation that best fits the data.

b. Plot the logistic function found in part a and the original data in the same window. Does the logistic function seem to fit the data from 1927 on? Before 1927?

c. To get a better fit, subtract 0.99 from each value of the population in the table. (This makes the population in 1804 small, but not 0 or negative.) Find a logistic function that fits the new data.

d. Plot the logistic function found in part c and the modified data in the same window. Does the logistic function now seem to be a better fit than in part b?

e. Based on the results from parts c and d, predict the limiting value of the world's population as time increases. For comparison, the *New York Times* article predicts a value of 10.73 billion. (*Hint:* After taking the limit, remember to add the 0.99 that was removed earlier.)

f. Based on the results from parts c and d, predict the limiting value of the world population as you go further and further back in time. Does that seem reasonable? Explain.

53. Worker Productivity A company has found that the rate at which a person new to the assembly line produces items is

$$\frac{dy}{dx} = 7.5e^{-0.3y},$$

where x is the number of days the person has worked on the line. How many items can a new worker be expected to produce on the eighth day if he produces none when $x = 0$?

Physical Sciences

54. Radioactive Decay The amount of a radioactive substance decreases exponentially, with a decay constant of 3% per month.

a. Write a differential equation to express the rate of change.

b. Find a general solution to the differential equation from part a.

c. If there are 75 g at the start of the decay process, find a particular solution for the differential equation from part a.

d. Find the amount left after 10 months.

55. Snowplow One morning snow began to fall at a heavy and constant rate. A snowplow started out at 8:00 A.M. At 9:00 A.M. it had traveled 2 miles. By 10:00 A.M. it had traveled 3 miles. Assuming that the snowplow removes a constant volume of snow per hour, determine the time at which it started snowing. (*Hint:* Let t denote the time since the snow started to fall, and let T be the time when the snowplow started out. Let x, the distance the snowplow has traveled, and h, the height of the snow, be functions of t. The assumption that a constant volume of snow per hour is removed implies that the speed of the snowplow times the height of the snow is a constant. Set up and solve differential equations involving dx/dt and dh/dt.) *Source: The American Mathematical Monthly*.

Newton's Law of Cooling Newton's law of cooling states that the rate of change of temperature of an object is proportional to the difference in temperature between the object and the surrounding medium. Thus, if T is the temperature of the object after t hours and T_M is the (constant) temperature of the surrounding medium, then

$$\frac{dT}{dt} = -k(T - T_M),$$

where k is a constant. Use this equation in Exercises 56–59.

56. Show that the solution of this differential equation is

$$T = Ce^{-kt} + T_M,$$

where C is a constant.

57. According to the solution of the differential equation for Newton's law of cooling, what happens to the temperature of an object after it has been in a surrounding medium with constant temperature for a long period of time? How well does this agree with reality?

Newton's Law of Cooling When a dead body is discovered, one of the first steps in the ensuing investigation is for a medical examiner to determine the time of death as closely as possible. Have you ever wondered how this is done? If the temperature of the medium (air, water, or whatever) has been fairly constant and less than 48 hours have passed since the death, Newton's law of cooling can be used. The medical examiner does not actually solve the equation for each case. Instead, a table based on the formula is consulted. Use Newton's law of cooling to work the following exercises. *Source: The College Mathematics Journal*.

58. Assume the temperature of a body at death is 98.6°F, the temperature of the surrounding air is 68°F, and at the end of one hour the body temperature is 90°F.

a. What is the temperature of the body after 2 hours?

b. When will the temperature of the body be 75°F?

c. Approximately when will the temperature of the body be within 0.01° of the surrounding air?

59. Suppose the air temperature surrounding a body remains at a constant 10°F, $C = 88.6$, and $k = 0.24$.

a. Determine a formula for the temperature at any time t.

 b. Use a graphing calculator to graph the temperature T as a function of time t on the window $[0, 30]$ by $[0, 100]$.

c. When does the temperature of the body decrease more rapidly: just after death, or much later? How do you know?

d. What will the temperature of the body be after 4 hours?

e. How long will it take for the body temperature to reach 40°F? Use your calculator graph to verify your answer.

YOUR TURN ANSWERS

1. $y = 2x^6 + (2/3)x^{3/2} + e^{5x}/5 + C$ **2.** $y = 3x^4 + 2x^3 - 4$
3. $y = ((3/2)x^2 + 3 \ln|x| + C)^{1/3}$ **4.** 3733

2 Linear First-Order Differential Equations

APPLY IT   What happens over time to the glucose level in a patient's bloodstream?
The solution to a linear differential equation gives us an answer in Example 4.

Recall that $f^{(n)}(x)$ represents the nth derivative of $f(x)$, and that $f^{(n)}(x)$ is called an nth-order derivative. By this definition, the derivative $f'(x)$ is first-order, $f''(x)$ is second-order, and so on. The *order of a differential equation* is that of the highest-order derivative in the equation. In this section only first-order differential equations are discussed.

A **linear first-order differential equation** is an equation of the form

$$\frac{dy}{dx} + P(x)y = Q(x).$$

Notice that a linear differential equation has a dy/dx term, a y term, and a term that is just a function of x. It does not have terms involving nonlinear expressions such as y^2 or e^y, nor does it have terms involving the product or quotient of y and dy/dx. Many useful models produce such equations. In this section we develop a general method for solving first-order linear differential equations.

EXAMPLE 1   **Linear Differential Equation**

Solve the equation

$$x\frac{dy}{dx} + 6y + 2x^4 = 0. \qquad (1)$$

SOLUTION   We need to first get the equation in the form of a linear first-order differential equation. Thus, dy/dx should have a coefficient of 1. To accomplish this, we divide both sides of the equation by x and rearrange the terms to get the linear differential equation

$$\frac{dy}{dx} + \frac{6}{x}y = -2x^3.$$

This equation is not separable and cannot be solved by the methods discussed so far. (Verify this.) Instead, multiply both sides of the equation by x^6 (the reason will be explained shortly) to get

$$x^6\frac{dy}{dx} + 6x^5y = -2x^9. \qquad (2)$$

On the left, $6x^5$, the coefficient of y, is the derivative of x^6, the coefficient of dy/dx. Recall the product rule for derivatives:

$$D_x(uv) = u\frac{dv}{dx} + \frac{du}{dx}v.$$

If $u = x^6$ and $v = y$, the product rule gives

$$D_x(x^6y) = x^6\frac{dy}{dx} + 6x^5y,$$

which is the left side of Equation (2). Substituting $D_x(x^6y)$ for the left side of Equation (2) gives

$$D_x(x^6y) = -2x^9.$$

Assuming $y = f(x)$, as usual, both sides of this equation can be integrated with respect to x and the result solved for y to get

$$x^6y = \int -2x^9\,dx = -2\left(\frac{x^{10}}{10}\right) + C = -\frac{x^{10}}{5} + C$$

$$y = -\frac{x^4}{5} + \frac{C}{x^6}. \tag{3}$$

Equation (3) is the general solution of Equation (2) and, therefore, of Equation (1).

This procedure has given us a solution, but what motivated our choice of the multiplier x^6? To see where x^6 came from, let $I(x)$ represent the multiplier, and multiply both sides of the general equation

$$\frac{dy}{dx} + P(x)y = Q(x)$$

by $I(x)$:

$$I(x)\frac{dy}{dx} + I(x)P(x)y = I(x)Q(x). \tag{4}$$

The method illustrated above will work only if the left side of the equation is the derivative of the product function $I(x) \cdot y$, which is

$$I(x)\frac{dy}{dx} + I'(x)y. \tag{5}$$

Comparing the coefficients of y in Equations (4) and (5) shows that $I(x)$ must satisfy

$$I'(x) = I(x)P(x),$$

or

$$\frac{I'(x)}{I(x)} = P(x).$$

Integrating both sides of this last equation gives

$$\ln|I(x)| = \int P(x)\,dx + C$$

$$|I(x)| = e^{\int P(x)\,dx + C}$$

or

$$I(x) = \pm e^C e^{\int P(x)\,dx}.$$

Only one value of $I(x)$ is needed, so let $C = 0$, so that $e^C = 1$, and use the positive result, giving

$$I(x) = e^{\int P(x)\,dx}.$$

In summary, choosing $I(x)$ as $e^{\int P(x)\,dx}$ and multiplying both sides of a linear first-order differential equation by $I(x)$ puts the equation in a form that can be solved by integration.

Integrating Factor

The function $I(x) = e^{\int P(x)\,dx}$ is called an **integrating factor** for the differential equation

$$\frac{dy}{dx} + P(x)y = Q(x).$$

For Equation (1), written as the linear differential equation

$$\frac{dy}{dx} + \frac{6}{x}y = -2x^3,$$

$P(x) = 6/x$, and the integrating factor is

$$I(x) = e^{\int (6/x)\,dx} = e^{6\ln|x|} = e^{\ln|x|^6} = e^{\ln x^6} = x^6.$$

This last step used the fact that $e^{\ln a} = a$ for all positive a.

In summary, we solve a linear first-order differential equation with the following steps.

Solving a Linear First-Order Differential Equation

1. Put the equation in the linear form $\dfrac{dy}{dx} + P(x)y = Q(x)$.
2. Find the integrating factor $I(x) = e^{\int P(x)\,dx}$.
3. Multiply each term of the equation from Step 1 by $I(x)$.
4. Replace the sum of terms on the left with $D_x[I(x)y]$.
5. Integrate both sides of the equation.
6. Solve for y.

EXAMPLE 2   Linear Differential Equation

Give the general solution of $\dfrac{dy}{dx} + 2xy = x$.

SOLUTION

Step 1 This equation is already in the required form.

Step 2 The integrating factor is

$$I(x) = e^{\int 2x\,dx} = e^{x^2}.$$

Step 3 Multiplying each term by e^{x^2} gives

$$e^{x^2}\frac{dy}{dx} + 2xe^{x^2}y = xe^{x^2}.$$

Step 4 The sum of terms on the left can now be replaced with $D_x(e^{x^2}y)$, to get

$$D_x(e^{x^2}y) = xe^{x^2}.$$

Step 5 Integrating on both sides gives

$$e^{x^2}y = \int xe^{x^2}\,dx,$$

or

$$e^{x^2}y = \frac{1}{2}e^{x^2} + C.$$

YOUR TURN 1
Give the general solution of
$$x\frac{dy}{dx} - y - x^2 e^x = 0, \, x > 0.$$

Step 6 Divide both sides by e^{x^2} to get the general solution

$$y = \frac{1}{2} + Ce^{-x^2}.$$

TRY YOUR TURN 1

EXAMPLE 3 Linear Differential Equation

Solve the initial value problem $2\left(\dfrac{dy}{dx}\right) - 6y - e^x = 0$ with $y(0) = 5$.

SOLUTION Write the equation in the required form by adding e^x to both sides and dividing both sides by 2:

$$\frac{dy}{dx} - 3y = \frac{1}{2}e^x.$$

The integrating factor is

$$I(x) = e^{\int(-3)\,dx} = e^{-3x}.$$

Multiplying each term by $I(x)$ gives

$$e^{-3x}\frac{dy}{dx} - 3e^{-3x}y = \frac{1}{2}e^x e^{-3x},$$

or

$$e^{-3x}\frac{dy}{dx} - 3e^{-3x}y = \frac{1}{2}e^{-2x}.$$

The left side can now be replaced by $D_x(e^{-3x}y)$ to get

$$D_x(e^{-3x}y) = \frac{1}{2}e^{-2x}.$$

Integrating on both sides gives

$$e^{-3x}y = \int \frac{1}{2}e^{-2x}\,dx,$$

$$e^{-3x}y = \frac{1}{2}\left(\frac{e^{-2x}}{-2}\right) + C.$$

Now, multiply both sides by e^{3x} to get

$$y = -\frac{e^x}{4} + Ce^{3x},$$

the general solution. Find the particular solution by substituting 0 for x and 5 for y:

$$5 = -\frac{e^0}{4} + Ce^0 = -\frac{1}{4} + C$$

or

$$\frac{21}{4} = C,$$

which leads to the particular solution

YOUR TURN 2
Solve the initial value problem
$$\frac{dy}{dx} + 2xy - xe^{-x^2} = 0 \text{ with}$$
$$y(0) = 3.$$

$$y = -\frac{e^x}{4} + \frac{21}{4}e^{3x}.$$

TRY YOUR TURN 2

Differential Equations

EXAMPLE 4   Glucose

Suppose glucose is infused into a patient's bloodstream at a constant rate of a grams per minute. At the same time, glucose is removed from the bloodstream at a rate proportional to the amount of glucose present. Then the amount of glucose, $G(t)$, present at time t satisfies

$$\frac{dG}{dt} = a - KG$$

for some constant K. Solve this equation for G. Does the glucose concentration eventually reach a constant? That is, what happens to G as $t \to \infty$? *Source: Ordinary Differential Equations with Applications.*

APPLY IT   **SOLUTION**   The equation can be written in the form of the linear first-order differential equation

$$\frac{dG}{dt} + KG = a. \qquad (6)$$

The integrating factor is

$$I(t) = e^{\int K\,dt} = e^{Kt}.$$

Multiply both sides of Equation (6) by $I(t) = e^{Kt}$.

$$e^{Kt}\frac{dG}{dt} + Ke^{Kt}G = ae^{Kt}$$

Write the left side as $D_t(e^{Kt}G)$ and solve for G by integrating on both sides.

$$D_t(e^{Kt}G) = ae^{Kt}$$

$$e^{Kt}G = \int ae^{Kt}dt$$

$$e^{Kt}G = \frac{a}{K}e^{Kt} + C$$

Multiply both sides by e^{-Kt} to get

$$G = \frac{a}{K} + Ce^{-Kt}.$$

NOTE

The equation in Example 4 can also be solved by separation of variables. You are asked to do this in Exercise 22.

As $t \to \infty$,

$$\lim_{t\to\infty} G = \lim_{t\to\infty}\left(\frac{a}{K} + Ce^{-Kt}\right) = \lim_{t\to\infty}\left(\frac{a}{K} + \frac{C}{e^{Kt}}\right) = \frac{a}{K}.$$

Thus, the glucose concentration stabilizes at a/K.

2   EXERCISES

Find the general solution for each differential equation.

1. $\frac{dy}{dx} + 3y = 6$

2. $\frac{dy}{dx} + 5y = 12$

3. $\frac{dy}{dx} + 2xy = 4x$

4. $\frac{dy}{dx} + 4xy = 4x$

5. $x\frac{dy}{dx} - y - x = 0, \quad x > 0$

6. $x\frac{dy}{dx} + 2xy - x^2 = 0$

7. $2\frac{dy}{dx} - 2xy - x = 0$

8. $3\frac{dy}{dx} + 6xy + x = 0$

9. $x\frac{dy}{dx} + 2y = x^2 + 6x, \quad x > 0$

10. $x^3\frac{dy}{dx} - x^2y = x^4 - 4x^3, \quad x > 0$

11. $y - x\frac{dy}{dx} = x^3, \quad x > 0$

12. $2xy + x^3 = x\frac{dy}{dx}$

199

Solve each differential equation, subject to the given initial condition.

13. $\dfrac{dy}{dx} + y = 4e^x$; $\quad y(0) = 50$

14. $\dfrac{dy}{dx} + 4y = 9e^{5x}$; $\quad y(0) = 25$

15. $\dfrac{dy}{dx} - 2xy - 4x = 0$; $\quad y(1) = 20$

16. $x\dfrac{dy}{dx} - 3y + 2 = 0$; $\quad y(1) = 8$

17. $x\dfrac{dy}{dx} + 5y = x^2$; $\quad y(2) = 12$

18. $2\dfrac{dy}{dx} - 4xy = 5x$; $\quad y(1) = 10$

19. $x\dfrac{dy}{dx} + (1 + x)y = 3$; $\quad y(4) = 50$

20. $\dfrac{dy}{dx} + 3x^2y - 2xe^{-x^3} = 0$; $\quad y(0) = 1000$

APPLICATIONS

Life Sciences

21. Population Growth The logistic equation introduced in Section 1,

$$\frac{dy}{dx} = k\left(1 - \frac{y}{N}\right)y \qquad (7)$$

can be written as

$$\frac{dy}{dx} = cy - py^2, \qquad (8)$$

where c and p are positive constants. Although this is a non-linear differential equation, it can be reduced to a linear equation by a suitable substitution for the variable y.

a. Letting $y = 1/z$ and $dy/dx = (-1/z^2)dz/dx$, rewrite Equation (8) in terms of z. Solve for z and then for y.

b. Let $z(0) = 1/y_0$ in part a and find a particular solution for y.

c. Find the limit of y as $x \to \infty$. This is the saturation level of the population.

22. Glucose Level Solve the glucose level example (Example 4) using separation of variables.

23. Drug Use The rate of change in the concentration of a drug with respect to time in a user's blood is given by

$$\frac{dC}{dt} = -kC + D(t),$$

where $D(t)$ is dosage at time t and k is the rate that the drug leaves the bloodstream. *Source: Mathematical Biosciences.*

a. Solve this linear equation to show that, if $C(0) = 0$, then

$$C(t) = e^{-kt}\int_0^t e^{ky}D(y)\,dy.$$

(Hint: To integrate both sides of the equation in Step 5 of "Solving a Linear First-Order Differential Equation," integrate from 0 to t, and change the variable of integration to y.)

b. Show that if $D(y)$ is a constant D, then

$$C(t) = \frac{D(1 - e^{-kt})}{k}.$$

24. Mouse Infection A model for the spread of an infectious disease among mice is

$$\frac{dN}{dt} = rN - \frac{\alpha r(\alpha + b + v)}{\beta\left[\alpha - r\left(1 + \dfrac{v}{b + \gamma}\right)\right]},$$

where N is the size of the population of mice, α is the mortality rate due to infection, b is the mortality rate due to natural causes for infected mice, β is a transmission coefficient for the rate that infected mice infect susceptible mice, v is the rate the mice recover from infection, and γ is the rate that mice lose immunity. *Source: Lectures on Mathematics in the Life Sciences.* Show that the solution to this equation, with the initial condition $N(0) = (\alpha + b + v)/\beta$, can be written as

$$N(t) = \frac{(\alpha + b + v)}{\beta R}[(R - \alpha)e^{rt} + \alpha],$$

where

$$R = \alpha - r\left(1 + \frac{v}{b + \gamma}\right).$$

Social Sciences

Immigration and Emigration If population is changed either by immigration or emigration, the exponential growth model discussed in Section 1 is modified to

$$\frac{dy}{dt} = ky + f(t),$$

where y is the population at time t and $f(t)$ is some (other) function of t that describes the net effect of the emigration/immigration. Assume $k = 0.02$ and $y(0) = 10{,}000$. Solve this differential equation for y, given the following functions $f(t)$.

25. $f(t) = e^t$ **26.** $f(t) = e^{-t}$

27. $f(t) = -t$ **28.** $f(t) = t$

Physical Sciences

29. Newton's Law of Cooling In Exercises 56–59 in the previous section, we saw that Newton's Law of Cooling states that the rate of change of the temperature of an object is proportional to the difference in temperature between the object and the surrounding medium. This leads to the differential equation

$$\frac{dT}{dt} = -k(T - T_M),$$

where T is the temperature of the object after time t, T_M is the temperature of the surrounding medium, and k is a constant. In the previous section, we solved this equation by separation of variables. Show that this equation is also linear, and find the solution by the method of this section.

3 Euler's Method

How many people have heard a rumor 3 hours after it is started? *This question will be answered in Exercise 35 at the end of this section.*

Applications sometimes involve differential equations such as

$$\frac{dy}{dx} = \frac{x + y}{y}$$

that cannot be solved by the methods discussed so far, but approximate solutions to these equations often can be found by numerical methods. For many applications, these approximations are quite adequate. In this section we introduce Euler's method, which is only one of numerous mathematical contributions made by Leonhard Euler (1707–1783) of Switzerland. (His name is pronounced "oiler.") He also introduced the $f(x)$ notation used throughout this text. Despite becoming blind during his later years, he was the most prolific mathematician of his era. In fact it took nearly 50 years after his death to publish the works he created in all mathematical fields during his lifetime.

Euler's method of solving differential equations gives approximate solutions to differential equations involving $y = f(x)$ where the initial values of x and y are known; that is, equations of the form

$$\frac{dy}{dx} = g(x, y), \qquad \text{with} \quad y(x_0) = y_0.$$

Geometrically, Euler's method approximates the graph of the solution $y = f(x)$ with a polygonal line whose first segment is tangent to the curve at the point (x_0, y_0), as shown in Figure 5.

FOR REVIEW

In linear approximation, we define Δy to be the actual change in y as x changed by an amount Δx:

$$\Delta y = f(x + \Delta x) - f(x).$$

The differential dy is an approximation to Δy. We find dy by following the tangent line from the point $(x, f(x))$, rather than by following the actual function. Then dy is found by using the formula $dy = (dy/dx)\, dx$ where $dx = \Delta x$. For example, let $f(x) = x^3$, $x = 1$, and $dx = \Delta x = 0.2$. Then $dy = f'(x)\, dx = 3x^2\, dx = 3(1^2)(0.2) = 0.6$. The actual change in y as x changes from 1 to 1.2 is

$$f(x + \Delta x) - f(x)$$
$$= f(1.2) - f(1)$$
$$= 1.2^3 - 1$$
$$= 0.728.$$

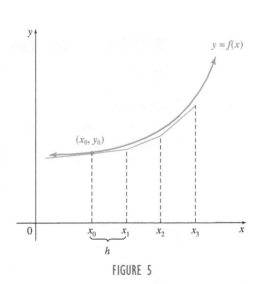

FIGURE 5

To use Euler's method, divide the interval from x_0 to another point x_n into n subintervals of equal width (see Figure 5.) The width of each subinterval is $h = (x_n - x_0)/n$.

Recall that if Δx is a small change in x, then the corresponding small change in y, Δy, is approximated by

$$\Delta y \approx dy = \frac{dy}{dx} \cdot \Delta x.$$

The differential dy is the change in y along the tangent line. On the interval from x_i to x_{i+1}, note that dy is just $y_{i+1} - y_i$, where y_i is the approximate solution at x_i. We also have $dy/dx = g(x_i, y_i)$ and $\Delta x = h$. Putting these into the previous equation yields

$$y_{i+1} - y_i = g(x_i, y_i)h$$
$$y_{i+1} = y_i + g(x_i, y_i)h.$$

Because y_0 is given, we can use the equation just derived with $i = 0$ to get y_1. We can then use y_1 and the same equation with $i = 1$ to get y_2 and continue in this manner until we get y_n. A summary of Euler's method follows.

Euler's Method

Let $y = f(x)$ be the solution of the differential equation

$$\frac{dy}{dx} = g(x, y), \quad \text{with} \quad y(x_0) = y_0,$$

for $x_0 \leq x \leq x_n$. Let $x_{i+1} = x_i + h$, where $h = (x_n - x_0)/n$ and

$$y_{i+1} = y_i + g(x_i, y_i)h,$$

for $0 \leq i \leq n - 1$. Then

$$f(x_{i+1}) \approx y_{i+1}.$$

As the following examples will show, the accuracy of the approximation varies for different functions. As h gets smaller, however, the approximation improves, although making h too small can make things worse. (See the discussion at the end of this section.) Euler's method is not difficult to program; it then becomes possible to try smaller and smaller values of h to get better and better approximations.

EXAMPLE 1   Euler's Method

Use Euler's method to approximate the solution of $dy/dx + 2xy = x$, with $y(0) = 1.5$, for $[0, 1]$. Use $h = 0.1$.

**Method 1
Calculating by Hand**

SOLUTION

The general solution of this equation was found in Example 2 of the last section, so the results using Euler's method can be compared with the actual solution. Begin by writing the differential equation in the required form as

$$\frac{dy}{dx} = x - 2xy, \quad \text{so that} \quad g(x, y) = x - 2xy.$$

Since $x_0 = 0$ and $y_0 = 1.5$,

$$g(x_0, y_0) = 0 - 2(0)(1.5) = 0,$$

and

$$y_1 = y_0 + g(x_0, y_0)h = 1.5 + 0(0.1) = 1.5.$$

Now $x_1 = 0.1$, $y_1 = 1.5$, and $g(x_1, y_1) = 0.1 - 2(0.1)(1.5) = -0.2$. Then

$$y_2 = 1.5 + (-0.2)(0.1) = 1.48.$$

The 11 values for x_i and y_i for $0 \leq i \leq 10$ are shown in the table below, together with the actual values using the result from Example 2 in the last section. (Since the result was only a general solution, replace x with 0 and y with 1.5 to get the particular solution $y = 1/2 + e^{-x^2}$.)

The results in the table look quite good. The graphs in Figure 6 show that the polygonal line follows the actual graph of $f(x)$ quite closely.

| Approximate Solution Using $h = 0.1$ | | | |
x_i	Euler's Method y_i	Actual Solution $f(x_i)$	Difference $y_i - f(x_i)$
0	1.5	1.5	0
0.1	1.5	1.49004983	0.0099502
0.2	1.48	1.46078944	0.0192106
0.3	1.4408	1.41393119	0.0268688
0.4	1.384352	1.35214379	0.0322082
0.5	1.31360384	1.27880078	0.0348031
0.6	1.23224346	1.19767633	0.0345671
0.7	1.14437424	1.11262639	0.0317478
0.8	1.05416185	1.02729242	0.0268694
0.9	0.96549595	0.94485807	0.0206379
1.0	0.88170668	0.86787944	0.0138272

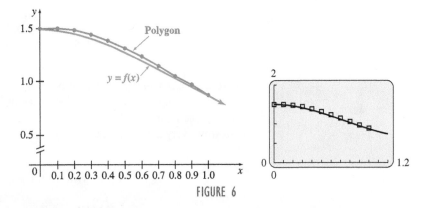

FIGURE 6

Method 2
Graphing Calculator

A graphing calculator can readily implement Euler's method. To do this example on a TI-84 Plus, start x with the value of $x_0 - h$ by storing -0.1 in X, store y_0, or 1.5, in Y, and put $X - 2X*Y$ into the function Y_1. Then the command $X + .1 \rightarrow X : Y + Y_1 * .1 \rightarrow Y$ gives the next value of y, which is still 1.5. Continue to press the ENTER key to get subsequent values of y.

Method 3
Spreadsheet

Euler's method can also be performed on a spreadsheet. In Microsoft Excel, for example, store the values of x in column A and the initial value of y in B1. Then put the command "$=B1+(A1-2*A1*B1)*.1$" into B2 to get the next value of y, using the formula for $g(x, y)$ in this example. Copy this formula into the rest of column B to get subsequent values of y.

YOUR TURN 1 Use Euler's method to approximate the solution of $dy/dx - x^2y^2 = 1$, with $y(0) = 2$, for [0,1]. Use $h = 0.2$.

TRY YOUR TURN 1

Differential Equations

Euler's method produces a very good approximation for this differential equation because the slope of the solution $f(x)$ is not steep in the interval under investigation. The next example shows that such good results cannot always be expected.

EXAMPLE 2   Euler's Method

Use Euler's method to solve $dy/dx = 3y + (1/2)e^x$, with $y(0) = 5$, for $[0, 1]$, using 10 subintervals.

SOLUTION   This is the differential equation of Example 3 in the last section. The general solution found there, with the initial condition given above, leads to the particular solution

$$y = -\frac{1}{4}e^x + \frac{21}{4}e^{3x}.$$

To solve by Euler's method, start with $g(x, y) = 3y + (1/2)e^x$, $x_0 = 0$, and $y_0 = 5$. For $n = 10$, $h = (1 - 0)/10 = 0.1$ again, and

$$y_{i+1} = y_i + g(x_i, y_i)h = y_i + \left(3y_i + \frac{1}{2}e^{x_i}\right)h.$$

For y_1, this gives

$$y_1 = y_0 + \left(3y_0 + \frac{1}{2}e^{x_0}\right)h$$

$$= 5 + \left[3(5) + \frac{1}{2}(e^0)\right](0.1)$$

$$= 5 + (15.5)(0.1) = 6.55.$$

Similarly,

$$y_2 = 6.55 + \left[3(6.55) + \frac{1}{2}e^{0.1}\right](0.1)$$

$$= 6.55 + (19.65 + 0.55258546)(0.1)$$

$$= 8.57025855.$$

These and the remaining values for the interval $[0, 1]$ are shown in the table below.

In this example the absolute value of the differences grows very rapidly as x_i gets farther from x_0. See Figure 7. These large differences come from the term e^{3x} in the solution; this term grows very quickly as x increases.

	Approximate Solution Using $h = 0.1$		
x_i	Euler's Method y_i	Actual Solution $f(x_i)$	Difference $y_i - f(x_i)$
0	5	5	0
0.1	6.55	6.810466	−0.260466
0.2	8.570259	9.260773	−0.690514
0.3	11.202406	12.575452	−1.373045
0.4	14.630621	17.057658	−2.427037
0.5	19.094399	23.116687	−4.022289
0.6	24.905154	31.305119	−6.399965
0.7	32.467806	42.368954	−9.901147
0.8	42.308836	57.315291	−15.006455
0.9	55.112764	77.503691	−22.390927
1	71.769573	104.769498	−32.999925

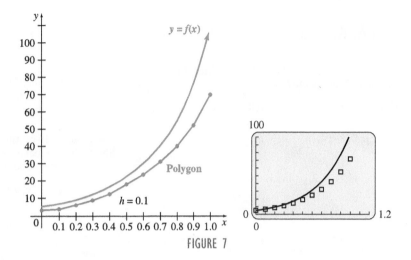

FIGURE 7

As these examples show, numerical methods may produce large errors. The error often can be reduced by using more subintervals of smaller width—letting $n = 100$ or 1000, for example. Approximations for the function in Example 3 with $n = 100$ and $h = (1 - 0)/100 = 0.01$ are shown in the table below. The approximations are considerably improved.

	Approximate Solution Using $h = 0.01$		
x_i	Euler's Method y_i	Actual Solution $f(x_i)$	Difference $y_i - f(x_i)$
0	5	5	0
0.1	6.779418	6.810466	−0.031048
0.2	9.177101	9.260773	−0.083672
0.3	12.406341	12.575452	−0.169111
0.4	16.753855	17.057658	−0.303803
0.5	22.605046	23.116687	−0.511642
0.6	30.477945	31.305119	−0.827175
0.7	41.068839	42.368954	−1.300115
0.8	55.313581	57.315291	−2.001710
0.9	74.469995	77.503691	−3.033695
1	100.228621	104.769498	−4.540878

We could improve the accuracy of Euler's method by using a smaller h, but there are two difficulties. First, this requires more calculations and, consequently, more time. Such calculations are usually done by computer, so the increased time may not matter. But this introduces a second difficulty: The increased number of calculations causes more round-off error, so there is a limit to how small we can make h and still get improvement. The preferred way to get greater accuracy is to use a more sophisticated procedure, such as the Runge-Kutta method. Such methods are beyond the scope of this text but are discussed in numerical analysis and differential equations courses.*

*For example, see Nagle, R. K., E. B. Saff, and A. D. Snider, *Fundamentals of Differential Equations*, 8th ed., Pearson, 2012.

3 EXERCISES

Use Euler's method to approximate the indicated function value to 3 decimal places, using $h = 0.1$.

1. $\dfrac{dy}{dx} = x^2 + y^2$; $y(0) = 2$; find $y(0.5)$

2. $\dfrac{dy}{dx} = xy + 4$; $y(0) = 0$; find $y(0.5)$

3. $\dfrac{dy}{dx} = 1 + y$; $y(0) = 2$; find $y(0.6)$

4. $\dfrac{dy}{dx} = x + y^2$; $y(0) = 0$; find $y(0.6)$

5. $\dfrac{dy}{dx} = x + \sqrt{y}$; $y(0) = 1$; find $y(0.4)$

6. $\dfrac{dy}{dx} = 1 + \dfrac{y}{x}$; $y(1) = 0$; find $y(1.4)$

7. $\dfrac{dy}{dx} = 2x\sqrt{1 + y^2}$; $y(1) = 2$; find $y(1.5)$

8. $\dfrac{dy}{dx} = e^{-y} + e^x$; $y(1) = 1$; find $y(1.5)$

Use Euler's method to approximate the indicated function value to 3 decimal places, using $h = 0.1$. Next, solve the differential equation and find the indicated function value to 3 decimal places. Compare the result with the approximation.

9. $\dfrac{dy}{dx} = -4 + x$; $y(0) = 1$; find $y(0.4)$

10. $\dfrac{dy}{dx} = 4x + 3$; $y(1) = 0$; find $y(1.5)$

11. $\dfrac{dy}{dx} = x^3$; $y(0) = 4$; find $y(0.5)$

12. $\dfrac{dy}{dx} = \dfrac{3}{x}$; $y(1) = 2$; find $y(1.4)$

13. $\dfrac{dy}{dx} = 2xy$; $y(1) = 1$; find $y(1.6)$

14. $\dfrac{dy}{dx} = x^2 y$; $y(0) = 1$; find $y(0.6)$

15. $\dfrac{dy}{dx} = ye^x$; $y(0) = 2$; find $y(0.4)$

16. $\dfrac{dy}{dx} = \dfrac{2x}{y}$; $y(0) = 3$; find $y(0.6)$

17. $\dfrac{dy}{dx} + y = 2e^x$; $y(0) = 100$; find $y(0.3)$

18. $\dfrac{dy}{dx} - 2y = e^{2x}$; $y(0) = 10$; find $y(0.4)$

Use Method 2 or 3 in Example 1 to construct a table like the ones in the examples for $0 \le x \le 1$, with $h = 0.2$.

19. $\dfrac{dy}{dx} = \sqrt[3]{x}$; $y(0) = 0$ 20. $\dfrac{dy}{dx} = y$; $y(0) = 1$

21. $\dfrac{dy}{dx} = 4 - y$; $y(0) = 0$

22. $\dfrac{dy}{dx} = x - 2xy$; $y(0) = 1$

Solve each differential equation and graph the function $y = f(x)$ and the polygonal approximation on the same axes. (The approximations were found in Exercises 19–22.)

23. $\dfrac{dy}{dx} = \sqrt[3]{x}$; $y(0) = 0$ 24. $\dfrac{dy}{dx} = y$; $y(0) = 1$

25. $\dfrac{dy}{dx} = 4 - y$; $y(0) = 0$

26. $\dfrac{dy}{dx} = x - 2xy$; $y(0) = 1$

27. **a.** Use Euler's method with $h = 0.2$ to approximate $f(1)$, where $f(x)$ is the solution to the differential equation

$$\frac{dy}{dx} = y^2; y(0) = 1.$$

   b. Solve the differential equation in part a using separation of variables, and discuss what happens to $f(x)$ as x approaches 1.

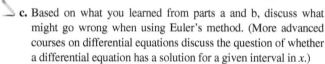   **c.** Based on what you learned from parts a and b, discuss what might go wrong when using Euler's method. (More advanced courses on differential equations discuss the question of whether a differential equation has a solution for a given interval in x.)

APPLICATIONS

Solve Exercises 28–35 using Euler's method.

Business and Economics

28. **Bankruptcy** Suppose 125 small business firms are threatened by bankruptcy. If y is the number bankrupt by time t, then $125 - y$ is the number not yet bankrupt by time t. The rate of change of y is proportional to the product of y and $125 - y$. Let 2010 correspond to $t = 0$. Assume 20 firms are bankrupt at $t = 0$.

   a. Write a differential equation using the given information. Use 0.002 for the constant of proportionality.

   b. Approximate the number of firms that are bankrupt in 2015, using $h = 1$.

Life Sciences

29. **Growth of Algae** The phosphate compounds found in many detergents are highly water soluble and are excellent fertilizers for algae. Assume that there are 5000 algae present at time $t = 0$ and conditions will support at most 500,000 algae. Assume that the rate of growth of algae, in the presence of sufficient phosphates, is proportional both to the number present (in thousands) and to the difference between 500,000 and the number present (in thousands).

   a. Write a differential equation using the given information. Use 0.01 for the constant of proportionality.

   b. Approximate the number present when $t = 2$, using $h = 0.5$.

30. Immigration An island is colonized by immigration from the mainland, where there are 100 species. Let the number of species on the island at time t (in years) equal y, where $y = f(t)$. Suppose the rate at which new species immigrate to the island is

$$\frac{dy}{dt} = 0.02(100 - y^{1/2}).$$

Use Euler's method with $h = 0.5$ to approximate y when $t = 5$ if there were 10 species initially.

31. Insect Population A population of insects, y, living in a circular colony grows at a rate

$$\frac{dy}{dt} = 0.05y - 0.1y^{1/2},$$

where t is time in weeks. If there were 60 insects initially, use Euler's method with $h = 1$ to approximate the number of insects after 6 weeks.

32. Whale Population Under certain conditions a population may exhibit a polynomial growth rate function. A population of blue whales is growing according to the function

$$\frac{dy}{dt} = -y + 0.02y^2 + 0.003y^3.$$

Here y is the population in thousands and t is measured in years. Use Euler's method with $h = 1$ to approximate the population in 4 years if the initial population is 15,000.

33. Goat Growth The growth of male Saanen goats can be approximated by the equation

$$\frac{dW}{dt} = -0.01189W + 0.92389W^{0.016},$$

where W is the weight (in kilograms) after t weeks. *Source: Annales de Zootechnie.* Find the weight of a goat at 5 weeks, given that the weight at birth is 3.65 kg. Use Euler's method with $h = 1$.

Social Sciences

34. Learning In an early article describing how people learn, the rate of change of the probability that a person performs a task correctly (p) with respect to time (t) is given by

$$\frac{dp}{dt} = \frac{2k}{\sqrt{m}}(p - p^2)^{3/2},$$

where k and m are constants related to the rate that the person learns the task. *Source: The Journal of General Psychology.* For this exercise, let $m = 4$ and $k = 0.5$.

a. Letting $p = 0.1$ when $t = 0$, use Method 2 or 3 in Example 1 to construct a table for t_i and p_i like the ones in the examples for $0 \le x \le 30$, with $h = 5$.

b. Based on your answer to part a, what does p seem to approach as t increases? Explain why this answer makes sense.

35. APPLY IT Spread of Rumors A rumor spreads through a community of 500 people at the rate

$$\frac{dN}{dt} = 0.02(500 - N)N^{1/2},$$

where N is the number of people who have heard the rumor at time t (in hours). Use Euler's method with $h = 0.5$ to find the number who have heard the rumor after 3 hours, if only 2 people heard it initially.

YOUR TURN ANSWER

1.

x_i	y_i
0	2
0.2	2.2
0.4	2.43872
0.6	2.82903537
0.8	3.60528313
1.0	5.46903563

4 Applications of Differential Equations

APPLY IT How do the populations of a predator and its prey change over time? We will answer this question in Example 2 using a pair of differential equations.

Continuous Deposits An amount of money A invested at an annual interest rate r, compounded continuously, grows according to the differential equation

$$\frac{dA}{dt} = rA,$$

where t is the time in years. Suppose money is deposited into this account at a rate of D dollars per year and that the money is deposited at a rate that is essentially constant and continuous. The differential equation for the growth of the account then becomes

$$\frac{dA}{dt} = rA + D.$$

EXAMPLE 1 Continuous Deposits

When Michael was born, his grandfather arranged to deposit $5000 in an account for him at 8% annual interest compounded continuously. Grandfather plans to add to the account "continuously" at the rate of $1000 a year. How much will be in the account when Michael is 18?

SOLUTION Here $r = 0.08$ and $D = 1000$, so the differential equation is

$$\frac{dA}{dt} = 0.08A + 1000.$$

Separate the variables and integrate on both sides.

$$\frac{1}{0.08A + 1000}dA = dt$$

$$\frac{1}{0.08}\ln(0.08A + 1000) = t + C$$

$$\ln(0.08A + 1000) = 0.08t + K \qquad \text{\small } K = 0.08C$$

$$0.08A + 1000 = e^{0.08t + K} \qquad \text{\small Apply the function } e^x \text{ to both sides.}$$

$$0.08A = -1000 + e^{0.08t}e^{K}$$

$$0.08A = -1000 + Me^{0.08t} \qquad \text{\small } M = e^K$$

$$A = -12{,}500 + \frac{M}{0.08}e^{0.08t}$$

Use the fact that the initial amount deposited was $5000 to find M.

$$5000 = -12{,}500 + \frac{M}{0.08}e^{(0.08)0}$$

$$5000 = -12{,}500 + \frac{M}{0.08}(1)$$

$$1400 = M$$

$$A = -12{,}500 + \frac{1400}{0.08}e^{0.08t}$$

$$A = -12{,}500 + 17{,}500e^{0.08t}$$

YOUR TURN 1 Modify Example 1 so that the initial amount is $6000, the interest rate is 5%, $1200 a year is added continuously, and Michael must wait until he is 21 to collect.

When Michael is 18, $t = 18$, the amount in the account will be

$$A = -12{,}500 + 17{,}500e^{(0.08)18}$$

$$= -12{,}500 + 17{,}500e^{1.44}$$

$$\approx 61{,}362.18,$$

or about $61,400. TRY YOUR TURN 1

A Predator-Prey Model

The Austrian mathematician A. J. Lotka (1880–1949) and the Italian mathematician Vito Volterra (1860–1940) proposed the following simple model for the way in which the fluctuations of populations of a predator and its prey affect each other. *Source: Elements of Mathematical Biology.* Let $x = f(t)$ denote the population of

Differential Equations

the predator and $y = g(t)$ denote the population of the prey at time t. The predator might be a wolf and its prey a moose, or the predator might be a ladybug and the prey an aphid.

Assume that if there were no predators present, the population of prey would increase at a rate py proportional to their number, but that the predators consume the prey at a rate qxy proportional to the product of the number of prey and the number of predators. The net rate of change dy/dt of y is the rate of increase of the prey minus the rate at which the prey are eaten, that is,

$$\frac{dy}{dt} = py - qxy,$$ (1)

with positive constants p and q.

Assume that if there were no prey, the predators would starve and their population would *decrease* at a rate rx proportional to their number, but that in the presence of prey the rate of growth of the population of predators is increased by an amount sxy. These assumptions give a second differential equation,

$$\frac{dx}{dt} = -rx + sxy,$$ (2)

with additional positive constants r and s.

Equations (1) and (2) form a system of differential equations known as the **Lotka-Volterra equations**. They cannot be solved for x and y as functions of t, but an equation relating the variables x and y can be found. Dividing Equation (1) by Equation (2) gives the separable differential equation

$$\frac{dy}{dx} = \frac{dy/dt}{dx/dt} = \frac{py - qxy}{-rx + sxy}$$

or

$$\frac{dy}{dx} = \frac{y(p - qx)}{x(sy - r)}.$$ (3)

Equation (3) is solved for specific values of the constants p, q, r, and s in the next example.

EXAMPLE 2 Predator-Prey

Suppose that $x = f(t)$ (hundreds of predators) and $y = g(t)$ (thousands of prey) satisfy the Lotka-Volterra Equations (1) and (2) with $p = 3$, $q = 1$, $r = 4$, and $s = 2$. Suppose that at a time when there are 100 predators ($x = 1$), there are 1000 prey ($y = 1$). Find an equation relating x and y.

APPLY IT   **SOLUTION** With the given values of the constants, p, q, r, and s, Equation (3) reads

$$\frac{dy}{dx} = \frac{y(3 - x)}{x(2y - 4)}.$$

Separating the variables yields

$$\frac{2y - 4}{y} dy = \frac{3 - x}{x} dx,$$

or

$$\int \left(2 - \frac{4}{y}\right) dy = \int \left(\frac{3}{x} - 1\right) dx.$$

Evaluating the integrals gives

$$2y - 4 \ln y = 3 \ln x - x + C.$$

(It is not necessary to use absolute value for the logarithms since x and y are positive.) Use the initial conditions $x = 1$ and $y = 1$ to find C.

$$2 - 4(0) = 3(0) - 1 + C$$
$$C = 3$$

The desired equation is

$$x + 2y - 3 \ln x - 4 \ln y = 3. \tag{4}$$

A graph of Equation (4), in Figure 8, shows that the solution is located on a closed curve. By looking at the original differential equation for y,

$$\frac{dy}{dt} = y(3 - x),$$

we can see that when $x < 3$ (the left side of the curve), then $dy/dt > 0$, so y increases. Similarly, when $x > 3$ (the right side of the curve), y decreases. This means that when there are few predators, the population of prey increases, but when there are many predators, the population of prey decreases, as we would expect. Similarly, by looking at the original differential equation for x,

$$\frac{dx}{dt} = x(2y - 4),$$

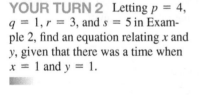

YOUR TURN 2 Letting $p = 4$, $q = 1$, $r = 3$, and $s = 5$ in Example 2, find an equation relating x and y, given that there was a time when $x = 1$ and $y = 1$.

confirm that when there are few prey ($y < 2$), the population of predators decreases (as we would expect, because the predators don't have enough to eat), and when there are many prey ($y > 2$), the population of predators increases. Convince yourself that, for these reasons, the solution (x, y) must move clockwise on the curve in Figure 8. The pattern repeats indefinitely.
                                                                                    TRY YOUR TURN 2

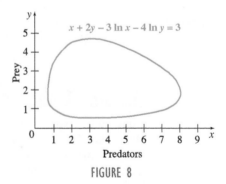

FIGURE 8

Epidemics   Under certain conditions, the spread of a contagious disease can be described with the logistic growth model, as in the next example.

EXAMPLE 3   **Spread of an Epidemic**

Consider a population of size N that satisfies the following conditions.

1. Initially there is only one infected individual.

2. All uninfected individuals are susceptible, and infection occurs when an uninfected individual contacts an infected individual.

3. Contact between any two individuals is just as likely as contact between any other two individuals.

4. Infected individuals remain infectious.

Let t = the time (in days) and y = the number of individuals infected at time t. At any moment there are $(N - y)y$ possible contacts between an uninfected individual and an infected individual. Thus, it is reasonable to assume that the rate of spread of the disease satisfies the following logistic equation (discussed in Section 10.1):

$$\frac{dy}{dt} = k\left(1 - \frac{y}{N}\right)y. \tag{5}$$

As shown in Section 10.1, the general solution of Equation (5) is

$$y = \frac{N}{1 + be^{-kt}}, \tag{6}$$

where $b = (N - y_0)/y_0$. Since just one individual is infected initially, $y_0 = 1$. Substituting these values into Equation (6) gives

$$y = \frac{N}{1 + (N - 1)e^{-kt}} \tag{7}$$

as the specific solution of Equation (5).

The infection rate dy/dt will be a maximum when its derivative is 0, that is, when $d^2y/dt^2 = 0$. Since

$$\frac{dy}{dt} = k\left(1 - \frac{y}{N}\right)y,$$

we have

$$\frac{d^2y}{dt^2} = k\left[\left(1 - \frac{y}{N}\right)\left(\frac{dy}{dt}\right) + y\left(-\frac{1}{N}\right)\left(\frac{dy}{dt}\right)\right]$$

$$= k\left(1 - \frac{2y}{N}\right)\left(\frac{dy}{dt}\right)$$

$$= k\left(1 - \frac{2y}{N}\right)k\left(1 - \frac{y}{N}\right)y$$

$$= k^2y\left(1 - \frac{y}{N}\right)\left(1 - \frac{2y}{N}\right).$$

Set $\dfrac{d^2y}{dt^2} = 0$ to get

$$y = 0, \qquad 1 - \frac{y}{N} = 0, \quad \text{or} \quad 1 - \frac{2y}{N} = 0.$$

That is, $\dfrac{d^2y}{dt^2} = 0$ when $y = 0$, $y = N$, or $y = \dfrac{N}{2}$.

Notice that since the infection rate $\dfrac{dy}{dt} = 0$ when $y = 0$ or $y = N$, the maximum infection rate does not occur there. Also observe that $\dfrac{d^2y}{dt^2} > 0$ when $0 < y < \dfrac{N}{2}$ and $\dfrac{d^2y}{dt^2} < 0$ when $\dfrac{N}{2} < y < N$. Thus, the maximum infection rate occurs when exactly half the total population is still uninfected and equals

$$\frac{dy}{dt} = k\left(1 - \frac{N/2}{N}\right)\frac{N}{2} = \frac{kN}{4}.$$

Letting $y = N/2$ in Equation (7) and solving for t shows that the maximum infection rate occurs at time

$$t_m = \frac{\ln(N-1)}{k}.$$

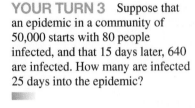

YOUR TURN 3 Suppose that an epidemic in a community of 50,000 starts with 80 people infected, and that 15 days later, 640 are infected. How many are infected 25 days into the epidemic?

Because y is a function of t, the infection rate dy/dt is also a function of t. Its graph, shown in Figure 9, is called the *epidemic curve*. It is symmetric about the line $t = t_m$.

TRY YOUR TURN 3

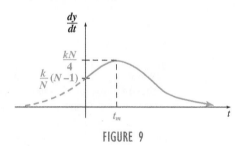

FIGURE 9

Mixing Problems
The mixing of two solutions can lead to a first-order differential equation, as the next example shows.

EXAMPLE 4 Salt Concentration

Suppose a tank contains 100 gal of a solution of dissolved salt and water, which is kept uniform by stirring. If pure water is allowed to flow into the tank at the rate of 4 gal per minute, and the mixture flows out at the rate of 3 gal per minute (see Figure 10), how much salt will remain in the tank after t minutes if 15 lb of salt are in the mixture initially? *Source: Ordinary Differential Equations with Boundary Value Problems.*

SOLUTION Let the amount of salt present in the tank at any specific time be $y = f(t)$. The net rate at which y changes is given by

$$\frac{dy}{dt} = (\text{Rate of salt in}) - (\text{Rate of salt out}).$$

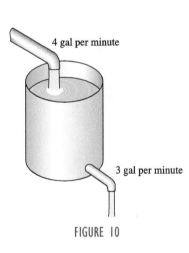

4 gal per minute

3 gal per minute

FIGURE 10

Since pure water is coming in, the rate of salt entering the tank is zero. The rate at which salt is leaving the tank is the product of the amount of salt per gallon (in V gallons) and the number of gallons per minute leaving the tank:

$$\text{Rate of salt out} = \left(\frac{y}{V}\ \text{lb per gal}\right)(3\ \text{gal per minute}).$$

The differential equation, therefore, can be written as

$$\frac{dy}{dt} = -\frac{3y}{V}; \quad y(0) = 15,$$

where $y(0)$ is the initial amount of salt in the solution. We must take into account the fact that the volume, V, of the mixture is not constant but is determined by

$$\frac{dV}{dt} = (\text{Rate of liquid in}) - (\text{Rate of liquid out}) = 4 - 3 = 1,$$

or

$$\frac{dV}{dt} = 1,$$

from which

$$V(t) = t + C_1.$$

Because the volume is known to be 100 at time $t = 0$, we have $C_1 = 100$, and

$$\frac{dy}{dt} = \frac{-3y}{t + 100}; \quad y(0) = 15,$$

a separable equation with solution

$$\frac{dy}{y} = \frac{-3}{t + 100}dt$$

$$\ln y = -3\ln(t + 100) + C.$$

Since $y = 15$ when $t = 0$,

$$\ln 15 = -3\ln 100 + C$$
$$\ln 15 + 3\ln 10^2 = C$$
$$\ln(15 \times 10^6) = C.$$

Finally,

$$\ln y = \ln(t + 100)^{-3} + \ln(15 \times 10^6)$$
$$= \ln[(t + 100)^{-3}(15 \times 10^6)]$$
$$y = \frac{15 \times 10^6}{(t + 100)^3}.$$

TRY YOUR TURN 4

YOUR TURN 4 Suppose that a tank initially contains 500 liters of a solution of water and 5 kg of salt. Suppose that pure water flows in at a rate of 6 L/min, and the solution flows out at a rate of 4 L/min. How many kg of salt remain after 20 minutes?

4 EXERCISES

APPLICATIONS

Business and Economics

1. Continuous Deposits Kimberly Austin deposits $5000 in an IRA at 6% interest compounded continuously for her retirement in 10 years. She intends to make continuous deposits at the rate of $3000 a year until she retires. How much will she have accumulated at that time?

2. Continuous Deposits In Exercise 1, how long will it take Kimberly to accumulate $30,000 in her retirement account?

3. Continuous Deposits To provide for a future expansion, a company plans to make continuous deposits to a savings account at the rate of $50,000 per year, with no initial deposit. The managers want to accumulate $500,000. How long will it take if the account earns 10% interest compounded continuously?

4. Continuous Deposits Suppose the company in Exercise 3 wants to accumulate $500,000 in 3 years. Find the approximate yearly deposit that will be required.

5. Continuous Deposits An investor deposits $8000 into an account that pays 6% compounded continuously and then begins to *withdraw* from the account continuously at a rate of $1200 per year.

a. Write a differential equation to describe the situation.

b. How much will be left in the account after 2 years?

c. When will the account be completely depleted?

Life Sciences

6. Predator-Prey Explain in your own words why the solution (x, y) must move clockwise on the curve in Figure 8.

7. Competing Species The system of equations

$$\frac{dy}{dt} = 4y - 2xy$$
$$\frac{dx}{dt} = -3x + 2xy$$

describes the influence of the populations (in thousands) of two competing species on their growth rates.

a. Following Example 2, find an equation relating x and y, assuming $y = 1$ when $x = 1$.

b. Find values of x and y so that both populations are constant. (*Hint:* Set both differential equations equal to 0.)

8. Symbiotic Species When two species, such as the rhinoceros and birds pictured below, coexist in a symbiotic (dependent) relationship, they either increase together or decrease together. Typical equations for the growth rates of two such species might be

$$\frac{dx}{dt} = -4x + 4xy$$

$$\frac{dy}{dt} = -3y + 2xy.$$

Thinkstock

a. Find an equation relating x and y if $x = 5$ when $y = 1$.

b. Find values of x and y so that both populations are constant. (See Exercise 7.)

c. A graph of the relationship found in part a is shown in the figure. Based on the differential equations for the growth rate and this graph, what happens to both populations when $y > 1$? When $y < 1$?

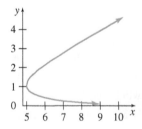

9. Spread of an Epidemic The native Hawaiians lived for centuries in isolation from other peoples. When foreigners finally came to the islands they brought with them diseases such as measles, whooping cough, and smallpox, which decimated the population. Suppose such an island has a native population of 5000, and a sailor from a visiting ship introduces measles, which has an infection rate of 0.00005. Also suppose that the model for spread of an epidemic described in Example 3 applies.

a. Write an equation for the number of natives who remain uninfected. Let t represent time in days.

b. How many are uninfected after 30 days?

c. How many are uninfected after 50 days?

d. When will the maximum infection rate occur?

10. Spread of an Epidemic In Example 3, the number of infected individuals is given by Equation (7).

a. Show that the number of uninfected individuals is given by

$$N - y = \frac{N(N-1)}{N - 1 + e^{kt}}.$$

b. Graph the equation in part a and Equation (7) on the same axes when $N = 100$ and $k = 1$.

c. Find the common inflection point of the two graphs.

d. What is the significance of the common inflection point?

e. What are the limiting values of y and $N - y$?

11. Spread of an Epidemic An influenza epidemic spreads at a rate proportional to the product of the number of people infected and the number not yet infected. Assume that 100 people are infected at the beginning of the epidemic in a community of 20,000 people, and 400 are infected 10 days later.

a. Write an equation for the number of people infected, y, after t days.

b. When will half the community be infected?

12. Spread of an Epidemic The Gompertz growth law,

$$\frac{dy}{dt} = kye^{-at},$$

for constants k and a, is another model used to describe the growth of an epidemic. Repeat Exercise 11, using this differential equation with $a = 0.02$.

13. Spread of Gonorrhea Gonorrhea is spread by sexual contact, takes 3 to 7 days to incubate, and can be treated with antibiotics. There is no evidence that a person ever develops immunity. One model proposed for the rate of change in the number of men infected by this disease is

$$\frac{dy}{dt} = -ay + b(f - y)Y,$$

where y is the fraction of men infected, f is the fraction of men who are promiscuous, Y is the fraction of women infected, and a and b are appropriate constants. *Source: An Introduction to Mathematical Modeling.*

a. Assume $a = 1$, $b = 1$, and $f = 0.5$. Choose $Y = 0.01$, and solve for y using $y = 0.02$ when t is 0 as an initial condition. Round your answer to 3 decimal places.

b. A comparable model for women is

$$\frac{dY}{dt} = -AY + B(F - Y)y,$$

where F is the fraction of women who are promiscuous and A and B are constants. Assume $A = 1$, $B = 1$, and $F = 0.03$. Choose $y = 0.1$ and solve for Y, using $Y = 0.01$ as an initial condition.

Social Sciences

Spread of a Rumor The equation developed in the text for the spread of an epidemic also can be used to describe diffusion of information. In a population of size N, let y be the number who have heard a particular piece of information. Then

$$\frac{dy}{dt} = k\left(1 - \frac{y}{N}\right)y$$

for a positive constant k. Use this model in Exercises 14–16.

14. Suppose a rumor starts among 3 people in a certain office building. That is, $y_0 = 3$. Suppose 500 people work in the building and 50 people have heard the rumor in 2 days. Using Equation (6), write an equation for the number who have heard the rumor in t days. How many people will have heard the rumor in 5 days?

15. A rumor spreads at a rate proportional to the product of the number of people who have heard it and the number who have not heard it. Assume that 3 people in an office with 45 employees heard the rumor initially, and 12 people have heard it 3 days later.

   a. Write an equation for the number, y, of people who have heard the rumor in t days.

   b. When will 30 employees have heard the rumor?

16. A news item is heard on the late news by 5 of the 100 people in a small community. By the end of the next day 20 people have heard the news. Using Equation (6), write an equation for the number of people who have heard the news in t days. How many have heard the news after 3 days?

17. Repeat Exercise 15 using the Gompertz growth law,

$$\frac{dy}{dt} = kye^{-at},$$

   for constants k and a, with $a = 0.1$.

Physical Sciences

18. Salt Concentration A tank holds 100 gal of water that contains 20 lb of dissolved salt. A brine (salt) solution is flowing into the tank at the rate of 2 gal per minute while the solution flows out of the tank at the same rate. The brine solution entering the tank has a salt concentration of 2 lb per gal.

   a. Find an expression for the amount of salt in the tank at any time.

   b. How much salt is present after 1 hour?

   c. As time increases, what happens to the salt concentration?

19. Solve Exercise 18 if the brine solution is introduced at the rate of 3 gal per minute while the rate of outflow remains the same.

20. Solve Exercise 18 if the brine solution is introduced at the rate of 1 gal per minute while the rate of outflow stays the same.

21. Solve Exercise 18 if pure water is added instead of brine.

22. Chemical in a Solution Five grams of a chemical is dissolved in 100 liters of alcohol. Pure alcohol is added at the rate of 2 liters per minute and at the same time the solution is being drained at the rate of 1 liter per minute.

   a. Find an expression for the amount of the chemical in the mixture at any time.

   b. How much of the chemical is present after 30 minutes?

23. Solve Exercise 22 if a 25% solution of the same mixture is added instead of pure alcohol.

24. Soap Concentration A prankster puts 4 lb of soap in a fountain that contains 200 gal of water. To clean up the mess a city crew runs clear water into the fountain at the rate of 8 gal per minute allowing the excess solution to drain off at the same rate. How long will it be before the amount of soap in the mixture is reduced to 1 lb?

YOUR TURN ANSWERS

1. $61,729.53
2. $x + 5y - 4\ln x - 3\ln y = 6$
3. 2483
4. 4.29 kg

CHAPTER REVIEW

SUMMARY

In this chapter, we studied differential equations, which are equations involving derivatives. Our goal has been to find a function that satisfies the equation. We learned to solve two different types of equations:

   • separable equations, using separation of variables, and
   • linear equations, using an integrating factor.

For equations that cannot be solved by either of the previous two methods, we introduced a numerical method known as Euler's method.

Differential equations have a large number of applications; some of those we studied in this chapter include:

   • continuous deposits;
   • the logistic equation for populations;
   • a predator-prey model;
   • and mixing problems.

General Solution of $\dfrac{dy}{dx} = g(x)$ The general solution of the differential equation $dy/dx = g(x)$ is

$$y = \int g(x)\,dx.$$

Separable Differential Equation   An equation is separable if it can be written in the form

$$\frac{dy}{dx} = \frac{p(x)}{q(y)}.$$

By separating the variables, it is transformed into the equation

$$\int q(y)\,dy = \int p(x)\,dx.$$

Solving a Linear First-Order Differential Equation

1. Put the equation in the linear form

$$\frac{dy}{dx} + P(x)y = Q(x).$$

2. Find the integrating factor $I(x) = e^{\int P(x)\,dx}$.

3. Multiply each term of the equation from Step 1 by $I(x)$.

4. Replace the sum of terms on the left with $D_x[I(x)y]$.

5. Integrate both sides of the equation.

6. Solve for y.

Euler's Method   Let $y = f(x)$ be the solution of the differential equation

$$\frac{dy}{dx} = g(x, y), \text{ with } y(x_0) = y_0,$$

for $x_0 \le x \le x_n$. Let $x_{i+1} = x_i + h$, where $h = (x_n - x_0)/n$ and

$$y_{i+1} = y_i + g(x_i, y_i)h,$$

for $0 \le i \le n - 1$. Then

$$f(x_{i+1}) \approx y_{i+1}.$$

KEY TERMS

differential equation

1

general solution
particular solution
initial condition
initial value problem

separable differential
  equation
separation of variables
growth constant
carrying capacity
logistic growth model
logistic equation
logistic curve

2

linear first-order
  differential equation
integrating factor

3

Euler's method

4

Lotka-Volterra equations

REVIEW EXERCISES

CONCEPT CHECK

Determine whether each of the following statements is true or false, and explain why.

 1. To determine a particular solution to a differential equation, you first must find a general solution to the differential equation.

 2. The function $y = e^{2x} + 5$ satisfies the differential equation $\dfrac{dy}{dx} = 2y$.

 3. The function $y = \dfrac{100}{1 + 99e^{-5t}}$ satisfies the differential equation $\dfrac{dy}{dt} = 5\left(1 - \dfrac{y}{100}\right)y$.

 4. The differential equation $y\dfrac{dy}{dx} + xy = 2500e^y$ is a first-order linear differential equation.

 5. Every differential equation is either separable or linear.

6. It is possible to solve the following differential equation using the method of separation of variables.

$$x\frac{dy}{dx} = (x + 1)(y + 1)$$

 7. It is possible to solve the following differential equation using the method of separation of variables.

$$\frac{dy}{dx} = x^2 + 4y^2$$

8. The function $I(x) = x^3$ can be used as an integrating factor for the differential equation

$$\frac{dy}{dx} + 3\frac{y}{x} = \frac{1}{x^2}.$$

 9. The function $I(x) = e^{5x}$ can be used as an integrating factor for the differential equation

$$x\frac{dy}{dx} + 5y = e^{2x}.$$

 10. Euler's method can be used to find the general solution to a differential equation.

11. If Euler's method is being used to solve the differential equation $\dfrac{dy}{dx} = x + \sqrt{y + 4}$ with $h = 0.1$, then
$$y_{i+1} = y_i + 0.1(x_i + \sqrt{y_i + 4}).$$

 12. The differential equation describing continuous deposits is separable.

PRACTICE AND EXPLORATIONS

 13. What is a differential equation? What is it used for?

14. What is the difference between a particular solution and a general solution to a differential equation?

15. How can you tell that a differential equation is separable? That it is linear?

16. Can a differential equation be both separable and linear? Explain why not, or give an example of an equation that is both.

Classify each equation as separable, linear, both, or neither.

17. $y\dfrac{dy}{dx} = 2x + y$

18. $\dfrac{dy}{dx} + y^2 = xy^2$

19. $\sqrt{x}\,\dfrac{dy}{dx} = \dfrac{1 + \ln x}{y}$

20. $\dfrac{dy}{dx} = xy + e^x$

21. $\dfrac{dy}{dx} + x = xy$

22. $\dfrac{x}{y}\dfrac{dy}{dx} = 4 + x^{3/2}$

23. $x\dfrac{dy}{dx} + y = e^x(1 + y)$

24. $\dfrac{dy}{dx} = x^2 + y^2$

Find the general solution for each differential equation.

25. $\dfrac{dy}{dx} = 3x^2 + 6x$

26. $\dfrac{dy}{dx} = 4x^3 + 6x^5$

27. $\dfrac{dy}{dx} = 4e^{2x}$

28. $\dfrac{dy}{dx} = \dfrac{1}{3x + 2}$

29. $\dfrac{dy}{dx} = \dfrac{3x + 1}{y}$

30. $\dfrac{dy}{dx} = \dfrac{e^x + x}{y - 1}$

31. $\dfrac{dy}{dx} = \dfrac{2y + 1}{x}$

32. $\dfrac{dy}{dx} = \dfrac{3 - y}{e^x}$

33. $\dfrac{dy}{dx} + y = x$

34. $x^4\dfrac{dy}{dx} + 3x^3y = 1$

35. $x \ln x\,\dfrac{dy}{dx} + y = 2x^2$

36. $x\dfrac{dy}{dx} + 2y - e^{2x} = 0$

Find the particular solution for each initial value problem. (Some solutions may give y implicitly.)

37. $\dfrac{dy}{dx} = x^2 - 6x; \quad y(0) = 3$

38. $\dfrac{dy}{dx} = 5(e^{-x} - 1); \quad y(0) = 17$

39. $\dfrac{dy}{dx} = (x + 2)^3 e^y; \quad y(0) = 0$

40. $\dfrac{dy}{dx} = (3 - 2x)y; \quad y(0) = 5$

41. $\dfrac{dy}{dx} = \dfrac{1 - 2x}{y + 3}; \quad y(0) = 16$

42. $\sqrt{x}\,\dfrac{dy}{dx} = xy; \quad y(1) = 4$

43. $e^x\dfrac{dy}{dx} - e^xy = x^2 - 1; \quad y(0) = 42$

44. $\dfrac{dy}{dx} + 3x^2y = x^2; \quad y(0) = 2$

Differential Equations

45. $x\dfrac{dy}{dx} - 2x^2y + 3x^2 = 0;\quad y(0) = 15$

46. $x^2\dfrac{dy}{dx} + 4xy - e^{2x^3} = 0;\quad y(1) = e^2$

47. When is Euler's method useful?

Use Euler's method to approximate the indicated function value for $y = f(x)$ to 3 decimal places, using $h = 0.2$.

48. $\dfrac{dy}{dx} = x + y^{-1};\quad y(0) = 1;\quad$ find $y(1)$

49. $\dfrac{dy}{dx} = e^x + y;\quad y(0) = 1;\quad$ find $y(0.6)$

50. Let $y = f(x)$ and $dy/dx = (x/2) + 4$, with $y(0) = 0$. Use Euler's method with $h = 0.1$ to approximate $y(0.3)$ to 3 decimal places. Then solve the differential equation and find $f(0.3)$ to 3 decimal places. Also, find $y_3 - f(x_3)$.

51. Let $y = f(x)$ and $dy/dx = 3 + \sqrt{y}$, with $y(0) = 0$. Construct a table for x_i and y_i like the one in Section 10.3, Example 2, for $[0, 1]$, with $h = 0.2$. Then graph the polygonal approximation of the graph of $y = f(x)$.

52. What is the logistic equation? Why is it useful?

APPLICATIONS

Business and Economics

53. Marginal Sales The marginal sales (in hundreds of dollars) of a computer software company are given by

$$\frac{dy}{dx} = 6e^{0.3x},$$

where x is the number of months the company has been in business. Assume that sales were 0 initially.

a. Find the sales after 6 months.

b. Find the sales after 12 months.

54. Production Rate The rate at which a new worker in a certain factory produces items is given by

$$\frac{dy}{dx} = 0.1(150 - y),$$

where y is the number of items produced by the worker per day, x is the number of days worked, and the maximum production per day is 150 items. Assume that the worker produces 15 items at the beginning of the first day on the job ($x = 0$).

a. Find the number of items the new worker will produce in 10 days.

b. Determine the number of days for a new worker to produce 100 items per day.

55. Continuous Withdrawals A retirement savings account contains \$300,000 and earns 5% interest compounded continuously. The retiree makes *continuous* withdrawals of \$20,000 per year.

a. Write a differential equation to describe the situation.

b. How much will be left in the account after 10 years?

56. In Exercise 55, approximately how long will it take to use up the account?

Life Sciences

57. Effect of Insecticide After use of an experimental insecticide, the rate of decline of an insect population is

$$\frac{dy}{dt} = \frac{-10}{1 + 5t},$$

where t is the number of hours after the insecticide is applied. Assume that there were 50 insects initially.

a. How many are left after 24 hours?

b. How long will it take for the entire population to die?

58. Growth of a Mite Population A population of mites grows at a rate proportional to the number present, y. If the growth constant is 10% and 120 mites are present at time $t = 0$ (in weeks), find the number present after 6 weeks.

59. Competing Species Find an equation relating x to y given the following equations, which describe the interaction of two competing species and their growth rates.

$$\frac{dx}{dt} = 0.2x - 0.5xy$$
$$\frac{dy}{dt} = -0.3y + 0.4xy$$

Find the values of x and y for which both growth rates are 0.

60. Smoke Content in a Room The air in a meeting room of 15,000 ft^3 has a smoke content of 20 parts per million (ppm). An air conditioner is turned on, which brings fresh air (with no smoke) into the room at a rate of 1200 ft^3 per minute and forces the smoky air out at the same rate. How long will it take to reduce the smoke content to 5 ppm?

61. In Exercise 60, how long will it take to reduce the smoke content to 10 ppm if smokers in the room are adding smoke at the rate of 5 ppm per minute?

62. Spread of Influenza A small, isolated mountain community with a population of 700 is visited by an outsider who carries influenza. After 6 weeks, 300 people are uninfected.

a. Write an equation for the number of people who remain uninfected at time t (in weeks).

b. Find the number still uninfected after 7 weeks.

c. When will the maximum infection rate occur?

63. Population Growth Let

$$y = \frac{N}{1 + be^{-kt}}.$$

If y is y_1, y_2, and y_3 at times t_1, t_2, and $t_3 = 2t_2 - t_1$ (that is, at three equally spaced times), then prove that

$$N = \frac{1/y_1 + 1/y_3 - 2/y_2}{1/(y_1y_3) - 1/y_2^2}.$$

Population Growth In the following table of U.S. Census figures, *y* is the population in millions. *Source: U.S. Census Bureau.*

Year	y	Year	y
1790	3.9	1910	92.0
1800	5.3	1920	105.7
1810	7.2	1930	122.8
1820	9.6	1940	131.7
1830	12.9	1950	150.7
1840	17.1	1960	179.3
1850	23.2	1970	203.3
1860	31.4	1980	226.5
1870	39.8	1990	248.7
1880	50.2	2000	281.4
1890	62.9	2010	308.7
1900	76.0		

64. Use Exercise 63 and the table to find the following.

a. Find *N* using the years 1800, 1850, and 1900.

b. Find *N* using the years 1850, 1900, and 1950.

c. Find *N* using the years 1870, 1920, and 1970.

d. Explain why different values of *N* were obtained in parts a–c. What does this suggest about the validity of this model and others?

65. Let $t = 0$ correspond to 1870, and let every decade correspond to an increase in *t* of 1.

a. Use 1870, 1920, and 1970 to find *N*, 1870 to find *b*, and 1920 to find *k* in the equation

$$y = \frac{N}{1 + be^{-kt}}.$$

b. Estimate the population of the United States in 2010 and compare your estimate to the actual population in 2010.

c. Predict the populations of the United States in 2030 and 2050.

66. Let $t = 0$ correspond to 1790, and let every decade correspond to an increase in *t* of 1. Use a calculator with logistic regression capability to complete the following.

a. Plot the data points. Do the points suggest that a logistic function is appropriate here?

b. Use the logistic regression function on your calculator to determine the logistic equation that best fits the data.

c. Plot the logistic equation from part a on the same graph as the data points. How well does the logistic equation seem to fit the data?

d. What seems to be the limiting size of the U.S. population?

Social Sciences

67. Education Researchers have proposed that the amount a full-time student is educated (x) changes with respect to the student's age *t* according to the differential equation

$$\frac{dx}{dt} = 1 - kx,$$

where *k* is a constant measuring the rate that education depreciates due to forgetting or technological obsolescence. *Source: Operations Research.*

a. Solve the equation using the method of separation of variables.

b. Solve the equation using an integrating factor.

c. What does *x* approach over time?

68. Spread of a Rumor A rumor spreads through the offices of a company with 200 employees, starting in a meeting with 10 people. After 3 days, 35 people have heard the rumor.

a. Write an equation for the number of people who have heard the rumor in *t* days. (*Hint:* Refer to Exercises 14–16 in Section 10.4.)

b. How many people have heard the rumor in 5 days?

Physical Sciences

69. Newton's Law of Cooling A roast at a temperature of 40°F is put in a 300°F oven. After 1 hour the roast has reached a temperature of 150°F. Newton's law of cooling states that

$$\frac{dT}{dt} = k(T - T_M),$$

where *T* is the temperature of an object, the surrounding medium has temperature T_M at time *t*, and *k* is a constant. Use Newton's law to find the temperature of the roast after 2 hours.

70. In Exercise 69, how long does it take for the roast to reach a temperature of 250°F?

71. Air Resistance Recall that the acceleration of gravity is a constant if air resistance is ignored. But air resistance cannot always be ignored, or parachutes would be of little use. In the presence of air resistance, the equation for acceleration also contains a term roughly proportional to the velocity squared. Since acceleration forces a falling object downward and air resistance pushed it upward, the air resistance term is opposite in sign to the acceleration of gravity. Thus,

$$a(t) = \frac{dv}{dt} = g - kv^2,$$

where *g* and *k* are positive constants. Future calculations will be simpler if we replace *g* and *k* by the squared constants G^2 and K^2, giving

$$\frac{dv}{dt} = G^2 - K^2v^2.$$

a. Use separation of variables and the fact that

$$\frac{1}{G^2 - K^2v^2} = \frac{1}{2G}\left(\frac{1}{G - Kv} + \frac{1}{G + Kv}\right)$$

to solve the differential equation above. Assume $v < G/K$, which is certainly true when the object starts falling (with $v = 0$). Write your solution in the form of v as a function of t.

b. Find $\lim_{t \to \infty} v(t)$, where $v(t)$ is the solution you found in part a. What does this tell you about a falling object in the presence of air resistance?

c. According to *Harper's Index*, the terminal velocity of a cat falling from a tall building is 60 mph. *Source: Harper's.* Use your answers from part b, plus the fact that 60 mph = 88 ft per second and g, the acceleration of gravity, is 32 ft per second^2, to find a formula for the velocity of a falling cat (in ft per second) as a function of time (in seconds). (*Hint:* Find K in terms of G. Then substitute into the answer from part a.)

EXTENDED APPLICATION

POLLUTION OF THE GREAT LAKES

Industrial nations are beginning to face the problems of water pollution. Lakes present a problem, because a polluted lake contains a considerable amount of water that must somehow be cleaned. The main cleanup mechanism is the natural process of gradually replacing the water in the lake. This application deals with pollution in the Great Lakes. The basic idea is to regard the flow in the Great Lakes as a mixing problem.

We make the following assumptions.

1. Rainfall and evaporation balance each other, so the average rates of inflow and outflow are equal.

2. The average rates of inflow and outflow do not vary much seasonally.

3. When water enters the lake, perfect mixing occurs, so that the pollutants are uniformly distributed.

4. Pollutants are not removed from the lake by decay, sedimentation, or in any other way except outflow.

5. Pollutants flow freely out of the lake; they are not retained (as DDT is).

(The first two are valid assumptions; however, the last three are questionable.)

We will use the following variables in the discussion to follow.

V = volume of the lake

P_L = pollution concentration in the lake at time t

P_i = pollution concentration in the inflow to the lake at time t

r = rate of flow

t = time in years

Source: An Introduction to Mathematical Modeling.

By the assumptions stated above, the net change in total pollutants during the time interval Δt is (approximately)

$$V \cdot \Delta P_L = (P_i - P_L)(r \cdot \Delta t),$$

where ΔP_L is the change in the pollution concentration. Dividing this equation by Δt and by V and taking the limit as $\Delta t \to 0$, we get the differential equation

$$\frac{dP_L}{dt} = \frac{(P_i - P_L)r}{V}.$$

Since we are treating V and r as constants, we replace r/V with k, so the equation can be written as the first-order linear equation

$$\frac{dP_L}{dt} + kP_L = kP_i.$$

The solution is

$$P_L(t) = e^{-kt}\left[P_L(0) + k\int_0^t P_i(x)e^{kx}\, dx \right]. \tag{1}$$

Figure 11 shows values of $1/k$ for each lake (except Huron) measured in years. *If the model is reasonable*, the numbers in the figure can be used in Equation (1) to determine the effect of various pollution abatement schemes. Lake Ontario is excluded from the discussion because about 84% of its inflow comes from Erie and can be controlled only indirectly.

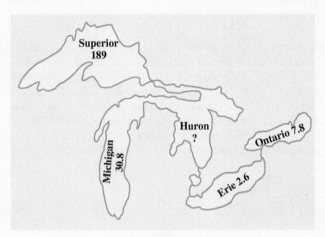

FIGURE 11

The fastest possible cleanup will occur if all pollution inflow ceases. This means that $P_i = 0$. In this case, Equation (1) leads to

$$t = \frac{1}{k} \ln\left(\frac{P_L(0)}{P_L(t)}\right).$$

From this we can tell the length of time necessary to reduce pollution to a given percentage of its present level. For example, from the figure, for Lake Superior $1/k = 189$. Thus, to reduce pollution to 50% of its present level, $P_L(0)$, we want

$$\frac{P_L(t)}{P_L(0)} = 0.5 \quad \text{or} \quad \frac{P_L(0)}{P_L(t)} = 2,$$

from which

$$t = 189 \ln 2 \approx 131.$$

The following figures, representing years, were found in this way. Fortunately, the pollution in Lake Superior is quite low at present.

As mentioned before, assumptions 3, 4, and 5 are questionable. For persistent pollutants like DDT, the estimated cleanup times may be too low. For other pollutants, how assumptions 4 and 5 affect cleanup times is unclear. However, the values of $1/k$ given in the figure probably provide rough lower bounds for the cleanup times of persistent pollutants.

Lake	50%	20%	10%	5%
Erie	2	4	6	8
Michigan	21	50	71	92
Superior	131	304	435	566

EXERCISES

1. Calculate the number of years to reduce pollution in Lake Erie to each level.
   a. 40%
   b. 30%

2. Repeat Exercise 1 for Lake Michigan.

3. Repeat Exercise 1 for Lake Superior.

4. We claim that Equation (1) is a solution of the differential equation

$$\frac{dP_L}{dt} + kP_L(t) = kP_i(t),$$

where t measures time from the present. The constant $k = r/V$ measures how quickly the water in the lake is replaced through inflow and corresponding outflow. The constant $P_L(0)$ is the current pollution level.

   a. To show that Equation (1) does define a solution of the differential equation, multiply both sides of Equation (1) by e^{kt} and then differentiate both sides with respect to t. Remember from the section on the Fundamental Theorem of Calculus that you can differentiate an integral by using the version of the Fundamental Theorem that says

$$\frac{d}{dt} \int_a^t f(x)\, dx = f(t).$$

   b. When you substitute $t = 0$ into the right-hand side of Equation (1), you should get $P_L(0)$. Do you? What happens to the integral? What happens to the factor of e^{-kt}?

   c. The map indicates a value of 30.8 for Lake Michigan. What value of k does this correspond to? What percent of the water in Lake Michigan is replaced each year by inflow? Which lake has the biggest annual water turnover?

5. Suppose that instead of assuming that all pollution inflow immediately ceases, we model $P_i(t)$ by a decaying exponential of the form $a \cdot e^{-pt}$, where p is a constant that tells us how fast the inflow is being cleaned of pollution. To simplify things, we'll also assume that initially the inflow and the lake have the same pollution concentration, so $a = P_L(0)$. Now substitute $P_L(0)e^{-px}$ for $P_i(x)$ in Equation (1), and evaluate the integral as a function of t.

6. When you simplify the right-hand side of Equation (1) using your new expression for the integral, and then factor out and divide by $P_L(0)$, you'll get the following nice expression for the ratio $P_L(t)/P_L(0)$:

$$\frac{P_L(t)}{P_L(0)} = \frac{1}{k - p}\left(ke^{-pt} - pe^{-kt}\right).$$

   a. Suppose that for Lake Michigan the constant p is equal to 0.02. Use a graph of the ratio $P_L(t)/P_L(0)$ to estimate how long it will take to reduce pollution to 50% of its current value. How does this compare with the time, assuming pollution-free inflow?

   b. If the constant p has the value 0 for Lake Michigan, what does that tell you about the pollution level in the inflow? In this case, what happens to the ratio $P_L(t)/P_L(0)$ over time?

221

7. At the website Wolfram|Alpha.com, you can enter "$y'(t) = (f(t) - y) * k, y(0) = a$" to solve the initial value problem in this Extended Application, where we have used $y(t)$ to represent $P_L(t)$, $f(t)$ to represent $P_i(t)$, and a to represent $P_L(0)$. Try this, and verify that the solution is equivalent to Equation (1).

8. Repeat Exercise 7, but in place of $f(t)$, put $a * e \wedge (-p * t)$, the form of $P_L(t)$ used in Exercises 5 and 6. Verify that the solution is equivalent to the solution given in Exercise 6.

9. Repeat Exercise 8, trying other functions of t in place of $f(t)$, such as t^3. Find which functions give a recognizable answer, and verify that answer using Equation (1).

DIRECTIONS FOR GROUP PROJECT

Suppose you and three others are employed by an agency that is concerned about the environmental health of one of the Great Lakes. Choose one of the lakes, and collect information about levels of pollution in it. Then, using the information you collected along with the information given in this application, prepare a public presentation for a local community organization that describes the lake and gives possible timelines for reducing pollution in the lake. Use presentation software such as Microsoft PowerPoint.

ANSWERS TO SELECTED EXERCISES

Exercises 1

For exercises ...	1,2	3,4,17–20	5–16,21–32, 38,39,53	35	36,37,41,42, 49–51,54	40,47,48,52	43–46,56–59
Refer to example ...	1	3	4,5,6	2	5	7	6

1. $y = -2x^2 + 2x^3 + C$ **3.** $y = x^4/2 + C$ **5.** $y^2 = 2x^3/3 + C$ **7.** $y = ke^{x^2}$ **9.** $y = ke^{x^3-x^2}$ **11.** $y = Cx$
13. $\ln(y^2 + 6) = x + C$ **15.** $y = -1/(e^{2x}/2 + C)$ **17.** $y = x^2 - x^3 + 5$ **19.** $y = -2xe^{-x} - 2e^{-x} + 44$ **21.** $y^2 = x^4/2 + 25$
23. $y = e^{x^2 + 3x}$ **25.** $y^2/2 - 3y = x^2 + x - 4$ **27.** $y = -3/(3 \ln|x| - 4)$ **29.** $y = (e^{x-1} - 3)/(e^{x-1} - 2)$ **35. a.** 1011.75
b. 1024.52 **c.** No **37.** About 13.9 yr **39.** $q = C/p^2$ **41.** d **43. a.** $I = 2.4 - 1.4e^{-0.088W}$ **b.** I approaches 2.4.
45. a. $dw/dt = k(C - 17.5w)$; the calorie intake per day is constant. **b.** lb/calorie **c.** $dw/dt = (C - 17.5w)/3500$
d. $w = C/17.5 - e^{-0.005M}e^{-0.005t}/17.5$ **e.** $w = C/17.5 + (w_0 - C/17.5)e^{-0.005t}$

47. a. 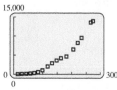 **b.** $y = \dfrac{25{,}538}{1 + 110.28e^{-0.01819t}}$ **c.** 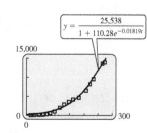 **d.** 25,538

49. $y = 35.6e^{0.02117t}$ **51. a.** $k \approx 0.8$ **b.** 11 **c.** 55 **d.** About 3000 **53.** About 10 **55.** 7:22:55 A.M. **57.** The temperature approaches T_M, the temperature of the surrounding medium. **59. a.** $T = 88.6e^{-0.24t} + 10$ **b.**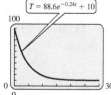
c. Just after death—the graph shows that the most rapid decrease occurs in the first few hours. **d.** About 43.9°F **e.** About 4.5 hours

Exercises 2

For exercises ...	1–20,25–29
Refer to example ...	2–4

1. $y = 2 + Ce^{-3x}$ **3.** $y = 2 + Ce^{-x^2}$ **5.** $y = x \ln x + Cx$ **7.** $y = -1/2 + Ce^{x^2/2}$
9. $y = x^2/4 + 2x + C/x^2$ **11.** $y = -x^3/2 + Cx$ **13.** $y = 2e^x + 48e^{-x}$ **15.** $y = -2 + 22e^{x^2 - 1}$ **17.** $y = x^2/7 + 2560/(7x^5)$
19. $y = (3 + 197e^{4-x})/x$ **21. a.** $y = c/(p + Kce^{-cx})$ **b.** $y = cy_0/[py_0 + (c - py_0)e^{-cx}]$ **c.** c/p
25. $y = 1.02e^t + 9999e^{0.02t}$ (rounded) **27.** $y = 50t + 2500 + 7500e^{0.02t}$ **29.** $T = Ce^{-kt} + T_M$

Exercises 3

For exercises ...	1–35
Refer to example ...	1,2

1. 8.273 **3.** 4.315 **5.** 1.491 **7.** 6.191 **9.** $-0.540; -0.520$ **11.** 4.010; 4.016 **13.** 3.806; 4.759
15. 3.112; 3.271 **17.** 73.505; 74.691

19.

x_i	y_i	$y(x_i)$	$y_i - y(x_i)$
0	0	0	0
0.2	0	0.08772053	-0.08772053
0.4	0.11696071	0.22104189	-0.10408118
0.6	0.26432197	0.37954470	-0.11522273
0.8	0.43300850	0.55699066	-0.12398216
1.0	0.61867206	0.75000000	-0.13132794

21.

x_i	y_i	$y(x_i)$	$y_i - y(x_i)$
0	0	0	0
0.2	0.8	0.725077	0.07492
0.4	1.44	1.3187198	0.12128
0.6	1.952	1.8047535	0.14725
0.8	2.3616	2.2026841	0.15892
1.0	2.68928	2.5284822	0.16080

23.

25.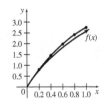

27. a. 4.109   **b.** $y = 1/(1 - x)$; y approaches ∞.
29. a. $dy/dt = 0.01y\,(500 - y) = 5y - 0.01y^2$
b. About 484 thousand
31. About 75   **33.** About 8.07 kg
35. About 157 people

Exercises 4

For exercises . . .	1–5	6–8	9–17	18–24
Refer to example . . .	1	2	3	4

1. $50,216.53   **3.** About 6.9 years   **5. a.** $dA/dt = 0.06A - 1200$ **b.** $6470.04
c. 8.51 years   **7. a.** $2y - 3 \ln y - 4 \ln x + 2x = 4$ **b.** $x = 2, y = 3/2$, or $x = 0, y = 0$ **9. a.** $y = 24{,}995{,}000/(4999 + e^{0.25t})$
b. 3672   **c.** 91   **d.** 34th day   **11. a.** $y = 20{,}000/(1 + 199e^{-0.14t})$ or $20{,}000e^{0.14t}/(e^{0.14t} + 199)$ **b.** About 38 days
13. a. $y = 0.005 + 0.015e^{-1.010t}$ **b.** $Y = 0.00727e^{-1.1t} + 0.00273$ **15. a.** $y = 45/(1 + 14e^{-0.54t})$ **b.** About 6 days
17. a. $y = 347e^{-4.24e^{-0.1t}}$ **b.** About 5.5 days   **19. a.** $y = [2(t + 100)^3 - 1{,}800{,}000]/(t + 100)^2$ **b.** About 250 lb of salt
c. Increases   **21. a.** $y = 20e^{-0.02t}$ **b.** About 6 lb of salt   **c.** Decreases   **23. a.** $y = [0.25\,(t + 100)^2 - 2000]/(t + 100)$
b. About 17.1 g

Chapter Review Exercises

For exercises . . .	1–3,6,7,13,14,25–32, 37–42,52–54,57,58, 63–67,69–71	5,15–24	4,8,9,33–36,43–46	10,11,47–51	12,55,56,59–62,68
Refer to section . . .	1	1, 2	2	3	4

1. True   **2.** False   **3.** True   **4.** False   **5.** False   **6.** True   **7.** False   **8.** True   **9.** False   **10.** False   **11.** True   **12.** True
17. Neither   **19.** Separable   **21.** Both   **23.** Linear   **25.** $y = x^3 + 3x^2 + C$ **27.** $y = 2e^{2x} + C$ **29.** $y^2 = 3x^2 + 2x + C$
31. $y = (Cx^2 - 1)/2$ **33.** $y = x - 1 + Ce^{-x}$ **35.** $y = (x^2 + C)/\ln x$ **37.** $y = x^3/3 - 3x^2 + 3$ **39.** $y = -\ln [5 - (x + 2)^4/4]$
41. $y^2 + 6y = 2x - 2x^2 + 352$ **43.** $y = -x^2e^{-x}/2 - xe^{-x}/2 + e^{-x}/4 + 41.75e^x$ **45.** $y = 3/2 + 27e^{x^2}/2$ **49.** 2.608
51.

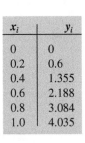

x_i	y_i
0	0
0.2	0.6
0.4	1.355
0.6	2.188
0.8	3.084
1.0	4.035

53. a. $10,099   **b.** $71,196   **55. a.** $dA/dt = 0.05A - 20{,}000$
b. $235,127.87   **57. a.** About 40   **b.** About 1.44×10^{10} hours
59. $0.2 \ln y - 0.5y + 0.3 \ln x - 0.4x = C$; $x = 3/4$ units, $y = 2/5$ units
61. It is not possible (t is negative).   **65. a.** $N = 329, b = 7.23; k = 0.247$
b. $y \approx 268$ million, which is less than the table value of 308.7 million.
c. About 289 million for 2030, about 303 million for 2050
67. a. and b. $x = 1/k + Ce^{-kt}$ **c.** $1/k$ **69.** 213°
71. a. $v = (G/K)(e^{2GKt} - 1)/(e^{2GKt} + 1)$ **b.** G/K
c. $v = 88(e^{0.727t} - 1)/(e^{0.727t} + 1)$

SAMPLE SOURCES

Section 1

1. From Fisher, J. C. and R. H. Pry, "A Simple Substitution Model of Technological Change," *Technological Forecasting and Social Change*, Vol. 3, 1971–1972. Copyright © 1972 by Elsevier Science Publishing Co., Inc. Reprinted by permission of the publisher.
2. From http://www.fabrics-manufacturers.com/consumption-statistics.html.
3. Exercise 40 from http://www.internetworldstats.com/emarketing.htm.
4. Exercise 41 from Problem 27 from May 2003 Course 1 Examination of the *Education and Examination Committee of the Society of Actuaries*. Reprinted by permission of the Society of Actuaries.
5. Exercise 43 from Specht, R. L., "Dark Island Heath (Ninety-Mile Plain, South Australia) V: The Water Relationships in Heath Vegetation and Pastures on the Makin Sand," *Australian Journal of Botany*, Vol. 5, No. 2, Sept. 1957, pp. 151–172.
6. Exercises 45 and 46 from Segal, Arthur C., "A Linear Diet Model," *The College Mathematics Journal*, Vol. 18, No. 1, Jan. 1987.
7. Exercise 47 from http://news.bbc.co.uk/2/hi/uk_news/8083179.stm.
8. Exercise 48 from Population Division of the Dept. of Economic and Social Affairs of the UN Secretariat, *World Population Prospects: The 2008 Revision*.
9. Exercises 49 and 50 from http://www.census.gov/population/www/projections/usinterimproj/.
10. Exercise 52 from *The New York Times*, Nov. 17, 1996, p. 3.
11. Exercise 55 first appeared in the *American Mathematical Monthly*, Vol. 44, Dec. 1937.
12. Exercises 58 and 59 from Callas, Dennis and David J. Hildreth, "Snapshots of Applications in Mathematics," *The College Mathematics Journal*, Vol. 26, No. 2, March 1995.

Section 2

1. Example 4 from Andrews, Larry C., *Ordinary Differential Equations with Applications*, Scott, Foresman and Company, 1982, p. 79.
2. Exercise 23 from Hoppensteadt, F. C. and J. D. Murray, "Threshold Analysis of a Drug Use Epidemic Model," *Mathematical Biosciences*, Vol. 53, No. 1/2, Feb. 1981, pp. 79–87.
3. Exercise 24 from Anderson, Roy M., "The Persistence of Direct Life Cycle Infectious Diseases Within Populations of Hosts," in *Lectures on Mathematics in the Life Sciences, Vol. 12: Some Mathematical Questions in Biology*, American Mathematical Society, 1979, pp. 1–67.

Section 3

1. Exercise 33 from France, J., J. Kijkstra and M. S. Dhanoa, "Growth Functions and Their Application in Animal Science," *Annales de Zootechnie*, Vol. 45 (Supplement), 1996, pp. 165–174.

2. Exercise 34 from Thurstone, L. L., "The Learning Function," *The Journal of General Psychology*, Vol. 3, No. 4, Oct. 1930, pp. 469–493.

Section 4

1. From Lotka, A. J., *Elements of Mathematical Biology*, Dover, 1956.
2. From Andrews, Larry C., *Ordinary Differential Equations with Boundary Value Problems*, HarperCollins Publishers, Inc., 1991, pp. 85–86. Reprinted by permission of the author.
3. Exercise 13 from Bender, Edward A., *An Introduction to Mathematical Modeling*. Copyright © 1978 by John Wiley and Sons, Inc. Reprinted by permission.

Review Exercise

1. Exercises 64–66 from http://www.census.gov/prod/ www/abs/ma.html.
2. Exercise 67 from Southwick, Lawrence, Jr. and Stanley Zionts, "An Optimal-Control-Theory Approach to the Education-Investment Decision," *Operations Research*, Vol. 22, 1974, pp. 1156–1174.
3. Exercise 71 from *Harper's*, Oct. 1994, p. 13.

Extended Application

1. From Bender, Edward A., *An Introduction to Mathematical Modeling*. Copyright © 1978 by John Wiley & Sons, Inc. Reprinted by permission from *An Introduction to Mathematical Modeling* by Edward A. Bender (Dover, 2000).

CREDITS

Example 7: Data from Fisher, J.C., and R. H. Pry, "A Simple Substitution Model of Technological Change," *Technological Forecasting and Social Change*," Vol. 3, 1971-1972, © 1972   Exercise 41: Copyright © Society of Actuaries. Used by permission. Example 4: Larry C. Andrews   Exercise 13: From Bender, Edward A., *An Introduction to Mathematical Modeling*, 1978. Published by Dover Publications. Reprinted by permission of the author.   Extended Application: From Bender, Edward A., *An Introduction to Mathematical Modeling*, 1978, 2000. Reprinted by permission of Dover Publications.

Probability and Calculus

Though earthquakes may appear to strike at random, the times between quakes can be modeled with an exponential density function. Such *continuous probability models* have many applications in science, engineering, and medicine. In an exercise in Section 1 of this chapter we'll use an exponential density function to describe the times between major earthquakes in Southern California, and in Section 3 we will compute the mean and standard deviation for this distribution.

In recent years, probability has become increasingly useful in fields ranging from manufacturing to medicine, as well as in all types of research. The foundations of probability were laid in the seventeenth century by Blaise Pascal (1623–1662) and Pierre de Fermat (1601–1665), who investigated *the problem of the points*. This problem dealt with the fair distribution of winnings in an interrupted game of chance between two equally matched players whose scores were known at the time of the interruption.

Probability has advanced from a study of gambling to a well-developed, deductive mathematical system. In this chapter we give a brief introduction to the use of calculus in probability.

Continuous Probability Models

APPLY IT

What is the probability that there is a bird's nest within 0.5 kilometers of a given point?
In Example 3, we will answer the question posed above.

In this section, we show how calculus is used to find the probability of certain events. Before discussing probability, however, we need to introduce some new terminology.

Suppose that a bank is studying the transaction times of its tellers. The lengths of time spent on observed transactions, rounded to the nearest minute, are shown in the following table.

Frequency of Transaction Times										
Time	1	2	3	4	5	6	7	8	9	10
Frequency	3	5	9	12	15	11	10	6	3	1 (Total: 75)

The table shows, for example, that 9 of the 75 transactions in the study took 3 minutes, 15 transactions took 5 minutes, and 1 transaction took 10 minutes. Because the time for any particular transaction is a random event, the number of minutes for a transaction is called a **random variable**. The frequencies can be converted to probabilities by dividing each frequency by the total number of transactions (75) to get the results shown in the next table.*

Probability of Transaction Times										
Time	1	2	3	4	5	6	7	8	9	10
Probability	0.04	0.07	0.12	0.16	0.20	0.15	0.13	0.08	0.04	0.01

Because each value of the random variable is associated with just one probability, this table defines a function. Such a function is called a **probability function**, and it has the following special properties.

*One definition of the *probability of an event* is the number of outcomes that favor the event divided by the total number of equally likely outcomes in an experiment.

Probability Function of a Random Variable

If the function f is a probability function with domain $\{x_1, x_2, \ldots, x_n\}$, and $f(x_i)$ is the probability that event x_i occurs, then for $1 \leq i \leq n$,

$$0 \leq f(x_i) \leq 1,$$

and

$$f(x_1) + f(x_2) + \cdots + f(x_n) = 1.$$

Note that $f(x_i) = 0$ implies that event x_i will not occur and $f(x_i) = 1$ implies that event x_i will occur.

The information in the second table can be displayed graphically with a special kind of bar graph called a **histogram**. The bars of a histogram have the same width, and their heights are determined by the probabilities of the various values of the random variable. See Figure 1.

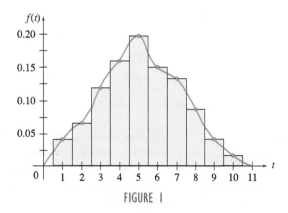

FIGURE 1

The probability function in the second table is a **discrete probability function** because it has a finite domain—the integers from 1 to 10, inclusive. A discrete probability function has a finite domain or an infinite domain that can be listed. For example, if we flip a coin until we get heads, and let the random variable be the number of flips, then the domain is $1, 2, 3, 4, \ldots$. On the other hand, the distribution of heights (in inches) of college women includes infinitely many possible measurements, such as 53, 54.2, 66.5, 72.$\overline{3}$, and so on, *within some real number interval*. Probability functions with such domains are called *continuous probability distributions*.

Continuous Probability Distribution

A **continuous random variable** can take on any value in some interval of real numbers. The distribution of this random variable is called a **continuous probability distribution**.

Some probability functions are inherently discrete. For example, the number of houses that a real estate agent sells in a year must be an integer, such as 0, 1, or 2, and could never take on any value in between. But the bank example discussed earlier is different, because you could think of it as a simplification of a continuous distribution. It would be possible to time the teller transactions with greater precision—to the nearest tenth of a minute, or even to the nearest 1/60 of a minute if desired. Theoretically, at least, t could take on any positive real-number value between, say, 0 and 11 minutes. The graph of the probabilities $f(t)$ of these transaction times can be thought of as the continuous curve shown in Figure 1. As indicated in Figure 1, the curve was derived from our table by connecting the points at the tops of the bars in the corresponding histogram and smoothing the resulting polygon into a curve.

To clarify some concepts in probability, we will follow the common convention of using capital letters to indicate random variables and lower case letters to indicate the values that the random variables take on. For example, to indicate the probability that a random variable takes on the value 2, we will write $P(X = 2)$. To indicate the probability that a random variable takes on the arbitrary value x, we will write $P(X = x)$.

For a discrete probability function, the area of each bar (or rectangle) gives the probability of a particular transaction time. Thus, by considering the possible transaction times T as all the real numbers between 0 and 11, the area under the curve of Figure 2 between any two values of T can be interpreted as the probability that a transaction time will be between those two numbers. For example, the shaded region in Figure 2 corresponds to the probability that T is between a and b, written $P(a \le T \le b)$.

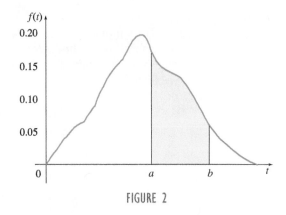

FIGURE 2

FOR REVIEW

Consider the connection between area and the definite integral. For example, here we solve the following:

Find the area between the x-axis and the graph of $f(x) = x^2$ from $x = 1$ to $x = 4$.

Answer: $\int_1^4 x^2\, dx = 21$

It was shown earlier that the definite integral of a continuous function f, where $f(x) \ge 0$, gives the area under the graph of $f(x)$ from $x = a$ to $x = b$. If a function f can be found to describe a continuous probability distribution, then the definite integral can be used to find the area under the curve from a to b that represents the probability that x will be between a and b.

If X is a continuous random variable whose distribution is described by the function f on $[a, b]$, then

$$P(a \le X \le b) = \int_a^b f(x)\, dx.$$

Probability Density Functions

A function f that describes a continuous probability distribution is called a *probability density function*. Such a function must satisfy the following conditions.

Probability Density Function

The function f is a **probability density function** of a random variable X in the interval $[a, b]$ if

1. $f(x) \ge 0$ for all x in the interval $[a, b]$; and

2. $\int_b^a f(x)\, dx = 1$.

Intuitively, Condition 1 says that the probability of a particular event can never be negative. Condition 2 says that the total probability for the interval must be 1; *something must happen.*

Now evaluate the integral. The indefinite integral was found in part (a).

$$P(0 \le X \le 0.5) = \int_0^{0.5} 2xe^{-x^2} \, dx = \left. (-e^{-x^2}) \right|_0^{0.5}$$

$$= -e^{-(0.5)^2} - (-e^0) = -e^{-0.25} + 1$$

$$\approx -0.7788 + 1 = 0.2212$$

The probability that a bird's nest will be found within 0.5 km of the given point is about 0.22.　　　　**TRY YOUR TURN 3**

YOUR TURN 3 Using the probability density function of Example 3, find the probability that there is a bird's nest within 1 km of the given point.

TECHNOLOGY

EXAMPLE 4　Computing Mortality

According to the National Center for Health Statistics, if we start with 100,000 people who are 50 years old, we can expect a certain number of them to die within each 5-year interval, as indicated by the following table.* *Source: National Vital Statistics Reports.*

Life Table		
Years from Age 50	Midpoint of Interval	Number Dying in Each Interval
0–5	2.5	2565
5–10	7.5	3659
10–15	12.5	5441
15–20	17.5	7622
20–25	22.5	10,498
25–30	27.5	13,858
30–35	32.5	16,833
35–40	37.5	16,720
40–45	42.5	13,211
45–50	47.5	7068
50–55	52.5	2525

(a) Plot the data.

SOLUTION　Figure 4 shows that the plot appears to have the shape of a polynomial.

(b) Find a polynomial equation that models the number of deaths, $N(t)$, as a function of the number of years, t, since age 50. Use the midpoints and the number of deaths in each interval from the table above.

SOLUTION　The highest degree polynomial that the regression feature on a TI-84 Plus calculator can find is fourth degree. As Figure 5(a) shows, this roughly captures the behavior of the data, but it has two drawbacks. For one, it doesn't reach the highest data points. Also, it's decreasing in the beginning when it should be increasing. Higher degree polynomials can be fit using Excel or using the Multiple Regression tool on the Statistics with List Editor application for the TI-89. We were thus able to find that the function

$$N(t) = 5.03958 \times 10^{-5}t^6 - 0.006603t^5 + 0.2992t^4 - 6.0507t^3 +$$
$$67.867t^2 - 110.3t + 2485.1$$

fits the data quite well, as shown in Figure 5(b).

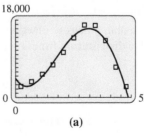
(a)

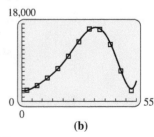
(b)

FIGURE 5

18,000

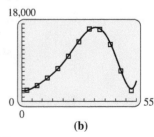

0 ⌊_____⌋ 55
0

FIGURE 4

*For simplicity, we have placed all those who lived past 100 in the class of those who lived from 100 to 105.

(c) Use the answer from part (b) to find a probability density function for the random variable T representing the number of additional years that a 50-year-old person lives.

SOLUTION We will construct a density function $S(t) = kN(t)$ by finding a suitable constant k, as we did in Example 2. The graph of the function turns up after $t = 52.5$, which is unlikely for the actual mortality function, so we will restrict the domain of the density function to the interval $[0, 52.5]$, even though this ignores those who live more than 102.5 years. Using the integration feature on our calculator, we find that

$$\int_0^{52.5} S(t)\,dt = k\int_0^{52.5} N(t)\,dt = 497{,}703k.$$

Notice that this number is close to the product of 5 years (interval length) and 100,000 (the total number of people). This is not a coincidence! We set the above integral equal to 1 to get $k = 1/497{,}703$. The function defined by

$$S(t) = \frac{1}{497{,}703}\, N(t)$$

$$= \frac{1}{497{,}703}\,(5.03958 \times 10^{-5}t^6 - 0.006603t^5 + 0.2992t^4$$

$$- 6.0507t^3 + 67.867t^2 - 110.3t + 2485.1)$$

is a probability density function for $[0, 52.5]$ because

$$\int_0^{52.5} S(t)\,dt = 1, \quad \text{and } S(t) \ge 0 \text{ for all } t \text{ in } [0, 52.5].$$

(d) Find the probability that a randomly chosen 50-year-old person will live at least until age 70.

SOLUTION Again using the integration feature on our calculator,

$$P(T \ge 20) = \int_{20}^{52.5} S(t)\,dt \approx 0.8054.$$

Thus a 50-year-old person has a 80.54% chance of living at least until age 70.

Notice that this value could also be estimated from the table by finding the number of people who have not died by age 70 and then dividing this number by 100,000. Thus, according to our table, there are 80,713 people still alive at age 70, representing 80.7% of the original population. As you can see, our estimate agrees quite well with the actual number.

Another important concept in probability is the *cumulative distribution function*, which gives the probability that a random variable X is less than or equal to an arbitrary value x.

Cumulative Distribution Function

If f is a probability density function of a random variable in the interval $[a, b]$, then the **cumulative distribution function** is defined as

$$F(x) = P(X \le x) = \int_a^x f(t)\,dt$$

for $x \ge a$. Also, $F(x) = 0$ for $x < a$.

NOTE

1. We integrate with respect to the variable t in the integral, rather than x, because we are already using x for the upper limit on the integral. It doesn't matter what variable of integration is used in a definite integral, since that variable doesn't appear in the final answer. We just need to use a variable that's not being used for another purpose.

2. If the random variable is defined on the interval $(-\infty, \infty)$, simply replace a with $-\infty$ in the above definition.

EXAMPLE 5 **Cumulative Distribution Function**

Consider the random variable X defined in Example 3, giving the distance (in kilometers) from a given point to the nearest bird's nest, with probability density function $f(x) = 2xe^{-x^2}$ for $x \geq 0$.

(a) Find the cumulative distribution function for this random variable.

SOLUTION The cumulative distribution function is given by

$$F(x) = P(X \leq x) = \int_0^x 2te^{-t^2}\, dt \qquad \text{Use the density function with } t \text{ as the variable}$$

$$= -e^{-t^2}\Big|_0^x \qquad \text{Use the antiderivative found in Example 3.}$$

$$= -e^{-x^2} + 1$$

for $x \geq 0$. The cumulative distribution function can be written as $F(x) = 1 - e^{-x^2}$ for $x \geq 0$. Note that for $x < 0$, $F(x) = 0$.

YOUR TURN 4 Use part (a) of Example 5 to calculate the probability that there is a bird's nest within 1 km of the given point.

(b) Use the solution to part (a) to calculate the probability that there is a bird's nest within 0.5 km of the given point.

SOLUTION To find $P(X \leq 0.5)$, calculate $F(0.5) = 1 - e^{-0.5^2} \approx 0.2212$. Notice that this is the same answer that we found in Example 3(b). **TRY YOUR TURN 4**

EXERCISES

Decide whether the functions defined as follows are probability density functions on the indicated intervals. If not, tell why.

1. $f(x) = \dfrac{1}{9}x - \dfrac{1}{18};\ [2, 5]$

2. $f(x) = \dfrac{1}{3}x - \dfrac{1}{6};\ [3, 4]$

3. $f(x) = \dfrac{x^2}{21};\ [1, 4]$

4. $f(x) = \dfrac{3}{98}x^2;\ [3, 5]$

5. $f(x) = 4x^3;\ [0, 3]$

6. $f(x) = \dfrac{x^3}{81};\ [0, 3]$

7. $f(x) = \dfrac{x^2}{16};\ [-2, 2]$

8. $f(x) = 2x^2;\ [-1, 1]$

9. $f(x) = \dfrac{5}{3}x^2 - \dfrac{5}{90};\ [-1, 1]$

10. $f(x) = \dfrac{3}{13}x^2 - \dfrac{12}{13}x + \dfrac{45}{52};\ [0, 4]$

Find a value of k that will make f a probability density function on the indicated interval.

11. $f(x) = kx^{1/2};\ [1, 4]$

12. $f(x) = kx^{3/2};\ [4, 9]$

13. $f(x) = kx^2;\ [0, 5]$

14. $f(x) = kx^2;\ [-1, 2]$

15. $f(x) = kx;\ [0, 3]$

16. $f(x) = kx;\ [2, 3]$

17. $f(x) = kx;\ [1, 5]$

18. $f(x) = kx^3;\ [2, 4]$

Find the cumulative distribution function for the probability density function in each of the following exercises.

19. Exercise 1

20. Exercise 2

21. Exercise 3

22. Exercise 4

23. Exercise 11

24. Exercise 12

25. The total area under the graph of a probability density function always equals _____.

26. In your own words, define a random variable.

27. What is the difference between a discrete probability function and a probability density function?

28. Why is $P(X = c) = 0$ for any number c in the domain of a probability density function?

Show that each function defined as follows is a probability density function on the given interval; then find the indicated probabilities.

29. $f(x) = \frac{1}{2}(1 + x)^{-3/2}$; $[0, \infty)$

    a. $P(0 \leq X \leq 2)$ **b.** $P(1 \leq X \leq 3)$

    c. $P(X \geq 5)$

30. $f(x) = e^{-x}$; $[0, \infty)$

    a. $P(0 \leq X \leq 1)$ **b.** $P(1 \leq X \leq 2)$

    c. $P(X \leq 2)$

31. $f(x) = (1/2)e^{-x/2}$; $[0, \infty)$

    a. $P(0 \leq X \leq 1)$ **b.** $P(1 \leq X \leq 3)$

    c. $P(X \geq 2)$

32. $f(x) = \dfrac{20}{(x + 20)^2}$; $[0, \infty)$

    a. $P(0 \leq X \leq 1)$ **b.** $P(1 \leq X \leq 5)$

    c. $P(X \geq 5)$

33. $f(x) = \begin{cases} \dfrac{x^3}{12} & \text{if } 0 \leq x \leq 2 \\ \dfrac{16}{3x^3} & \text{if } x > 2 \end{cases}$

    a. $P(0 \leq X \leq 2)$ **b.** $P(X \geq 2)$

    c. $P(1 \leq X \leq 3)$

34. $f(x) = \begin{cases} \dfrac{20x^4}{9} & \text{if } 0 \leq x \leq 1 \\ \dfrac{20}{9x^5} & \text{if } x > 1 \end{cases}$

    a. $P(0 \leq X \leq 1)$ **b.** $P(X \geq 1)$

    c. $P(0 \leq X \leq 2)$

APPLICATIONS

Business and Economics

35. Life Span of a Computer Part The life (in months) of a certain electronic computer part has a probability density function defined by

$$f(t) = \frac{1}{2}e^{-t/2} \quad \text{for } t \text{ in } [0, \infty).$$

Find the probability that a randomly selected component will last the following lengths of time.

    a. At most 12 months

    b. Between 12 and 20 months

    c. Find the cumulative distribution function for this random variable.

    d. Use the answer to part c to find the probability that a randomly selected component will last at most 6 months.

36. Machine Life A machine has a useful life of 4 to 9 years, and its life (in years) has a probability density function defined by

$$f(t) = \frac{1}{11}\left(1 + \frac{3}{\sqrt{t}}\right).$$

Find the probabilities that the useful life of such a machine selected at random will be the following.

    a. Longer than 6 years

    b. Less than 5 years

    c. Between 4 and 7 years

    d. Find the cumulative distribution function for this random variable.

    e. Use the answer to part d to find the probability that a randomly selected machine has a useful life of at most 8 years.

37. Machine Part The lifetime of a machine part has a continuous distribution on the interval $(0, 40)$ with probability density function f, where $f(x)$ is proportional to $(10 + x)^{-2}$. Calculate the probability that the lifetime of the machine part is less than 6. Choose one of the following. *Source: Society of Actuaries.*

    a. 0.04   **b.** 0.15   **c.** 0.47   **d.** 0.53   **e.** 0.94

38. Insurance An insurance policy pays for a random loss X subject to a deductible of C, where $0 < C < 1$. The loss amount is modeled as a continuous random variable with density function

$$f(x) = \begin{cases} 2x & \text{for } 0 < x < 1 \\ 0 & \text{otherwise.} \end{cases}$$

Given a random loss X, the probability that the insurance payment is less than 0.5 is equal to 0.64. Calculate C. Choose one of the following. (*Hint:* The payment is 0 unless the loss is greater than the deductible, in which case the payment is the loss minus the deductible.) *Source: Society of Actuaries.*

    a. 0.1   **b.** 0.3   **c.** 0.4   **d.** 0.6   **e.** 0.8

Life Sciences

39. Petal Length The length of a petal on a certain flower varies from 1 cm to 4 cm and has a probability density function defined by

$$f(x) = \frac{1}{2\sqrt{x}}.$$

Find the probabilities that the length of a randomly selected petal will be as follows.

    a. Greater than or equal to 3 cm

    b. Less than or equal to 2 cm

    c. Between 2 cm and 3 cm

40. Clotting Time of Blood The clotting time of blood is a random variable t with values from 1 second to 20 seconds and probability density function defined by

$$f(t) = \frac{1}{(\ln 20)t}.$$

Find the following probabilities for a person selected at random.

a. The probability that the clotting time is between 1 and 5 seconds

b. The probability that the clotting time is greater than 10 seconds

41. Flour Beetles Researchers who study the abundance of the flour beetle, *Tribolium castaneum*, have developed a probability density function that can be used to estimate the abundance of the beetle in a population. The density function, which is a member of the gamma distribution, is

$$f(x) = 1.185 \times 10^{-9} x^{4.5222} e^{-0.049846x},$$

where x is the size of the population. *Source: Ecology*.

a. Estimate the probability that a randomly selected flour beetle population is between 0 and 150.

b. Estimate the probability that a randomly selected flour beetle population is between 100 and 200.

42. Flea Beetles The mobility of an insect is an important part of its survival. Researchers have determined that the probability that a marked flea beetle, *Phyllotreta cruciferae* and *Phyllotreta striolata*, will be recaptured within a certain distance and time after release can be calculated from the probability density function

$$p(x, t) = \frac{e^{-x^2/(4Dt)}}{\int_0^L e^{-u^2/(4Dt)}\, du},$$

where t is the time after release (in hours), x is the distance (in meters) from the release point that recaptures occur, L is the maximum distance from the release point that recaptures can occur, and D is the diffusion coefficient. *Source: Ecology Monographs*.

a. If $t = 12$, $L = 6$, and $D = 38.3$, find the probability that a flea beetle will be recaptured within 3 m of the release point.

b. Using the same values for t, L, and D, find the probability that a flea beetle will be recaptured between 1 and 5 m of the release point.

Social Sciences

43. Social Network The number of U.S. users (in millions) on Facebook, a computer social network, in 2009 is given in the table below. *Source: Inside Facebook*.

Age Interval (years)	Midpoint of Interval (year)	Number of Users in Each Interval (millions)
13–17	15	6.049
18–25	21.5	19.461
26–34	30	13.423
35–44	39.5	9.701
45–54	49.5	4.582
55–65	60	2.849
Total		56.065

a. Plot the data. What type of function appears to best match this data?

b. Use the regression feature on your graphing calculator to find a quartic equation that models the number of years, t, since birth and the number of Facebook users, $N(t)$. Use the midpoint value to estimate the point in each interval for the age of the Facebook user. Graph the function with the plot of the data. Does the function resemble the data?

c. By finding an appropriate constant k, find a function $S(t) = kN(t)$ that is a probability density function describing the probability of the age of a Facebook user. (*Hint:* Because the function in part b is negative for values less than 13.4 and greater than 62.0, restrict the domain of the density function to the interval [13.4, 62.0]. That is, integrate the function you found in part b from 13.4 to 62.0.)

d. For a randomly chosen person who uses Facebook, find the probabilities that the person was at least 35 but less than 45 years old, at least 18 but less than 35 years old, and at least 45 years old. Compare these with the actual probabilities.

44. Time to Learn a Task The time required for a person to learn a certain task is a random variable with probability density function defined by

$$f(t) = \frac{8}{7(t-2)^2}.$$

The time required to learn the task is between 3 and 10 minutes. Find the probabilities that a randomly selected person will learn the task in the following lengths of time.

a. Less than 4 minutes

b. More than 5 minutes

Physical Sciences

45. Annual Rainfall The annual rainfall in a remote Middle Eastern country varies from 0 to 5 in. and is a random variable with probability density function defined by

$$f(x) = \frac{5.5 - x}{15}.$$

Find the following probabilities for the annual rainfall in a randomly selected year.

a. The probability that the annual rainfall is greater than 3 in.

b. The probability that the annual rainfall is less than 2 in.

c. The probability that the annual rainfall is between 1 in. and 4 in.

46. Earthquakes The time between major earthquakes in the Southern California region is a random variable with probability density function

$$f(t) = \frac{1}{960} e^{-t/960},$$

where t is measured in days. *Source: Journal of Seismology*.

a. Find the probability that the time between a major earthquake and the next one is less than 365 days.

b. Find the probability that the time between a major earthquake and the next one is more than 960 days.

47. Earthquakes The time between major earthquakes in the Taiwan region is a random variable with probability density function

$$f(t) = \frac{1}{3650.1}e^{-t/3650.1},$$

where t is measured in days. *Source: Journal of Seismology*.

a. Find the probability that the time between a major earthquake and the next one is more than 1 year but less than 3 years.

b. Find the probability that the time between a major earthquake and the next one is more than 7300 days.

General Interest

48. Drunk Drivers The frequency of alcohol-related traffic fatalities has dropped in recent years but is still high among young people. Based on data from the National Highway Traffic Safety Administration, the age of a randomly selected, alcohol-impaired driver in a fatal car crash is a random variable with probability density function given by

$$f(t) = \frac{4.045}{t^{1.532}} \quad \text{for } t \text{ in } [16, 80].$$

Find the following probabilities of the age of such a driver. *Source: Traffic Safety Facts*.

a. Less than or equal to 25

b. Greater than or equal to 35

c. Between 21 and 30

d. Find the cumulative distribution function for this random variable.

e. Use the answer to part d to find the probability that a randomly selected alcohol-impaired driver in a fatal car crash is at most 21 years old.

49. Driving Fatalities Consider that driver fatality rates are highest for the youngest and oldest drivers. When adjusted for the number of miles driven by people in each age group, the number of drivers in fatal crashes goes down with age, and the age of a randomly selected driver in a fatal car crash is a random variable with probability density function given by

$$f(t) = 0.06049e^{-0.03211t} \quad \text{for } t \text{ in } [16, 84].$$

Find the following probabilities of the age of such a driver. *Source: National Highway Traffic Safety Administration*.

a. Less than or equal to 25

b. Greater than or equal to 35

c. Between 21 and 30

d. Find the cumulative distribution function for this random variable.

e. Use the answer to part d to find the probability that a randomly selected driver in a fatal crash is at most 21 years old.

50. Length of a Telephone Call The length of a telephone call (in minutes), t, for a certain town is a continuous random variable with probability density function defined by

$$f(t) = 3t^{-4}, \quad \text{for } t \text{ in } [1, \infty).$$

Find the probabilities for the following situations.

a. The call lasts between 1 and 2 minutes.

b. The call lasts between 3 and 5 minutes.

c. The call lasts longer than 3 minutes.

51. Time of Traffic Fatality The National Highway Traffic Safety Administration records the time of day of fatal crashes. The following table gives the time of day (in hours since midnight) and the frequency of fatal crashes. *Source: The National Highway Traffic Safety Administration*.

Time of Day	Midpoint of Interval (hours)	Frequency
0–3	1.5	4486
3–6	4.5	2774
6–9	7.5	3236
9–12	10.5	3285
12–15	13.5	4356
15–18	16.5	5325
18–21	19.5	5342
21–24	22.5	4952
Total		33,756

a. Plot the data. What type of function appears to best match this data?

b. Use the regression feature on your graphing calculator to find a cubic equation that models the time of day, t, and the number of traffic fatalities, $T(t)$. Use the midpoint value to estimate the time in each interval. Graph the function with the plot of the data. Does the graph fit the data?

c. By finding an appropriate constant k, find a function $S(t) = kT(t)$ that is a probability density function describing the probability of a traffic fatality at a particular time of day.

d. For a randomly chosen traffic fatality, find the probabilities that the accident occurred between 12 am and 2 am ($t = 0$ to $t = 2$) and between 4 pm and 5:30 pm ($t = 16$ to $t = 17.5$).

YOUR TURN ANSWERS

1. $P\left(\frac{3}{2} \le X \le 2\right) = \frac{1}{3}$ **2.** $k = 1/64$

3. 0.6321   **4.** 0.6321

2 Expected Value and Variance of Continuous Random Variables

What is the average age of a drunk driver in a fatal car crash?
You will be asked to answer this question in Exercise 40.

It often is useful to have a single number, a typical or "average" number, that represents a random variable. The *mean* or *expected value* for a discrete random variable is found by multiplying each value of the random variable by its corresponding probability, as follows.

Expected Value

Suppose the random variable X can take on the n values, $x_1, x_2, x_3, \ldots, x_n$. Also, suppose the probabilities that each of these values occurs are, respectively, $p_1, p_2, p_3, \ldots, p_n$. Then the **mean**, or **expected value**, of the random variable is

$$\mu = x_1 p_1 + x_2 p_2 + x_3 p_3 + \cdots + x_n p_n = \sum_{i=1}^{n} x_i p_i.$$

For the banking example in the previous section, the expected value is given by

$$\mu = 1(0.04) + 2(0.07) + 3(0.12) + 4(0.16) + 5(0.20) + 6(0.15)$$
$$+ 7(0.13) + 8(0.08) + 9(0.04) + 10(0.01)$$
$$= 5.09.$$

Thus, the average time a person can expect to spend with the bank teller is 5.09 minutes.

This definition can be extended to continuous random variables by using definite integrals. Suppose a continuous random variable has probability density function f on $[a, b]$. We can divide the interval from a to b into n subintervals of length Δx, where $\Delta x = (b - a)/n$. In the ith subinterval, the probability that the random variable takes a value close to x_i is approximately $f(x_i) \Delta x$, and so

$$\mu \approx \sum_{i=1}^{n} x_i f(x_i) \Delta x.$$

As $n \to \infty$, the limit of this sum gives the expected value

$$\mu = \int_{a}^{b} x f(x) \, dx.$$

The **variance** of a probability distribution is a measure of the *spread* of the values of the distribution. For a discrete distribution, the variance is found by taking the expected value of the squares of the differences of the values of the random variable and the mean. If the random variable X takes the values $x_1, x_2, x_3, \ldots, x_n$, with respective probabilities $p_1, p_2, p_3, \ldots, p_n$ and mean μ, then the variance of X is

$$\text{Var}(X) = \sum_{i=1}^{n} (x_i - \mu)^2 p_i.$$

Think of the variance as the expected value of $(X - \mu)^2$, which measures how far X is from the mean μ. The **standard deviation** of X is defined as

$$\sigma = \sqrt{\text{Var}(X)}.$$

For the banking example in the previous section, the variance and standard deviation are

$$
\begin{aligned}
\text{Var}(X) = & (1 - 5.09)^2(0.04) + (2 - 5.09)^2(0.07) + (3 - 5.09)^2(0.12) \\
& + (4 - 5.09)^2(0.16) + (5 - 5.09)^2(0.20) + (6 - 5.09)^2(0.15) \\
& + (7 - 5.09)^2(0.13) + (8 - 5.09)^2(0.08) + (9 - 5.09)^2(0.04) \\
& + (10 - 5.09)^2(0.01) \\
= & \ 4.1819
\end{aligned}
$$

and

$$
\sigma = \sqrt{\text{Var}(X)} \approx 2.0450.
$$

Like the mean or expected value, the variance of a continuous random variable is an integral.

$$
\text{Var}(X) = \int_a^b (x - \mu)^2 f(x) \, dx
$$

To find the standard deviation of a continuous probability distribution, like that of a discrete distribution, we find the square root of the variance. The formulas for the expected value, variance, and standard deviation of a continuous probability distribution are summarized here.

Expected Value, Variance, and Standard Deviation

If X is a continuous random variable with probability density function f on $[a, b]$, then the expected value of X is

$$
E(X) = \mu = \int_a^b x f(x) \, dx.
$$

The variance of X is

$$
\text{Var}(X) = \int_a^b (x - \mu)^2 f(x) \, dx,
$$

and the standard deviation of X is

$$
\sigma = \sqrt{\text{Var}(X)}.
$$

NOTE In the formulas for expected value, variance, and standard deviation, and all other formulas in this section, it is possible that $a = -\infty$ or $b = \infty$, in which case the density function f is defined on $[a, \infty)$, $(-\infty, b]$, or $(-\infty, \infty)$. In this case, the integrals in these formulas become improper integrals. Example 2 will illustrate the procedure for dealing with them.

Geometrically, the expected value (or mean) of a probability distribution represents the balancing point of the distribution. If a fulcrum were placed at μ on the x-axis, the figure would be in balance. See Figure 6.

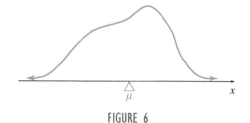

FIGURE 6

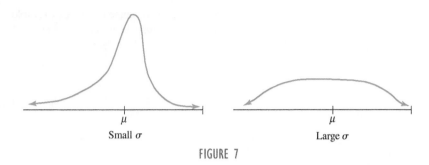

FIGURE 7

The variance and standard deviation of a probability distribution indicate how closely the values of the distribution cluster about the mean. These measures are most useful for comparing different distributions, as in Figure 7.

EXAMPLE 1   Expected Value and Variance

Find the expected value and variance of the random variable X with probability density function defined by $f(x) = (3/26)x^2$ on $[1, 3]$.

SOLUTION   By the definition of expected value just given,

$$\mu = \int_1^3 xf(x)\,dx$$

$$= \int_1^3 x\left(\frac{3}{26}x^2\right)dx$$

$$= \frac{3}{26}\int_1^3 x^3\,dx$$

$$= \frac{3}{26}\left(\frac{x^4}{4}\right)\Big|_1^3 = \frac{3}{104}(81 - 1) = \frac{30}{13},$$

or about 2.3077.

The variance is

$$\text{Var}(X) = \int_1^3 \left(x - \frac{30}{13}\right)^2\left(\frac{3}{26}x^2\right)dx$$

$$= \int_1^3 \left(x^2 - \frac{60}{13}x + \frac{900}{169}\right)\left(\frac{3}{26}x^2\right)dx \qquad \text{Square } \left(x - \frac{30}{13}\right).$$

$$= \frac{3}{26}\int_1^3 \left(x^4 - \frac{60}{13}x^3 + \frac{900}{169}x^2\right)dx \qquad \text{Multiply.}$$

$$= \frac{3}{26}\left(\frac{x^5}{5} - \frac{60}{13}\cdot\frac{x^4}{4} + \frac{900}{169}\cdot\frac{x^3}{3}\right)\Big|_1^3 \qquad \text{Integrate.}$$

$$= \frac{3}{26}\left[\left(\frac{243}{5} - \frac{60(81)}{52} + \frac{900(27)}{169(3)}\right) - \left(\frac{1}{5} - \frac{60}{52} + \frac{300}{169}\right)\right]$$

$$\approx 0.2592.$$

From the variance, the standard deviation is $\sigma \approx \sqrt{0.2592} \approx 0.5091$. The expected value and standard deviation are shown on the graph of the probability density function in Figure 8.   TRY YOUR TURN 1

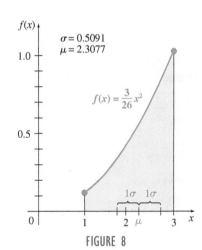

FIGURE 8

YOUR TURN 1   Repeat Example 1 for the probability density function $f(x) = \dfrac{8}{3x^3}$ on $[1, 2]$.

Calculating the variance in the last example was a messy job. An alternative version of the formula for the variance is easier to compute. This alternative formula is derived as follows.

$$\text{Var}(X) = \int_a^b (x - \mu)^2 f(x) dx$$

$$= \int_a^b (x^2 - 2\mu x + \mu^2) f(x) dx$$

$$= \int_a^b x^2 f(x) \, dx - 2\mu \int_a^b x f(x) \, dx + \mu^2 \int_a^b f(x) dx \qquad (1)$$

By definition,

$$\int_a^b x f(x) \, dx = \mu,$$

and, since $f(x)$ is a probability density function,

$$\int_a^b f(x) \, dx = 1.$$

Substitute back into Equation (1) to get the alternative formula,

$$\text{Var}(X) = \int_a^b x^2 f(x) \, dx - 2\mu^2 + \mu^2 = \int_a^b x^2 f(x) \, dx - \mu^2.$$

Alternative Formula for Variance

If X is a random variable with probability density function f on $[a, b]$, and if $E(X) = \mu$, then

$$\textbf{Var}(X) = \int_a^b x^2 f(x) \, dx - \mu^2.$$

CAUTION   Notice that the term μ^2 comes *after* the dx and so is *not* integrated.

EXAMPLE 2   Variance

Use the alternative formula for variance to compute the variance of the random variable X with probability density function defined by $f(x) = 3/x^4$ for $x \geq 1$.

SOLUTION   To find the variance, first find the expected value:

$$\mu = \int_1^\infty x f(x) dx = \int_1^\infty x \cdot \frac{3}{x^4} \, dx = \int_1^\infty \frac{3}{x^3} \, dx$$

$$= \lim_{b \to \infty} \int_1^b \frac{3}{x^3} \, dx = \lim_{b \to \infty} \left(\frac{3}{-2x^2} \right) \Big|_1^b = \frac{3}{2},$$

or 1.5. Now find the variance by the alternative formula for variance:

$$\text{Var}(X) = \int_1^\infty x^2 \left(\frac{3}{x^4} \right) dx - \left(\frac{3}{2} \right)^2$$

$$= \int_1^\infty \frac{3}{x^2} \, dx - \frac{9}{4}$$

$$= \lim_{b \to \infty} \int_1^b \frac{3}{x^2} \, dx - \frac{9}{4}$$

$$= \lim_{b \to \infty} \left(\frac{-3}{x} \right) \Big|_1^b - \frac{9}{4}$$

$$= 3 - \frac{9}{4} = \frac{3}{4}, \quad \text{or } 0.75. \qquad \text{TRY YOUR TURN 2}$$

YOUR TURN 2   Repeat Example 2 for the probability density function $f(x) = 4/x^5$ for $x \geq 1$.

EXAMPLE 3 Passenger Arrival

A recent study has shown that airline passengers arrive at the gate with the amount of time (in hours) before the scheduled flight time given by the probability density function $f(t) = (3/4)(2t - t^2)$ for $0 \le t \le 2$.

(a) Find and interpret the expected value for this distribution.

SOLUTION The expected value is

$$\mu = \int_0^2 t \left(\frac{3}{4} \right)(2t - t^2)dt = \int_0^2 \left(\frac{3}{4} \right)(2t^2 - t^3)dt$$

$$= \left(\frac{3}{4} \right)\left(\frac{2t^3}{3} - \frac{t^4}{4} \right)\Big|_0^2 = \left(\frac{3}{4} \right)\left(\frac{16}{3} - 4 \right) = 1.$$

This result indicates that passengers arrive at the gate an average of 1 hour before the scheduled flight time.

(b) Compute the standard deviation.

SOLUTION First compute the variance. We use the alternative formula.

$$\text{Var}(T) = \int_0^2 t^2 \left(\frac{3}{4} \right)(2t - t^2)dt - 1^2$$

$$= \int_0^2 \left(\frac{3}{4} \right)(2t^3 - t^4)dt - 1$$

$$= \left(\frac{3}{4} \right)\left(\frac{t^4}{2} - \frac{t^5}{5} \right)\Big|_0^2 - 1$$

$$= \left(\frac{3}{4} \right)\left(8 - \frac{32}{5} \right) - 1 = \frac{6}{5} - 1 = \frac{1}{5}$$

The standard deviation is $\sigma = \sqrt{1/5} \approx 0.45$.

(c) Calculate the probability that passengers will arrive at the gate within one standard deviation of the mean.

SOLUTION Since the mean, or expected value, is 1 and the standard deviation is approximately 0.45, we are calculating the probability that passengers will arrive between

$$\mu - \sigma = 1 - 0.45 = 0.55 \text{ hours}$$

and

$$\mu + \sigma = 1 + 0.45 = 1.45 \text{ hours}$$

before the scheduled flight time. The probability is given by

$$P(0.55 \le T \le 1.45) = \int_{0.55}^{1.45} \frac{3}{4}(2t - t^2)dt.$$

Evaluating the integral gives

$$\int_{0.55}^{1.45} \frac{3}{4}(2t - t^2)dt = \frac{3}{4}\left(t^2 - \frac{t^3}{3} \right)\Big|_{0.55}^{1.45} \approx 0.6294.$$

The probability that passengers will arrive within one standard deviation of the mean is about 0.63.

TECHNOLOGY

EXAMPLE 4 Life Expectancy

In the previous section of this chapter we used statistics compiled by the National Center for Health Statistics to determine a probability density function that can be used to study the proportion of all 50-year-olds who will be alive in t years. The function is given by

$$S(t) = \frac{1}{497{,}703}(5.03958 \times 10^{-5}t^6 - 0.006603t^5 + 0.2992t^4$$
$$- 6.0507t^3 + 67.867t^2 - 110.3t + 2485.1)$$

for $0 \leq t \leq 52.5$.

(a) Find the life expectancy of a 50-year-old person.

SOLUTION Since this is a complicated function that is tedious to integrate analytically, we will employ the integration feature on a TI-84 Plus calculator to calculate

$$\mu = \int_0^{52.5} tS(t)dt \approx 30.38 \text{ years.}$$

According to life tables, the life expectancy of a person between the ages of 50 and 55 is 30.6 years. Our estimate is remarkably accurate given the limited number of data points and the function used in our original analysis. Life expectancy is generally calculated with techniques from life table analysis. *Source: National Center for Health Statistics.*

(b) Find the standard deviation of this probability function.

SOLUTION Using the alternate formula, we first calculate the variance.

$$\text{Var}(T) = \int_0^{52.5} t^2 S(t)dt - \mu^2 = 1057.7195 - (30.38)^2 \approx 134.775$$

Thus, $\sigma = \sqrt{\text{Var}(T)} \approx 11.61$ years.

As we mentioned earlier, the expected value is also referred to as the mean of the random variable. It is a type of average. There is another type of average, known as the *median*, that is often used. It is the value of the random variable for which there is a 50% probability of being larger and a 50% probability of being smaller. The precise definition is as follows.

Median

If X is a random variable with probability density function f on $[a, b]$, then the **median** of X is the number m such that

$$\int_a^m f(x)dx = \frac{1}{2}.$$

The median is particularly useful when the random variable is not distributed symmetrically about the mean. An example of this would be a random variable representing the price of homes in a city. There is a small probability that a home will be much more expensive than most of the homes in the city, and this tends to make the mean abnormally high. The median price is a better representation of the average price of a home.

EXAMPLE 5 Median

Find the median for the random variable described in Example 2, with density function defined by $f(x) = 3/x^4$ for $x \geq 1$.

SOLUTION According to the formula,

$$\int_1^m \frac{3}{x^4} dx = \frac{1}{2}.$$

Evaluating the integral on the left, we have

$$-\frac{1}{x^3}\bigg|_1^m = -\frac{1}{m^3} + 1.$$

Set this equal to 1/2.

$$-\frac{1}{m^3} + 1 = \frac{1}{2}$$

$$\frac{1}{2} = \frac{1}{m^3} \qquad \text{Subtract 1/2 from both sides, and add } 1/m^3.$$

$$m^3 = 2 \qquad \text{Cross multiply.}$$

$$m = \sqrt[3]{2}$$

YOUR TURN 3 Repeat Example 5 for the probability density function $f(x) = 4/x^5$ for $x \geq 1$.

The median value is, therefore, $\sqrt[3]{2} \approx 1.2599$. Notice that this is smaller than the mean of 1.5 found in Example 2. This is because the random variable can take on arbitrarily large values, which pulls up the mean but doesn't affect the median. **TRY YOUR TURN 3**

Using the notion of cumulative distribution function from the previous section, we can say that the median m is the value for which the cumulative distribution function is 0.5; that is, $F(m) = 0.5$.

2 EXERCISES

In Exercises 1–8, a probability density function of a random variable is defined. Find the expected value, the variance, and the standard deviation. Round answers to the nearest hundredth.

1. $f(x) = \frac{1}{4}$; $[3, 7]$

2. $f(x) = \frac{1}{10}$; $[0, 10]$

3. $f(x) = \frac{x}{8} - \frac{1}{4}$; $[2, 6]$

4. $f(x) = 2(1 - x)$; $[0, 1]$

5. $f(x) = 1 - \frac{1}{\sqrt{x}}$; $[1, 4]$

6. $f(x) = \frac{1}{11}\left(1 + \frac{3}{\sqrt{x}}\right)$; $[4, 9]$

7. $f(x) = 4x^{-5}$; $[1, \infty)$

8. $f(x) = 3x^{-4}$; $[1, \infty)$

9. What information does the mean (expected value) of a continuous random variable give?

10. Suppose two random variables have standard deviations of 0.10 and 0.23, respectively. What does this tell you about their distributions?

In Exercises 11–14, the probability density function of a random variable is defined.

a. Find the expected value to the nearest hundredth.

b. Find the variance to the nearest hundredth.

c. Find the standard deviation. Round to the nearest hundredth.

d. Find the probability that the random variable has a value greater than the mean.

e. Find the probability that the value of the random variable is within 1 standard deviation of the mean. Use the value of the standard deviation to the accuracy of your calculator.

11. $f(x) = \frac{\sqrt{x}}{18}$; $[0, 9]$

12. $f(x) = \frac{x^{-1/3}}{6}$; $[0, 8]$

13. $f(x) = \frac{1}{4}x^3$, $[0, 2]$

14. $f(x) = \frac{3}{16}(4 - x^2)$; $[0, 2]$

For Exercises 15–20, (a) find the median of the random variable with the probability density function given, and (b) find the probability that the random variable is between the expected value (mean) and the median. The expected value for each of these functions was found in Exercises 1–8.

15. $f(x) = \frac{1}{4}$; $[3, 7]$

16. $f(x) = \frac{1}{10}$; $[0, 10]$

17. $f(x) = \frac{x}{8} - \frac{1}{4}$; $[2, 6]$

18. $f(x) = 2(1 - x)$; $[0, 1]$

19. $f(x) = 4x^{-5}$; $[1, \infty)$

20. $f(x) = 3x^{-4}$; $[1, \infty)$

Find the expected value, the variance, and the standard deviation, when they exist, for each probability density function.

21. $f(x) = \begin{cases} \dfrac{x^3}{12} & \text{if } 0 \le x \le 2 \\ \dfrac{16}{3x^3} & \text{if } x > 2 \end{cases}$

22. $f(x) = \begin{cases} \dfrac{20x^4}{9} & \text{if } 0 \le x \le 1 \\ \dfrac{20}{9x^5} & \text{if } x > 1 \end{cases}$

23. Let X be a continuous random variable with density function

$$f(x) = \begin{cases} \dfrac{|x|}{10} & \text{for } -2 \le x \le 4 \\ 0 & \text{otherwise.} \end{cases}$$

Calculate the expected value of X. *Source: Society of Actuaries.* Choose one of the following.

a. $1/5$ **b.** $3/5$ **c.** 1 **d.** $28/15$ **e.** $12/5$

APPLICATIONS

Business and Economics

24. Life of a Light Bulb The life (in hours) of a certain kind of light bulb is a random variable with probability density function defined by

$$f(t) = \frac{1}{58\sqrt{t}} \quad \text{for } t \text{ in } [1,900].$$

a. What is the expected life of such a bulb?

b. Find σ.

c. Find the probability that one of these bulbs lasts longer than 1 standard deviation above the mean.

d. Find the median life of these bulbs.

25. Machine Life The life (in years) of a certain machine is a random variable with probability density function defined by

$$f(t) = \frac{1}{11}\left(1 + \frac{3}{\sqrt{t}}\right) \quad \text{for } t \text{ in } [4, 9].$$

a. Find the mean life of this machine.

b. Find the standard deviation of the distribution.

c. Find the probability that a particular machine of this kind will last longer than the mean number of years.

26. Life of an Automobile Part The life span of a certain automobile part (in months) is a random variable with probability density function defined by

$$f(t) = \frac{1}{2}e^{-t/2} \quad \text{for } t \text{ in } [0, \infty).$$

a. Find the expected life of this part.

b. Find the standard deviation of the distribution.

c. Find the probability that one of these parts lasts less than the mean number of months.

d. Find the median life of these parts.

27. Losses After Deductible A manufacturer's annual losses follow a distribution with density function

$$f(x) = \begin{cases} \dfrac{2.5(0.6)^{2.5}}{x^{3.5}} & \text{for } x > 0.6 \\ 0 & \text{otherwise.} \end{cases}$$

To cover its losses, the manufacturer purchases an insurance policy with an annual deductible of 2. What is the mean of the manufacturer's annual losses not paid by the insurance policy? Choose one of the following. (*Hint:* The loss not paid by the insurance policy will equal the actual loss if the actual loss is less than the deductible. Otherwise it will equal the deductible.) *Source: Society of Actuaries.*

a. 0.84 **b.** 0.88 **c.** 0.93 **d.** 0.95 **e.** 1.00

28. Insurance Reimbursement An insurance policy reimburses a loss up to a benefit limit of 10. The policyholder's loss, Y, follows a distribution with density function:

$$f(y) = \begin{cases} \dfrac{2}{y^3} & \text{for } y > 1 \\ 0 & \text{otherwise.} \end{cases}$$

What is the expected value of the benefit paid under the insurance policy? Choose one of the following. (*Hint:* The benefit paid will be equal to the actual loss if the actual loss is less than the limit. Otherwise it will equal the limit.) *Source: Society of Actuaries.*

a. 1.0 **b.** 1.3 **c.** 1.8 **d.** 1.9 **e.** 2.0

29. Insurance Claims An insurance company's monthly claims are modeled by a continuous, positive random variable X, whose probability density function is proportional to $(1 + x)^{-4}$, where $0 < x < \infty$. Determine the company's expected monthly claims. Choose one of the following. *Source: Society of Actuaries.*

a. $1/6$ **b.** $1/3$ **c.** $1/2$ **d.** 1 **e.** 3

30. Dental Insurance An insurance policy reimburses dental expense, X, up to a maximum benefit of 250. The probability density function for X is

$$f(x) = \begin{cases} ce^{-0.004x} & \text{for } x \ge 0 \\ 0 & \text{otherwise,} \end{cases}$$

where c is a constant. Calculate the median benefit for this policy. Choose one of the following. (*Hint:* As long as the expenses are less than 250, the expenses and the benefit are equal.) *Source: Society of Actuaries.*

a. 161 **b.** 165 **c.** 173 **d.** 182 **e.** 250

Life Sciences

31. Blood Clotting Time The clotting time of blood (in seconds) is a random variable with probability density function defined by

$$f(t) = \frac{1}{(\ln 20)t} \quad \text{for } t \text{ in } [1, 20].$$

a. Find the mean clotting time.

b. Find the standard deviation.

c. Find the probability that a person's blood clotting time is within 1 standard deviation of the mean.

d. Find the median clotting time.

32. Length of a Leaf The length of a leaf on a tree is a random variable with probability density function defined by

$$f(x) = \frac{3}{32}(4x - x^2) \quad \text{for } x \text{ in } [0, 4].$$

a. What is the expected leaf length?

b. Find σ for this distribution.

c. Find the probability that the length of a given leaf is within 1 standard deviation of the expected value.

33. Petal Length The length (in centimeters) of a petal on a certain flower is a random variable with probability density function defined by

$$f(x) = \frac{1}{2\sqrt{x}} \quad \text{for } x \text{ in } [1, 4].$$

a. Find the expected petal length.

b. Find the standard deviation.

c. Find the probability that a petal selected at random has a length more than 2 standard deviations above the mean.

d. Find the median petal length.

34. Flea Beetles As we saw in Exercise 42 of the previous section, the probability that a marked flea beetle, *Phyllotreta cruciferae* and *Phyllotreta striolata*, will be recaptured within a certain distance and time after release can be calculated from the probability density function

$$p(x, t) = \frac{e^{-x^2/(4Dt)}}{\int_0^L e^{-u^2/(4Dt)}\, du},$$

where t is the time (in hours) after release, x is the distance (in meters) from the release point that recaptures occur, L is the maximum distance from the release point that recaptures can occur, and D is the diffusion coefficient. If $t = 12$, $L = 6$, and $D = 38.3$, find the expected recapture distance. *Source: Ecology Monographs.*

35. Flour Beetles As we saw in Exercise 41 of the previous section, a probability density function has been developed to estimate the abundance of the flour beetle, *Tribolium castaneum*. The density function, which is a member of the gamma distribution, is

$$f(x) = 1.185 \times 10^{-9} x^{4.5222} e^{-0.049846x},$$

where x is the size of the population. Calculate the expected size of a flour beetle population. (*Hint:* Use 1000 as the upper limit of integration.) *Source: Ecology.*

Social Sciences

36. Time to Learn a Task In Exercise 44 of the previous section, the probability density function for the time required for a person to learn a certain task was given by

$$f(t) = \frac{8}{7(t - 2)^2},$$

for $3 \le t \le 10$ minutes. Find the median time for a person to learn the task.

37. Social Network In Exercise 43 of the previous section, the probability density function for the number of U.S. users of Facebook, a computer social network, was found to be

$$S(t) = \frac{1}{466.26}(- 0.00007445t^4 + 0.01243t^3 - 0.7419t^2 + 18.18t - 137.5)$$

where t was the number of years since birth on [13.4, 62.0]. Calculate the expected age of a Facebook user, as well as the standard deviation. *Source: Inside Facebook.*

Physical Sciences

38. Earthquakes The time between major earthquakes in the Southern California region is a random variable with probability density function defined by

$$f(t) = \frac{1}{960}e^{-t/960},$$

where t is measured in days. *Source: Journal of Seismology.* Find the expected value and the standard deviation of this probability density function.

39. Annual Rainfall The annual rainfall in a remote Middle Eastern country is a random variable with probability density function defined by

$$f(x) = \frac{5.5 - x}{15}, \quad \text{for } x \text{ in } [0, 5].$$

a. Find the mean annual rainfall.

b. Find the standard deviation.

c. Find the probability of a year with rainfall less than 1 standard deviation below the mean.

General Interest

40. Drunk Drivers In the last section, we saw that the age of a randomly selected, alcohol-impaired driver in a fatal car crash is a random variable with probability density function given by

$$f(t) = \frac{4.045}{t^{1.532}} \quad \text{for } t \text{ in } [16, 80].$$

Source: Traffic Safety Facts.

a. APPLY IT Find the expected age of a drunk driver in a fatal car crash.

b. Find the standard deviation of the distribution.

c. Find the probability that such a driver will be younger than 1 standard deviation below the mean.

d. Find the median age of a drunk driver in a fatal car crash.

41. Driving Fatalities In the last section, we saw that the age of a randomly selected driver in a fatal car crash is a random variable with probability density function given by

$$f(t) = 0.06049e^{-0.03211t} \quad \text{for } t \text{ in } [16, 84].$$

Source: National Highway Traffic Safety Administration.

a. Find the expected age of a driver in a fatal car crash.

b. Find the standard deviation of the distribution.

c. Find the probability that such a driver will be younger than 1 standard deviation below the mean.

d. Find the median age of a driver in a fatal car crash.

42. Length of a Telephone Call The length of a telephone call (in minutes), t, for a certain town is a continuous random variable with probability density function defined by

$$f(t) = 3t^{-4}$$

for t in $[1, \infty)$. Find the expected length of a phone call.

43. Time of Traffic Fatality In Exercise 51 of the previous section, the probability density function for the number of fatal traffic accidents was found to be

$$S(t) = \frac{1}{101{,}370}\left(-2.564t^3 + 99.11t^2 - 964.6t + 5631\right)$$

where t is the number of hours since midnight on $[0, 24]$. Calculate the expected time of day at which a fatal accident will occur. *Source: The National Highway Traffic Safety Administration.*

YOUR TURN ANSWERS

1. 4/3, 0.0706   **2.** 2/9   **3.** $\sqrt[4]{2} \approx 1.1892$

3 Special Probability Density Functions

APPLY IT   **What is the probability that the maximum outdoor temperature will be higher than 24°C? What is the probability that a flashlight battery will last longer than 40 hours?**
These questions, presented in Examples 1 and 2, can be answered if the probability density function for the maximum temperature and for the life of the battery are known.

In practice, it is not feasible to construct a probability density function for every experiment. Instead, a researcher uses one of several probability density functions that are well known, matching the shape of the experimental distribution to one of the known distributions. In this section we discuss some of the most commonly used probability distributions.

Uniform Distribution
The simplest probability distribution occurs when the probability density function of a random variable remains constant over the sample space. In this case, the random variable is said to be *uniformly distributed* over the sample space. The probability density function for the **uniform distribution** is defined by

$$f(x) = \frac{1}{b-a} \quad \text{for } x \text{ in } [a, b],$$

where a and b are constant real numbers. The graph of $f(x)$ is shown in Figure 9.

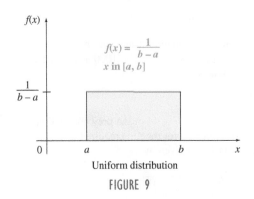

Uniform distribution

FIGURE 9

Since $b - a$ is positive, $f(x) \geq 0$, and

$$\int_a^b \frac{1}{b-a}\,dx = \frac{1}{b-a}x\Big|_a^b = \frac{1}{b-a}(b-a) = 1.$$

Therefore, the function is a probability density function.

The expected value for the uniform distribution is

$$\mu = \int_a^b \left(\frac{1}{b-a}\right)x\,dx = \left(\frac{1}{b-a}\right)\frac{x^2}{2}\Big|_a^b$$

$$= \frac{1}{2(b-a)}(b^2 - a^2) = \frac{1}{2}(b+a). \quad b^2 - a^2 = (b-a)(b+a)$$

The variance is given by

$$\text{Var}(X) = \int_a^b \left(\frac{1}{b-a}\right)x^2\,dx - \left(\frac{b+a}{2}\right)^2$$

$$= \left(\frac{1}{b-a}\right)\frac{x^3}{3}\Big|_a^b - \frac{(b+a)^2}{4}$$

$$= \frac{1}{3(b-a)}(b^3 - a^3) - \frac{1}{4}(b+a)^2$$

$$= \frac{b^2 + ab + a^2}{3} - \frac{b^2 + 2ab + a^2}{4} \quad b^3 - a^3 = (b-a)(b^2 + ab + a^2)$$

$$= \frac{b^2 - 2ab + a^2}{12}. \quad \text{Get a common denominator; subtract.}$$

Thus

$$\text{Var}(X) = \frac{1}{12}(b-a)^2, \quad \text{Factor.}$$

and

$$\sigma = \frac{1}{\sqrt{12}}(b-a).$$

These properties of the uniform distribution are summarized below.

Uniform Distribution

If X is a random variable with probability density function

$$f(x) = \frac{1}{b-a} \quad \text{for } x \text{ in } [a,b],$$

then

$$\mu = \frac{1}{2}(b+a) \quad \text{and} \quad \sigma = \frac{1}{\sqrt{12}}(b-a).$$

EXAMPLE 1 **Daily Temperature**

A couple is planning to vacation in San Francisco. They have been told that the maximum daily temperature during the time they plan to be there ranges from 15°C to 27°C. Assume that the probability of any temperature between 15°C and 27°C is equally likely for any given day during the specified time period.

(a) What is the probability that the maximum temperature on the day they arrive will be higher than 24°C?

APPLY IT

SOLUTION   If the random variable T represents the maximum temperature on a given day, then the uniform probability density function for T is defined by $f(t) = 1/12$ for the interval $[15, 27]$. By definition,

$$P(T > 24) = \int_{24}^{27} \frac{1}{12}\, dt = \frac{1}{12}t \Big|_{24}^{27} = \frac{1}{4}.$$

(b) What average maximum temperature can they expect?

SOLUTION   The expected maximum temperature is

$$\mu = \frac{1}{2}(27 + 15) = 21,$$

or 21°C.

(c) What is the probability that the maximum temperature on a given day will be one standard deviation or more below the mean?

SOLUTION   First find σ.

$$\sigma = \frac{1}{\sqrt{12}}(27 - 15) = \frac{12}{\sqrt{12}} = \sqrt{12} = 2\sqrt{3} \approx 3.464.$$

One standard deviation below the mean indicates a temperature of $21 - 3.464 = 17.536$°C.

$$P(T \le 17.536) = \int_{15}^{17.536} \frac{1}{12}\, dt = \frac{1}{12}t \Big|_{15}^{17.536} \approx 0.2113$$

The probability is about 0.21 that the temperature will not exceed 17.5°C.

TRY YOUR TURN 1

YOUR TURN 1   The next vacation for the couple in Example 1 is to a desert with a maximum daily temperature that uniformly ranges from 27°C to 42°C. Find the expected maximum temperature and the probability that the maximum temperature will be within one standard deviation of the mean.

Exponential Distribution
The next distribution is very important in reliability and survival analysis. When manufactured items and living things have a constant failure rate over a period of time, the exponential distribution is used to describe their probability of failure. In this case, the random variable is said to be *exponentially distributed* over the sample space. The probability density function for the **exponential distribution** is defined by

$$f(x) = ae^{-ax} \qquad \text{for } x \text{ in } [0, \infty),$$

where a is a positive constant. The graph of $f(x)$ is shown in Figure 10.

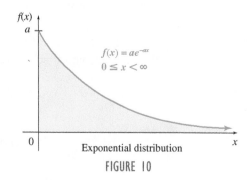

FIGURE 10

Here $f(x) \ge 0$, since e^{-ax} and a are both positive for all values of x. Also,

$$\int_0^{\infty} ae^{-ax}\, dx = \lim_{b \to \infty} \int_0^b ae^{-ax}\, dx$$

$$= \lim_{b \to \infty} \left(-e^{-ax}\right)\Big|_0^b = \lim_{b \to \infty}\left(\frac{-1}{e^{ab}} + \frac{1}{e^0}\right) = 1,$$

so the function is a probability density function.

The expected value and the standard deviation of the exponential distribution can be found using integration by parts. The results are given below. (See Exercise 20 at the end of this section.)

Exponential Distribution

If X is a random variable with probability density function

$$f(x) = ae^{-ax} \quad \text{for } x \text{ in } [0, \infty),$$

then

$$\mu = \frac{1}{a} \quad \text{and} \quad \sigma = \frac{1}{a},$$

EXAMPLE 2 Flashlight Battery

Suppose the useful life (in hours) of a flashlight battery is the random variable T, with probability density function given by the exponential distribution

$$f(t) = \frac{1}{20}e^{-t/20} \quad \text{for } t \geq 0.$$

(a) Find the probability that a particular battery, selected at random, has a useful life of less than 100 hours.

SOLUTION The probability is given by

$$P(T \leq 100) = \int_0^{100} \frac{1}{20}e^{-t/20}\, dt = \frac{1}{20}(-20e^{-t/20})\Big|_0^{100}$$

$$= -(e^{-100/20} - e^0) = -(e^{-5} - 1)$$

$$\approx 1 - 0.0067 = 0.9933.$$

(b) Find the expected value and standard deviation of the distribution.

SOLUTION Use the formulas given above. Both μ and σ equal $1/a$, and since $a = 1/20$ here,

$$\mu = 20 \quad \text{and} \quad \sigma = 20.$$

This means that the average life of a battery is 20 hours, and no battery lasts less than 1 standard deviation below the mean.

APPLY IT

YOUR TURN 2 Repeat Example 2 for a flashlight battery with a useful life given by the probability density function $f(t) = \frac{1}{25}e^{-t/25}$ for $t \geq 0$.

(c) What is the probability that a battery will last longer than 40 hours?

SOLUTION The probability is given by

$$P(T > 40) = \int_{40}^{\infty} \frac{1}{20}e^{-t/20}\, dt = \lim_{b \to \infty}(-e^{-t/20})\Big|_{40}^{b} = \frac{1}{e^2} \approx 0.1353,$$

or about 14%.

TRY YOUR TURN 2

Normal Distribution

The **normal distribution**, with its well-known bell-shaped graph, is undoubtedly the most important probability density function. It is widely used in various applications of statistics. The random variables associated with these applications are said to be normally distributed. The probability density function for the normal distribution has the following characteristics.

Normal Distribution

If μ and σ are real numbers, $\sigma > 0$, and if X is a random variable with probability density function defined by

$$f(x) = \frac{1}{\sigma\sqrt{2\pi}}e^{-(x-\mu)^2/(2\sigma^2)} \quad \text{for } x \text{ in } (-\infty, \infty),$$

then

$$E(X) = \mu \quad \text{and} \quad \text{Var}(X) = \sigma^2, \quad \text{with standard deviation } \sigma.$$

Notice that the definition of the probability density function includes σ, which is the standard deviation of the distribution.

Advanced techniques can be used to show that

$$\int_{-\infty}^{\infty} \frac{1}{\sigma\sqrt{2\pi}}e^{-(x-\mu)^2/(2\sigma^2)}\, dx = 1.$$

Deriving the expected value and standard deviation for the normal distribution also requires techniques beyond the scope of this text.

Each normal probability distribution has associated with it a bell-shaped curve, called a **normal curve**, such as the one in Figure 11. Each normal curve is symmetric about a vertical line through the mean, μ. Vertical lines at points $+1\sigma$ and -1σ from the mean show the inflection points of the graph. (See Exercise 22 at the end of this section.) A normal curve never touches the x-axis; it extends indefinitely in both directions.

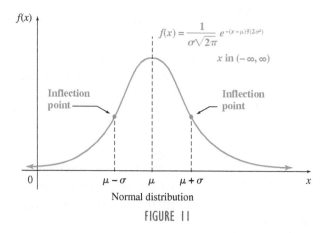

Normal distribution

FIGURE 11

The development of the normal curve is credited to the Frenchman Abraham De Moivre (1667–1754). Three of his publications dealt with probability and associated topics: *Annuities upon Lives* (which contributed to the development of actuarial studies), *Doctrine of Chances*, and *Miscellanea Analytica*.

Many different normal curves have the same mean. In such cases, a larger value of σ produces a "flatter" normal curve, while smaller values of σ produce more values near the mean, resulting in a "taller" normal curve. See Figure 12.

It would be far too much work to calculate values for the normal probability distribution for various values of μ and σ. Instead, values are calculated for the **standard normal**

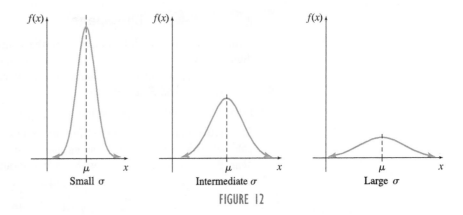

FIGURE 12

distribution, which has $\mu = 0$ and $\sigma = 1$. The graph of the standard normal distribution is shown in Figure 13.

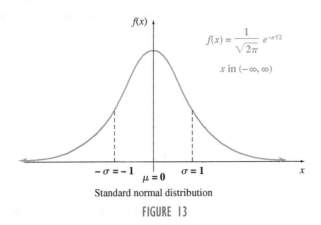

$$f(x) = \frac{1}{\sqrt{2\pi}} e^{-x^2/2}$$

x in $(-\infty, \infty)$

Standard normal distribution

FIGURE 13

Probabilities for the standard normal distribution come from the definite integral

$$\int_a^b \frac{1}{\sqrt{2\pi}} e^{-x^2/2}\, dx.$$

Since $f(x) = e^{-x^2/2}$ does not have an antiderivative that can be expressed in terms of functions used in this course, numerical methods are used to find values of this definite integral. Look through an Area Under the Standard Normal Curve table. Each value in the table is the total area under the standard normal curve to the left of the number z.

If a normal distribution does not have $\mu = 0$ and $\sigma = 1$, we use the following theorem, which is proved in Exercise 21.

z-Scores Theorem
Suppose a normal distribution has mean μ and standard deviation σ. The area under the associated normal curve that is to the left of the value x is exactly the same as the area to the left of

$$z = \frac{x - \mu}{\sigma}$$

for the standard normal curve.

Using this result, the table can be used for *any* normal distribution, regardless of the values of μ and σ. The number z in the theorem is called a z-**score**.

EXAMPLE 3   Life Spans

According to actuarial tables, life spans in the United States are approximately normally distributed with a mean of about 75 years and a standard deviation of about 16 years. By computing the areas under the associated normal curve, find the following probabilities. *Source: Psychological Science.*

(a) Find the probability that a randomly selected person lives less than 88 years.

SOLUTION Let T represent the life span of a random individual. To find $P(T < 88)$, we calculate the corresponding z-score using $t = 88$, $\mu = 75$, and $\sigma = 16$. Round to the nearest hundredths, since this is the extent of our normal curve table.

$$z = \frac{88 - 75}{16} = \frac{13}{16} \approx 0.81$$

Look up 0.81 in the normal curve table in the Appendix. The corresponding area is 0.7910. Thus, the shaded area shown in Figure 14 is 0.7910. This means that the probability of a randomly selected person living less than 88 years is $P(T < 88) = P(Z < 0.81) = 0.7910$, or about 79%.

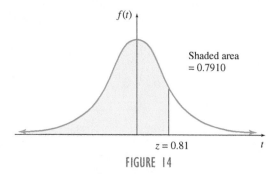

FIGURE 14

(b) Find the probability that a randomly selected person lives more than 67 years.

SOLUTION   To calculate $P(T > 67)$, first find the corresponding z-score.

$$z = \frac{67 - 75}{16} = -0.5$$

From the normal curve table, the area to the *left* of $z = -0.5$ is 0.3085. Therefore, the area to the *right* is $P(T > 67) = P(Z > -0.5) = 1 - 0.3085 = 0.6915$. See Figure 15. Thus, the probability of a randomly selected person living more than 67 years is 0.6915, or about 69%.

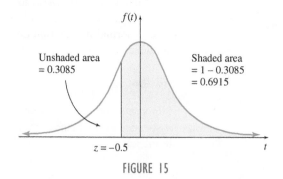

FIGURE 15

(c) Find the probability that a randomly selected person lives between 61 and 70 years.

SOLUTION   Find z-scores for both values.

$$z = \frac{61 - 75}{16} = -0.88 \qquad \text{and} \qquad z = \frac{70 - 75}{16} = -0.31$$

YOUR TURN 3 Using the information provided in Example 3, find the probability that a randomly selected person lives (a) more than 79 years and (b) between 67 and 83 years.

Start with the area to the left of $z = -0.31$ and subtract the area to the left of $z = -0.88$. Thus,

$$P(61 \leq T \leq 70) = P(-0.88 \leq Z \leq -0.31) = 0.3783 - 0.1894 = 0.1889.$$

The required area is shaded in Figure 16. The probability of a randomly selected person living between 61 and 70 years is about 19%. **TRY YOUR TURN 3**

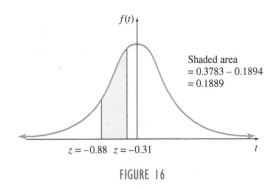

FIGURE 16

It's worth noting that there is always some error in approximating a discrete distribution with a continuous distribution. For example, when T is the life span of a randomly selected person, then $P(T = 65)$ is clearly positive, but if T is a normal random variable, then $P(T = 65) = 0$, since it represents no area. The problem is that a person's age jumps from 65 to 66, but a continuous random variable takes on all real numbers in between. If we were to measure a person's age to the nearest nanosecond, the probability that someone's age is exactly 65 years and 0 nanoseconds would be virtually 0.

Furthermore, a bit of thought shows us that the approximation of life spans by a normal distribution can't be perfect. After all, three standard deviations to the left and right of 75 give $75 - 3 \times 16 = 27$ and $75 + 3 \times 16 = 123$. Because of the symmetry of the normal distribution, $P(T < 27)$ and $P(T > 123)$ should be equal. Yet there are people who die before the age of 27, and no human has been verified to live beyond the age of 123.

TECHNOLOGY NOTE

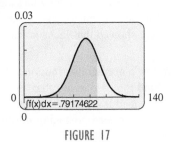

FIGURE 17

As an alternative to using the normal curve table, we can use a graphing calculator. Enter the formula for the normal distribution into the calculator, using $\mu = 75$ and $\sigma = 16$. Plot the function on a window that contains at least four standard deviations to the left and right of μ; for Example 3(a), we will let $0 \leq t \leq 140$. Then use the integration feature (under CALC on a TI-84 Plus) to find the area under the curve to the left of 88.

The result is shown in Figure 17. In place of $-\infty$, we have used $t = 0$ as the left endpoint. This is far enough to the left of $\mu = 75$ that it can be considered as $-\infty$ for all practical purposes. It also makes sense in this application, since life span can't be a negative number. You can verify that choosing a slightly different lower limit makes little difference in the answer. In fact, the answer of 0.79174622 is more accurate than the answer of 0.7910 that we found in Example 3(a), where we needed to round $13/16 = 0.8125$ to 0.81 in order to use the table.

We could get the answer on a TI-84 Plus without generating a graph using the command `fnInt` and entering $\int_0^{88}(\texttt{Y}_1)\texttt{dx}$, where $\texttt{Y}_1$ is the formula for the normal distribution with $\mu = 75$ and $\sigma = 16$.

The numerical integration method works with any probability density function. In addition, many graphing calculators are programmed with information about specific density functions, such as the normal. We can solve the first part of Example 3 on the TI-84 Plus by entering `normalcdf` $(-1\texttt{E}99,88,75,16)$. The calculator responds with 0.7917476687. ($-1\texttt{E}99$ stands for -1×10^{99}, which the calculator uses for $-\infty$.) If you use this method in the exercises, your answers will differ slightly from those at the end of the chapter, which were generated using the normal curve table.

The *z*-scores are actually standard deviation multiples; that is, a *z*-score of 2.5 corresponds to a value 2.5 standard deviations above the mean. For example, looking up $z = 1.00$ and $z = -1.00$ in the table shows that

$$0.8413 - 0.1587 = 0.6826,$$

so that 68.26% of the area under a normal curve is within 1 standard deviation of the mean. Also, using $z = 2.00$ and $z = -2.00$,

$$0.9772 - 0.0228 = 0.9544,$$

meaning 95.44% of the area is within 2 standard deviations of the mean. These results, summarized in Figure 18, can be used to get a quick estimate of results when working with normal curves.

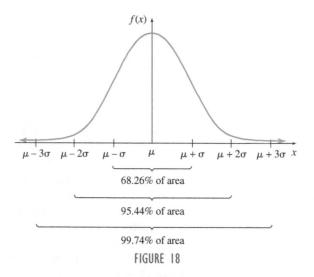
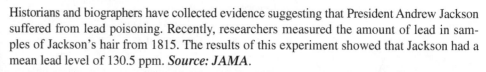
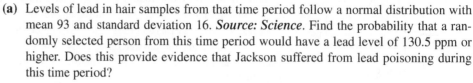

FIGURE 18

Manufacturers make use of the fact that a normal random variable is almost always within 3 standard deviations of the mean to design control charts. When a sample of items produced by a machine has a mean farther than 3 standard deviations from the desired specification, the machine is assumed to be out of control, and adjustments are made to ensure that the items produced meet the tolerance required.

EXAMPLE 4 Lead Poisoning

Historians and biographers have collected evidence suggesting that President Andrew Jackson suffered from lead poisoning. Recently, researchers measured the amount of lead in samples of Jackson's hair from 1815. The results of this experiment showed that Jackson had a mean lead level of 130.5 ppm. *Source: JAMA*.

(a) Levels of lead in hair samples from that time period follow a normal distribution with mean 93 and standard deviation 16. *Source: Science*. Find the probability that a randomly selected person from this time period would have a lead level of 130.5 ppm or higher. Does this provide evidence that Jackson suffered from lead poisoning during this time period?

SOLUTION $P(X \geq 130.5) = P\left(Z \geq \dfrac{130.5 - 93}{16}\right) = P(Z \geq 2.34) = 0.0096$

Since this probability is so low, it is likely that Jackson suffered from lead poisoning during this time period.*

---

*Although this provides evidence that Andrew Jackson had elevated lead levels, the authors of the paper concluded that Andrew Jackson did not die from lead poisoning.

(b) Today's normal lead levels follow a normal distribution with approximate mean of 10 ppm and standard deviation of 5 ppm. *Source: Clinical Chemistry.* By today's standards, calculate the probability that a randomly selected person from today would have a lead level of 130.5 ppm or higher. From this, can we conclude that Andrew Jackson had lead poisoning?

SOLUTION $P(X \geq 130.5) = P\left(Z \geq \dfrac{130.5 - 10}{5}\right) = P(Z \geq 24.1) \approx 0$

By today's standards, which may not be valid for this experiment, Jackson certainly suffered from lead poisoning.

3 EXERCISES

Find (a) the mean of the distribution, (b) the standard deviation of the distribution, and (c) the probability that the random variable is between the mean and 1 standard deviation above the mean.

1. The length (in centimeters) of the leaf of a certain plant is a continuous random variable with probability density function defined by

$$f(x) = \frac{5}{7} \quad \text{for } x \text{ in } [3, 4.4].$$

2. The price of an item (in hundreds of dollars) is a continuous random variable with probability density function defined by

$$f(x) = 4 \quad \text{for } x \text{ in } [2.75, 3].$$

3. The length of time (in years) until a particular radioactive particle decays is a random variable t with probability density function defined by

$$f(t) = 4e^{-4t} \quad \text{for } t \text{ in } [0, \infty).$$

4. The length of time (in years) that a seedling tree survives is a random variable t with probability density function defined by

$$f(t) = 0.05e^{-0.05t} \quad \text{for } t \text{ in } [0, \infty).$$

5. The length of time (in days) required to learn a certain task is a random variable t with probability density function defined by

$$f(t) = \frac{e^{-t/3}}{3} \quad \text{for } t \text{ in } [0, \infty).$$

6. The distance (in meters) that seeds are dispersed from a certain kind of plant is a random variable x with probability density function defined by

$$f(x) = 0.1e^{-0.1x} \quad \text{for } x \text{ in } [0, \infty).$$

Find the proportion of observations of a standard normal distribution that are between the mean and the given number of standard deviations above the mean.

7. 3.50

8. 1.68

Find the proportion of observations of a standard normal distribution that are between the given z-scores.

9. 1.28 and 2.05

10. -2.13 and -0.04

Find a z-score satisfying the conditions given in Exercises 11–14. (*Hint:* Use the table backwards.)

11. 10% of the total area is to the left of z.

12. 2% of the total area is to the left of z.

13. 18% of the total area is to the right of z.

14. 22% of the total area is to the right of z.

15. Describe the standard normal distribution. What are its characteristics?

16. What is a z-score? How is it used?

17. Describe the shape of the graph of each probability distribution.

   a. Uniform   **b.** Exponential   **c.** Normal

In the second section of this chapter, we defined the median of a probability distribution as an integral. The median also can be defined as the number m such that $P(X \leq m) = P(X \geq m)$.

18. Find an expression for the median of the uniform distribution.

19. Find an expression for the median of the exponential distribution.

20. Verify the expected value and standard deviation of the exponential distribution given in the text.

21. Prove the z-scores theorem. (*Hint:* Write the formula for the normal distribution with mean μ and standard deviation σ, using t instead of x as the variable. Then write the integral representing the area to the left of the value x, and make the substitution $u = (t - \mu)/\sigma$.)

22. Show that a normal random variable has inflection points at $x = \mu - \sigma$ and $x = \mu + \sigma$.

23. Use Simpson's rule with $n = 140$, or use the integration feature on a graphing calculator, to approximate the following integrals.

   a. $\displaystyle\int_0^{35} 0.5e^{-0.5x}\,dx$ **b.** $\displaystyle\int_0^{35} 0.5xe^{-0.5x}\,dx$

   c. $\displaystyle\int_0^{35} 0.5x^2 e^{-0.5x}\,dx$

24. Use your results from Exercise 23 to verify that, for the exponential distribution with $a = 0.5$, the total probability is 1, and both the mean and the standard deviation are equal to $1/a$.

25. Use Simpson's rule with $n = 40$, or the integration feature on a graphing calculator, to approximate the following for the standard normal probability distribution. Use limits of -6 and 6 in place of $-\infty$ and ∞.

a. The mean   **b.** The standard deviation

26. A very important distribution for analyzing the reliability of manufactured goods is the Weibull distribution, whose probability density function is defined by

$$f(x) = abx^{b-1}e^{-ax^b} \quad \text{for } x \text{ in } [0, \infty),$$

where a and b are constants. Notice that when $b = 1$, this reduces to the exponential distribution. The Weibull distribution is more general than the exponential, because it applies even when the failure rate is not constant. Use Simpson's rule with $n = 100$, or the integration feature on a graphing calculator, to approximate the following for the Weibull distribution with $a = 4$ and $b = 1.5$. Use a limit of 3 in place of ∞.

a. The mean   **b.** The standard deviation

27. Determine the cumulative distribution function for the uniform distribution.

28. Determine the cumulative distribution function for the exponential distribution.

APPLICATIONS

Business and Economics

29. Insurance Sales The amount of insurance (in thousands of dollars) sold in a day by a particular agent is uniformly distributed over the interval $[10, 85]$.

a. What amount of insurance does the agent sell on an average day?

b. Find the probability that the agent sells more than $50,000 of insurance on a particular day.

30. Fast-Food Outlets The number of new fast-food outlets opening during June in a certain city is exponentially distributed, with a mean of 5.

a. Give the probability density function for this distribution.

b. What is the probability that the number of outlets opening is between 2 and 6?

31. Sales Expense A salesperson's monthly expenses (in thousands of dollars) are exponentially distributed, with an average of 4.25 (thousand dollars).

a. Give the probability density function for the expenses.

b. Find the probability that the expenses are more than $10,000.

In Exercises 32–34, assume a normal distribution.

32. Machine Accuracy A machine that fills quart bottles with apple juice averages 32.8 oz per bottle, with a standard deviation of 1.1 oz. What are the probabilities that the amount of juice in a bottle is as follows?

a. Less than 1 qt

b. At least 1 oz more than 1 qt

33. Machine Accuracy A machine produces screws with a mean length of 2.5 cm and a standard deviation of 0.2 cm. Find the probabilities that a screw produced by this machine has lengths as follows.

a. Greater than 2.7 cm

b. Within 1.2 standard deviations of the mean

34. Customer Expenditures Customers at a certain pharmacy spend an average of $54.40, with a standard deviation of $13.50. What are the largest and smallest amounts spent by the middle 50% of these customers?

35. Insured Loss An insurance policy is written to cover a loss, X, where X has a uniform distribution on $[0, 1000]$. At what level must a deductible be set in order for the expected payment to be 25% of what it would be with no deductible? Choose one of the following. (*Hint:* Use a variable, such as D, for the deductible. The payment is 0 if the loss is less than D, and the loss minus D if the loss is greater than D.) *Source: Society of Actuaries.*

a. 250   **b.** 375   **c.** 500   **d.** 625   **e.** 750

36. High-Risk Drivers The number of days that elapse between the beginning of a calendar year and the moment a high-risk driver is involved in an accident is exponentially distributed. An insurance company expects that 30% of high-risk drivers will be involved in an accident during the first 50 days of a calendar year. What portion of high-risk drivers are expected to be involved in an accident during the first 80 days of a calendar year? Choose one of the following. *Source: Society of Actuaries.*

a. 0.15   **b.** 0.34   **c.** 0.43   **d.** 0.57   **e.** 0.66

37. Printer Failure The lifetime of a printer costing $200 is exponentially distributed with mean 2 years. The manufacturer agrees to pay a full refund to a buyer if the printer fails during the first year following its purchase, and a one-half refund if it fails during the second year. If the manufacturer sells 100 printers, how much should it expect to pay in refunds? Choose one of the following. *Source: Society of Actuaries.*

a. 6321   **b.** 7358   **c.** 7869   **d.** 10,256   **e.** 12,642

38. Electronic Device The time to failure of a component in an electronic device has an exponential distribution with a median of four hours. Calculate the probability that the component will work without failing for at least five hours. Choose one of the following. *Source: Society of Actuaries.*

a. 0.07   **b.** 0.29   **c.** 0.38   **d.** 0.42   **e.** 0.57

Life Sciences

39. Insect Life Span The life span of a certain insect (in days) is uniformly distributed over the interval $[20, 36]$.

a. What is the expected life of this insect?

b. Find the probability that one of these insects, randomly selected, lives longer than 30 days.

40. Location of a Bee Swarm A swarm of bees is released from a certain point. The proportion of the swarm located at least 2 m from the point of release after 1 hour is a random variable that is exponentially distributed with $a = 2$.

a. Find the expected proportion under the given conditions.

b. Find the probability that fewer than 1/3 of the bees are located at least 2 m from the release point after 1 hour.

41. Digestion Time The digestion time (in hours) of a fixed amount of food is exponentially distributed with $a = 1$.

a. Find the mean digestion time.

b. Find the probability that the digestion time is less than 30 minutes.

42. Pygmy Heights The average height of a member of a certain tribe of pygmies is 3.2 ft, with a standard deviation of 0.2 ft. If the heights are normally distributed, what are the largest and smallest heights of the middle 50% of this population?

43. Finding Prey H. R. Pulliam found that the time (in minutes) required by a predator to find a prey is a random variable that is exponentially distributed, with $\mu = 25$. *Source: American Naturalist*.

a. According to this distribution, what is the longest time within which the predator will be 90% certain of finding a prey?

b. What is the probability that the predator will have to spend more than 1 hour looking for a prey?

44. Life Expectancy According to the National Center for Health Statistics, the life expectancy for a 55-year-old African American female is 26.1 years. Assuming that from age 55, the survival of African American females follows an exponential distribution, determine the following probabilities. *Source: National Vital Statistics Report*.

a. The probability that a randomly selected 55-year-old African American female will live beyond 80 years of age (at least 25 more years)

b. The probability that a randomly selected 55-year-old African American female will live less than 20 more years

45. Life Expectancy According to the National Center for Health Statistics, life expectancy for a 70-year-old African American male is 12.3 years. Assuming that from age 70, the survival of African American males follows an exponential distribution, determine the following probabilities. *Source: National Vital Statistics Report*.

a. The probability that a randomly selected 70-year-old African American male will live beyond 90 years of age

b. The probability that a randomly selected 70-year-old African American male will live between 10 and 20 more years

46. Mercury Poisoning Historians and biographers have collected evidence that suggests that President Andrew Jackson suffered from mercury poisoning. Recently, researchers measured the amount of mercury in samples of Jackson's hair from 1815. The results of this experiment showed that Jackson had a mean mercury level of 6.0 ppm. *Source: JAMA*.

a. Levels of mercury in hair samples from that time period followed a normal distribution with mean 6.9 and standard deviation 4.6. *Source: Science of the Total Environment*. Find the probability that a randomly selected person from that time period would have a mercury level of 6.0 ppm or higher. Discuss whether this provides evidence that Jackson suffered from mercury poisoning during this time period.

b. Today's accepted normal mercury levels follow a normal distribution with approximate mean 0.6 ppm and standard deviation 0.3 ppm. *Source: Clinical Chemistry*. By today's standards, how likely is it that a randomly selected person from today would have a mercury level of 6.0 ppm or higher? Discuss whether we can conclude from this that Andrew Jackson suffered from mercury poisoning.

Social Sciences

47. Dating a Language Over time, the number of original basic words in a language tends to decrease as words become obsolete or are replaced with new words. In 1950, C. Feng and M. Swadesh established that of the original 210 basic ancient Chinese words from 950 A.D., 167 were still being used. The proportion of words that remain after t millennia is a random variable that is exponentially distributed with $a = 0.229$. *Source: The UMAP Journal*.

a. Find the life expectancy and standard deviation of a Chinese word.

b. Calculate the probability that a randomly chosen Chinese word will remain after 2000 years.

Physical Sciences

48. Rainfall The rainfall (in inches) in a certain region is uniformly distributed over the interval $[32, 44]$.

a. What is the expected number of inches of rainfall?

b. What is the probability that the rainfall will be between 38 and 40 in.?

49. Dry Length Days Researchers have shown that the number of successive dry days that occur after a rainstorm for particular regions of Catalonia, Spain, is a random variable that is distributed exponentially with a mean of 8 days. *Source: International Journal of Climatology*.

a. Find the probability that 10 or more successive dry days occur after a rainstorm.

b. Find the probability that fewer than 2 dry days occur after a rainstorm.

50. Earthquakes The proportion of the times (in days) between major earthquakes in the north-south seismic belt of China is a random variable that is exponentially distributed, with $a = 1/609.5$. *Source: Journal of Seismology*.

a. Find the expected number of days and the standard deviation between major earthquakes for this region.

b. Find the probability that the time between a major earthquake and the next one is more than 1 year.

General Interest

51. Soccer The time between goals (in minutes) for the Wolves soccer team in the English Premier League during a recent season can be approximated by an exponential distribution with $a = 1/90$. *Source: The Mathematical Spectrum*.

a. The Wolves scored their first goal of the season 71 minutes into their first game. Find the probability that the time for a goal is no more than 71 minutes.

b. It was 499 minutes later (in game time) before the Wolves scored their next goal. Find the probability that the time for a goal is 499 minutes or more.

52. Football The margin of victory over the point spread (defined as the number of points scored by the favored team minus the number of points scored by the underdog minus the point spread, which is the difference between the previous two, as predicted by oddsmakers) in National Football League games has been found to be normally distributed with mean 0 and standard deviation 13.861. Suppose New England is favored over Miami by 3 points. What is the probability that New England wins? (*Hint:* Calculate the probability that the margin of victory over the point spread is greater than -3.) *Source: The American Statistician.*

YOUR TURN ANSWERS

1. 34.5°C, 0.5774
2. (a) 0.9817, (b) 25 and 25, (c) 0.2019
3. (a) 0.4013 (b) 0.3830

CHAPTER REVIEW

SUMMARY

In this chapter, we gave a brief introduction to the use of calculus in the study of probability. In particular, the idea of a random variable and its connection to a probability density function and a cumulative distribution function were given. We explored four important concepts:

- expected value (the average value of a random variable that we would expect in the long run),
- variance (a measure of the spread of the values of a distribution),
- standard deviation (the square root of the variance), and
- median (the value of a random variable for which there is a 50% probability of being larger and a 50% probability of being smaller).

Integration techniques were used to determine probabilities, expected value, and variance of continuous random variables. Three probability density functions that have a wide range of applications were studied in detail:

- uniform (when the probability density function remains constant over the sample space),
- exponential (for items that have a constant failure rate over time), and
- normal (for random variables with a bell-shaped distribution).

Probability Density Function on [a, b]	**1.** $f(x) \geq 0$ for all x in the interval $[a, b]$.
	2. $\int_a^b f(x)\,dx = 1$.
	3. $P(c \leq X \leq d) = \int_c^d f(x)\,dx$ for c, d in $[a, b]$.
Cumulative Distribution Function	$F(x) = P(X \leq x) = \int_a^x f(t)\,dt$
Expected Value for a Density Function on [a, b]	$E(X) = \mu = \int_a^b x f(x)\,dx$
Variance for a Density Function on [a, b]	$\mathrm{Var}(X) = \int_a^b (x - \mu)^2 f(x)\,dx$
Alternative Formula for Variance	$\mathrm{Var}(X) = \int_a^b x^2 f(x)\,dx - \mu^2$
Standard Deviation	$\sigma = \sqrt{\mathrm{Var}(X)}$
Median	The value m such that $\int_a^m f(x)\,dx = \dfrac{1}{2}$.

Uniform Distribution $\quad f(x) = \dfrac{1}{b-a}$ on $[a, b]$

$$\mu = \frac{1}{2}(b + a) \quad \text{and} \quad \sigma = \frac{1}{\sqrt{12}}(b - a)$$

Exponential Distribution $\quad f(x) = ae^{-ax}$ on $[0, \infty)$

$$\mu = \frac{1}{a} \quad \text{and} \quad \sigma = \frac{1}{a}$$

Normal Distribution $\quad f(x) = \dfrac{1}{\sigma\sqrt{2\pi}}\, e^{-(x-\mu)^2/(2\sigma^2)}$ on $(-\infty, \infty)$

$$E(X) = \mu \quad \text{and} \quad \text{Var}(X) = \sigma^2$$

z-Scores Theorem $\quad$ For a normal curve with mean μ and standard deviation σ, the area to the left of x is the same as the area to the left of

$$z = \frac{x - \mu}{\sigma}$$

for the standard normal curve.

KEY TERMS

1

random variable
probability function
histogram
discrete probability function
continuous random variable

continuous probability
  distribution
probability density
  function
cumulative distribution
  function

2

mean
expected value
variance
standard deviation
median

3

uniform distribution
exponential distribution
normal distribution
normal curve
standard normal distribution
z-score

REVIEW EXERCISES

CONCEPT CHECK

Determine whether each of the following statements is true or false, and explain why.

___ **1.** A continuous random variable can take on values greater than 1.

___ **2.** A probability density function can take on values greater than 1.

___ **3.** A continuous random variable can take on values less than 0.

___ **4.** A probability density function can take on values less than 0.

___ **5.** The expected value of a random variable must always be at least 0.

___ **6.** The variance of a random variable must always be at least 0.

___ **7.** The expected value of a uniform random variable is the average of the endpoints of the interval over which the density function is positive.

___ **8.** For an exponential random variable, the expected value and standard deviation are always equal.

___ **9.** The normal distribution and the exponential distribution have approximately the same shape.

___ **10.** In the standard normal distribution, the expected value is 1 and the standard deviation is 0.

PRACTICE AND EXPLORATIONS

11. In a probability function, the y-values (or function values) represent _____.

12. Define a continuous random variable.

13. Give the two conditions that a probability density function for $[a, b]$ must satisfy.

14. In a probability density function, the probability that X equals a specific value, $P(X = c)$, is _____.

Decide whether each function defined as follows is a probability density function for the given interval.

15. $f(x) = \sqrt{x}$; $[4, 9]$

16. $f(x) = \dfrac{1}{27}(2x + 4)$; $[1, 4]$

17. $f(x) = 0.7e^{-0.7x}$; $[0, \infty)$

18. $f(x) = 0.4$; $[4, 6.5]$

In Exercises 19 and 20, find a value of k that will make $f(x)$ define a probability density function for the indicated interval.

19. $f(x) = kx^2$; $[1, 4]$ **20.** $f(x) = k\sqrt{x}$; $[4, 9]$

21. The probability density function of a random variable X is defined by

$$f(x) = \frac{1}{10} \quad \text{for } x \text{ in } [10, 20].$$

Find the following probabilities.

    a. $P(X \le 12)$ **b.** $P(X \ge 31/2)$ **c.** $P(10.8 \le X \le 16.2)$

22. The probability density function of a random variable X is defined by

$$f(x) = 1 - \frac{1}{\sqrt{x - 1}} \quad \text{for } x \text{ in } [2, 5].$$

Find the following probabilities.

    a. $P(X \ge 3)$ **b.** $P(X \le 4)$ **c.** $P(3 \le X \le 4)$

23. Describe what the expected value or mean of a probability distribution represents geometrically.

24. The probability density functions shown in the graphs have the same mean. Which has the smallest standard deviation?

a.

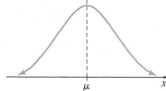

b.

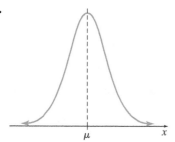

c.

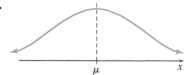

For the probability density functions defined in Exercises 25–28, find (a) the expected value, (b) the variance, (c) the standard deviation, (d) the median, and (e) the cumulative distribution function.

25. $f(x) = \frac{2}{9}(x - 2)$; $[2, 5]$ **26.** $f(x) = \frac{1}{5}$; $[4, 9]$

27. $f(x) = 5x^{-6}$; $[1, \infty)$

28. $f(x) = \frac{1}{20}\left(1 + \frac{3}{\sqrt{x}}\right)$; $[1, 9]$

29. The probability density function of a random variable is defined by $f(x) = 4x - 3x^2$ for x in $[0, 1]$. Find the following for the distribution.

    a. The mean   **b.** The standard deviation

    c. The probability that the value of the random variable will be less than the mean

    d. The probability that the value of the random variable will be within 1 standard deviation of the mean

30. Find the median of the random variable of Exercise 29. Then find the probability that the value of the random variable will lie between the median and the mean of the distribution.

For Exercises 31 and 32, find (a) the mean of the distribution, (b) the standard deviation of the distribution, and (c) the probability that the value of the random variable is within 1 standard deviation of the mean.

31. $f(x) = 0.01e^{-0.01x}$ for x in $[0, \infty)$

32. $f(x) = \frac{5}{112}(1 - x^{-3/2})$ for x in $[1, 25]$

In Exercises 33–40, find the proportion of observations of a standard normal distribution for each region.

33. The region to the left of $z = -0.43$

34. The region to the right of $z = 1.62$

35. The region between $z = -1.17$ and $z = -0.09$

36. The region between $z = -1.39$ and $z = 1.28$

37. The region that is 1.2 standard deviations or more below the mean

38. The region that is up to 2.5 standard deviations above the mean

39. Find a z-score so that 52% of the area under the normal curve is to the right of z.

40. Find a z-score so that 21% of the area under the normal curve is to the left of z.

The topics in this short chapter involved material you've studied previously, including functions, domain and range, exponential functions, area and integration, improper integrals, integration by parts, and numerical integration. For the following special probability density functions, give

    a. the type of distribution;

    b. the domain and range;

    c. the graph;

    d. the mean and standard deviation;

    e. $P(\mu - \sigma \le X \le \mu + \sigma)$.

41. $f(x) = 0.05$ for x in $[10, 30]$

42. $f(x) = e^{-x}$ for x in $[0, \infty)$

43. $f(x) = \frac{e^{-x^2}}{\sqrt{\pi}}$ for x in $(-\infty, \infty)$ (*Hint:* $\sigma = 1/\sqrt{2}$.)

44. The chi-square distribution is important in statistics for testing whether data comes from a specified distribution and for testing the independence of two characteristics of a set of data.

When a quantity called the *degrees of freedom* is equal to 4, the probability density function is given by

$$f(x) = \frac{xe^{-x/2}}{4} \text{ for } x \text{ in } [0, \infty).$$

a. Verify that this is a probability density function by noting that $f(x) \geq 0$ and by finding $P(0 \leq X < \infty)$.

b. Find $P(0 \leq X \leq 3)$.

45. When the degrees of freedom in the chi-square distribution (see the previous exercise) is 1, the probability density function is given by

$$f(x) = \frac{x^{-1/2}e^{-x/2}}{\sqrt{2\pi}} \text{ for } x \text{ in } (0, \infty).$$

Calculating probabilities is now complicated by the fact that the density function cannot be antidifferentiated. Numerical integration is complicated because the density function becomes unbounded as x approaches 0.

a. Show that one application of integration by parts (or column integration with just two rows, similar to Example 2 in Section 1 on Integration by Parts) allows $P(0 < X \leq b)$ to be rewritten as

$$\frac{1}{\sqrt{2\pi}} \left[2x^{1/2}e^{-x/2} \Big|_0^b + \int_0^b x^{1/2}e^{-x/2}\, dx \right].$$

b. Using Simpson's rule with $n = 12$ in the result from part a, approximate $P(0 < X \leq 1)$.

c. Using Simpson's rule with $n = 12$ in the result from part a, approximate $P(0 < X \leq 10)$.

d. What should be the limit as $b \to \infty$ of the expression in part a? Do the results from parts b and c support this?

APPLICATIONS

Business and Economics

46. Mutual Funds The price per share (in dollars) of a particular mutual fund is a random variable x with probability density function defined by

$$f(x) = \frac{3}{4}(x^2 - 16x + 65) \quad \text{for } x \text{ in } [8, 9].$$

a. Find the probability that the price will be less than $8.50.

b. Find the expected value of the price.

c. Find the standard deviation.

47. Machine Repairs The time (in years) until a certain machine requires repairs is a random variable t with probability density function defined by

$$f(t) = \frac{5}{112}(1 - t^{-3/2}) \quad \text{for } t \text{ in } [1, 25].$$

a. Find the probability that no repairs are required in the first three years by finding the probability that a repair will be needed in years 4 through 25.

b. Find the expected value for the number of years before the machine requires repairs.

c. Find the standard deviation.

48. Retail Outlets The number of new outlets for a clothing manufacturer is an exponential distribution with probability density function defined by

$$f(x) = \frac{1}{6}e^{-x/6} \quad \text{for } x \text{ in } [0, \infty).$$

Find the following for this distribution.

a. The mean

b. The standard deviation

c. The probability that the number of new outlets will be greater than the mean

49. Product Repairs The number of repairs required by a new product each month is exponentially distributed with an average of 8.

a. What is the probability density function for this distribution?

b. Find the expected number of repairs per month.

c. Find the standard deviation.

d. What is the probability that the number of repairs per month will be between 5 and 10?

50. Useful Life of an Appliance Part The useful life of a certain appliance part (in hundreds of hours) is 46.2, with a standard deviation of 15.8. Find the probability that one such part would last for at least 6000 (60 hundred) hours. Assume a normal distribution.

51. Equipment Insurance A piece of equipment is being insured against early failure. The time from purchase until failure of the equipment is exponentially distributed with mean 10 years. The insurance will pay an amount x if the equipment fails during the first year, and it will pay $0.5x$ if failure occurs during the second or third year. If failure occurs after the first three years, no payment will be made. At what level must x be set if the expected payment made under this insurance is to be 1000? *Source: Society of Actuaries.* Choose one of the following.

a. 3858 b. 4449 c. 5382 d. 5644 e. 7235

Life Sciences

52. Weight Gain of Rats The weight gain (in grams) of rats fed a certain vitamin supplement is a continuous random variable with probability density function defined by

$$f(x) = \frac{8}{7}x^{-2} \quad \text{for } x \text{ in } [1, 8].$$

a. Find the mean of the distribution.

b. Find the standard deviation of the distribution.

c. Find the probability that the value of the random variable is within 1 standard deviation of the mean.

53. Movement of a Released Animal The distance (in meters) that a certain animal moves away from a release point is exponentially distributed, with a mean of 100 m. Find the probability that the animal will move no farther than 100 m away.

54. Snowfall The snowfall (in inches) in a certain area is uniformly distributed over the interval $[2, 30]$.

a. What is the expected snowfall?

b. What is the probability of getting more than 20 inches of snow?

55. Body Temperature of a Bird The body temperature (in degrees Celsius) of a particular species of bird is a continuous random variable with probability density function defined by

$$f(x) = \frac{3}{19{,}696}(x^2 + x) \quad \text{for } x \text{ in } [38, 42].$$

a. What is the expected body temperature of this species?

b. Find the probability of a body temperature below the mean.

56. Average Birth Weight The average birth weight of infants in the United States is 7.8 lb, with a standard deviation of 1.1 lb. Assuming a normal distribution, what is the probability that a newborn will weigh more than 9 lb?

57. Heart Muscle Tension In a pilot study on tension of the heart muscle in dogs, the mean tension was 2.2 g, with a standard deviation of 0.4 g. Find the probability of a tension of less than 1.9 g. Assume a normal distribution.

58. Life Expectancy According to the National Center for Health Statistics, the life expectancy for a 65-year-old American male is 17.0 years. Assuming that from age 65, the survival of American males follows an exponential distribution, determine the following probabilities. *Source: National Vital Statistics Report.*

a. The probability that a randomly selected 65-year-old American male will live beyond 80 years of age (at least 15 more years)

b. The probability that a randomly selected 65-year-old American male will live less than 10 more years

59. Life Expectancy According to the National Center for Health Statistics, the life expectancy for a 50-year-old American female is 32.5 years. Assuming that from age 50, the survival of American females follows an exponential distribution, determine the following probabilities. *Source: National Vital Statistics Report.*

a. The probability that a randomly selected 50-year-old American female will live beyond 90 years of age (at least 40 more years)

b. The probability that a randomly selected 50-year-old American female will live between 30 and 50 more years

Social Sciences

60. Assaults The number of deaths in the United States caused by assault (murder) for each age group is given in the following table. *Source: National Vital Statistics.*

a. Plot the data. What type of function appears to best match this data?

Age Interval (years)	Midpoint of Interval (year)	Number Dying in Each Interval
0–14	7	1096
15–24	19.5	5729
25–34	29.5	4729
35–44	39.5	3013
45–54	49.5	2207
55–64	59.5	1011
65–74	69.5	397
75–84	79.5	274
85 +	89.5 (est)	32
Total		18,488

b. Use the regression feature on your graphing calculator to find a quartic equation that models the number of years, t, since birth and the number of deaths caused by assault, $N(t)$. Use the midpoint value to estimate the point in each interval when the person died. Graph the function with the plot of the data. Does the function resemble the data?

c. By finding an appropriate constant k, find a function $S(t) = kN(t)$ that is a probability density function describing the probability of death by assault. (*Hint:* Because the function in part b is negative for values less than 5.2 and greater than 88.9, restrict the domain of the density function to the interval $[5.2, 88.9]$. That is, integrate the function you found in part b from 5.2 to 88.9.)

d. For a randomly chosen person who was killed by assault, find the probabilities that the person killed was less than 25 years old, at least 45 but less than 65 years old, and at least 75 years old, and compare these with the actual probabilities.

e. Estimate the expected age at which a person will die by assault.

f. Find the standard deviation of this distribution.

Physical Sciences

61. Earthquakes The time between major earthquakes in the Taiwan region is a random variable with probability density function defined by

$$f(t) = \frac{1}{3650.1}e^{-t/3650.1},$$

where t is measured in days. Find the expected value and standard deviation of this probability density function. *Source: Journal of Seismology.*

General Interest

62. State-Run Lotteries The average state "take" on lotteries is 40%, with a standard deviation of 13%. Assuming a normal distribution, what is the probability that a state-run lottery will have a "take" of more than 50%?

EXTENDED APPLICATION

EXPONENTIAL WAITING TIMES

We have seen in this chapter how probabilities that are spread out over continuous time intervals can be modeled by continuous probability density functions. The exponential distribution you met in the last section of this chapter is often used to model *waiting times,* the gaps between events that are randomly distributed in time, such as decays of a radioactive nucleus or arrivals of customers in the waiting line at a bank. In this application we investigate some properties of the exponential family of distributions.

Suppose that in a badly run subway system, the times between arrivals of subway trains at your station are exponentially distributed with a mean of 10 minutes. Sometimes trains arrive very close together, sometimes far apart, but if you keep track over many days, you'll find that the *average* time between trains is 10 minutes. According to the last section of this chapter, the exponential distribution with density function $f(t) = ae^{-at}$ has mean $1/a$, so the probability density function for our interarrival times is

$$f(t) = \frac{1}{10} e^{-t/10}.$$

First let's see what these waiting times look like. We have used a random-number generator from a statistical software package to draw 25 waiting times from this distribution. Figure 19 shows cumulative arrival times, which is what you would observe if you recorded the arrival time of each train measured in minutes from an arbitrary 0 point.

You can see that 25 trains arrive in a span of about 260 minutes, so the average interarrival time was indeed close to 10 minutes. You may also notice that there are some large gaps and some cases where trains arrived very close together.

To get a better feeling for the distribution of long and short interarrival times, look at the following list, which gives the 25 interarrival times in minutes, sorted from smallest to largest.

0.016	4.398	15.659
0.226	4.573	15.954
0.457	5.415	16.403
0.989	9.570	18.978
1.576	10.413	20.736
1.988	10.916	33.013
2.738	13.109	39.073
3.133	13.317	
3.895	14.622	

You can see that there were some very short waits. (In fact, the shortest time between trains is only 1 second, which means our model needs to be adjusted somehow to allow for the time trains spend stopped in the station.) The longest time between trains was 39 minutes, almost four times as long as the average! Although the exponential model exaggerates the irregularities of typical subway service, the problem of pile-ups and long gaps is very real for public transportation, especially for bus routes that are subject to unpredictable traffic delays. Anyone who works at a customer service job is also familiar with this behavior: The waiting line at a bank may be empty for minutes at a stretch, and then several customers walk in at nearly the same time. In this case, the customer interarrival times are exponentially distributed.

Planners who are involved with scheduling need to understand this "clumping" behavior. One way to explore it is to find probabilities for ranges of interarrival times. Here integrals are the natural tool. For example, if we want to estimate the fraction of interarrival times that will be less than 2 minutes, we compute

$$\frac{1}{10} \int_0^2 e^{-t/10} \, dt = 1 - e^{-1/5} \approx 0.1813.$$

So on average, 18% of the interarrival times will be less than 2 minutes, which indicates that clustering of trains will be a problem in our system. (If you have ridden a system like the one in New York City, you may have boarded a train that was ordered to "stand by" for several minutes to spread out a cluster of trains.) We can also compute the probability of a gap of 30 minutes or longer. It will be

$$\frac{1}{10} \int_{30}^\infty e^{-t/10} \, dt = e^{-3} \approx 0.0498.$$

So in a random sample of 25 interarrival times we might expect one or two long waits, and our simulation, which includes times of 33 and 39 minutes, is not a fluke. Of course, the rider's experience depends on when she arrives at the station, which is another random input to our model. If she arrives in the middle of a cluster, she'll get a train right away, but if she arrives at the beginning of a long gap she may have a half-hour wait. So we would also like to model the rider's *waiting time,* the time between the rider's arrival at the station and the arrival of the next train.

A remarkable fact about the exponential distribution is that if our passenger arrives at the station at a random time, the distribution of the rider's waiting times is *the same* as the distribution of

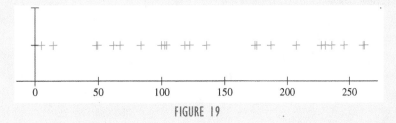

FIGURE 19

interarrival times (that is, exponential with mean 10 minutes). At first this seems paradoxical; since she usually arrives between trains, she should wait less, on average, than the average time between trains. But remember that she's more likely to arrive at the station in one of those long gaps. In our simulation, 72 out of 260 minutes is taken up with long gaps, and even if the rider arrives at the middle of such a gap she'll still wait longer than 15 minutes. Because of this feature the exponential distribution is often called *memoryless:* If you dip into the process at random, it is as if you were starting all over. If you arrive at the station just as a train leaves, your waiting time for the next one still has an exponential distribution with mean 10 minutes. The next train doesn't "know" anything about the one that just left.*

Because the riders' waiting times are exponential, the calculations we have already made tell us what riders will experience: A wait of less than 2 minutes has probability about 0.18. The average wait is 10 minutes, but long waits of more than 30 minutes are not all that rare (probability about 0.05).

Customers waiting for service care about the average wait, but they may care even more about the *predictability* of the wait. In this chapter we stated that the standard deviation for an exponential distribution is the same as the mean, so in our model the standard deviation of riders' waiting times will be 10 minutes. This indicates that a wait of twice the average length is not a rare event. (See Exercise 3.)

Let's compare the experience of riders on our exponential subway with the experience of riders of a perfectly regulated service in which trains arrive *exactly* 10 minutes apart. We'll still assume that the passenger arrives at random. But now the waiting time is uniformly distributed on the time interval [0 minutes, 10 minutes]. This uniform distribution has density function

$$f(t) = \begin{cases} \dfrac{1}{10} & \text{for } 0 \le t \le 10 \\ 0 & \text{otherwise} \end{cases}$$

The mean waiting time is

$$\int_0^{10} \frac{1}{10} \cdot t\, dt = 5 \text{ minutes}$$

and the standard deviation of the waiting times is

$$\sqrt{\int_0^{10} \frac{(t-5)^2}{10} dt} = \sqrt{\frac{25}{3}} \approx 2.89 \text{ minutes.}$$

Clearly the rider has a better experience on this system. Even though the same average number of trains is running per hour as in the exponential subway, the average wait for the uniform subway is only 5 minutes with a standard deviation of 2.89 minutes, and no one ever waits longer than 10 minutes!

*See Chapter 1 in Volume 2 of Feller, William, *An Introduction to Probability Theory and Its Applications,* 2nd ed., New York: Wiley, 1971.

Any subway run is subject to unpredictable accidents and variations, and this random input is always pushing the riders' waiting times toward the exponential model. Indeed, even with uniform scheduling of trains, there will be service bottlenecks because the exponential distribution is also a reasonable model (over a short time period) for interarrival times of *passengers* entering the station. The goal of schedulers is to move passengers efficiently in spite of random train delays and random input of passengers. One proposed solution, the PRT or personal rapid transit system, uses small vehicles holding just a few passengers that can be scheduled to match a fluctuating demand.

The subway scheduling problem is part of a branch of statistics called *queueing theory*, the study of any process in which inputs arrive at a service point and wait in a line or queue to be served. Examples include telephone calls arriving at a customer service center, our passengers entering the subway station, packets of information traveling through the Internet, and even pieces of code waiting for a processor in a multiprocessor computer. The following Web sites provide a small sampling of work in this very active research area.

- *http://web2.uwindsor.ca/math/hlynka/queue.html* (A collection of information on queueing theory)

- *http://faculty.washington.edu/jbs/itrans/ingsim.htm* (an article on scheduling a PRT)

EXERCISES

1. If X is a continuous random variable, $P(a \le X \le b)$ is the same as $P(a < X < b)$. Since these are different events, how can they have the same probability?

2. Someone who rides the subway back and forth to work each weekday makes about 40 trips a month. On the exponential subway, how many times a month can this commuter expect a wait longer than half an hour?

3. Find the probability that a rider of the exponential subway waits more than 20 minutes for a train; that is, find the probability of a wait more than twice as long as the average.

4. On the exponential subway, what is the probability that a randomly arriving passenger has a wait of between 9 and 10 minutes? What is the corresponding probability on the uniform subway?

5. If our system is aiming for an average interarrival time of 10 minutes, we might set a tolerance of plus or minus 2 minutes and try to keep the interarrival times between 8 and 12 minutes. Under the exponential model, what fraction of interarrival times fall in this range? How about under the uniform model?

6. Most mathematical software includes routines for generating "pseudo-random" numbers (that is, numbers that behave randomly even though they are generated by arithmetic). That's what we used to simulate the exponential waiting times for our subway system. But a source on the Internet (http://www.fourmilab.ch/hotbits/) delivers random numbers based on the times between decay events in a sample of Krypton-85. As noted above, the waiting times between decay events have an exponential distribution, so we can see what nature's random numbers look like. Here's a short sample:

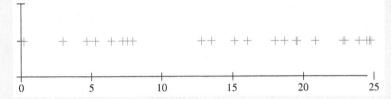

Actually, this source builds its random numbers from random bits, that is, 0's and 1's that occur with equal probability. See if you can think of a way of turning a sequence of exponential waiting times into a random sequence of 0's and 1's.

DIRECTIONS FOR GROUP PROJECT

Find a situation in which you and your group can gather actual wait times, such as a bus stop, doctor's office, teller line at a bank, or check-out line at a grocery store. Collect data on interarrival/service times and determine the mean service time. Using this average, determine whether the data appears to follow an exponential distribution. Develop a table that lists the percentage of the time that particular waiting times occur using both the data and the exponential function. Construct a poster that could be placed near the location where people wait that estimates the waiting time for service.

ANSWERS TO SELECTED EXERCISES

Exercises 1

For exercises . . .	1–10	11–18,29–34	19–24,35c,d,36c,d, 48d,e,49d,e	35a,b,36a,b,39–42,44–47, 48a,b,c,49a,b,c,50	43,51
Refer to example . . .	1	2	5	3	4

1. Yes **3.** Yes **5.** No; $\int_0^3 4x^3\, dx \neq 1$
7. No; $\int_{-2}^2 x^2/16\, dx \neq 1$
9. No; $f(x) < 0$ for some x values in $[-1, 1]$. **11.** $k = 3/14$ **13.** $k = 3/125$ **15.** $k = 2/9$ **17.** $k = 1/12$
19. $F(x) = (x^2 - x - 2)/18, 2 \leq x \leq 5$ **21.** $F(x) = (x^3 - 1)/63, 1 \leq x \leq 4$ **23.** $F(x) = (x^{3/2} - 1)/7, 1 \leq x \leq 4$
25. 1 **29. a.** 0.4226 **b.** 0.2071 **c.** 0.4082 **31. a.** 0.3935 **b.** 0.3834 **c.** 0.3679 **33. a.** 1/3 **b.** 2/3 **c.** 295/432
35. a. 0.9975 **b.** 0.0024 **c.** $F(t) = 1 - e^{-t/2}, t \geq 0$ **d.** 0.9502 **37.** c **39. a.** 0.2679 **b.** 0.4142 **c.** 0.3178
41. a. 0.8131 **b.** 0.4901
43. a. 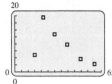 polynomial function **b.** $N(t) = -0.00007445t^4 + 0.01243t^3 - 0.7419t^2 + 18.18t - 137.5$

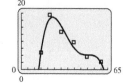 Yes

c. $S(t) = \dfrac{1}{466.26}(-0.00007445t^4 + 0.01243t^3 - 0.7419t^2 + 18.18t - 137.5)$ **d.** Estimates: 0.1688, 0.5896, 0.1610; actual:
0.1730, 0.5865, 0.1325 **45. a.** 0.2 **b.** 0.6 **c.** 0.6 **47. a.** 0.1640 **b.** 0.1353 **49. a.** 0.2829 **b.** 0.4853 **c.** 0.2409
d. $F(t) = 1.8838(0.5982 - e^{-0.03211t}), 16 \leq t \leq 84$ **e.** 0.1671
51. a. 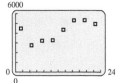 A polynomial function **b.** $T(t) = -2.564t^3 + 99.11t^2 - 964.6t + 5631$

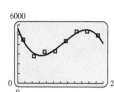

c. $S(t) = \dfrac{1}{101,370}(-2.564t^3 + 99.11t^2 - 964.6t + 5631)$ **d.** 0.09457; 0.07732

Exercises 2

For exercises . . .	1–6,11–14	7,8	11d,e–14d,e,24–26,31–33, 34,35,38–42	15a–20a,24d,26d,31d, 33d,36,40d,41d	37,43
Refer to example . . .	1	2	3	5	4

1. $\mu = 5$; Var$(X) \approx 1.33$; $\sigma \approx 1.15$
3. $\mu = 14/3 \approx 4.67$; Var$(X) \approx 0.89$; $\sigma \approx 0.94$ **5.** $\mu = 2.83$; Var$(X) \approx 0.57$; $\sigma \approx 0.76$
7. $\mu = 4/3 \approx 1.33$; Var$(X) = 2/9 \approx 0.22$; $\sigma \approx 0.47$ **11. a.** 5.40 **b.** 5.55 **c.** 2.36 **d.** 0.5352 **e.** 0.6043 **13. a.** 1.6
b. 0.11 **c.** 0.33 **d.** 0.5904 **e.** 0.6967 **15. a.** 5 **b.** 0 **17. a.** 4.828 **b.** 0.0553 **19. a.** $\sqrt[4]{2} \approx 1.189$ **b.** 0.1836
21. 16/5; does not exist; does not exist **23.** d **25. a.** 6.409 yr **b.** 1.447 yr **c.** 0.4910 **27.** c **29.** c **31. a.** 6.342 seconds
b. 5.135 sec **c.** 0.7518 **d.** 4.472 sec **33. a.** 2.333 cm **b.** 0.8692 cm **c.** 0 **d.** 2.25 cm **35.** 111 **37.** 31.75 years; 11.55
years **39. a.** 1.806 **b.** 1.265 **c.** 0.1886 **41. a.** 38.51 years **b.** 17.56 years **c.** 0.1656 **d.** 34.26 years **43.** About 1 pm

Exercises 3

For exercises . . .	1,2,29,35,39,48	3–6,30,31,36–38,40, 41,43–45,47,49–51	7–14,32–34,42,52	46
Refer to example . . .	1	2	3	4

1. a. 3.7 cm **b.** 0.4041 cm **c.** 0.2886
3. a. 0.25 years **b.** 0.25 years **c.** 0.2325
5. a. 3 days **b.** 3 days **c.** 0.2325 **7.** 49.98% **9.** 8.01% **11.** −1.28 **13.** 0.92 **19.** $m = (-\ln 0.5)/a$ or $(\ln 2)/a$
23. a. 1.00000 **b.** 1.99999 **c.** 8.00000 **25. a.** $\mu \approx 0$ **b.** $\sigma = 0.9999999251 \approx 1$ **27.** $F(x) = (x - a)/(b - a), a \leq x \leq b$
29. a. $47,500 **b.** 0.4667 **31. a.** $f(x) = 0.235e^{-0.235x}$ on $[0, \infty)$ **b.** 0.0954 **33. a.** 0.1587 **b.** 0.7698 **35.** c **37.** d
39. a. 28 days **b.** 0.375 **41. a.** 1 hour **b.** 0.3935 **43. a.** 58 minutes **b.** 0.0907 **45. a.** 0.1967 **b.** 0.2468
47. a. 4.37 millennia; 4.37 millennia **b.** 0.6325 **49. a.** 0.2865 **b.** 0.2212 **51. a.** 0.5457 **b.** 0.0039

Chapter Review Exercises

1. True **2.** True **3.** True **4.** False **5.** False **6.** True
7. True **8.** True **9.** False **10.** False **11.** probabilities
13. 1. $f(x) \geq 0$ for all x in $[a, b]$; 2. $\int_a^b f(x)\,dx = 1$

For exercises . . .	1–4,11–22,41, 46a–47a,60a-d	5,6,23–31,42, 46b,c–47b,c,52, 55,60e,f,61	7–10,33–40,43, 48–51,53,54,56, 57–59,62
Refer to section . . .	1	2	3

15. Not a probability density function **17.** Probability density function **19.** $k = 1/21$ **21. a.** $1/5 = 0.2$ **b.** $9/20 = 0.45$
c. 0.54 **25. a.** 4 **b.** 0.5 **c.** 0.7071 **d.** 4.121 **e.** $F(x) = (x - 2)^2/9, 2 \leq x \leq 5$ **27. a.** 5/4 **b.** $5/48 \approx 0.1042$
c. 0.3227 **d.** 1.149 **e.** $F(x) = 1 - 1/x^5, x \geq 1$ **29. a.** 0.5833 **b.** 0.2444 **c.** 0.4821 **d.** 0.6114 **31. a.** 100
b. 100 **c.** 0.8647 **33.** 33.36% **35.** 34.31% **37.** 11.51% **39.** -0.05 **41. a.** Uniform **b.** Domain: [10, 30], range: {0.05}
c.
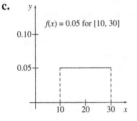
$f(x) = 0.05$ for [10, 30]
d. $\mu = 20; \sigma \approx 5.77$ **e.** 0.577 **43. a.** Normal **b.** Domain: $(-\infty, \infty)$, range: $(0, 1/\sqrt{\pi}]$
c.
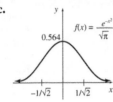
$f(x) = \dfrac{e^{-x^2}}{\sqrt{\pi}}$
d. $\mu = 0; \sigma = 1/\sqrt{2}$ **e.** 0.6826 **45. b.** 0.6819 **c.** 0.9716
d. 1; yes **47. a.** 0.9107 **b.** 13.57 years **c.** 6.68 years
49. a. $f(x) = e^{-x/8}/8; [0, \infty)$ **b.** 8 **c.** 8 **d.** 0.2488 **51.** d
53. 0.6321 **55. a.** 40.07°C **b.** 0.4928 **57.** 0.2266
59. a. 0.2921 **b.** 0.1826 **61.** 3650.1 days; 3650.1 days

SAMPLE SOURCES

Section 1

1. Example 4 from *National Vital Statistics Reports*, Vol. 54, No. 13, April 19, 2006, Table 6, p. 25.
2. Exercise 37 from Problem 34 from May 2003 Course 1 *Examination of the Education and Examination Committee of the Society of Actuaries*. Reprinted by permission of the Society of Actuaries.
3. Exercise 38 from Problem 40 from the 2005 Sample Exam P of the *Education and Examination Committee of the Society of Actuaries*. Reprinted by permission of the Society of Actuaries.
4. Exercise 41 from Dennis, Brian and Robert F. Costantino, "Analysis of Steady-State Populations with the Gamma Abundance Model: Application to *Tribolium*," *Ecology*, Vol. 69, No. 4, Aug. 1988, pp. 1200–1213.
5. Exercise 42 from Karevia, Peter, "Experimental and Mathematical Analysis of Herbivore Movement: Quantifying the Influence of Plant Spacing and Quality on Foraging Discrimination," *Ecology Monographs*, Vol. 2, No. 3, Sept. 1982, pp. 261–282.
6. Exercise 43 from "Number of U.S. Facebook Users Over 35 Nearly Doubles in Last 60 Days," March 25, 2009, http://www.insidefacebook.com/2009/03/25/number-of-us-facebook-users-over-35-nearly-doubles-in-last-60-days/.

7. Exercises 46 and 47 from Wang, Jeen-Hwa and Chiao-Hui Kuo, "On the Frequency Distribution of Interoccurrence Times of Earthquakes," *Journal of Seismology*, Vol. 2, 1998, pp. 351–358.
8. Exercise 48 from Traffic Safety Facts, 2008 Data, NHTA'S National Center for Statistics and Analysis, http://www-nrd.nhtsa.dot.gov/pubs/811155.pdf.
9. Exercise 49 from http://www-nrd.nhtsa.dot.gov/pdf/nrd-30/NCSA/RNotes/1998/AgeSex96.pdf.
10. Exercise 51 from Fatal Crashes by Time of Day and Day of Week, USA, Year: 2008. FARS Encyclopedia: Crashes–Time. http://www-fars.nhtsa.dot.gov/Crashes/CrashesTime.aspx.

Section 2

1. Example 4 from National Center for Health Statistics, *Method for Constructing Complete Annual U.S. Life Tables*, Series 2, No. 129, Dec. 1999.
2. Exercise 23 from Problem 12 from May 2003 Course 1 Examination of the *Education and Examination Committee of the Society of Actuaries*. Reprinted by permission of the Society of Actuaries.
3. Exercise 27 from Problem 51 from the 2005 Sample Exam P of the *Education and Examination Committee of the Society of Actuaries*. Reprinted by permission of the Society of Actuaries.

4. Exercise 28 from Problem 53 from the 2005 Sample Exam P of the *Education and Examination Committee of the Society of Actuaries*. Reprinted by permission of the Society of Actuaries.
5. Exercise 29 from Problem 55 from the 2005 Sample Exam P of the *Education and Examination Committee of the Society of Actuaries*. Reprinted by permission of the Society of Actuaries.
6. Exercise 30 from Problem 68 from the 2005 Sample Exam P of the *Education and Examination Committee of the Society of Actuaries*. Reprinted by permission of the Society of Actuaries.
7. Exercise 34 from Kareiva, Peter, "Experimental and Mathematical Analyses of Herbivore Movement: Quantifying the Influence of Plant Spacing and Quality on Foraging Discrimination," *Ecology Monographs*, Vol. 2, No. 3, 1982, pp. 261–282.
8. Exercise 35 from Dennis, Brian and Robert F. Costantino, "Analysis of Steady-State Population with the Gamma Abundance Model: Application to *Tribolium*," *Ecology*, Vol. 69, No. 4, Aug. 1988, pp. 1200–1213.

CREDITS

Sequences and Series

From Chapter 12 of *Calculus with Applications*. Tenth Edition. Margaret L. Lial, Raymond N. Greenwell, Nathan P. Ritchey.

Sequences and Series

**Extended Application:
Living Assistance and Subsidized Housing**

In sports that place high stress on the body, such as basketball, professional athletes often have relatively short playing careers. In Section 2 of this chapter we look at annuities, a kind of investment that allows a player to use her current high earnings to purchase a sequence of guaranteed annual payments that will begin when she retires.

Image Source/SuperStock

608

272

A function whose domain is the set of natural numbers, such as

$$a(n) = 2n, \quad \text{for} \quad n = 1, 2, 3, 4, \ldots$$

is a **sequence**. The sequence $a(n) = 2n$ can be written by listing its *terms*, $2, 4, 6, 8, \ldots,$ $2n, \ldots$. The letter n is used instead of x as a variable to emphasize the fact that the domain includes only natural numbers. For the same reason, a is used instead of f to name the function.

Sequences have many different applications; one example is the sequence of payments used to pay off a car loan or a home mortgage. (For most practical problems, the domain is a *subset* of the set of natural numbers.) This use of sequences is discussed in Section 2. The remaining sections of this chapter cover topics related to sequences.

| Geometric Sequences

APPLY IT If a person saved 1¢ on June 1, 2¢ on June 2, 4¢ on June 3, and so forth, continuing the pattern of saving twice as much each day as the previous day, how much would she have saved by the last day of June?
We will answer this question in Example 6 of this section.

In our definition of sequence we used the example $a(n) = 2n$. The range values of this sequence function,

$$a(1) = 2, \quad a(2) = 4, \quad a(3) = 6, \ldots,$$

are called the **elements** or **terms** of the sequence. Instead of writing $a(5)$ for the fifth term of a sequence, it is customary to write a_5; for the sequence above

$$a_5 = 10.$$

In the same way, for the sequence above, $a_1 = 2$, $a_2 = 4$, $a_8 = 16$, $a_{20} = 40$, and $a_{51} = 102$.

The symbol a_n is used for the **general** or **nth term** of a sequence. For example, for the sequence $4, 7, 10, 13, 16, \ldots$ the general term might be given by $a_n = 1 + 3n$. This formula for a_n can be used to find any term of the sequence that might be needed. For example, the first three terms of the sequence are

$$a_1 = 1 + 3(1) = 4, \qquad a_2 = 1 + 3(2) = 7, \qquad \text{and} \qquad a_3 = 1 + 3(3) = 10.$$

Also, $a_8 = 25$ and $a_{12} = 37$.

EXAMPLE 1 Sequence

Find the first four terms of the sequence having general term $a_n = -4n + 2$.

SOLUTION Replace n, in turn, with 1, 2, 3, and 4.

$$\text{If } n = 1, \quad a_1 = -4(1) + 2 = -4 + 2 = -2.$$
$$\text{If } n = 2, \quad a_2 = -4(2) + 2 = -8 + 2 = -6.$$
$$\text{If } n = 3, \quad a_3 = -4(3) + 2 = -12 + 2 = -10.$$
$$\text{If } n = 4, \quad a_4 = -4(4) + 2 = -16 + 2 = -14.$$

YOUR TURN 1 Find the first four terms of the sequence having general term $a_n = 3n - 6$.

The first four terms of this sequence are $-2, -6, -10,$ and -14.   TRY YOUR TURN 1

A sequence in which each term after the first is found by *multiplying* the preceding term by the same number is called a **geometric sequence**. The ratio of any two consecutive terms is a constant r,

$$r = \frac{a_{n+1}}{a_n}, \quad \text{where } n \geq 1,$$

called the **common ratio**. For example, to find r in the following sequence:

$$3, -6, 12, -24, 48, -96, \ldots$$

take $-6/3$ or $12/(-6)$ or $-24/12$, etc. and get $r = -2$. Thus, it is a geometric sequence in which each term after the first is found by multiplying the preceding term by the number -2, the common ratio.

If a is the first term of a geometric sequence and r is the common ratio, then the second term is given by $a_2 = ar$ and the third term by $a_3 = a_2 r = ar^2$. Also, $a_4 = ar^3$ and $a_5 = ar^4$. These results are generalized below.

General Term of a Geometric Sequence

If a geometric sequence has first term a and common ratio r, then

$$a_n = ar^{n-1}.$$

EXAMPLE 2 Geometric Sequences

Find the indicated term for each geometric sequence.

(a) Find a_7 for $6, 24, 96, 384, \ldots$.

SOLUTION Here $a = a_1 = 6$. To verify that the sequence is geometric, divide each term except the first by the preceding term.

$$\frac{24}{6} = \frac{96}{24} = \frac{384}{96} = 4$$

Since the ratio is constant, the sequence is geometric with $r = 4$. To find a_7, use the formula for a_n with $n = 7$, $a = 6$, and $r = 4$.

$$a_7 = 6(4)^{7-1} = 6(4)^6 = 6(4096) = 24{,}576$$

(b) Find a_6 for $8, -16, 32, -64, 128, \ldots$.

YOUR TURN 2 Find a_7 for $2, -6, 18, -54, \ldots$.

SOLUTION As before, verify that $r = -16/8 = 32/(-16) = -64/32 = 128/(-64) = -2$. Here $a = a_1 = 8$, so

$$a_6 = 8(-2)^{6-1} = 8(-2)^5 = 8(-32) = -256. \quad \text{TRY YOUR TURN 2}$$

EXAMPLE 3 Depreciation

A new machine is purchased for $150,000. Each year the machine loses 25% of its value. Find its value at the end of the sixth year.

SOLUTION Since the machine loses 25% of its value each year, it retains 75% of its value. At the end of its first year, its value is 75% of $150,000. Its value at the end of each of the following years is 75% of the previous year's value. These values form a geometric sequence, with $r = 0.75$. If we let $a = a_1 = 150{,}000$ then the value at the end of the first year is a_2, at the end of the second year is a_3, and so on. The value at the end of the sixth year is

YOUR TURN 3 A machine purchased for $10,000 loses 10% of its value each year. Find its value at the end of its tenth year.

$$a_7 = 150{,}000(0.75)^{7-1} = 150{,}000(0.75)^6 = 26{,}696.77734.$$

The value of the machine is $26,696.78 at the end of the sixth year. TRY YOUR TURN 3

In the next section we will need to know how to find the sum of the first n terms of a geometric sequence. To get a general rule for finding such a sum, begin by writing the sum S_n of the first n terms of a geometric sequence with first term $a = a_1$ and common ratio r as

$$S_n = a_1 + a_2 + a_3 + \cdots + a_n.$$

Since $a_n = ar^{n-1}$, this sum can be written as

$$S_n = a + ar + ar^2 + \cdots + ar^{n-1}. \tag{1}$$

If $r = 1$, all the terms are equal to a, and $S_n = n \cdot a$, the correct result for this case. If $r \neq 1$, multiply both sides of Equation (1) by r, obtaining

$$rS_n = ar + ar^2 + ar^3 + \cdots + ar^n. \tag{2}$$

Now subtract corresponding sides of Equation (1) from Equation (2):

$$rS_n - S_n = ar^n - a.$$

Factoring yields

$$S_n(r - 1) = a(r^n - 1),$$

and dividing by $r - 1$ on both sides gives

$$S_n = \frac{a(r^n - 1)}{r - 1}.$$

This result is summarized below.

Sum of The First n Terms of a Geometric Sequence

If a geometric sequence has first term a and common ratio r, then the sum of the first n terms, S_n, is given by

$$S_n = \frac{a(r^n - 1)}{r - 1}, \quad \text{where } r \neq 1.$$

EXAMPLE 4   Summing Terms of a Geometric Sequence

Find the sum of the first six terms of the geometric sequence $3, 12, 48, \ldots$.

Method 1
Using the Formula

SOLUTION   Here $a = a_1 = 3$ and $r = 4$. Find S_6, the sum of the first six terms, by the formula above.

$$S_6 = \frac{3(4^6 - 1)}{4 - 1} \qquad \text{Let } n = 6, a = 3, r = 4.$$
$$= \frac{3(4096 - 1)}{3}$$
$$= 4095$$

Method 2
Graphing Calculator

The sum of a sequence can be conveniently calculated on a TI-84 Plus calculator using the command $\texttt{sum(seq(3*4\^N, N, 0, 5))}$ as shown in Figure 1. Notice that to find the sum of the first six terms of the sequence we begin with $\texttt{N} = 0$ and end with $\texttt{N} = 5$ for a total of 4095.

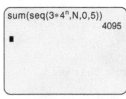

```
sum(seq(3*4ⁿ,N,0,5))
                  4095
■
```

FIGURE 1

YOUR TURN 4   Find the sum of the first seven terms of the geometric sequence $2, -8, 32, \ldots$.

TRY YOUR TURN 4

Using summation notation, we can write $S_n = a + ar + ar^2 + \cdots + ar^{n-1}$ as

$$S_n = \sum_{i=0}^{n-1} ar^i.$$

EXAMPLE 5 **Summing Terms of a Geometric Sequence**

Use the formula for the sum of the first n terms of a geometric sequence to evaluate the following sum.

$$\sum_{i=0}^{8} \frac{1}{2}(-2)^i$$

YOUR TURN 5
Evaluate the sum $\sum_{i=0}^{4} 81\left(\frac{1}{3}\right)^i$.

SOLUTION   Here $a = 1/2$ and $r = -2$. The summation is from $i = 0$ to $n-1 = 8$, so $n = 9$. Using the formula gives

$$S_9 = \frac{\frac{1}{2}[(-2)^9 - 1]}{-2 - 1} = \frac{\frac{1}{2}(-512 - 1)}{-3} = \frac{\frac{1}{2}(-513)}{-3} = 85.5.$$

TRY YOUR TURN 5

EXAMPLE 6 **Savings**

A person saved 1¢ on June 1, 2¢ on June 2, 4¢ on June 3, and so forth, continuing the pattern of saving twice as much each day as the previous day. How much would she have saved by the end of June?

APPLY IT   **SOLUTION**   This is a geometric sequence with $a = 1$ and $r = 2$. We want to find S_{30}.

$$S_{30} = \frac{1(2^{30} - 1)}{2 - 1} = 1{,}073{,}741{,}823$$

By the end of June, the person will have saved 1,073,741,823 cents, or \$10,737,418.23!

EXERCISES

List the first n terms of the geometric sequence satisfying the following conditions.

1. $a_1 = 2, r = 3, n = 4$ **2.** $a_1 = 4, r = 2, n = 5$

3. $a_1 = 1/2, r = 4, n = 4$ **4.** $a_1 = 2/3, r = 6, n = 3$

5. $a_3 = 6, a_4 = 12, n = 5$ **6.** $a_2 = 9, a_3 = 3, n = 4$

Find a_5 and a_n for the following geometric sequences.

7. $a_1 = 4, r = 3$ **8.** $a_1 = 8, r = 4$

9. $a_1 = -3, r = -5$ **10.** $a_1 = -4, r = -2$

11. $a_2 = 12, r = 1/2$ **12.** $a_3 = 2, r = 1/3$

13. $a_4 = 64, r = -4$ **14.** $a_4 = 81, r = -3$

For each sequence that is geometric, find r and a_n.

15. $6, 12, 24, 48, \ldots$ **16.** $4, 16, 64, 256, \ldots$

17. $3/4, 3/2, 3, 6, 12, \ldots$ **18.** $-7, -5, -3, -1, 1, 3, \ldots$

19. $4, 8, -16, 32, 64, -128, \ldots$ **20.** $6, 8, 10, 12, 14, \ldots$

21. $-5/8, 5/12, -5/18, 5/27, \ldots$

22. $7/4, -7/12, 7/36, -7/108, \ldots$

Find the sum of the first five terms of each geometric sequence.

23. $3, 6, 12, 24, \ldots$ **24.** $5, 20, 80, 320, \ldots$

25. $12, -6, 3, -3/2, \ldots$ **26.** $18, -3, 1/2, -1/12, \ldots$

27. $a_1 = 3, r = -2$ **28.** $a_1 = -5, r = 4$

29. $a_1 = 6.324, r = 2.598$ **30.** $a_1 = -2.772, r = -1.335$

Use the formula for the sum of the first n terms of a geometric sequence to evaluate the following sums.

31. $\displaystyle\sum_{i=0}^{7} 8(2)^i$ **32.** $\displaystyle\sum_{i=0}^{6} 4(3)^i$

33. $\displaystyle\sum_{i=0}^{8} \frac{3}{2}(4)^i$ **34.** $\displaystyle\sum_{i=0}^{9} \frac{3}{4}(2)^i$

35.

36. $\sum_{i=0}^{5} \frac{3}{2}(-2)^i$

37. $\sum_{i=0}^{8} 64\left(\frac{1}{2}\right)^i$

38. $\sum_{i=0}^{6} 81\left(\frac{2}{3}\right)^i$

APPLICATIONS

Business and Economics

39. Depreciation A certain machine annually loses 20% of the value it had at the beginning of that year. If its initial value is $12,000, find its value at the following times.

  a. The end of the fifth year

  b. The end of the eighth year

40. Income An oil well produced $4,000,000 of income its first year. Each year thereafter, the well produced 3/4 as much income as the previous year. What is the total amount of income produced by the well in 8 years?

41. Savings Suppose you could save $1 on January 1, $2 on January 2, $4 on January 3, and so on. What amount would you save on January 31? What would be the total amount of your savings during January?

42. Depreciation Each year a machine loses 30% of the value it had at the beginning of the year. Find the value of the machine at the end of 6 years if it cost $200,000 new.

Life Sciences

43. Population The population of a certain colony of bacteria increases by 5% each hour. After 7 hours, what is the percent increase in the population over the initial population?

Physical Sciences

44. Radioactive Decay The half-life of a radioactive substance is the time it takes for half the substance to decay. Suppose the half-life of a substance is 3 years and that 10^{15} molecules of the substance are present initially. How many molecules will be unchanged after 15 years?

45. Rotation of a Wheel A bicycle wheel rotates 400 times per minute. If the rider removes his or her feet from the pedals, the wheel will start to slow down. Each minute, it will rotate only 3/4 as many times as in the preceding minute. How many times will the wheel rotate in the fifth minute after the rider's feet are removed from the pedals?

General Interest

46. Thickness of a Paper Stack A piece of paper is 0.008 in. thick.

  a. Suppose the paper is folded in half, so that its thickness doubles, for 12 times in a row. How thick is the final stack of paper?

  b. Suppose it were physically possible to fold the paper 50 times in a row. How thick would the final stack of paper be?

47. Sports In the NCAA Men's Basketball Tournament, 64 teams are initially paired off. By playing a series of single-elimination games, a champion is crowned. *Source: Mathematics Teacher*.

  a. Write a geometric sequence whose sum determines the number of games that must be played to determine the champion team.

  b. How many games must be played to produce the champion?

  c. Generalize parts a and b to a tournament where 2^n teams are initially present.

  d. Discuss a quick way to determine the answers to parts b and c, based on the fact that each game produces one loser, and all teams except the champion lose one game.

48. Game Shows Some game shows sponsor tournaments where in each game, three individuals play against each other, yielding one winner and two losers. The winners of three such games then play each other, until the final game of three players produces a tournament winner. Suppose 81 people begin such a tournament. *Source: Mathematics Teacher*.

  a. Write a geometric sequence whose sum determines the number of games that must be played to determine the tournament champion.

  b. How many games must be played to produce the champion?

  c. Generalize parts a and b to a tournament where 3^n players are initially present.

  d. Further generalize parts a and b to a tournament where t^n players are initially present.

▰ YOUR TURN ANSWERS

1. −3, 0, 3, 6   **2.** 1458   **3.** $3486.78   **4.** 6554   **5.** 121

2 Annuities: An Application of Sequences

APPLY IT   Suppose $1500 is deposited at the end of each year for the next 6 years in an account paying 8% per year, compounded annually. How much will be in the account after 6 years?

Such a sequence of equal payments made at equal periods of time is called an **annuity**. If each payment is made at the end of a period, and if the frequency of payments is the same as the frequency of compounding, the annuity is called an **ordinary annuity**. The time between payments is the **payment period**, and the time from the beginning of the first period to the end of the last period is called the **term of the annuity**. The **amount of the** annuity, the final sum on deposit in the account, is defined as the sum of the compound amounts of all the payments, compounded to the end of the term.

Figure 2 shows the annuity described above. To find the amount of this annuity, look at each of the $1500 payments separately. The first of these payments will produce a compound amount of

$$1500(1 + 0.08)^5 = 1500(1.08)^5$$

at the end of 6 years. Use 5 as the exponent instead of 6 because the money is deposited at the *end* of the first year and thus earns interest for only 5 years.

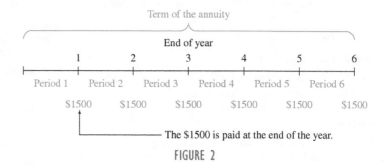

FIGURE 2

The second payment of $1500 will produce a compound amount (at the end of 5 years) of $1500(1.08)^4$. As shown in Figure 3, the total amount of the annuity is

$$1500(1.08)^5 + 1500(1.08)^4 + 1500(1.08)^3 + 1500(1.08)^2$$
$$+ 1500(1.08)^1 + 1500. \tag{1}$$

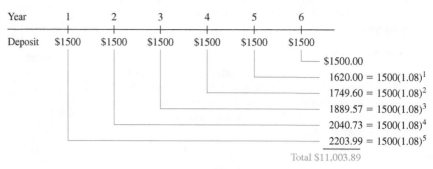

FIGURE 3

(The last payment earns no interest.) Reversing the order of the terms, so the last term is first, shows that Equation (1) is the sum of the terms of a geometric sequence with $a = 1500, r = 1.08$, and $n = 6$. Using the formula for the sum of the first n terms of a geometric sequence gives

$$1500 + 1500(1.08)^1 + 1500(1.08)^2 + 1500(1.08)^3$$
$$+ 1500(1.08)^4 + 1500(1.08)^5 = \frac{1500(1.08^6 - 1)}{1.08 - 1}$$
$$\approx \$11,003.89.$$

To generalize this result, suppose that R dollars are paid into an account at the end of each period for n periods, at a rate of interest i per period. The first payment of R dollars will produce a compound amount of $R(1 + i)^{n-1}$ dollars, the second payment will produce

$R(1 + i)^{n-2}$ dollars, and so on; the final payment earns no interest and contributes just R dollars to the total. If S represents the future value (or sum) of the annuity, then

$$S = R(1 + i)^{n-1} + R(1 + i)^{n-2} + R(1 + i)^{n-3} + \cdots + R(1 + i) + R,$$

or, written in reverse order,

$$S = R + R(1 + i)^1 + R(1 + i)^2 + \cdots + R(1 + i)^{n-1}.$$

This is the sum of the first n terms of the geometric sequence having first term R and common ratio $1 + i$. Using the formula for the sum of the first n terms of a geometric sequence gives

$$S = \frac{R[(1 + i)^n - 1]}{(1 + i) - 1} = \frac{R[(1 + i)^n - 1]}{i} = R\left[\frac{(1 + i)^n - 1}{i}\right].$$

The quantity in brackets is commonly written $s_{\overline{n}|i}$ (read "s-angle-n at i"), so that

$$S = R \cdot s_{\overline{n}|i}.$$

 **TECHNOLOGY NOTE**

Values of $s_{\overline{n}|i}$ can be found by a calculator. The TI-84 Plus has a special Finance menu with this formula built in.

Our work with annuities can be summarized as follows.

Amount of Annuity

The amount S of an annuity of payments of R dollars each, made at the end of each period for n consecutive interest periods at a rate of interest i per period, is given by

$$S = R\left[\frac{(1 + i)^n - 1}{i}\right] \qquad \text{or} \qquad S = R \cdot s_{\overline{n}|i}.$$

NOTE In this section we are assuming that each payment is made at the end of a period, as is the case in an ordinary annuity. There are situations in which each payment is made at the beginning of a period; this is known as an *annuity due*. The details are slightly different, and we will not go into them here. For more information, see Chapter 5 of our textbook, *Finite Mathematics*, by Lial, Greenwell, and Ritchey.

EXAMPLE 1 Annuity

Erin D'Aquanni is an athlete who feels that her playing career will last 7 more years. To prepare for her future, she deposits $22,000 at the end of each year for 7 years in an account paying 8% compounded annually. How much will she have on deposit after 7 years?

SOLUTION Her deposits form an ordinary annuity with $R = 22,000$, $n = 7$, and $i = 0.08$. The amount of this annuity is (by the formula above)

$$S = 22,000\left[\frac{(1.08)^7 - 1}{0.08}\right].$$

YOUR TURN 1 In Example 1, how much will Erin have on deposit after 7 years if she deposits $22,000 annually and earns only 5% interest?

The number in brackets, $s_{\overline{7}|0.08}$, is 8.92280336, so that

$$S = 22,000(8.92280336) = 196,301.67,$$

or $196,301.67.

TRY YOUR TURN 1

EXAMPLE 2 Annuity

Suppose $1000 is deposited at the end of each 6-month period for 5 years in an account paying 6% per year compounded semiannually. Find the amount of the annuity.

SOLUTION Interest of $i = 0.06/2 = 0.03$ is earned semiannually. In 5 years there are $5 \times 2 = 10$ semiannual periods. Since $s_{\overline{10}|0.03} = [(1.03)^{10} - 1]/0.03 = 11.46388$, the $1000 deposits will produce a total of

$$S = 1000(11.46388) = 11{,}463.88,$$

or $11,463.88.

TRY YOUR TURN 2

YOUR TURN 2 Suppose $125 is deposited monthly for 5 years into an account paying 2% per year compounded monthly. Find the amount of the annuity.

The formula for S involves the variables R, i, and n. The next example shows how to solve for one of these other variables.

EXAMPLE 3 Annuity

Melissa Abruzese wants to buy an expensive video camera three years from now. She plans to deposit an equal amount at the end of each quarter for three years in order to accumulate enough money to pay for the camera. Melissa expects the camera to cost $2400 at that time. The bank pays 6% interest per year compounded quarterly. Find the amount of each of the 12 equal deposits she must make.

SOLUTION This example describes an ordinary annuity with $S = 2400$. Since interest is compounded quarterly, $i = 0.06/4 = 0.015$ and $n = 3 \cdot 4 = 12$ periods. The unknown here is the amount of each payment, R. By the formula for the amount of an annuity given above,

$$2400 = R \cdot s_{\overline{12}|0.015}$$
$$2400 = R\left[\frac{1.015^{12} - 1}{0.015}\right]$$
$$2400 = R(13.04121)$$
$$R = 184.03, \qquad \text{Divide both sides by 13.04121.}$$

or $184.03.

TRY YOUR TURN 3

YOUR TURN 3 Repeat Example 3 if the interest rate is only 2.5% compounded quarterly.

Sinking Fund

A **sinking fund** is a fund set up to receive periodic payments; these periodic payments plus the interest on them are designed to produce a given total at some time in the future. As an example, a corporation might set up a sinking fund to receive money that will be needed to pay off a loan in the future. The deposits in Examples 1 and 3 form sinking funds.

EXAMPLE 4 Sinking Fund

The Toussaints are close to retirement. They agree to sell an antique urn to a local museum for $17,000. Their tax adviser suggests that they defer receipt of this money until they retire, 5 years in the future. (At that time, they might well be in a lower tax bracket.) The museum agrees to pay them the $17,000 in a lump sum in 5 years. Find the amount of each payment the museum must make into a sinking fund so that it will have the necessary $17,000 in 5 years. Assume that the museum can earn 8% compounded annually on its money and that the payments are made annually.

SOLUTION These payments make up an ordinary annuity. The annuity will amount to $17,000 in 5 years at 8% compounded annually, so

$$17{,}000 = R \cdot s_{\overline{5}|0.08}$$
$$R = \frac{17{,}000}{s_{\overline{5}|0.08}} = \frac{17{,}000}{5.86660} \approx 2897.76,$$

or $2897.76. If the museum deposits $2897.76 at the end of each year for 5 years in an account paying 8% compounded annually, it will have the needed $17,000. This result is shown in the following table. In other cases, the last payment might differ slightly from the others due to rounding R to the nearest penny.

	Sinking Fund Amounts		
Payment Number	Amount of Deposit	Interest Earned	Total in Account
1	$2897.76	$0	$2897.76
2	$2897.76	$231.82	$6027.34
3	$2897.76	$482.19	$9407.29
4	$2897.76	$752.58	$13,057.63
5	$2897.76	$1044.61	$17,000.00

Present Value of an Annuity

As shown above, if a deposit of R dollars is made at the end of each period for n periods, at a rate of interest i per period, then the account will contain

$$S = R \cdot s_{\overline{n}|i} = R\left[\frac{(1 + i)^n - 1}{i}\right]$$

dollars after n periods. Now suppose we want to find the *lump sum P* that must be deposited today at a rate of interest i per period in order to produce the same amount S after n periods.

First recall that P dollars deposited today will amount to $P(1 + i)^n$ dollars after n periods at a rate of interest i per period. This amount, $P(1 + i)^n$, should be the same as S, the amount of the annuity. Substituting $P(1 + i)^n$ for S in the formula above gives

$$P(1 + i)^n = R\left[\frac{(1 + i)^n - 1}{i}\right].$$

To solve this equation for P, multiply both sides of the equation by $(1 + i)^{-n}$.

$$P = R(1 + i)^{-n}\left[\frac{(1 + i)^n - 1}{i}\right]$$

Use the distributive property and the fact that $(1 + i)^{-n}(1 + i)^n = 1$.

$$P = R\left[\frac{(1 + i)^{-n}(1 + i)^n - (1 + i)^{-n}}{i}\right] = R\left[\frac{1 - (1 + i)^{-n}}{i}\right]$$

The amount P is called the **present value of the annuity**. The quantity in brackets is abbreviated as $a_{\overline{n}|i}$.

Present Value of an Annuity

The present value P of an annuity of payments of R dollars each, made at the end of each period for n consecutive interest periods at a rate of interest i per period is given by

$$P = R\left[\frac{1 - (1 + i)^{-n}}{i}\right] \qquad \text{or} \qquad P = R \cdot a_{\overline{n}|i}.$$

EXAMPLE 5   Present Value

What lump sum deposited today at 6% interest compounded annually will yield the same total amount as payments of $1500 at the end of each year for 12 years, also at 6% compounded annually?

SOLUTION Find the present value of an annuity of $1500 per year for 12 years at 6% compounded annually. From the present value formula, $a_{\overline{12}|0.06} = [1 - (1.06)^{-12}]/0.06 = 8.383844$, so

$$P = 1500(8.383844) = 12{,}575.77,$$

or $12,575.77. A lump sum deposit of $12,575.77 today at 6% compounded annually will yield the same total after 12 years as deposits of $1500 at the end of each year for 12 years at 6% compounded annually.

Check this result as follows. The compound amount in 12 years of a deposit of $12,575.77 today at 6% compounded annually can be found by the formula $A = P(1 + i)^n$:

$$12{,}575.77(1.06)^{12} = (12{,}575.77)(2.012196) \approx 25{,}304.91,$$

or $25,304.91. On the other hand, a deposit of $1500 into an annuity at the end of each year for 12 years, at 6% compounded annually, gives an amount of

$$1500[(1.06)^{12} - 1]/0.06 = 1500(16.86994) = 25{,}304.91,$$

or $25,304.91.

In summary, there are two ways to have $25,304.91 in 12 years at 6% compounded annually—a single deposit of $12,575.77 today, or payments of $1500 at the end of each year for 12 years.   TRY YOUR TURN 4 ▬

> **YOUR TURN 4** Repeat Example 5 if the annual interest rate is 4.5% and the payments are $2500 at the end of each year for 12 years.

The formula above can be used if the lump sum is known and the periodic payment of the annuity must be found. The next example shows how to do this.

EXAMPLE 6   Payments

A used car costs $6000. After a down payment of $1000, the balance will be paid off in 36 monthly payments with interest of 12% per year, compounded monthly. Find the amount of each payment.

SOLUTION   A single lump sum payment of $5000 today would pay off the loan, so $5000 is the present value of an annuity of 36 monthly payments with interest of $12\%/12 = 1\%$ per month. We can find R, the amount of each payment, by using the formula

$$P = R \cdot a_{\overline{n}|i}$$

and replacing P with 5000, n with 36, and i with 0.01. From the present value formula, $a_{\overline{36}|0.01} = 30.10751$, so

$$5000 = R(30.10751)$$
$$R \approx 166.07$$

or $166.07. Monthly payments of $166.07 each will be needed.   TRY YOUR TURN 5 ▬

> **YOUR TURN 5** A used car costs $11,000, and there is no down payment. The car will be paid off in 48 monthly payments with interest of 6% per year, compounded monthly. Find the amount of each payment.

Amortization   A loan is **amortized** if both the principal and interest are paid by a sequence of equal periodic payments. In Example 6 above, a loan of $5000 at 12% interest compounded monthly could be amortized by paying $166.07 per month for 36 months, or (it turns out) $131.67 per month for 48 months.

EXAMPLE 7   Amortization

A speculator agrees to pay $15,000 for a parcel of land. Payments will be made twice each year for 4 years at an interest rate of 12% compounded semiannually.

(a) Find the amount of each payment.

SOLUTION If the speculator immediately paid $15,000, there would be no need for any payments at all. Thus, $15,000 is the present value of an annuity of R dollars, with $2 \cdot 4 = 8$ periods, and $i = 0.12/2 = 0.06$ per period. If P is the present value of an annuity,

$$P = R \cdot a_{\overline{n}|i}.$$

In this example, $P = 15,000$, with

$$15,000 = R \cdot a_{\overline{8}|0.06}$$

or

$$R = \frac{15,000}{a_{\overline{8}|0.06}}.$$
$$= \frac{15,000}{6.20979} \approx 2415.54,$$

or $2415.54. Each payment is $2415.54.

(b) Find the portion of the first payment that is applied to the reduction of the debt.

SOLUTION Interest is 12% per year, compounded semiannually. During the first period, the entire $15,000 is owed. Interest on this amount for 6 months (1/2 year) is found by the formula for simple interest, $I = Prt$, so that

$$I = 15,000(0.12)\left(\frac{1}{2}\right) = 900,$$

or $900. At the end of 6 months, the speculator makes a payment of $2415.54; since $900 of this represents interest, a total of

$$\$2415.54 - \$900 = \$1515.54$$

is applied to the reduction of the original debt.

(c) Find the balance due after 6 months.

SOLUTION The original balance due is $15,000. After 6 months, $1515.54 is applied to reduction of the debt. The debt owed after 6 months is

$$\$15,000 - \$1515.54 = \$13,484.46.$$

(d) How much interest is owed for the second 6-month period? How much will be applied to the debt?

SOLUTION A total of $13,484.46 is owed for the second 6 months. Interest on this amount is

$$I = 13,484.46(0.12)\left(\frac{1}{2}\right) \approx 809.07,$$

or $809.07. A payment of $2415.54 is made at the end of this period; a total of

$$\$2415.54 - \$809.07 = \$1606.47$$

is applied to the reduction of the debt.

Continuing this process gives the *amortization schedule* shown below. As the schedule shows, each payment is the same, except perhaps for a small adjustment in the final payment. Payment 0 represents the original amount of the loan.

Amortization Schedule				
Payment Number	Amount of Payment	Interest for Period	Portion to Principal	Principal at End of Period
0	—	—	—	$15,000.00
1	$2415.54	$900	$1515.54	$13,484.46
2	$2415.54	$809.07	$1606.47	$11,877.99
3	$2415.54	$712.68	$1702.86	$10,175.13
4	$2415.54	$610.51	$1805.03	$8370.10
5	$2415.54	$502.21	$1913.33	$6456.77
6	$2415.54	$387.41	$2028.13	$4428.64
7	$2415.54	$265.72	$2149.82	$2278.82
8	$2415.54	$136.73	$2278.82	$0

The unpaid balance of a loan after x payments is equivalent to the present value of an annuity after $n - x$ consecutive payments and is given by the function

$$y = R\left[\frac{1 - (1 + i)^{-(n-x)}}{i}\right]$$

For Example 7, the unpaid balance after two payments is

$$y = 2415.54\left[\frac{1 - (1 + 0.12/2)^{-(8-2)}}{0.12/2}\right] \approx 11{,}877.99,$$

or $11,877.99.

This formula can also be used to produce a graph of the unpaid balance. For Example 7, the graph of

$$y = 2415.54\left[\frac{1 - (1 + 0.12/2)^{-(8-x)}}{0.12/2}\right]$$

is shown in Figure 4.

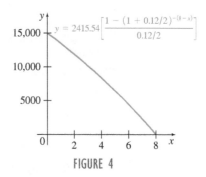

FIGURE 4

EXAMPLE 8 Amortization

The Millers buy a house for $174,000, with a down payment of $26,000. Interest is charged at 7.25% per year for 30 years compounded monthly. Find the amount of each monthly payment to amortize the loan.

Method 1
Calculation by Hand

SOLUTION Here, the present value, P, is 148,000 (or 174,000 − 26,000). Also, $i = 0.0725/12 \approx 0.0060416667$, and $n = 12 \cdot 30 = 360$. The monthly payment R must be found. From the formula for the present value of an annuity,

$$148,000 = R \cdot a_{\overline{360}|0.0060416667}$$

$$= R\left[\frac{1 - (1 + 0.0060416667)^{-360}}{0.0060416667}\right]$$

$$= R\left(\frac{1 - 0.1143540397}{0.0060416667}\right)$$

$$= R\left(\frac{0.8856459603}{0.0060416667}\right),$$

or

$$R \approx 1009.62.$$

Monthly payments of $1009.62 will be required to amortize the loan.

Method 2
Graphing Calculator

We can find the monthly payments to amortize this loan using the Finance Application of a TI-84 Plus calculator. To solve this problem, press the APPS button on the calculator and then select the `Finance` option. To input the particular information into the application, select the `TVM Solver` as shown in Figure 5 and then press ENTER. Then input the relevant values needed for the Solver, as shown in Figure 6. Note that the value of PMT is zero in `TVM Solver`. At this point, the particular value of PMT does not matter since we are going to calculate that value. Once the information is input into the solver, you must press 2nd QUIT to leave `TVM Solver`. To find the payment, press APPS, then `Finance`, and then select the `tvm_Pmt` button and press ENTER twice. The result shown in Figure 7 agrees with our work above.

YOUR TURN 6 In Example 8, suppose the house costs $256,000, and the Millers make a down payment of $32,000. If interest is charged at 4.9% per year for 30 years compounded monthly, find the amount of each monthly payment.

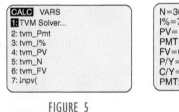

FIGURE 5   FIGURE 6   FIGURE 7

TRY YOUR TURN 6

2   EXERCISES

Find the amount of each ordinary annuity. (Interest is compounded annually.)

1. $R = \$120, i = 0.05, n = 10$

2. $R = \$1500, i = 0.04, n = 12$

3. $R = \$9000, i = 0.06, n = 18$

4. $R = \$80,000, i = 0.07, n = 24$

5. $R = \$11,500, i = 0.055, n = 30$

6. $R = \$13,400, i = 0.045, n = 25$

Find the amount of each ordinary annuity based on the information given.

7. $R = \$10,500$, 10% interest compounded semiannually for 7 years

8. $R = \$4200$, 6% interest compounded semiannually for 11 years

9. $R = \$1800$, 8% interest compounded quarterly for 12 years

10. $R = \$5300$, 4% interest compounded quarterly for 9 years

Find the periodic payments that will amount to the given sums under the given conditions.

11. $S = \$10,000$; interest is 8% compounded annually; payments are made at the end of each year for 12 years.

12. $S = \$80,000$; interest is 6% compounded semiannually; payments are made at the end of each semiannual period for 9 years.

13. $S = \$50,000$; interest is 12% compounded quarterly; payments are made at the end of each quarter for 8 years.

14. $S = \$8000$; interest is 4% compounded monthly; payments are made at the end of each month for 5 years.

Find the present value of each ordinary annuity.

15. Payments of $5000 are made annually for 11 years at 6% compounded annually.

16. Payments of $1280 are made annually for 9 years at 7% compounded annually.

17. Payments of $1400 are made semiannually for 8 years at 6% compounded semiannually.

18. Payments of $960 are made semiannually for 16 years at 5% compounded semiannually.

19. Payments of $50,000 are made quarterly for 10 years at 8% compounded quarterly.

20. Payments of $9800 are made quarterly for 15 years at 4% compounded quarterly.

Find the lump sum deposited today that will yield the same total amount as payments of $10,000 at the end of each year for 15 years, at the following interest rates. Interest is compounded annually.

21. 4%   22. 5%

23. 6%   24. 8%

Find the payments necessary to amortize each loan.

25. $2500, 16% compounded quarterly, 6 quarterly payments

26. $1000, 8% compounded annually, 9 annual payments

27. $90,000, 8% compounded annually, 12 annual payments

28. $41,000, 12% compounded semiannually, 10 semiannual payments

29. $55,000, 6% compounded monthly, 36 monthly payments

30. $6800, 12% compounded monthly, 24 monthly payments

APPLICATIONS

Business and Economics

31. Amount of an Annuity Sara Swangard wants to deposit $12,000 at the end of each year for 9 years into an annuity.

   a. Sara's local bank offers an account paying 5% interest compounded annually. Find the final amount she will have on deposit.

   b. Sara's brother-in-law works in a bank that pays 3% compounded annually. If she deposits her money in this bank instead, how much money will she have in her account?

   c. How much would Sara lose over 9 years by using her brother-in-law's bank instead of her local bank?

32. Amount of an Annuity For 8 years, Tobi Casper deposits $100 at the end of each month into an annuity paying 6% annual interest compounded monthly.

   a. Find the total amount Tobi deposits into the account over the 8 years.

   b. Find the final amount Tobi will have on deposit at the end of the 8 years.

   c. How much interest did Tobi earn?

33. Sinking Fund Steve Day wants $20,000 in 8 years.

   a. What amount should he deposit at the end of each quarter at 6% annual interest compounded quarterly to accumulate the $20,000?

   b. Find his quarterly deposit if the money is deposited at 4% compounded quarterly.

34. Sinking Fund Megan Donnelly wants to buy a car that she estimates will cost $24,000 in 5 years. How much money must she deposit at the end of each quarter at 5% interest compounded quarterly in order to have enough in 5 years to pay for her car?

35. Sinking Fund Harv's Meats will need to buy a new deboner machine in 4 years. At that time Harv expects the machine to cost $12,000. To accumulate enough money to pay for the machine, Harv decides to deposit a sum of money at the end of each 6-month period in an account paying 4% compounded semiannually. How much should each payment be?

36. Sinking Fund A firm must pay off $40,000 worth of bonds in 7 years.

   a. Find the amount of each annual payment to be made into a sinking fund, if the money earns 6% compounded annually.

   b. What annual payment should be made if the firm can get interest of 8% compounded annually?

Individual Retirement Accounts With Individual Retirement Accounts (IRAs), a worker whose income does not exceed certain limits can deposit up to a certain amount annually, with taxes deferred on the principal and interest. To attract depositors, banks have been advertising the amount that would accumulate by retirement. Suppose a 40-year-old person deposits $2000 per year until age 65. Find the total in the account with the interest rates stated in Exercises 37–40. Assume semiannual compounding with payments of $1000 made at the end of each semiannual period.

37. 6%   38. 8%   39. 10%   40. 12%

41. Sinking Fund Rebecca Nasman sells some land in Nevada. She will be paid a lump sum of $60,000 in 7 years. Until then, the buyer pays 8% interest, compounded quarterly.

   a. Find the amount of each quarterly interest payment.

   b. The buyer sets up a sinking fund so that enough money will be present to pay off the $60,000. The buyer wants to make semiannual payments into the sinking fund; the account pays 6% compounded semiannually. Find the amount of each payment into the fund.

   c. Prepare a table showing the amount in the sinking fund after each deposit.

42. Sinking Fund Jerry Higgins bought a rare stamp for his collection. He agreed to pay a lump sum of $4000 after 5 years. Until then, he pays 6% interest, compounded semiannually.

a. Find the amount of each semiannual interest payment.

b. Jerry sets up a sinking fund so that enough money will be present to pay off the $4000. He wants to make annual payments into the fund. The account pays 8% compounded annually. Find the amount of each payment into the fund.

c. Prepare a table showing the amount in the sinking fund after each deposit.

43. Investment In 1995, Oseola McCarty donated $150,000 to the University of Southern Mississippi to establish a scholarship fund. What is unusual about her is that the entire amount came from what she was able to save each month from her work as a washer woman, a job she began in 1916 at the age of 8, when she dropped out of school. *Source: The New York Times*.

a. How much would Ms. McCarty have to put into her savings account at the end of every 3 months to accumulate $150,000 over 79 years? Assume she received an interest rate of 5.25% compounded quarterly.

b. Answer part a using a 2% and a 7% interest rate.

AP Images

44. Present Value of an Annuity What lump sum deposited today at 5% compounded annually for 8 years will provide the same amount as $1000 deposited at the end of each year for 8 years at 6% compounded annually?

45. Present Value of an Annuity In his will the late Mr. Hudspeth said that each child in his family could have an annuity of $2000 at the end of each year for 9 years or the equivalent present value. If money can be deposited at 8% compounded annually, what is the present value?

46. Lottery Winnings In the "Million Dollar Lottery," a winner is paid a million dollars at the rate of $50,000 per year for 20 years. Assume that these payments form an ordinary annuity and that the lottery managers can invest money at 6% compounded annually. Find the lump sum that the management must put away to pay off the "million dollar" winner.

47. Lottery Winnings In most states, the winnings of million-dollar lottery jackpots are divided into equal payments given annually for 20 years. (In Colorado, the results are distributed over 25 years.) This means that the present value of the jackpot is worth less than the stated prize, with the actual value determined by the interest rate at which the money could be invested. *Source: The New York Times Magazine*.

a. Find the present value of a $1 million lottery jackpot distributed in equal annual payments over 20 years, using an interest rate of 5%.

b. Find the present value of a $1 million lottery jackpot distributed in equal annual payments over 20 years, using an interest rate of 9%.

c. Calculate the answer for part a using the 25-year distribution time in Colorado.

d. Calculate the answer for part b using the 25-year distribution time in Colorado.

48. Car Payments Kristina Walters buys a new car costing $22,000. She agrees to make payments at the end of each month for 4 years. If she pays 9% interest, compounded monthly, what is the amount of each payment? Find the total amount of interest Kristina will pay.

House Payments Find the monthly house payment necessary to amortize each of the loans in Exercises 49–52. Then find the unpaid balance after 5 years for each loan. Assume that interest is compounded monthly.

49. $249,560 at 7.75% for 25 years

50. $170,892 at 8.11% for 30 years

51. $353,700 at 7.95% for 30 years

52. $196,511 at 7.57% for 25 years

53. Annuity When Ms. Thompson died, she left $25,000 to her husband, which he deposited at 6% compounded annually. He wants to make annual withdrawals from the account so that the money (principal and interest) is gone in exactly 8 years.

a. Find the amount of each withdrawal.

b. Find the amount of each withdrawal if the money must last 12 years.

54. Annuity The trustees of a college have accepted a gift of $150,000. The donor has directed the trustees to deposit the money in an account paying 6% per year, compounded semiannually. The trustees may withdraw an equal amount of money at the end of each 6-month period; the money must last 5 years.

a. Find the amount of each withdrawal.

b. Find the amount of each withdrawal if the money must last 7 years.

55. Amortization An insurance firm pays $4000 for a new printer for its computer. It amortizes the loan for the printer in 4 annual payments at 8% compounded annually. Prepare an amortization schedule for this machine.

56. Amortization Certain large semitrailer trucks cost $72,000 each. Ace Trucking buys such a truck and agrees to pay for it with a loan that will be amortized with 9 semiannual payments at 9.5% compounded semiannually. Prepare an amortization schedule for this truck.

57. Amortization A printer manufacturer charges $1048 for a high-speed printer. A firm of tax accountants buys 8 of these machines. They make a down payment of $1200 and agree to amortize the balance with monthly payments at 10.5% compounded monthly for 4 years. Prepare an amortization schedule showing the first six payments.

58. Amortization When Barbara Essenmacher opened her law office, she bought $14,000 worth of law books and $7200 worth of office furniture. She paid $1200 down and agreed to amortize the balance with semiannual payments for 5 years at 8% compounded semiannually. Prepare an amortization schedule for this purchase.

YOUR TURN ANSWERS

1. $179,124.19   2. $7880.92

3. $193.22   4. $22,796.45

5. $258.34   6. $1188.83

3 Taylor Polynomials at 0

APPLY IT

How can we determine the length of time before a machine part must be replaced?

We shall see in Exercise 39 that a Taylor polynomial can be used to approximate the answer to this question.

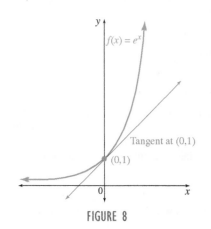

FIGURE 8

Although exponential and logarithmic functions are quite different from polynomials, they can be closely approximated by polynomials. These approximating polynomials are called **Taylor polynomials** after British mathematician Brook Taylor (1685–1731), who published his work on them in 1715.

One of the most useful nonpolynomial functions is the exponential function $f(x) = e^x$. Let us begin our discussion of Taylor polynomials by finding polynomials that approximate e^x for values of x close to 0. As a first approximation to e^x, choose the straight line that is tangent to the graph of $f(x) = e^x$ at the point $(0, 1)$. (See Figure 8.) Since the slope of a tangent line is given by the derivative of the function, and the derivative of $f(x) = e^x$ is $f'(x) = e^x$, the slope of the tangent line at $x = 0$ is $f'(0) = e^0 = 1$.

The tangent line goes through $(0, f(0)) = (0, 1)$ and has slope $f'(0) = 1$. By the point-slope form of the equation of a line, the equation of the tangent line is

$$y - y_1 = m(x - x_1)$$
$$y - f(0) = f'(0)(x - 0)$$
$$y = f(0) + f'(0) \cdot x,$$

or, after substituting 1 for $f(0)$ and 1 for $f'(0)$,

$$y = 1 + x.$$

If $P_1(x)$ is used to represent $1 + x$, then

$$P_1(x) = 1 + x$$

is called the *Taylor polynomial of degree 1* for $f(x) = e^x$ at $x = 0$.

To be useful, $P_1(x)$ should approximate e^x for values of x close to 0. To check the accuracy of this approximation, compare values of $P_1(x)$ and values of e^x, for x close to 0, in the following table.

\multicolumn{3}{c}{**Approximations and Exact Values of e^x**}		
x	$P_1(x) = 1 + x$	$f(x) = e^x$
-1	0	0.3678794412
-0.1	0.9	0.904837418
-0.01	0.99	0.9900498337
-0.001	0.999	0.9990004998
0	1	1
0.001	1.001	1.0010005
0.01	1.01	1.010050167
0.1	1.1	1.105170918
1	2	2.718281828

This table agrees with the graph in Figure 8: the polynomial $P_1(x)$ is a good approximation for $f(x) = e^x$ only when x is close to 0.

For the polynomial $P_1(x)$,

$$P_1(0) = f(0) \qquad \text{and} \qquad P_1'(0) = f'(0);$$

that is, $P_1(x)$ and $f(x)$ are equal at 0 and their derivatives are equal at 0. A better approximation could be found with a curve. Since $P_1(x)$ is first-degree, we use a second-degree polynomial and require the second derivatives to be equal at 0. If $P_1(x)$ is written as

$$P_1(x) = a_0 + a_1 x,$$

with $a_0 = f(0)$ and $a_1 = f'(0)$, then a second-degree polynomial can be written as

$$P_2(x) = a_0 + a_1 x + a_2 x^2.$$

Just as above, we want

$$P_2(0) = f(0) \qquad \text{and} \qquad P_2'(0) = f'(0),$$

but we also want

$$P_2''(0) = f''(0).$$

Since $P_2(0) = a_0$, and $f(0) = 1$, then $a_0 = 1$. Also, $P_2'(x) = a_1 + 2a_2 x$, so $P_2'(0) = a_1$. Since $f'(0) = e^0 = 1$, we also must have $a_1 = 1$. Finally, $P_2''(x) = 2a_2$. Since $f''(x) = e^x$, $P_2''(0) = 2a_2$ and $f''(0) = 1$, so that

$$2a_2 = 1$$

$$a_2 = \frac{1}{2}.$$

Our second approximation, the *Taylor polynomial of degree 2 for $f(x) = e^x$ at $x = 0$*, is thus

$$P_2(x) = 1 + x + \frac{1}{2}x^2.$$

A graph of this polynomial, along with the graph of $f(x) = e^x$, is shown in Figure 9.

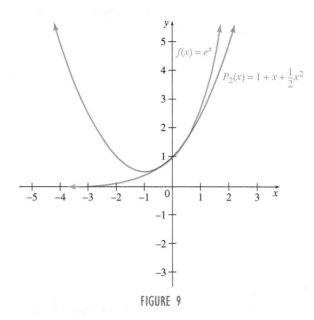

FIGURE 9

As above, the accuracy of this approximation can be checked with a table comparing values of $P_2(x)$ with those of $P_1(x)$ and $f(x)$, as shown.

	Approximations and Exact Values of e^x		
x	$P_1(x) = 1 + x$	$P_2(x) = 1 + x + \dfrac{1}{2}x^2$	$f(x) = e^x$
-1	0	0.5	0.3678794412
-0.1	0.9	0.905	0.9048374180
-0.01	0.99	0.99005	0.9900498337
-0.001	0.999	0.9990005	0.9990004998
0	1	1	1
0.001	1.001	1.0010005	1.001000500
0.01	1.01	1.01005	1.010050167
0.1	1.1	1.105	1.105170918
1	2	2.5	2.718281828

Although the approximations provided by $P_2(x)$ are better than those provided by $P_1(x)$, they are still accurate only for values of x close to 0. A better approximation would be given by a polynomial $P_3(x)$ that equals $f(x)$ when $x = 0$ and has the first, second, and *third* derivatives of $P_3(x)$ and $f(x) = e^x$ equal when $x = 0$. If we let

$$P_3(x) = a_0 + a_1x + a_2x^2 + a_3x^3,$$

—FOR REVIEW—

Recall that $P_3^{(n)}(x)$ represents the nth derivative of $P_3(x)$.

we can find the first three derivatives:

$$P_3^{(1)}(x) = a_1 + 2a_2x + 3a_3x^2$$
$$P_3^{(2)}(x) = 2a_2 + 6a_3x$$
$$P_3^{(3)}(x) = 6a_3.$$

Letting $x = 0$ in $P_3(x)$ and in each derivative, in turn, yields

$$P_3(0) = a_0, \qquad P_3^{(1)}(0) = a_1, \qquad P_3^{(2)}(0) = 2a_2, \qquad P_3^{(3)}(0) = 6a_3.$$

Since $f(0) = 1$, $f^{(1)}(0) = 1$, $f^{(2)}(0) = 1$, and $f^{(3)}(0) = 1$ for $f(x) = e^x$,

$$a_0 = 1, \qquad a_1 = 1, \qquad a_2 = \frac{1}{2}, \qquad \text{and} \qquad a_3 = \frac{1}{6},$$

with

$$P_3(x) = 1 + x + \frac{1}{2}x^2 + \frac{1}{6}x^3.$$

A graph of $f(x) = e^x$ and $P_3(x)$ is shown in Figure 10.

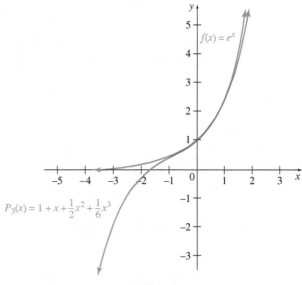

FIGURE 10

To generalize the work above, let $f(x) = e^x$ be approximated by

$$P_n(x) = a_0 + a_1 x + a_2 x^2 + \cdots + a_n x^n,$$

where

$$P_n(0) = f(0),$$
$$P_n^{(1)}(0) = f^{(1)}(0)$$
$$\vdots$$
$$P_n^{(n)}(0) = f^{(n)}(0).$$

Taking derivatives of $P_n(x)$ gives

$$P_n^{(1)}(x) = a_1 + 2a_2 x + 3a_3 x^2 + \cdots + n \cdot a_n x^{n-1}$$
$$P_n^{(2)}(x) = 2a_2 + 2 \cdot 3a_3 x + \cdots + n(n-1)a_n x^{n-2}$$
$$P_n^{(3)}(x) = 2 \cdot 3a_3 + \cdots + n(n-1)(n-2)a_n x^{n-3}$$
$$\vdots$$
$$P_n^{(n)}(x) = n(n-1)(n-2)(n-3)\cdots 3 \cdot 2 \cdot 1 \cdot a_n = n!a_n.$$

The symbol $n!$ (read "n-factorial") is used for the product

$$n(n-1)(n-2)(n-3)\cdots 3\cdot 2\cdot 1.$$

For example, $3! = 3\cdot 2\cdot 1 = 6$, while $5! = 120$. By convention, $0! = 1$.* If we use factorials and replace x with 0, the various derivatives of $P_n(x)$ become

$$P_n^{(1)}(0) = 1!a_1$$
$$P_n^{(2)}(0) = 2!a_2$$
$$P_n^{(3)}(0) = 3!a_3$$
$$\vdots$$
$$P_n^{(n)}(0) = n!a_n.$$

For every value of n, $f^{(n)}(0) = 1$. Setting corresponding derivatives equal gives

$$1!a_1 = 1$$
$$2!a_2 = 1$$
$$3!a_3 = 1$$
$$\vdots$$
$$n!a_n = 1,$$

from which

$$a_1 = \frac{1}{1!}, \quad a_2 = \frac{1}{2!}, \quad a_3 = \frac{1}{3!}, \quad \cdots, \quad a_n = \frac{1}{n!}.$$

Finally, the *Taylor polynomial of degree n* for $f(x) = e^x$ at $x = 0$ is

$$P_n(x) = 1 + \frac{1}{1!}x + \frac{1}{2!}x^2 + \frac{1}{3!}x^3 + \cdots + \frac{1}{n!}x^n.$$

Using the convention that the *zeroth derivative* of $y = f(x)$ is just f itself, and using Σ to represent a sum, we can write this result in the following way.

Taylor Polynomial for $f(x) = e^x$
The **Taylor polynomial of degree n** for $f(x) = e^x$ at $x = 0$ is

$$P_n(x) = \sum_{i=0}^{n} \frac{f^{(i)}(0)}{i!}x^i = \sum_{i=0}^{n} \frac{1}{i!}x^i.$$

*The symbol $n!$ for the product

$$n(n-1)(n-2)(n-3)\cdots 3\cdot 2\cdot 1$$

came into use during the late 19th century, although it was by no means the only symbol for n-factorial. Another popular symbol was $\lfloor n$. The exclamation point notation has won out, probably because it is more convenient for printers of textbooks.

Taylor polynomials of degree up to 10 for $f(x) = e^x$ are shown in Figure 11.

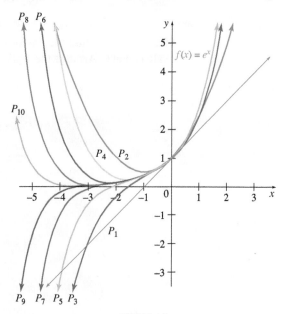

FIGURE 11

TECHNOLOGY NOTE Graphing calculators simplify the creation of a sequence of Taylor polynomials. For example, to create Taylor polynomials of degree 1, 2, and 3 for e^x on a TI-84 Plus, let $Y_1 = 1 + X$, $Y_2 = Y_1 + X^2/2$, and $Y_3 = Y_2 + X^3/6$.

EXAMPLE 1 Taylor Polynomial

Use a Taylor polynomial of degree 5 to approximate $e^{-0.2}$.

SOLUTION In the work above, we found Taylor polynomials for e^x at $x = 0$. As the graphs in Figure 11 suggest, these polynomials can be used to find approximate values of e^x for values of x near 0. The Taylor polynomial of degree 5 for $f(x) = e^x$ is

$$P_5(x) = 1 + \frac{1}{1!}x + \frac{1}{2!}x^2 + \frac{1}{3!}x^3 + \frac{1}{4!}x^4 + \frac{1}{5!}x^5.$$

Replacing x with -0.2 gives

$$1 + \frac{1}{1!}(-0.2) + \frac{1}{2!}(-0.2)^2 + \frac{1}{3!}(-0.2)^3 + \frac{1}{4!}(-0.2)^4$$

$$+ \frac{1}{5!}(-0.2)^5 \approx 0.8187307.$$

YOUR TURN 1 Use a Taylor polynomial of degree 5 to approximate $e^{-0.15}$.

Using a calculator to evaluate $e^{-0.2}$ directly gives 0.8187308, which agrees with our approximation to 6 decimal places. **TRY YOUR TURN 1**

Generalizing our work in finding the Taylor polynomials for $f(x) = e^x$ leads to the following definition of Taylor polynomials for any appropriate function f.

Taylor Polynomial of Degree n
Let f be a function that can be differentiated n times at 0. The Taylor polynomial of degree n for f at 0 is

NOTE
Because of the $f(0)$ term, a Taylor polynomial of degree n has $n + 1$ terms.

$$P_n(x) = f(0) + \frac{f^{(1)}(0)}{1!}x + \frac{f^{(2)}(0)}{2!}x^2 + \frac{f^{(3)}(0)}{3!}x^3 + \cdots + \frac{f^{(n)}(0)}{n!}x^n = \sum_{i=0}^{n} \frac{f^{(n)}(0)}{i!}x^i.$$

EXAMPLE 2   Taylor Polynomial

Let $f(x) = \sqrt{x + 1}$. Find the Taylor polynomial of degree 4 at $x = 0$.

SOLUTION   To find the Taylor polynomial of degree 4, use the first four derivatives of f, evaluated at 0. Arrange the work as follows.

Calculations for Taylor Polynomial	
Derivative	**Value at 0**
$f(x) = \sqrt{x + 1} = (x + 1)^{1/2}$	$f(0) = 1$
$f^{(1)}(x) = \dfrac{1}{2}(x + 1)^{-1/2} = \dfrac{1}{2(x + 1)^{1/2}}$	$f^{(1)}(0) = \dfrac{1}{2}$
$f^{(2)}(x) = -\dfrac{1}{4}(x + 1)^{-3/2} = \dfrac{-1}{4(x + 1)^{3/2}}$	$f^{(2)}(0) = -\dfrac{1}{4}$
$f^{(3)}(x) = \dfrac{3}{8}(x + 1)^{-5/2} = \dfrac{3}{8(x + 1)^{5/2}}$	$f^{(3)}(0) = \dfrac{3}{8}$
$f^{(4)}(x) = -\dfrac{15}{16}(x + 1)^{-7/2} = \dfrac{-15}{16(x + 1)^{7/2}}$	$f^{(4)}(0) = -\dfrac{15}{16}$

Now use the definition of a Taylor polynomial.

$$
\begin{aligned}
P_4(x) &= f(0) + \frac{f^{(1)}(0)}{1!}x + \frac{f^{(2)}(0)}{2!}x^2 + \frac{f^{(3)}(0)}{3!}x^3 + \frac{f^{(4)}(0)}{4!}x^4 \\
&= 1 + \frac{1/2}{1!}x + \frac{-1/4}{2!}x^2 + \frac{3/8}{3!}x^3 + \frac{-15/16}{4!}x^4 \\
&= 1 + \frac{1}{2}x - \frac{1}{8}x^2 + \frac{1}{16}x^3 - \frac{5}{128}x^4
\end{aligned}
$$

YOUR TURN 2 Let $f(x) = \sqrt{x + 4}$. Find the Taylor polynomial of degree 4 at $x = 0$.

TRY YOUR TURN 2

EXAMPLE 3   Approximation

Use the result of Example 2 to approximate $\sqrt{0.9}$.

SOLUTION   To approximate $\sqrt{0.9}$, we must evaluate $f(-0.1) = \sqrt{-0.1 + 1} = \sqrt{0.9}$. Using $P_4(x)$ from Example 2, with $x = -0.1$, gives

$$
\begin{aligned}
P_4(-0.1) &= 1 + \frac{1}{2}(-0.1) - \frac{1}{8}(-0.1)^2 + \frac{1}{16}(-0.1)^3 - \frac{5}{128}(-0.1)^4 \\
&= 1 - 0.05 - 0.00125 - 0.0000625 - 0.000003906 = 0.948683594.
\end{aligned}
$$

YOUR TURN 3 Use the result of Your Turn 2 to approximate $\sqrt{4.05}$.

Thus, $\sqrt{0.9} \approx 0.948683594$. A calculator gives a value of 0.9486832981 for the square root of 0.9.

TRY YOUR TURN 3

EXAMPLE 4   Taylor Polynomial

Find the Taylor polynomial of degree n at $x = 0$ for

$$
f(x) = \frac{1}{1 - x}.
$$

Sequences and Series

SOLUTION As above, find the first n derivatives, and evaluate each at 0.

Calculations for Taylor Polynomial	
Derivative	**Value at 0**
$f(x) = \dfrac{1}{1-x} = (1-x)^{-1}$	$f(0) = 1$
$f^{(1)}(x) = -1(1-x)^{-2}(-1) = (1-x)^{-2}$	$f^{(1)}(0) = 1 = 1!$
$f^{(2)}(x) = 2(1-x)^{-3}$	$f^{(2)}(0) = 2 = 2!$
$f^{(3)}(x) = 3!(1-x)^{-4}$	$f^{(3)}(0) = 3!$
$f^{(4)}(x) = 4!(1-x)^{-5}$	$f^{(4)}(0) = 4!$

Continuing this process,

$$f^{(n)}(x) = n!(1-x)^{-1-n} \quad \text{and} \quad f^{(n)}(0) = n!.$$

By the definition of Taylor polynomials,

$$P_n(x) = 1 + \frac{1!}{1!}x + \frac{2!}{2!}x^2 + \frac{3!}{3!}x^3 + \frac{4!}{4!}x^4 + \cdots + \frac{n!}{n!}x^n$$

$$= 1 + x + x^2 + x^3 + x^4 + \cdots + x^n.$$

EXAMPLE 5 **Approximation**

Use a Taylor polynomial of degree 4 to approximate $1/0.98$.

SOLUTION Use the function f from Example 4, with $x = 0.02$, to get

$$f(0.02) = \frac{1}{1 - 0.02} = \frac{1}{0.98}.$$

Based on the result obtained in Example 4,

$$P_4(x) = 1 + x + x^2 + x^3 + x^4,$$

with

$$P_4(0.02) = 1 + (0.02) + (0.02)^2 + (0.02)^3 + (0.02)^4$$

$$= 1 + 0.02 + 0.0004 + 0.000008 + 0.00000016$$

$$= 1.02040816.$$

A calculator gives $1/0.98 = 1.020408163$.

3 EXERCISES

For the functions defined as follows, find the Taylor polynomials of degree 4 at 0.

1. $f(x) = e^{-2x}$

2. $f(x) = e^{3x}$

3. $f(x) = e^{x+1}$

4. $f(x) = e^{-x}$

5. $f(x) = \sqrt{x+9}$

6. $f(x) = \sqrt{x+16}$

7. $f(x) = \sqrt[3]{x-1}$

8. $f(x) = \sqrt[3]{x+8}$

9. $f(x) = \sqrt[4]{x+1}$

10. $f(x) = \sqrt[4]{x+16}$

11. $f(x) = \ln(1-x)$

12. $f(x) = \ln(1+2x)$

13. $f(x) = \ln(1+2x^2)$

14. $f(x) = \ln(1-x^3)$

15. $f(x) = xe^{-x}$

16. $f(x) = x^2 e^x$

17. $f(x) = (9-x)^{3/2}$

18. $f(x) = (1+x)^{3/2}$

19. $f(x) = \dfrac{1}{1+x}$

20. $f(x) = \dfrac{1}{x-1}$

Use Taylor polynomials of degree 4 at $x = 0$, found in Exercises 1–14 above, to approximate the quantities in Exercises 21–34. Round answers to 4 decimal places.

21. $e^{-0.04}$

22. $e^{0.06}$

23. $e^{1.02}$

24. $e^{-0.07}$

25. $\sqrt{8.92}$

26. $\sqrt{16.3}$

27. $\sqrt[3]{-1.05}$

28. $\sqrt[3]{7.91}$

29. $\sqrt[4]{1.06}$

30. $\sqrt[4]{15.88}$

31. ln 0.97

32. ln 1.06

33. ln 1.008

34. ln 0.992

35. Find a polynomial of degree 3 such that $f(0) = 3$, $f'(0) = 6$, $f''(0) = 12$, and $f'''(0) = 24$.

36. Find a polynomial of degree 4 such that $f(0) = 1$, $f'(0) = 1$, $f''(0) = 2$, $f'''(0) = 6$, and $f^{(4)}(0) = 24$. Generalize this result to a polynomial of degree n, assuming that $f^{(n)}(0) = n!$

37. a. Generalize the result of Example 2 to show that if x is small compared with a,

$$(a + x)^{1/n} \approx a^{1/n} + \frac{xa^{1/n}}{na}.$$

b. Use the result of part a to approximate $\sqrt[3]{66}$ to 5 decimal places, and compare with the actual value.

APPLICATIONS

Business and Economics

38. Duration Let D represent *duration*, a term in finance that measures the length of time an investor must wait to receive half of the value of a cash flow stream totaling S dollars. Let r be the rate of interest and V the value of the investment. The value of S can be calculated by two formulas that are approximately equal:

$$S \approx V(1 + rD)$$

and

$$S \approx V(1 + r)^D.$$

a. Show that the first approximation follows from the second by using the Taylor polynomial of degree 1 for the function $f(r) = (1 + r)^D$. *Source: Robert D. Campbell.*

b. For $V = \$1000$, $r = 0.1$, and $D = 3.2$, calculate and compare the two expressions for S.

39. APPLY IT Replacement Time for a Part A book on management science gives the equation

$$\frac{e^{\lambda N}}{\lambda} - N = \frac{1}{\lambda} + k$$

to determine N, the time until a particular part can be expected to need replacing. (λ and k are constants for a particular machine.) To find a useful approximate value for N when λN is near 0, go through the following steps.

a. Find a Taylor polynomial of degree 2 at $N = 0$ for $e^{\lambda N}$.

b. Substitute this polynomial into the given equation and solve for N.

In Exercises 40–44, use a Taylor polynomial of degree 2 at $x = 0$ to approximate the desired value. Compare your answers with the results obtained by direct substitution.

40. Profit The profit (in thousands of dollars) when x thousand tons of apples are sold is

$$P(x) = \frac{20 + x^2}{50 + x}.$$

Find $P(0.3)$.

41. Profit The profit (in thousands of dollars) from the sale of x thousand packages of note paper is

$$P(x) = \ln(100 + 3x).$$

Find $P(0.6)$ if ln 100 is given as 4.605.

42. Cost For a certain electronic part, the cost to make the part declines as more parts are made. Suppose that the cost (in dollars) to manufacture the xth part is

$$C(x) = e^{-x/50}.$$

Find $C(5)$.

43. Revenue Revenue from selling agricultural products often increases at a slower and slower rate as more of the products are sold. Suppose the revenue from the xth unit of a product is

$$R(x) = 500 \ln\left(4 + \frac{x}{50}\right).$$

Find $R(10)$ if ln 4 is given as 1.386.

Life Sciences

44. Amount of a Drug in the Bloodstream The amount (in milliliters) of a certain drug in the bloodstream x minutes after being administered is

$$A(x) = \frac{6x}{1 + 10x}.$$

Find $A(0.05)$.

45. Species Survival According to a text on species survival, the probability P that a certain species survives is given by

$$P = 1 - e^{-2k},$$

where k is a constant. Use a Taylor polynomial to show that if k is small, P is approximately $2k$.

Physical Sciences

46. Electric Potential In the Extended Application for Chapter 4, the electric potential at a distance z from an electrically charged disk of radius R was given as

$$V = k_1(\sqrt{z^2 + R^2} - z),$$

where k_1 is a constant.

a. Suppose z is much larger than R. By writing $\sqrt{z^2 + R^2}$ as $z\sqrt{1 + R^2/z^2}$ and using the Taylor polynomial of degree 1 for $\sqrt{1 + x}$, show that the potential can be approximated by

$$V \approx \frac{k_2}{z},$$

the result given in the Extended Application, where k_2 is a constant.

b. Suppose z is much smaller than R. By writing $\sqrt{z^2 + R^2}$ as $R\sqrt{1 + z^2/R^2}$ and using the Taylor polynomial of degree 1 for $\sqrt{1 + x}$, show that the potential can be approximated by

$$V \approx k_1\left(R - z + \frac{z^2}{2R}\right),$$

the result given in the Extended Application.

YOUR TURN ANSWERS

1. 0.860708

2. $P_4(x) = 2 + \frac{1}{4}x - \frac{1}{64}x^2 + \frac{1}{512}x^3 - \frac{5}{16,384}x^4$

3. 2.0124612

4 Infinite Series

APPLY IT If some fraction of a particular gene in a population experiences a mutation each generation, can we expect that the entire population will have this mutation over time?

The answer to this question is found in Example 5 by considering the sum of an infinite series.

A repeating decimal such as $0.66666\ldots$ is really the sum of an infinite number of terms:

$$0.66666\ldots = 0.6 + 0.06 + 0.006 + 0.0006 + \cdots$$

$$= \frac{6}{10} + \frac{6}{10^2} + \frac{6}{10^3} + \frac{6}{10^4} + \cdots.$$

In this section we will show how an infinite number of terms can sometimes be added to get a finite sum by a limit process. To do this, we need the following definition.

Infinite Series

An **infinite series** is an expression of the form

$$a_1 + a_2 + a_3 + a_4 + \cdots + a_n + \cdots = \sum_{i=1}^{\infty} a_i.$$

To find the sum $a_1 + a_2 + a_3 + a_4 + \cdots + a_n + \cdots$, first find the sum S_n of the first n terms, called the **nth partial sum**. For example,

$$S_1 = a_1$$
$$S_2 = a_1 + a_2$$
$$S_3 = a_1 + a_2 + a_3$$
$$\vdots$$
$$S_n = a_1 + a_2 + a_3 + \cdots + a_n = \sum_{i=1}^{n} a_i.$$

EXAMPLE 1 Partial Sums

Find the first five partial sums for the sequence

$$1, \frac{1}{2}, \frac{1}{4}, \frac{1}{8}, \frac{1}{16}, \ldots.$$

SOLUTION By the definition of partial sum,

$$S_1 = 1$$
$$S_2 = 1 + \frac{1}{2} = \frac{3}{2}$$
$$S_3 = 1 + \frac{1}{2} + \frac{1}{4} = \frac{7}{4}$$
$$S_4 = 1 + \frac{1}{2} + \frac{1}{4} + \frac{1}{8} = \frac{15}{8}$$
$$S_5 = 1 + \frac{1}{2} + \frac{1}{4} + \frac{1}{8} + \frac{1}{16} = \frac{31}{16}.$$

YOUR TURN 1 Find the first five partial sums for the sequence $1, 1/4, 1/9, 1/16, 1/25, \ldots$

TRY YOUR TURN 1

As n gets larger, the partial sum $S_n = a_1 + a_2 + \cdots + a_n$ includes more and more terms from the infinite series. It is thus reasonable to define the *sum of the infinite series* as $\lim_{n \to \infty} S_n$, if it exists.

Sum of the Infinite Series

Let $S_n = a_1 + a_2 + a_3 + \cdots + a_n$ be the nth partial sum for the series $a_1 + a_2 + a_3 + \cdots + a_n + \cdots$. Suppose

$$\lim_{n \to \infty} S_n = L$$

for some real number L. Then L is called the **sum of the infinite series** $a_1 + a_2 + a_3 + \cdots + a_n + \cdots$, and the infinite series **converges**. If no such limit exists, then the infinite series has no sum and **diverges**.

Infinite Geometric Series

Some good examples of convergent and divergent series come from the study of infinite geometric series, which are the sums of the terms of geometric sequences, discussed in this chapter's first section. For example,

$$1, \frac{1}{2}, \frac{1}{4}, \frac{1}{8}, \frac{1}{16}, \cdots, \frac{1}{2^n}, \cdots$$

is a geometric sequence with first term $a_1 = 1$ and common ratio $r = 1/2$. The first five partial sums for this sequence were found in Example 1. To find S_n, the nth partial sum, use the formula given in the first section: The sum of the first n terms of a geometric sequence having first term $a = a_1$ and common ratio r is

$$S_n = \frac{a(r^n - 1)}{r - 1}.$$

For any value of n, S_n can be found for the geometric sequence by using the formula with $a = 1$ and $r = 1/2$.

$$S_n = \frac{a(r^n - 1)}{r - 1} = \frac{1\left[\left(\frac{1}{2}\right)^n - 1\right]}{\frac{1}{2} - 1}$$

$$= \frac{\left(\frac{1}{2}\right)^n - 1}{-\frac{1}{2}} = -2\left[\left(\frac{1}{2}\right)^n - 1\right] = 2\left[1 - \left(\frac{1}{2}\right)^n\right]$$

As n gets larger and larger, that is, as $n \to \infty$, the value of $(1/2)^n$ gets closer and closer to 0, so that

$$\lim_{n \to \infty} \left(\frac{1}{2}\right)^n = 0.$$

Using properties of limits,

$$\lim_{n \to \infty} S_n = \lim_{n \to \infty} 2\left[1 - \left(\frac{1}{2}\right)^n\right] = 2(1 - 0) = 2.$$

By the definition of the sum of an infinite series,

$$1 + \frac{1}{2} + \frac{1}{4} + \frac{1}{8} + \cdots = 2,$$

and the series converges.

To generalize from this example, start with the formula for the sum of the first n terms of a geometric sequence.

$$S_n = \frac{a(r^n - 1)}{r - 1}.$$

If r is in the interval $(-1, 1)$, then $\lim\limits_{n \to \infty} r^n = 0$. (Consider what happens to a small number as you raise it to a larger and larger power.) In that case,

$$\lim_{n \to \infty} S_n = \lim_{n \to \infty} \frac{a(r^n - 1)}{r - 1} = \frac{a(0 - 1)}{r - 1}$$
$$= \frac{a}{1 - r}.$$

On the other hand, if $r > 1$, then $\lim\limits_{n \to \infty} r^n = \infty$. (Consider what happens to a large number as you raise it to a larger and larger power.) In that case,

$$\lim_{n \to \infty} S_n = \infty,$$

and the series diverges because the terms of the series are getting larger and larger. If $r < -1$, then $\lim\limits_{n \to \infty} r^n$ does not exist, because r^n becomes larger and larger in magnitude while alternating in sign, and the same thing happens to the partial sums, so the series diverges. If $r = 1$, all the terms of the series equal a, so the series diverges (except in the trivial case when $a = 0$.) Finally, if $r = -1$, the terms of the series alternate between a and $-a$, and the partial sums alternate between a and 0, so the series diverges.

Sum of a Geometric Series

The infinite geometric series

$$a + ar + ar^2 + ar^3 + \cdots$$

converges, if r is in $(-1, 1)$, to the sum

$$\frac{a}{1 - r}.$$

The series diverges if r is not in $(-1, 1)$.

EXAMPLE 2   Geometric Series

Determine if the following geometric series converge. Give the sum of each convergent series.

(a) $3 + \dfrac{3}{8} + \dfrac{3}{64} + \dfrac{3}{512} + \cdots$

SOLUTION   This is a geometric series, with $a = a_1 = 3$ and $r = 1/8$. Since r is in $(-1, 1)$, the series converges and has sum

$$\frac{a}{1 - r} = \frac{3}{1 - 1/8} = \frac{3}{7/8} = 3 \cdot \frac{8}{7} = \frac{24}{7}.$$

(b) $\dfrac{3}{4} - \dfrac{9}{16} + \dfrac{27}{64} - \dfrac{81}{256} + \cdots$

SOLUTION This geometric series has $a = a_1 = 3/4$ and $r = -3/4$. Since r is in $(-1, 1)$, the series converges. The sum of the series is

$$\frac{3/4}{1 - (-3/4)} = \frac{3/4}{1 + 3/4} = \frac{3/4}{7/4} = \frac{3}{7}.$$

(c) $1 + 1.1 + (1.1)^2 + (1.1)^3 + (1.1)^4 + \cdots + (1.1)^{n-1} + \cdots$

SOLUTION This is a geometric series with common ratio $r = 1.1$. Since $r > 1$, the series diverges. (The partial sum S_n will eventually exceed any preassigned number, no matter how large.) TRY YOUR TURN 2

YOUR TURN 2 Determine if the following geometric series converge. Give the sum of each convergent series.

(a) $2 + 2/3 + 2/9 + 2/27 + \cdots$

(b) $5 - 5/4 + 5/16 - 5/64 + \cdots$

(c) $2 - 2(1.01) + 2(1.01)^2 - 2(1.01)^3 + \cdots$

EXAMPLE 3 Trains

Suppose a train leaves a station at noon travelling at 50 mph. Two hours later, on an adjacent track, a second train leaves the station heading in the same direction with a velocity of 60 mph. Determine the time at which the trains are both the same distance from the station.

(a) Solve this problem using algebra.

SOLUTION Let t be the number of hours since 2:00 pm. Since the first train left 2 hours earlier and has already traveled 100 miles, the total distance that the first train has traveled is $d_1 = 100 + 50t$. The second train has traveled $d_2 = 60t$. The two trains will be the same distance from the station when $d_1 = d_2$. Setting the two equations equal to each other and solving for t gives

$$d_1 = d_2$$
$$100 + 50t = 60t$$
$$100 = 10t$$
$$t = 10$$

The trains are equal distances from the station 10 hours after 2:00 pm, or at midnight.

(b) Solve this problem using a geometric series.

SOLUTION At 2:00 pm, the first train is 100 miles from the station. Since the second train is traveling at 60 mph, it will take $100/60 = 5/3$ hours to make up the 100 miles. But, during that $5/3$ hours, the first train will travel another $50(5/3) = 250/3$ miles. So the second train will have to travel another $(250/3)/60 = 50(5/3)/60 = (5/6)(5/3)$ hours to travel this distance. In the meantime, the first train has now traveled another $50(5/3)(5/6)$ miles. It will take the second train $(5/3)(5/6)(5/6)$ hours to make up this time, and so on. The total time that it takes for the trains to be an equal distance apart is found by summing the sequence of times it will take the second train to make up the distance. That is,

$$t = 5/3 + (5/3)(5/6) + (5/3)(5/6)^2 + (5/3)(5/6)^3 + \cdots$$

This is a geometric series, with $a = a_1 = 5/3$ and $r = 5/6$. Since r is in $(-1, 1)$, the series converges and the sum is

$$\frac{5/3}{1 - 5/6} = \frac{5/3}{1/6} = 10.$$

Thus, the trains will be an equal distance from the station 10 hours after 2:00, or at midnight. TRY YOUR TURN 3

YOUR TURN 3 Suppose Turtle starts a race at 8:00 am and travels at 15 feet per minute. Rabbit, who is much faster than Turtle, starts the race 6 hours later, traveling at 45 feet per minute. Determine the time when Rabbit catches up with Turtle.

EXAMPLE 4 Multiplier Effect

Suppose a company spends $1,000,000 on payroll in a certain city. Suppose also that the employees of the company reside in the city. Assume that on the average the inhabitants of this city spend 80% of their income in the same city. Then 80% of the original $1,000,000, or $(0.80)(\$1,000,000) = \$800,000$ will be spent in that city. An additional 80% of this $800,000, or $640,000, will in turn be spent in the city, as will 80% of the $640,000, and so on. Find the total expenditure in the city initiated by the original $1,000,000 payroll.

SOLUTION These amounts, $1,000,000, $800,000, $640,000, $512,000, and so on, form an infinite series with $a = a_1 = \$1,000,000$ and $r = 0.80$. The sum of these amounts is

$$\frac{a}{1 - r} = \frac{\$1,000,000}{1 - 0.80} = \$5,000,000.$$

The original $1,000,000 payroll leads to a total expenditure of $5,000,000 in the city. In economics, the quotient of these numbers, $5,000,000/$1,000,000 = 5, is called the *multiplier*.

EXAMPLE 5   Mutation

Retinoblastoma is a kind of cancer of the eye in children. Medical researchers believe that the disease depends on a single dominant gene, say A. Let a be the normal gene. It is believed that a fraction m of the population, $m = 2 \times 10^{-5}$, per generation will experience *mutation*, a sudden unaccountable change, of a into A. (We exclude the possibility of back mutations of A into a.) With medical care, approximately 70% of those affected with the disease survive. According to past data, the survivors reproduce at half the normal rate. The net fraction of affected persons who produce offspring is thus $r = 35\% = 0.35$. Since gene A is extremely rare, practically all the affected persons are of genotype Aa, so that we may neglect the few individuals of genotype AA. Find the total fraction of the population having the disease.

APPLY IT   **SOLUTION**   We start by defining the following variables.

m = fraction of population with disease due to mutation in this generation

mr = fraction of population with disease due to mutation in the previous generation

mr^2 = fraction of population with disease due to mutation two generations ago

mr^n = fraction of population with disease due to mutation n generations ago

The total fraction p of the population having the disease in this generation is thus

$$p = m + mr + mr^2 + \cdots + mr^n + \cdots$$

Use the formula for the sum of an infinite geometric series to find

$$p = \frac{m}{1 - r} = \frac{2 \times 10^{-5}}{1 - 0.35} \approx 3.1 \times 10^{-5}.$$

The fraction of the population having retinoblastoma is about 3×10^{-5}, or about 50% more than the fraction of each generation that experiences mutation.

4   EXERCISES

Identify which geometric series converge. Give the sum of each convergent series.

1. $20 + 10 + 5 + \dfrac{5}{2} + \cdots$

2. $1 + 0.8 + 0.64 + 0.512 + \cdots$

3. $2 + 6 + 18 + 54 + \cdots$

4. $3 + 6 + 12 + 24 + \cdots$

5. $27 + 9 + 3 + 1 + \cdots$

6. $64 + 16 + 4 + 1 + \cdots$

7. $100 + 10 + 1 + \cdots$

8. $44 + 22 + 11 + \cdots$

9. $\dfrac{5}{4} + \dfrac{5}{8} + \dfrac{5}{16} + \cdots$

10. $\dfrac{4}{5} + \dfrac{2}{5} + \dfrac{1}{5} + \cdots$

11. $\dfrac{1}{3} - \dfrac{2}{9} + \dfrac{4}{27} - \dfrac{8}{81} + \cdots$

12. $1 + \dfrac{1}{1.01} + \dfrac{1}{(1.01)^2} + \cdots$

13. $e - 1 + \dfrac{1}{e} - \dfrac{1}{e^2} + \cdots$

14. $e + e^2 + e^3 + e^4 + \cdots$

The nth term of a sequence is given. Calculate the first five partial sums.

15. $a_n = \dfrac{1}{n}$

16. $a_n = \dfrac{1}{n + 1}$

17. $a_n = \dfrac{1}{2n + 5}$

18. $a_n = \dfrac{1}{3n - 1}$

19. $a_n = \dfrac{1}{(n + 1)(n + 2)}$

20. $a_n = \dfrac{1}{(n + 3)(2n + 1)}$

21. The repeating decimal 0.222222 . . . can be expressed as infinite geometric series

$$0.2 + 0.2\left(\dfrac{1}{10}\right) + 0.2\left(\dfrac{1}{10}\right)^2 + 0.2\left(\dfrac{1}{10}\right)^3 + \cdots.$$

By finding the sum of the series, determine the rational number whose decimal expansion is 0.222222. . . .

22. The repeating decimal 0.18181818 . . . can be expressed as the infinite geometric series

$$0.18 + 0.18\left(\dfrac{1}{100}\right) + 0.18\left(\dfrac{1}{100}\right)^2 + 0.18\left(\dfrac{1}{100}\right)^3 + \cdots.$$

Determine the rational number whose decimal expression is 0.18181818 . . . .

23. The following classical formulas for computing the value of π were developed by François Viète (1540–1603) and Gottfried von Leibniz (1646–1716), respectively:

$$\dfrac{2}{\pi} = \dfrac{\sqrt{2}}{2} \cdot \dfrac{\sqrt{2 + \sqrt{2}}}{2} \cdot \dfrac{\sqrt{2 + \sqrt{2 + \sqrt{2}}}}{2} \cdots$$

and

$$\dfrac{\pi}{4} = 1 - \dfrac{1}{3} + \dfrac{1}{5} - \dfrac{1}{7} + \cdots.$$

Sources: Mathematics Teacher and A History of Mathematics.

a. Multiply the first three terms of Viète's formula together, and compare this with the sum of the first four terms of Leibniz's formula. Which formula is more accurate?

b. Use the table function on a graphing calculator or a spreadsheet to determine how many terms of the second formula must be added together to produce the same accuracy as the product of the first three terms of the first formula. [*Hint:* On a TI-84 Plus, use the command `Y1=4*sum(seq((-1)^(N-1)/(2N-1),N,1,X)).`]

APPLICATIONS

Business and Economics

24. **Production Orders** A sugar factory receives an order for 1000 units of sugar. The production manager thus orders production of 1000 units of sugar. He forgets, however, that the production of sugar requires some sugar (to prime the machines, for example), and so he ends up with only 900 units of sugar. He then orders an additional 100 units, and receives only 90 units. A further order for 10 units produces 9 units. Finally seeing he is wrong, the manager decides to try mathematics. He views the production process as an infinite geometric series with $a_1 = 1000$ and $r = 0.1$.

a. Using this, find the number of units of sugar that he should have ordered originally.

b. Afterwards, the manager realizes a much simpler solution to his problem. If x is the amount of sugar he orders, and he only gets 90% of what he orders, he should solve $0.9x = 1000$. What is the solution?

c. Explain why the answers to parts a and b are the same.

25. **Tax Rebate** The government claims to be able to stimulate the economy substantially by giving each taxpayer a $200 tax rebate. They reason that 90% of this amount, or $(0.90)(\$200) = \$180$, will be spent. An additional 90% of this $180 will then be spent, and so on.

a. If the government claim is true, how much total expenditure will result from this $200 rebate?

b. Calculate the value of the multiplier. (See Example 4.)

26. **Present Value** Recall computing the present value of a continuous flow of money. Suppose that instead of a continuous flow, an amount C is deposited each year, and the annual interest rate is r. Then the present value of the cash flow over n years is

$$P = C(1 + r)^{-1} + C(1 + r)^{-2} + C(1 + r)^{-3} + \cdots + C(1 + r)^{-n}.$$

a. Show that the present value can be simplified to

$$P = C\dfrac{(1 + r)^n - 1}{r(1 + r)^n}.$$

b. Show that the present value, taken over an infinite amount of time, is given by $P = C/r$.

27. **Malpractice Insurance** An insurance company determines it cannot write medical malpractice insurance profitably and stops selling the coverage. In spite of this action, the company will have to pay claims for many years on existing medical malpractice policies. The company pays 60 for medical malpractice claims the year after it stops selling the coverage. Each subsequent year's payments are 20% less than those of the previous year. Calculate the total medical malpractice payments that the company pays in all years after it stops selling the coverage. Choose one of the following. (*Hint:* When the problem says "pays 60," you can think of it as paying $60,000, but the units do not actually matter.) *Source: Society of Actuaries.*

a. 94

b. 150

c. 240

d. 300

e. 360

28. Automobile Insurance In modeling the number of claims filed by an individual under an automobile policy during a three-year period, an actuary makes the simplifying assumption that for all integers $n \geq 0$, $p_{n+1} = \dfrac{1}{5} p_n$, where p_n represents the probability that the policyholder files n claims during the period. Under this assumption, what is the probability that a policyholder files more than one claim during the period? Choose one of the following. (*Hint:* The total probability must equal 1.) *Source: Society of Actuaries*.

a. 0.04

b. 0.16

c. 0.20

d. 0.80

e. 0.96

Physical Sciences

29. Distance Mitzi drops a ball from a height of 10 m and notices that on each bounce the ball returns to about 3/4 of its previous height. About how far will the ball travel before it comes to rest?

30. Rotation of a Wheel After a person pedaling a bicycle removes his or her feet from the pedals, the wheel rotates 400 times the first minute. As it continues to slow down, in each minute it rotates only 3/4 as many times as in the previous minute. How many times will the wheel rotate before coming to a complete stop?

31. Pendulum Arc Length A pendulum bob swings through an arc 40 cm long on its first swing. Each swing thereafter, it swings only 80% as far as on the previous swing. How far will it swing altogether before coming to a complete stop?

General Interest

32. Perimeter A sequence of equilateral triangles is constructed as follows: The first triangle has sides 2 m in length. To get the next triangle, midpoints of the sides of the previous triangle are connected. If this process could be continued indefinitely, what would be the total perimeter of all the triangles?

33. Area What would be the total area of all the triangles of Exercise 32, disregarding the overlaps?

34. Trains Suppose a train leaves a station at noon traveling 100 mph. Two hours later, on an adjacent track, a second train leaves the station heading in the same direction traveling 125 mph. Determine when both trains are the same distance from the station.

a. Solve this problem using algebra.

b. Solve this problem using a geometric series. (See Example 3.)

35. Zeno's Paradox In the fifth century B.C., the Greek philosopher Zeno posed a paradox involving a race between Achilles (the fastest runner at the time) and a tortoise. The tortoise was given a head start, but once the race began, Achilles quickly reached the point where the tortoise had started. By then the tortoise had moved on to a new point. Achilles quickly reached that second point, but the tortoise had now moved to another point. Zeno concluded that Achilles could never reach the tortoise because every time he reached the point where the tortoise had been, the tortoise had moved on to a new point. This conclusion was absurd, yet people had trouble finding an error in Zeno's logic.

Suppose Achilles runs 10 m per second, the tortoise runs 1 m per second, and the tortoise has a 10-m head start.

a. Solve this problem using a geometric series. (See Example 3.)

b. Solve this problem using algebra.

c. Explain the error in Zeno's reasoning.

36. Bikers A famous story about the outstanding mathematician John von Neumann (1903–1957) concerns the following problem: Two bicyclists start 20 miles apart and head toward each other, each going 10 miles per hour. At the same time, a fly traveling 15 miles per hour leaves the front wheel of one bicycle, flies to the front wheel of the other bicycle, turns around and flies back to the wheel of the first bicycle, and so on, continuing in this manner until trapped between the two wheels. What total distance did the fly fly? There is a quick way to solve this problem. However, von Neumann allegedly solved this problem instantly by summing an infinite series. Solve this problem using both methods. *Source: American Mathematical Monthly*.

YOUR TURN ANSWERS

1. 1, 5/4, 49/36, 205/144, 5269/3600
2. (a) Converges to 3 (b) Converges to 4 (c) Diverges
3. 5 pm

5 Taylor Series

APPLY IT How many years will it take to double an amount invested at 9% annual interest?

Using Taylor series, we derive the rule of 70 and the rule of 72 to answer this question in Example 5.

As we saw in the previous section, the sum of the infinite geometric series having first term a and common ratio r is

$$\frac{a}{1 - r} \quad \text{for } r \text{ in } (-1, 1).$$

If the first term of an infinite geometric series is $a = 1$ and the common ratio is x, then the series is written

$$1 + x + x^2 + x^3 + x^4 + \cdots + x^{n-1} + \cdots.$$

If x is in $(-1, 1)$, then by the formula for the sum of an infinite geometric series, the sum of this series is

$$\frac{1}{1-x}.$$

That is,

$$\frac{1}{1-x} = 1 + x + x^2 + x^3 + x^4 + \cdots \quad \text{for } x \text{ in } (-1, 1).$$

The interval $(-1, 1)$ is called the **interval of convergence** for the series. This series is not an approximation for $1/(1-x)$; the sum of the series is actually *equal to* $1/(1-x)$ for any x in $(-1, 1)$.

Earlier in this chapter, we found that the Taylor polynomial of degree n at $x = 0$ for $1/(1-x)$ is

$$P_n(x) = 1 + x + x^2 + x^3 + x^4 + \cdots + x^n.$$

Since the series given above for $1/(1-x)$ is just an extension of this Taylor polynomial, it seems natural to call the series a *Taylor series*.

Taylor Series

If all derivatives of a function f exist at 0, then the **Taylor series** for f at 0 is defined to be

$$f(0) + f^{(1)}(0)x + \frac{f^{(2)}(0)}{2!}x^2 + \frac{f^{(3)}(0)}{3!}x^3 + \cdots.$$

The particular Taylor series at 0 is also called a **Maclaurin series**. Scotsman Colin Maclaurin (1698–1746) used this series in his work *Treatise of Fluxions*, published in 1742. In this text, we will only consider Taylor series at 0. Taylor series at other points, as well as methods for finding the interval of convergence, are beyond the scope of this text. For more information, see *Thomas' Calculus*, 12th ed., by Maurice D. Weir and Joel R. Hass, Addison-Wesley, 2010.

Calculations for Taylor Series	
Derivative	Value at 0
$f(x) = e^x$	$f(0) = 1$
$f^{(1)}(x) = e^x$	$f^{(1)}(0) = 1$
$f^{(2)}(x) = e^x$	$f^{(2)}(0) = 1$
$f^{(3)}(x) = e^x$	$f^{(3)}(0) = 1$
.	.
.	.
.	.
$f^{(n)}(x) = e^x$	$f^{(n)}(0) = 1$

EXAMPLE 1 Taylor Series

Find the Taylor series for $f(x) = e^x$ at 0.

SOLUTION Work as in Section 3. The result is in the table to the left. Using the definition given in this section, the Taylor series for $f(x) = e^x$ is

$$1 + x + \frac{1}{2!}x^2 + \frac{1}{3!}x^3 + \frac{1}{4!}x^4 + \cdots + \frac{1}{n!}x^n + \cdots.$$

While we cannot prove it here, the interval of convergence is $(-\infty, \infty)$.

The process for finding the interval of convergence for a given Taylor series is discussed in more advanced calculus courses. Three of the most common Taylor series are listed below, along with their intervals of convergence. Note that these three functions are equal to their respective Taylor series expansion for all values of x contained in the given interval of convergence. (As is customary, these series are written so that the initial term is a *zeroth* term.)

Common Taylor Series

$f(x)$	*Taylor Series*	*Interval of Convergence*
e^x	$1 + x + \dfrac{1}{2!}x^2 + \dfrac{1}{3!}x^3 + \cdots + \dfrac{1}{n!}x^n + \cdots$	$(-\infty, \infty)$
$\ln(1 + x)$	$x - \dfrac{x^2}{2} + \dfrac{x^3}{3} - \dfrac{x^4}{4} + \cdots + \dfrac{(-1)^n x^{n+1}}{n + 1} + \cdots$	$(-1, 1]$
$\dfrac{1}{1 - x}$	$1 + x + x^2 + x^3 + \cdots + x^n + \cdots$	$(-1, 1)$

Operations on Taylor Series

The first n terms of a Taylor series form a polynomial. Because of this, we would expect many of the operations on polynomials to generalize to Taylor series; some properties of series concerning these operations are given in the following theorems.

Operations on Taylor Series

Let f and g be functions having Taylor series with

$$f(x) = a_0 + a_1 x + a_2 x^2 + a_3 x^3 + \cdots + a_n x^n + \cdots$$

and

$$g(x) = b_0 + b_1 x + b_2 x^2 + b_3 x^3 + \cdots + b_n x^n + \cdots.$$

1. The Taylor series for $f + g$ is

$$(a_0 + b_0) + (a_1 + b_1)x + (a_2 + b_2)x^2 + \cdots$$
$$+ (a_n + b_n)x^n + \cdots,$$

for all x in the interval of convergence of both f and g. (Convergent series may be added term by term.)

2. For a real number c, the Taylor series for $c \cdot f(x)$ is

$$c \cdot a_0 + c \cdot a_1 x + c \cdot a_2 x^2 + \cdots + c \cdot a_n x^n + \cdots,$$

for all x in the interval of convergence of f.

3. For any positive integer k, the Taylor series for $x^k \cdot f(x)$ is

$$a_0 x^k + a_1 x^k \cdot x + a_2 x^k \cdot x^2 + \cdots + a_n x^k \cdot x^n + \cdots$$
$$= a_0 x^k + a_1 x^{k+1} + a_2 x^{k+2} + \cdots + a_n x^{k+n} + \cdots,$$

for all x in the interval of convergence of f.

These properties follow from the properties of derivatives and from the definition of a Taylor series.

305

EXAMPLE 2   Taylor Series

Find Taylor series for the following functions.

(a) $f(x) = 5e^x$

SOLUTION   Use property 2, with $c = 5$, along with the Taylor series for $f(x) = e^x$ given earlier. The Taylor series for $5e^x$ is

$$5 \cdot 1 + 5 \cdot x + 5 \cdot \frac{1}{2!}x^2 + 5 \cdot \frac{1}{3!}x^3 + \cdots + 5 \cdot \frac{1}{n!}x^n + \cdots$$

$$= 5 + 5x + \frac{5}{2!}x^2 + \frac{5}{3!}x^3 + \cdots + \frac{5}{n!}x^n + \cdots$$

for all x in $(-\infty, \infty)$.

(b) $f(x) = x^3 \ln(1 + x)$

SOLUTION   Use the Taylor series for $\ln(1 + x)$ with Property 3. With $k = 3$, this gives the Taylor series for $x^3 \ln(1 + x)$.

YOUR TURN 1   Find Taylor series for the following functions.
(a) $f(x) = -7 \ln(1 + x)$
(b) $g(x) = x^2/(1 - x)$

$$x^3 \cdot x - x^3 \cdot \frac{1}{2}x^2 + x^3 \cdot \frac{1}{3}x^3 - x^3 \cdot \frac{1}{4}x^4 + \cdots + \frac{x^3(-1)^n \cdot x^{n+1}}{n+1} + \cdots$$

$$= x^4 - \frac{1}{2}x^5 + \frac{1}{3}x^6 - \frac{1}{4}x^7 + \cdots + \frac{(-1)^n x^{4+n}}{n+1} + \cdots \quad \text{TRY YOUR TURN 1}$$

To see why the properties are so useful, try writing the Taylor series for $x^3 \ln(1 + x)$ directly from the definition of a Taylor series.

The final property of Taylor series is perhaps the most useful of all.

Composition with Taylor Series

Let a function f have a Taylor series such that

$$f(x) = a_0 + a_1 x + a_2 x^2 + a_3 x^3 + \cdots + a_n x^n + \cdots.$$

Then replacing each x with $g(x) = cx^k$ for some constant c and positive integer k gives the Taylor series for $f[g(x)]$:

$$a_0 + a_1 g(x) + a_2 [g(x)]^2 + a_3 [g(x)]^3 + \cdots + a_n [g(x)]^n + \cdots.$$

The interval of convergence of this new series may be different from that of the first series.

EXAMPLE 3   Composition with Taylor Series

Find the Taylor series for each function.

(a) $f(x) = e^{-x^2/2}$

SOLUTION   We know that the Taylor series for e^x is

$$1 + x + \frac{1}{2!}x^2 + \frac{1}{3!}x^3 + \cdots + \frac{1}{n!}x^n + \cdots$$

for all x in $(-\infty, \infty)$. Use the composition property, and replace each x with $-x^2/2$ to get the Taylor series for $e^{-x^2/2}$.

$$1 + \left(-\frac{x^2}{2}\right) + \frac{1}{2!}\left(-\frac{x^2}{2}\right)^2 + \frac{1}{3!}\left(-\frac{x^2}{2}\right)^3 + \cdots + \frac{1}{n!}\left(-\frac{x^2}{2}\right)^n + \cdots$$

$$= 1 - \frac{1}{2}x^2 + \frac{1}{2!2^2}x^4 - \frac{1}{3!2^3}x^6 + \cdots + \frac{(-1)^n}{n!2^n}x^{2n} + \cdots$$

The Taylor series for $e^{-x^2/2}$ has the same interval of convergence, $(-\infty, \infty)$, as the Taylor series for e^x.

(b) $f(x) = \dfrac{1}{1 + 4x}$

SOLUTION   Write $1/(1 + 4x)$ as

$$\frac{1}{1 + 4x} = \frac{1}{1 - (-4x)},$$

which is $1/(1 - x)$ with x replaced with $-4x$. Start with

$$\frac{1}{1 - x} = 1 + x + x^2 + x^3 + \cdots + x^n + \cdots,$$

which converges for x in $(-1, 1)$, and replace each x with $-4x$ to get

$$\frac{1}{1 + 4x} = \frac{1}{1 - (-4x)}$$
$$= 1 + (-4x) + (-4x)^2 + (-4x)^3 + \cdots + (-4x)^n + \cdots$$
$$= 1 - 4x + 16x^2 - 64x^3 + \cdots + (-1)^n 4^n x^n + \cdots.$$

The interval of convergence of the original series is $(-1, 1)$, or $-1 < x < 1$. Replacing x with $-4x$ gives

$$-1 < -4x < 1 \qquad \text{or} \qquad -\frac{1}{4} < x < \frac{1}{4},$$

so that the interval of convergence of the new series is $(-1/4, 1/4)$.

(c) $f(x) = \dfrac{1}{2 - x^2}$

SOLUTION   This function most nearly matches $1/(1 - x)$. To get 1 in the denominator, instead of 2, divide the numerator and denominator by 2.

$$\frac{1}{2 - x^2} = \frac{1/2}{1 - x^2/2}$$

Thus, we can find the Taylor series for $1/(2 - x^2)$ by starting with the Taylor series for $1/(1 - x)$, multiplying each term by $1/2$, and replacing each x with $x^2/2$.

$$\frac{1}{2 - x^2} = \frac{1/2}{1 - x^2/2}$$
$$= \frac{1}{2} \cdot 1 + \frac{1}{2} \cdot \left(\frac{x^2}{2}\right) + \frac{1}{2}\left(\frac{x^2}{2}\right)^2 + \frac{1}{2}\left(\frac{x^2}{2}\right)^3 + \cdots + \frac{1}{2}\left(\frac{x^2}{2}\right)^n + \cdots$$
$$= \frac{1}{2} + \frac{x^2}{4} + \frac{x^4}{8} + \frac{x^6}{16} + \cdots + \frac{x^{2n}}{2^{n+1}} + \cdots$$

YOUR TURN 2 Find the Taylor series for each function.
(a) $f(x) = \ln(2x^2 + 1)$

(b) $g(x) = \dfrac{3}{4 - x^2}$

The Taylor series for $1/(1 - x)$ is valid when $-1 < x < 1$. Replacing x with $x^2/2$ gives

$$-1 < \frac{x^2}{2} < 1 \qquad \text{or} \qquad -2 < x^2 < 2.$$

This inequality is satisfied by any x in the interval $(-\sqrt{2}, \sqrt{2})$.

TRY YOUR TURN 2

Although we do not go into detail in this text, the Taylor series we discuss may be differentiated and integrated term by term. This result is used in the next example.

EXAMPLE 4 Integrating a Taylor Series

The standard normal curve of statistics is given by

$$f(x) = \frac{1}{\sqrt{2\pi}}e^{-x^2/2}.$$

Find the area bounded by this curve and the lines $x = 0$, $x = 1$, and the x-axis.

SOLUTION The desired area is shown in Figure 12 below. By earlier methods, this area is given by the definite integral

$$\int_0^1 \frac{1}{\sqrt{2\pi}}e^{-x^2/2}dx = \frac{1}{\sqrt{2\pi}}\int_0^1 e^{-x^2/2}dx.$$

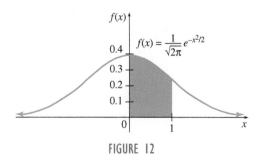

FIGURE 12

This integral cannot be evaluated by any method we have used, but recall that Example 3(a) gave the Taylor series for $f(x) = e^{-x^2/2}$:

$$e^{-x^2/2} = 1 - \frac{1}{2}x^2 + \frac{1}{2!2^2}x^4 - \frac{1}{3!2^3}x^6 + \cdots + \frac{(-1)^n}{n!2^n}x^{2n} + \cdots.$$

An approximation to $\int_0^1 e^{-x^2/2}dx$ can be found by integrating this series term by term. Using, say, the first six terms of this series gives

$$\frac{1}{\sqrt{2\pi}}\int_0^1 e^{-x^2/2}\,dx \approx \frac{1}{\sqrt{2\pi}}\int_0^1\left(1 - \frac{1}{2}x^2 + \frac{1}{2!2^2}x^4 - \frac{1}{3!2^3}x^6 + \frac{1}{4!2^4}x^8 - \frac{1}{5!2^5}x^{10}\right)dx$$

$$= \frac{1}{\sqrt{2\pi}}\int_0^1\left(1 - \frac{1}{2}x^2 + \frac{1}{8}x^4 - \frac{1}{48}x^6 + \frac{1}{384}x^8 - \frac{1}{3840}x^{10}\right)dx$$

$$= \frac{1}{\sqrt{2\pi}}\left(x - \frac{1}{6}x^3 + \frac{1}{40}x^5 - \frac{1}{336}x^7 + \frac{1}{3456}x^9 - \frac{1}{42,240}x^{11}\right)\Big|_0^1$$

$$= \frac{1}{\sqrt{2\pi}}\left(1 - \frac{1}{6} + \frac{1}{40} - \frac{1}{336} + \frac{1}{3456} - \frac{1}{42,240} - 0\right)$$

$$\approx \frac{1}{\sqrt{2(3.1416)}}(0.855623)$$

$$\approx 0.3413.$$

This result agrees with the value 0.3413 obtained from the normal curve table. We could have obtained a more accurate result by using more terms of the Taylor series.

In Example 4, we used terms of the Taylor series for $f(x) = e^{-x^2/2}$ up to the term containing x^{10}. This is exactly the same as finding the Taylor polynomial of degree 10 for the function. In general, taking terms up to degree n of a Taylor series is the same as finding the Taylor polynomial of degree n.

Recall that the **doubling time** (in years) for a quantity that increases at an annual rate r is given by

$$n = \frac{\ln 2}{\ln(1 + r)},$$

and we can approximate n using the rule of 70 and the rule of 72. Now we can derive these rules by using a Taylor series. As shown in the list of common Taylor series,

$$\ln(1 + x) = x - \frac{x^2}{2} + \frac{x^3}{3} - \frac{x^4}{4} + \cdots$$

for x in $(-1, 1]$. Further,

$$\ln(1 + x) = x - \left(\frac{x^2}{2} - \frac{x^3}{3}\right) - \left(\frac{x^4}{4} - \frac{x^5}{5}\right) - \cdots < x$$

because each term in parentheses is positive for x in $(-1, 1]$. Therefore, for $0 < r < 1$, the doubling time,

$$n = \frac{\ln 2}{\ln(1 + r)} = \frac{\ln 2}{r - \frac{r^2}{2} + \frac{r^3}{3} - \frac{r^4}{4} + \cdots},$$

is just slightly larger than the quotient

$$\frac{\ln 2}{r} \approx \frac{0.693}{r} = \frac{69.3}{100r}.$$

Since the actual value of

$$\ln(1 + r) = r - \frac{r^2}{2} + \frac{r^3}{3} - \frac{r^4}{4} + \cdots$$

is slightly smaller than r for $0 < r < 1$, the quotients

$$\frac{70}{100r} \quad \text{and} \quad \frac{72}{100r}$$

give good approximations for the doubling time, the *rule of 70* and the *rule of 72*.

Rule of 70 and Rule of 72

Rule of 70   If a quantity is increasing at a constant rate r compounded annually, where $0.001 \leq r \leq 0.05$,

$$\text{Doubling time} \approx \frac{70}{100r} \text{ years.}$$

Rule of 72   If a quantity is increasing at a constant rate r compounded annually, where $0.05 < r \leq 0.12$, then

$$\text{Doubling time} \approx \frac{72}{100r} \text{ years.}$$

The rule of 70 is used by demographers because populations usually grow at rates of less than 5 percent. The rule of 72 is preferred by economists and investors, since money frequently grows at a rate of between 5 percent and 12 percent. Because the difference between compounding continuously and compounding several times a year is small, both the rule of 70 and the rule of 72 can be used to approximate the doubling time in any interval.

EXAMPLE 5 Doubling Time

Find the doubling time for an investment at each interest rate.

(a) 9%

APPLY IT

SOLUTION By the formula for doubling time, at an interest rate of 9%, money will double in

$$\frac{\ln 2}{\ln(1 + 0.09)} \approx 8 \text{ years.}$$

(b) 1%

SOLUTION At an interest rate of 1%, money will double in

$$\frac{\ln 2}{\ln(1 + 0.01)} \approx 70 \text{ years.}$$

(c) Use the rule of 70 and the rule of 72 to verify the results in parts (a) and (b).

YOUR TURN 3 Repeat Example 5(c) for interest rates of 3.5% and 8%.

SOLUTION The rule of 70 predicts that at a growth rate of 1%, a population will double in 70 years, in agreement with part (b). The rule of 72 predicts that at an interest rate of 9%, money will double in 8 years, in agreement with part (a).   **TRY YOUR TURN 3**

The following table gives the actual doubling time n in years for various growth rates r, together with the approximate doubling times given by the rules of 70 and 72.

Doubling Times													
r	0.001	0.005	0.01	0.02	0.03	0.04	0.05	0.06	0.07	0.08	0.09	0.10	0.11	0.12
n	693	139	69.7	35.0	23.4	17.7	14.2	11.9	10.2	9.0	8.0	7.3	6.6	6.1
$\frac{70}{100r}$	700	140	70	35	23.3	17.5	14	11.7	10	8.8	7.8	7.0	6.4	5.8
$\frac{72}{100r}$	720	144	72	36	24	18	14.4	12	10.3	9	8	7.2	6.5	6

The last row in the table is particularly easy to compute because 72 has so many integral divisors. Therefore, the rule of 72 is frequently used by economists and investors for any interest rate r.

It can be shown that the rule of 70 will give the doubling time with an error of 2% or less if $0.001 \leq n \leq 0.05$, and the rule of 72 will give the doubling time with a 2% error or less if $0.05 < r \leq 0.12$. The above table shows the accuracy of the approximations, and the graph in Figure 13 shows that the graphs of

$$\frac{\ln 2}{\ln(1 + r)}, \quad \frac{70}{100r}, \quad \text{and} \quad \frac{72}{100r}$$

are virtually indistinguishable over the domains just indicated.

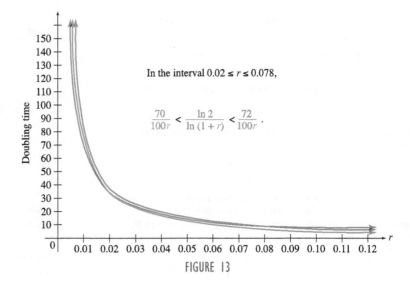

In the interval $0.02 \leq r \leq 0.078$,

$$\frac{70}{100r} < \frac{\ln 2}{\ln(1 + r)} < \frac{72}{100r}.$$

FIGURE 13

5   EXERCISES

Find the Taylor series for the functions defined as follows. Give the interval of convergence for each series.

1. $f(x) = \dfrac{6}{1 - x}$

2. $f(x) = \dfrac{-3}{1 - x}$

3. $f(x) = x^2 e^x$

4. $f(x) = x^5 e^x$

5. $f(x) = \dfrac{5}{2 - x}$

6. $f(x) = \dfrac{-3}{4 - x}$

7. $f(x) = \dfrac{8x}{1 + 3x}$

8. $f(x) = \dfrac{7x}{1 + 2x}$

9. $f(x) = \dfrac{x^2}{4 - x}$

10. $f(x) = \dfrac{9x^4}{1 - x}$

11. $f(x) = \ln(1 + 4x)$

12. $f(x) = \ln\left(1 - \dfrac{x}{2}\right)$

13. $f(x) = e^{4x^2}$

14. $f(x) = e^{-3x^2}$

15. $f(x) = x^3 e^{-x}$

16. $f(x) = x^4 e^{2x}$

17. $f(x) = \dfrac{2}{1 + x^2}$

18. $f(x) = \dfrac{6}{3 + x^2}$

19. $f(x) = \dfrac{e^x + e^{-x}}{2}$

20. $f(x) = \dfrac{e^x - e^{-x}}{2}$

21. $f(x) = \ln(1 + 2x^4)$

22. $f(x) = \ln(1 - 5x^2)$

23. Use the fact that

$$\frac{1 + x}{1 - x} = \frac{1}{1 - x} + \frac{x}{1 - x}$$

to find a Taylor series for $(1 + x)/(1 - x)$.

24. By properties of logarithms,

$$\ln\left(\frac{1 + x}{1 - x}\right) = \ln(1 + x) - \ln(1 - x).$$

Use this to find a Taylor series for $\ln[(1 + x)/(1 - x)]$.

25. Use the Taylor series for e^x to suggest that

$$e^x \approx 1 + x + \frac{x^2}{2}$$

for all x close to zero.

26. Use the Taylor series for e^{-x} to suggest that

$$e^{-x} \approx 1 - x + \frac{x^2}{2}$$

for all x close to zero.

27. Use the Taylor series for e^x to show that

$$e^x \geq 1 + x$$

for all x.

28. Use the Taylor series for e^{-x} to show that

$$e^{-x} \geq 1 - x$$

for all x.

Use the method in Example 4 (with five terms of the appropriate Taylor series) to approximate the areas of the following regions.

29. The region bounded by $f(x) = e^{x^2}$, $x = 0$, $x = 1/3$, and the x-axis

30. The region bounded by $f(x) = 1/(1 - x^3)$, $x = 0$, $x = 1/2$, and the x-axis

31. The region bounded by $f(x) = 1/(1 - \sqrt{x})$, $x = 1/4$, $x = 1/3$, and the x-axis

32. The region bounded by $f(x) = e^{\sqrt{x}}$, $x = 0$, $x = 1$, and the x-axis

As mentioned in Example 4, the equation of the standard normal curve is

$$f(x) = \frac{1}{\sqrt{2\pi}}e^{-x^2/2}.$$

Use the method in Example 4 (with five terms of the Taylor series) to approximate the area of the region bounded by the normal curve, the x-axis, $x = 0$, and the values of x in Exercise 33 and 34.

33. $x = 0.4$ **34.** $x = 0.6$

APPLICATIONS

Business and Economics

35. Investment Ray Mesing has invested \$12,000 in a certificate of deposit that has a 4.75% annual interest rate. Determine the doubling time for this investment using the doubling-time formula. How does this compare with the estimate given by the rule of 70?

36. Investment It is anticipated that a bank stock that Katie Vales has invested \$15,000 in will achieve an annual interest rate of 6%. Determine the doubling time for this investment using the doubling-time formula. How does this compare with the estimate given by the rule of 72?

Life Sciences

37. Infant Mortality Infant mortality is an example of a relatively rare event that can be described by the *Poisson distribution*, for which the probability of x occurrences is given by

$$f(x) = \frac{\lambda^x e^{-\lambda}}{x!}, \qquad x = 0, 1, 2, \ldots$$

a. Verify that f describes a probability distribution by showing that

$$\sum_{x=0}^{\infty} f(x) = 1.$$

b. Calculate the expected value for f, given by

$$\sum_{x=0}^{\infty} xf(x).$$

c. In 2010, the U.S. infant mortality rate was estimated at 6.14 per 1000 live births. Assuming that this is the expected value for a Poisson distribution, find the probability that in a random sample of 1000 live births, there were fewer than 4 cases of infant mortality. *Source: Central Intelligence Agency*.

General Interest

38. Baseball In the year 2010, the proportion of U.S. major league baseball players who were foreign born was 231 out of 833. Suppose we begin to randomly select major league players until we find one who is foreign born. Such an experiment can be described by the *geometric distribution*, for which the probability of success after x tries is given by

$$f(x) = (1 - p)^{x-1}p, \qquad x = 1, 2, 3, \ldots$$

where p is the probability of success on a given try. (*Note:* This formula is only accurate if the number of baseball players is very large, compared with the number that we select before meeting one who is foreign born.) *Source: Major League Baseball*.

a. Verify that f describes a probability distribution by showing that

$$\sum_{x=1}^{\infty} f(x) = 1.$$

b. Calculate the expected value for f, given by

$$\sum_{x=1}^{\infty} xf(x).$$

(*Hint:* Let $g(z) = p\sum_{x=1}^{\infty} z^x$, and evaluate $g'(1 - p)$.)

c. On average, how many major league baseball players would you expect to meet before meeting one who is foreign born?

d. What is the probability that you meet a foreign-born player within the first three major league players that you meet?

39. Trouble In the Milton Bradley game Trouble™, each player takes turns pressing a "popper" that contains a single die. To begin moving a game piece around the board a player must first pop a 6 on the die. The number of tries required to get a 6 can be described by the geometric distribution. (See Exercise 38.)

a. Using the result of Exercise 38b, what is the expected number of times a popper must be pressed before a success occurs?

b. What is the probability that you will have to press the popper four or more times before a 6 pops up?

YOUR TURN ANSWERS

1. (a) $-7x + 7x^2/2 - 7x^3/3 + 7x^4/4 + \cdots + \frac{7(-1)^n x^n}{n} + \cdots$, for all x in $(-1, 1]$

  (b) $x^2 + x^3 + x^4 + \cdots + x^n + \cdots$, for all x in $(-1, 1)$

2. (a) $2x^2 - 2x^4 + (8/3)x^6 - 4x^8 + \cdots + \frac{(-1)^{n+1} 2^n x^{2n}}{n} + \cdots$, for all x in $\left[-\frac{1}{\sqrt{2}}, \frac{1}{\sqrt{2}}\right]$

  (b) $3/4 + 3x^2/16 + 3x^4/64 + 3x^6/256 + \cdots + \frac{3x^{2n}}{4^{n+1}} + \cdots$, for all x in $(-2, 2)$

3. 20 yr; 9 yr

6 Newton's Method

APPLY IT How can the true interest rate be found, given the amount loaned, the number of payments, and the amount of each payment?
We will answer this question in Exercise 34 using a technique developed in this section.

Given a function f, a number r such that $f(r) = 0$ is called a zero of f. For example, if $f(x) = x^2 - 4x + 3$, then $f(3) = 0$ and $f(1) = 0$, so that both 3 and 1 are zeros of f. The zeros of linear and quadratic functions can be found with the methods of algebra. More complicated methods exist for finding zeros of third-degree or fourth-degree polynomial functions, but there is no general method for finding zeros of higher-degree polynomials.

In practical applications of mathematics, it is seldom necessary to find *exact* zeros of a function; usually a decimal approximation is all that is needed. We have seen earlier how a graphing calculator may be used to find approximate values of zeros. In this section, we will explore a calculus-based method to do the same. The method provides a sequence of values, c_1, $c_2, \ldots$, whose limit is the true value in a wide variety of applications. Of course, you may simply prefer to use the `zero` feature on your graphing calculator, but Newton's method is the basis for some of the techniques used by mathematicians to solve more complex problems.

The zeros of a differentiable function f can be approximated as follows. Find a closed interval $[a, b]$ so that $f(a)$ and $f(b)$ are of opposite sign, one positive and one negative. As suggested by Figure 14, this means there must exist at least one value c in the interval (a, b) such that $f(c) = 0$. This number c is a zero of the function f.

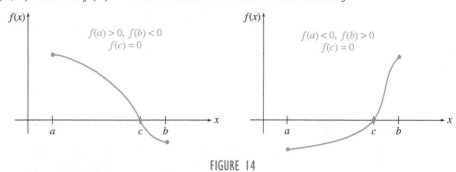

FIGURE 14

To find an approximate value for c, first make a guess for c. Let c_1 be the initial guess. (See Figure 15.) Then locate the point $(c_1, f(c_1))$ on the graph of $y = f(x)$ and identify the tangent line at this point. This tangent line will cut the x-axis at a point c_2. The number c_2 is often a better approximation of c than was c_1.

To locate c_2, first find the equation of the tangent line through $(c_1, f(c_1))$. The slope of this tangent line is $f'(c_1)$. The point-slope form of the equation of the tangent line is

$$y - f(c_1) = f'(c_1)(x - c_1).$$

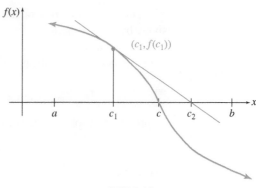

FIGURE 15

313

When $x = c_2$, we know that $y = 0$. Substituting into the equation of the tangent line gives

$$0 - f(c_1) = f'(c_1)(c_2 - c_1)$$

or

$$-\frac{f(c_1)}{f'(c_1)} = c_2 - c_1,$$

from which

$$c_2 = c_1 - \frac{f(c_1)}{f'(c_1)}.$$

If $f'(c_1)$ should be 0, the tangent line would be horizontal and not cut the x-axis. For this reason, assume $f'(c_1) \neq 0$. This new value, c_2, is usually a better approximation to c than was c_1. To improve the approximation further, locate the tangent line to the curve at $(c_2, f(c_2))$. Let this tangent cut the x-axis at c_3. (See Figure 16.) Find c_3 by a process similar to that used above: if $f'(c_2) \neq 0$,

$$c_3 = c_2 - \frac{f(c_2)}{f'(c_2)}.$$

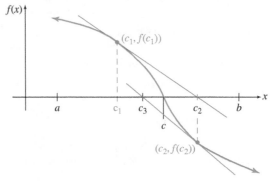

FIGURE 16

The approximation to c often can be improved by repeating this process as many times as desired. In general, if c_n is an approximation to c, a better approximation, c_{n+1}, frequently can be found by the following formula.

Newton's Method
If $f'(c_n) \neq 0$, then

$$c_{n+1} = c_n - \frac{f(c_n)}{f'(c_n)}.$$

This process of first obtaining a rough approximation for c, then replacing it successively by approximations that are often better, is called **Newton's method**, named after Sir Isaac Newton, the codiscoverer of calculus. An early version of this method appeared in his work *Method of Fluxions*, published in 1736.

EXAMPLE 1 **Newton's Method**

Approximate a solution for the equation

$$3x^3 - x^2 + 5x - 12 = 0$$

in the interval $[1, 2]$.

SOLUTION Let $f(x) = 3x^3 - x^2 + 5x - 12$, so that $f'(x) = 9x^2 - 2x + 5$. Check that $f(1) < 0$ with $f(2) > 0$. Since $f(1)$ and $f(2)$ have opposite signs, there is a solution for the equation in the interval $(1, 2)$. As an initial guess, let $c_1 = 1$. A better guess, c_2, can be found as follows.

$$c_2 = c_1 - \frac{f(c_1)}{f'(c_1)} = 1 - \frac{-5}{12} = 1.4167$$

A third approximation, c_3, can now be found.

$$c_3 = c_2 - \frac{f(c_2)}{f'(c_2)} = 1.4167 - \frac{1.6066}{20.230} = 1.3373$$

In the same way,

$$c_4 = 1.3373 - \frac{0.072895}{18.421} = 1.3333 \quad \text{and} \quad c_5 = 1.3333 - \frac{-6.111 \times 10^{-4}}{18.333} = 1.3333.$$

YOUR TURN 1 Approximate a solution for the equation $2x^3 - 5x^2 + 6x - 10 = 0$ on $[1, 3]$.

Subsequent approximations yield no further accuracy, either to the 4 decimal places to which we have rounded or to the digits displayed in a TI-84 Plus calculator. Thus $x = 1.3333$ is a reasonably accurate solution of $3x^3 - x^2 + 5x - 12 = 0$. (The exact solution is $4/3$.)

TRY YOUR TURN 1

TECHNOLOGY NOTE   Newton's method is easily implemented on a graphing calculator. For the previous example on a TI-84 Plus, start by storing 1 in X, the function $f(x)$ in Y_1, and the function $f'(x)$ in Y_2. The command $\text{X} - \text{Y}_1/\text{Y}_2 \to \text{X}$ gives the next value of x. Continue to press the ENTER key for subsequent calculations.

In Example 1 we had to go through five steps to get the degree of accuracy that we wanted. The solutions of similar polynomial equations usually can be found in about as many steps, although other types of equations might require more steps, particularly if the initial guess is far from the true solution.

In any case, if a solution can be found by Newton's method, it usually can be found by a computer in a small fraction of a second. But in some cases, the method will not find the solution, or will only do so for a good initial guess. Figure 17 shows an example in which Newton's method does not give a solution. Because of the symmetry of the graph in Figure 17, all the odd steps (c_3, c_5, and so forth) give c_1, while all the even steps (c_4, c_6, and so forth) give c_2, so the approximations never approach the true solution. Such cases are rare in practice. If you find that Newton's method is not producing a solution, verify that there is a solution, and then try a better initial guess.

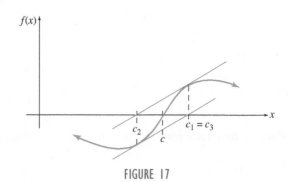

FIGURE 17

Newton's method also can be used to approximate the values of radicals, as shown by the next example.

EXAMPLE 2 Approximation

Approximate $\sqrt{12}$ to the nearest thousandth.

SOLUTION First, note that $\sqrt{12}$ is a solution of the equation $x^2 - 12 = 0$. Therefore, let $f(x) = x^2 - 12$, so that $f'(x) = 2x$. Since $3 < \sqrt{12} < 4$, use $c_1 = 3$ as the first approximation to $\sqrt{12}$. A better approximation is given by c_2:

$$c_2 = 3 - \frac{-3}{6} = 3.5.$$

Now find c_3 and c_4:

$$c_3 = 3.5 - \frac{0.25}{7} = 3.464,$$

YOUR TURN 2 Approximate $\sqrt[3]{15}$ to the nearest thousandth.

$$c_4 = 3.464 - \frac{-0.0007}{6.928} = 3.464.$$

Since $c_3 = c_4 = 3.464$, to the nearest thousandth, $\sqrt{12} = 3.464$.   **TRY YOUR TURN 2**

6 EXERCISES

Use Newton's method to find a solution for each equation in the given intervals. Find all solutions to the nearest hundredth.

1. $5x^2 - 3x - 3 = 0$; $[1, 2]$
2. $2x^2 - 8x + 3 = 0$; $[3, 4]$
3. $2x^3 - 6x^2 - x + 2 = 0$; $[3, 4]$
4. $-x^3 + 4x^2 - 5x + 4 = 0$; $[2, 3]$
5. $-3x^3 + 5x^2 + 3x + 2 = 0$; $[2, 3]$
6. $4x^3 - 5x^2 - 6x + 6 = 0$; $[1, 2]$
7. $2x^4 - 2x^3 - 3x^2 - 5x - 8 = 0$; $[-2, -1], [2, 3]$
8. $3x^4 + 4x^3 - 6x^2 - 2x - 12 = 0$; $[-3, -2], [1, 2]$
9. $4x^{1/3} - 2x^2 + 4 = 0$; $[-3, 0]$
10. $4x^{1/3} - 2x^2 + 4 = 0$; $[0, 3]$
11. $e^x + x - 2 = 0$; $[0, 3]$
12. $e^{2x} + 3x - 4 = 0$; $[0, 3]$
13. $x^2 e^{-x} + x^2 - 2 = 0$; $[0, 3]$
14. $x^2 e^{-x} + x^2 - 2 = 0$; $[-3, 0]$
15. $\ln x + x - 2 = 0$; $[1, 4]$
16. $2 \ln x + x - 3 = 0$; $[1, 4]$

Use Newton's method to find each root to the nearest thousandth.

17. $\sqrt{2}$
18. $\sqrt{3}$
19. $\sqrt{11}$
20. $\sqrt{15}$
21. $\sqrt{250}$
22. $\sqrt{300}$
23. $\sqrt[3]{9}$
24. $\sqrt[3]{15}$
25. $\sqrt[3]{100}$
26. $\sqrt[3]{121}$

Use Newton's method to find the critical points for the functions defined as follows. Approximate them to the nearest hundredth. Decide whether each critical point leads to a relative maximum or a relative minimum.

27. $f(x) = x^3 - 3x^2 - 18x + 4$
28. $f(x) = x^3 + 9x^2 - 6x + 4$
29. $f(x) = x^4 - 3x^3 + 6x - 1$
30. $f(x) = x^4 + 2x^3 - 5x + 2$

31. Use Newton's method to attempt to find a solution for the equation

$$f(x) = (x - 1)^{1/3} = 0$$

by starting with a value very close to 1, which is obviously the true solution. Verify that the approximations get worse with each iteration of Newton's method. This is one of those rare cases in which Newton's method doesn't work at all. Discuss why this is so by considering what happens to the tangent line at $x = 1$.

APPLICATIONS

Business and Economics

32. **Break-Even Point** For a particular product, the revenue and cost functions are

$$R(x) = 10x^{2/3} \quad \text{and} \quad C(x) = 2x - 9$$

Approximate the break-even point to the nearest hundredth.

33. **Manufacturing** A new manufacturing process produces savings of

$$S(x) = x^2 + 40x + 20$$

dollars after x years, with increased costs of

$$C(x) = x^3 + 5x^2 + 9$$

dollars. For how many years, to the nearest hundredth, should the process be used?

34. APPLY IT True Annual Interest Rate Federal government regulations require that people loaning money to consumers disclose the true annual interest rate of the loan. The formulas for calculating this interest rate are very complex. For example, suppose P dollars is loaned, with the money to be repaid in n monthly payments of M dollars each. Then the true annual interest rate is found by solving the equation

$$\frac{1 - (1 + i)^{-n}}{i} - \frac{P}{M} = 0$$

for i, the monthly interest rate, and then multiplying i by 12 to get the true annual rate. This equation can best be solved

by Newton's method. (This is how the financial function IRR (Internal Rate of Return) is computed in Microsoft Excel.)

a. Let $f(i) = \dfrac{1 - (1 + i)^{-n}}{i} - \dfrac{P}{M}$. Find $f'(i)$.

b. Form the quotient $f(i)/f'(i)$.

c. Suppose that $P = \$4000$, $n = 24$, and $M = \$197$. Let the initial guess for i be $i_1 = 0.01$. Use Newton's method and find i_2.

d. Find i_3. (*Note:* For the accuracy required by federal law, it is usually sufficient to stop after two successive values of i differ by no more than 10^{-7}.)

Find i_2 and i_3.

35. $P = \$600$, $M = \$57$, $n = 12$, $i_1 = 0.02$

36. $P = \$15,000$, $M = \$337$, $n = 60$, $i_1 = 0.01$

YOUR TURN ANSWERS

1. 2.177   **2.** 2.466

7 L'Hospital's Rule

Remember back to your study of *limits*. For example,

$$\lim_{x \to 1} \frac{x^2 + 1}{x + 4} = \frac{2}{5},$$

which can be found by direct substitution using the limit rules for a rational function. In this section we will use derivatives to find limits of quotients of functions that could not easily be found using previously learned techniques.

If we try to find

$$\lim_{x \to 1} \frac{x^2 - 1}{x - 1}$$

by evaluating the numerator and denominator at $x = 1$, we get

$$\frac{1^2 - 1}{1 - 1} = \frac{0}{0},$$

an **indeterminate form**. Any attempt to assign a value to $0/0$ leads to a meaningless result. The limit exists, however; as shown earlier, it is found by factoring.

$$\lim_{x \to 1} \frac{x^2 - 1}{x - 1} = \lim_{x \to 1} \frac{(x + 1)(x - 1)}{x - 1} = \lim_{x \to 1} (x + 1) = 2$$

As a second example,

$$\lim_{x \to 1} \frac{\ln x}{(x - 1)^2}$$

also leads to the indeterminate form $0/0$. Selecting values of x close to 1 and using a calculator gives the following table.

x	0.99	0.999	0.9999	1.0001	1.001	1.01
$\dfrac{\ln x}{(x - 1)^2}$	-100.5	-1000.5	$-10,000.5$	9999.5	999.5	99.5

As this table suggests, $\lim_{x \to 1} (\ln x)/(x - 1)^2$ does not exist.

In the first example, trying to find $\lim_{x\to 1}(x^2 - 1)/(x - 1)$ by evaluating the expression at $x = 1$ led to the indeterminate form $0/0$, but factoring the expression led to the actual limit, 2. Evaluating $\lim_{x\to 1}(\ln x)/(x - 1)^2$ in the second example led to the indeterminate form $0/0$, but using a table of values showed that this limit did not exist. **L'Hospital's rule** gives a quicker way to decide whether a quotient with the indeterminate form $0/0$ has a limit.

L'Hospital's Rule

Let f and g be functions and let a be a real number such that

$$\lim_{x\to a} f(x) = 0 \qquad \text{and} \qquad \lim_{x\to a} g(x) = 0,$$

or

$$\lim_{x\to a} f(x) = \pm\infty \qquad \text{and} \qquad \lim_{x\to a} g(x) = \pm\infty.$$

Let f and g have derivatives that exist at each point in some open interval containing a.

If $\lim_{x\to a} \dfrac{f'(x)}{g'(x)} = L$, then $\lim_{x\to a} \dfrac{f(x)}{g(x)} = L$.

If $\lim_{x\to a} \dfrac{f'(x)}{g'(x)}$ does not exist because $\left|\dfrac{f'(x)}{g'(x)}\right|$ becomes large without bound

for values of x near a, then $\lim_{x\to a} \dfrac{f(x)}{g(x)}$ also does not exist.

A partial proof of this rule is given at the end of this section. L'Hospital's rule is another example of a mathematical misnomer. Although named after the Marquis de l'Hospital (1661–1704), it was actually developed by Johann Bernoulli (1667–1748) in a textbook published in 1696. (Johann Bernoulli was the brother of Jakob Bernoulli, mentioned in the section on Antiderivatives.) L'Hospital was a student of Bernoulli and published, with a financial arrangement, the works of his teacher under his own name.

EXAMPLE 1   L'Hospital's Rule

Find $\lim_{x\to 2} \dfrac{3x - 6}{\sqrt{2 + x} - 2}$.

SOLUTION   It is very important to first make sure that the conditions of l'Hospital's rule are satisfied. Here

$$\lim_{x\to 2}(3x - 6) = 0 \qquad \text{and} \qquad \lim_{x\to 2}(\sqrt{2 + x} - 2) = 0.$$

Since the limits of both numerator and denominator are 0, l'Hospital's rule applies. Now take the derivatives of both numerator and denominator separately. (Do *not* use the quotient rule for derivatives.)

For $\quad f(x) = 3x - 6, \quad$ we have $f'(x) = 3$.

For $\quad g(x) = \sqrt{2 + x} - 2, \quad$ we have $g'(x) = \dfrac{1}{2\sqrt{2 + x}}$.

Find the limit of the quotient of the derivatives.

$$\lim_{x \to 2} \frac{f'(x)}{g'(x)} = \lim_{x \to 2} \frac{3}{1/(2\sqrt{2 + x})} = \lim_{x \to 2} 6\sqrt{2 + x} = 12.$$

By l'Hospital's rule, this result is the desired limit:

$$\lim_{x \to 2} \frac{3x - 6}{\sqrt{2 + x} - 2} = 12. \qquad \text{TRY YOUR TURN 1} \quad \blacksquare$$

YOUR TURN 1

Find $\displaystyle\lim_{x \to 4} \frac{3x - 12}{\sqrt[3]{x + 4} - 2}$.

EXAMPLE 2 **L'Hospital's Rule**

Find $\displaystyle\lim_{x \to 1} \frac{\ln x}{(x - 1)^2}$.

SOLUTION Make sure that l'Hospital's rule applies.

$$\lim_{x \to 1} \ln x = \ln 1 = 0 \quad \text{and} \quad \lim_{x \to 1} (x - 1)^2 = 0$$

Since the conditions of l'Hospital's rule are satisfied, we can now take the derivatives of the numerator and denominator separately.

$$D_x(\ln x) = \frac{1}{x} \quad \text{and} \quad D_x[(x - 1)^2] = 2(x - 1)$$

Next, we find the limit of the quotient of these derivatives:

$$\lim_{x \to 1} \frac{1/x}{2(x - 1)} = \lim_{x \to 1} \frac{1}{2x(x - 1)} \text{ does not exist.}$$

YOUR TURN 2

Find $\displaystyle\lim_{x \to 1} \frac{e^{x-1} - 1}{x^2 - 2x + 1}$.

By l'Hospital's rule, this means that

$$\lim_{x \to 1} \frac{\ln x}{(x - 1)^2} \text{ does not exist.} \qquad \text{TRY YOUR TURN 2} \quad \blacksquare$$

Before looking at more examples of l'Hospital's rule, consider the following summary.

Using L'Hospital's Rule

1. Be sure that $\displaystyle\lim_{x \to a} \frac{f(x)}{g(x)}$ leads to the indeterminate form $0/0$ or $\pm \infty / \pm \infty$.
2. Take the derivatives of f and g separately.
3. Find $\displaystyle\lim_{x \to a} \frac{f'(x)}{g'(x)}$; this limit, if it exists, equals $\displaystyle\lim_{x \to a} \frac{f(x)}{g(x)}$.
4. If necessary, apply l'Hospital's rule more than once.

EXAMPLE 3 **L'Hospital's Rule**

Find $\displaystyle\lim_{x \to 0} \frac{x^3}{e^x - 1}$.

SOLUTION The limit in the numerator is 0, as is the limit in the denominator, so that l'Hospital's rule applies. Taking derivatives separately in the numerator and denominator gives

$$\lim_{x \to 0} \frac{3x^2}{e^x} = \frac{0}{e^0} = \frac{0}{1} = 0.$$

YOUR TURN 3

Find $\displaystyle\lim_{x \to 0} \frac{x^3}{\ln(x + 1)}$.

By l'Hospital's rule,

$$\lim_{x \to 0} \frac{x^3}{e^x - 1} = 0. \qquad \text{TRY YOUR TURN 3} \quad \blacksquare$$

EXAMPLE 4   L'Hospital's Rule

Find $\lim\limits_{x \to 0} \dfrac{e^x - x - 1}{x^2}$.

SOLUTION   Find the limit in both the numerator and denominator to verify that l'Hospital's rule applies. Then take derivatives of both the numerator and denominator separately.

$$\lim_{x \to 0} \frac{e^x - 1}{2x} = \frac{e^0 - 1}{2 \cdot 0} = \frac{1 - 1}{0} = \frac{0}{0}$$

The result is still the indeterminate form $0/0$; use l'Hospital's rule a second time. Taking derivatives of $e^x - 1$ and $2x$ gives

$$\lim_{x \to 0} \frac{e^x}{2} = \frac{e^0}{2} = \frac{1}{2}.$$

Finally, by l'Hospital's rule,

$$\lim_{x \to 0} \frac{e^x - x - 1}{x^2} = \frac{1}{2}.$$ TRY YOUR TURN 4

YOUR TURN 4

Find $\lim\limits_{x \to 0} \dfrac{e^{3x} - \frac{9}{2}x^2 - 3x - 1}{x^3}$.

EXAMPLE 5   L'Hospital's Rule

Find $\lim\limits_{x \to 1} \dfrac{x^2 - 1}{\sqrt{x}}$.

SOLUTION   Taking derivatives of the numerator and denominator separately gives

$$\lim_{x \to 1} \frac{2x}{(1/2)x^{-1/2}} = \lim_{x \to 1} 4x^{3/2} = 4 \cdot 1^{3/2} = 4 \cdot 1 = 4. \quad \text{Incorrect}$$

Unfortunately, 4 is the wrong answer. What happened? We did not verify that the conditions of l'Hospital's rule were satisfied. In fact,

$$\lim_{x \to 1}(x^2 - 1) = 0, \quad \text{but} \quad \lim_{x \to 1} \sqrt{x} = 1 \neq 0.$$

Since l'Hospital's rule does not apply, we must use another method to find the limit. By substitution,

$$\lim_{x \to 1} \frac{x^2 - 1}{\sqrt{x}} = \frac{1^2 - 1}{\sqrt{1}} = \frac{0}{1} = 0.$$

L'Hospital's rule also applies when

$$\lim_{x \to a} f(x) = \infty \quad \text{and} \quad \lim_{x \to a} g(x) = \infty.$$

EXAMPLE 6   Limit of $0 \cdot \infty$ or ∞/∞

Find each of the following limits.

(a) $\lim\limits_{x \to 0^+} x \ln x$

SOLUTION   It is not immediately clear what the limit is. The factor x is getting smaller and smaller as x approaches 0, but the factor $\ln x$ is approaching $-\infty$. We have a limit of the form $0 \cdot \infty$. To evaluate this limit, use the fact that

$$x = \frac{1}{1/x}$$

to rewrite the expression as

$$x \ln x = \frac{\ln x}{1/x}.$$

Now both the numerator and the denominator become infinite in magnitude, and l'Hospital's rule applies to limits of the form ∞/∞.

$$\lim_{x \to 0^+} x \ln x = \lim_{x \to 0^+} \frac{\ln x}{1/x} \qquad \text{Rewrite as a quotient of the form } \infty/\infty.$$

$$= \lim_{x \to 0^+} \frac{1/x}{-1/x^2} \qquad \text{Differentiate the numerator and denominator.}$$

$$= \lim_{x \to 0^+} -x \qquad \text{Simplify.}$$

$$= 0$$

Therefore, by l'Hospital's rule,

$$\lim_{x \to 0^+} x \ln x = 0.$$

(b) $\lim_{x \to 0^+} x \, (\ln x)^2.$

SOLUTION This limit has the form $0 \cdot \infty$ and is similar to the limit in part (a), so we will handle it in the same manner.

$$\lim_{x \to 0^+} x \, (\ln x)^2 = \lim_{x \to 0^+} \frac{(\ln x)^2}{1/x} \qquad \text{Rewrite as a quotient of the form } \infty/\infty.$$

$$= \lim_{x \to 0^+} \frac{2(\ln x)(1/x)}{-1/x^2} \qquad \text{Differentiate the numerator and denominator.}$$

$$= \lim_{x \to 0^+} -2x(\ln x) \qquad \text{Simplify.}$$

This problem is similar to what we started with, but with $\ln x$ raised to the first power, rather than the second power. It seems that we have made progress, so let's try the same idea again.

$$\lim_{x \to 0^+} -2x(\ln x) = \lim_{x \to 0^+} \frac{-2 \ln x}{1/x} \qquad \text{Rewrite as a quotient of the form } \infty/\infty.$$

$$= \lim_{x \to 0^+} \frac{-2/x}{-1/x^2} \qquad \text{Differentiate the numerator and denominator.}$$

$$= \lim_{x \to 0^+} 2x \qquad \text{Simplify.}$$

$$= 0$$

YOUR TURN 5 Find $\lim_{x \to 0^+} x^2 \ln(3x)$.

(We could have avoided this second step by noticing that the limit at the end of the first step is just -2 times the limit in part (a).) Therefore, by l'Hospital's rule,

$$\lim_{x \to 0^+} x(\ln x)^2 = 0. \qquad \text{TRY YOUR TURN 5}$$

We could use the same idea as in Example 6 repeatedly to show that

$$\lim_{x \to 0^+} x(\ln x)^n = 0$$

for any positive integer n. You might recognize this limit from curve sketching. We have a way to demonstrate this result. The intuitive reason for this result is that although $\ln x$ approaches $-\infty$ as x approaches 0 from the right, the logarithm is a very slowly changing function, so it doesn't get large very quickly.

Limits at Infinity

L'Hospital's rule also applies to limits at infinity. The next example illustrates this idea.

EXAMPLE 7   Limit at Infinity

Find each of the following limits.

(a) $\lim\limits_{x \to \infty} xe^{-x}$

SOLUTION   As in the previous example, it's not obvious what the limit is. The factor x is getting larger and larger, but the factor e^{-x} is getting smaller and smaller. This is another example of a limit of the form $0 \cdot \infty$. To find out what happens to the product, we will rewrite the product as a quotient. This converts the problem to a limit of the form ∞/∞, as in the previous example.

$$\lim\limits_{x \to \infty} xe^{-x} = \lim\limits_{x \to \infty} \frac{x}{e^x} \qquad \text{Rewrite as a quotient of the form } \infty/\infty.$$

$$= \lim\limits_{x \to \infty} \frac{1}{e^x} \qquad \text{Differentiate the numerator and denominator.}$$

$$= 0$$

Therefore, by l'Hospital's rule.

$$\lim\limits_{x \to \infty} xe^{-x} = 0.$$

(b) $\lim\limits_{x \to \infty} x^n e^{-x}$, where n is a positive integer

SOLUTION   Like the limit in part (a), this limit is of the form $0 \cdot \infty$, and it can be evaluated by rewriting the product as a quotient.

$$\lim\limits_{x \to \infty} x^n e^{-x} = \lim\limits_{x \to \infty} \frac{x^n}{e^x} \qquad \text{Rewrite as a quotient of the form } \infty/\infty.$$

$$= \lim\limits_{x \to \infty} \frac{nx^{n-1}}{e^x} \qquad \text{Differentiate the numerator and denominator.}$$

This leaves us with a new problem similar to the original, but with the numerator of degree one less. We could continue to apply l'Hospital's rule until the numerator becomes $n!$, which happens to x^n when it is differentiated n times. Then

$$\lim\limits_{x \to \infty} \frac{n!}{e^x} = 0.$$

YOUR TURN 6

Find $\lim\limits_{x \to \infty} \dfrac{\ln x}{e^x}$ and $\lim\limits_{x \to \infty} \dfrac{\ln x}{x^2}$.

Therefore, by l'Hospital's rule,

$$\lim\limits_{x \to \infty} x^n e^{-x} = 0. \qquad \text{TRY YOUR TURN 6}$$

The limit in Example 7(b) may be familiar from curve sketching. We have a way to demonstrate this result. The intuitive reason for this result is that e^{-x} approaches 0 very rapidly as x goes to infinity. Alternatively, we could say that e^x gets large much faster than any power of x as x goes to infinity.

Proof of l'Hospital's Rule
Because the proof of l'Hospital's rule is too advanced for this text we will not prove it here. We will, however, prove the theorem for the special case where f, g, f', and g' are continuous on some open interval containing a, and $g'(a) \neq 0$. We will only consider the case in which

$$\lim\limits_{x \to a} f(x) = 0 \qquad \text{and} \qquad \lim\limits_{x \to a} g(x) = 0.$$

The assumption that f and g are continuous means that both $f(a) = 0$ and $g(a) = 0$. Thus,

$$\lim_{x \to a} \frac{f(x)}{g(x)} = \lim_{x \to a} \frac{f(x) - f(a)}{g(x) - g(a)}, \qquad f(a) = 0 \text{ and } g(a) = 0$$

where we subtracted 0 in both the numerator and denominator. Multiplying the numerator and denominator by $1/(x - a)$ gives

$$\lim_{x \to a} \frac{f(x)}{g(x)} = \lim_{x \to a} \frac{\dfrac{f(x) - f(a)}{x - a}}{\dfrac{g(x) - g(a)}{x - a}}.$$

By a property of limits, this becomes

$$\lim_{x \to a} \frac{f(x)}{g(x)} = \frac{\displaystyle\lim_{x \to a} \frac{f(x) - f(a)}{x - a}}{\displaystyle\lim_{x \to a} \frac{g(x) - g(a)}{x - a}}.$$

By the definition of the derivative, the limit in the numerator is $f'(a)$, and the limit in the denominator is $g'(a)$. From our assumption that both f' and g' are continuous, and if $g'(a) \neq 0$, the quotient on the right above becomes

$$\frac{f'(a)}{g'(a)} = \frac{\displaystyle\lim_{x \to a} f'(x)}{\displaystyle\lim_{x \to a} g'(x)} = \lim_{x \to a} \frac{f'(x)}{g'(x)}.$$

Thus,

$$\lim_{x \to a} \frac{f(x)}{g(x)} = \lim_{x \to a} \frac{f'(x)}{g'(x)},$$

which is what we wanted to show.

7   EXERCISES

Use l'Hospital's rule where applicable to find each limit.

1. $\displaystyle\lim_{x \to 1} \frac{x^3 + x^2 - x - 1}{x^2 - x}$

2. $\displaystyle\lim_{x \to 3} \frac{x^3 + x^2 - 11x - 3}{x^2 - 3x}$

3. $\displaystyle\lim_{x \to 0} \frac{x^5 - 2x^3 + 4x^2}{8x^5 - 2x^2 + 5x}$

4. $\displaystyle\lim_{x \to 0} \frac{8x^6 + 3x^4 - 9x}{9x^7 - 2x^4 + x^3}$

5. $\displaystyle\lim_{x \to 2} \frac{\ln(x - 1)}{x - 2}$

6. $\displaystyle\lim_{x \to 0} \frac{\ln(x + 1)}{x}$

7. $\displaystyle\lim_{x \to 0} \frac{e^x - 1}{x^4}$

8. $\displaystyle\lim_{x \to 0} \frac{e^{2x} - 1}{5x^2 - x}$

9. $\displaystyle\lim_{x \to 0} \frac{xe^x}{e^x - 1}$

10. $\displaystyle\lim_{x \to 0} \frac{xe^{-x}}{2e^{2x} - 2}$

11. $\displaystyle\lim_{x \to 0} \frac{e^x}{2x^3 + 9x^2 - 11x}$

12. $\displaystyle\lim_{x \to 0} \frac{e^x}{8x^5 - 3x^4}$

13. $\displaystyle\lim_{x \to 0} \frac{\sqrt{2 + x} - \sqrt{2}}{x}$

14. $\displaystyle\lim_{x \to 0} \frac{\sqrt{9 + x} - 3}{x}$

15. $\displaystyle\lim_{x \to 4} \frac{\sqrt{x} - 2}{x - 4}$

16. $\displaystyle\lim_{x \to 9} \frac{\sqrt{x} - 3}{x - 9}$

17. $\displaystyle\lim_{x \to 8} \frac{\sqrt[3]{x} - 2}{x - 8}$

18. $\displaystyle\lim_{x \to 27} \frac{\sqrt[3]{x} - 3}{x - 27}$

19. $\displaystyle\lim_{x \to 1} \frac{x^9 + 3x^8 + 4x^5 - 8}{x - 1}$

20. $\displaystyle\lim_{x \to 2} \frac{x^7 - 5x^6 + 5x^5 + 32}{x - 2}$

21. $\displaystyle\lim_{x \to 0} \frac{e^x + e^{-x} - 2}{x}$

22. $\displaystyle\lim_{x \to 0} \frac{e^x - 1 + x}{e^{-x} - 1 - x}$

23. $\displaystyle\lim_{x \to 3} \frac{\sqrt{x^2 + 7} - 4}{x^2 - 9}$

24. $\displaystyle\lim_{x \to 5} \frac{\sqrt{x^2 + 11} - 6}{x^2 - 25}$

25. $\displaystyle\lim_{x \to 0} \frac{1 + \frac{1}{3}x - (1 + x)^{1/3}}{x^2}$

26. $\displaystyle\lim_{x \to 0} \frac{2e^{5x} - 25x^2 - 10x - 2}{5x^3}$

27. $\displaystyle\lim_{x \to 0} \frac{\sqrt{1 + x} - \sqrt{1 - x}}{x}$

28. $\displaystyle\lim_{x \to 0} \frac{\sqrt{3 - x} - \sqrt{3 + x}}{x}$

29. $\displaystyle\lim_{x \to 0} \frac{\sqrt{x^2 - 5x + 4}}{x}$

30. $\displaystyle\lim_{x \to 1} \frac{\sqrt{x^2 + 5x + 9}}{x - 1}$

31. $\displaystyle\lim_{x \to 0} \frac{(5 + x)\ln(x + 1)}{e^x - 1}$

32. $\displaystyle\lim_{x \to 0} \frac{(7 - x)\ln(1 - x)}{e^{-x} - 1}$

33. $\lim\limits_{x\to 0^+} x^2 (\ln x)^2$

34. $\lim\limits_{x\to 0^+} x e^{1/x}$

35. $\lim\limits_{x\to 0^+} x \ln(e^x - 1)$

36. $\lim\limits_{x\to\infty} \dfrac{(\ln x)^2}{x}$

37. $\lim\limits_{x\to\infty} \dfrac{\sqrt{x}}{\ln(\ln x)}$

38. $\lim\limits_{x\to\infty} \dfrac{e^{\sqrt{x}}}{x^3}$

39. $\lim\limits_{x\to\infty} \dfrac{\ln(e^x + 1)}{5x}$

40. $\lim\limits_{x\to\infty} \dfrac{\ln(4e^{\sqrt{x}} - 1)}{3\sqrt{x}}$

41. $\lim\limits_{x\to\infty} x^5 e^{-0.001x}$

42. $\lim\limits_{x\to\infty} \dfrac{x^3 + 1}{x^2 \ln x}$

In Exercises 43–46, first get a common denominator; then find the limits that exist.

43. $\lim\limits_{x\to 0}\left(\dfrac{e^x}{x^2} - \dfrac{1}{x^2} - \dfrac{1}{x} \right)$

44. $\lim\limits_{x\to 0}\left(\dfrac{12e^x}{x^3} - \dfrac{12}{x^3} - \dfrac{12}{x^2} - \dfrac{6}{x} \right)$

45. $\lim\limits_{x\to 1}\left(\dfrac{x}{x - 1} - \dfrac{1}{\ln x} \right)$

46. $\lim\limits_{x\to 0}\left(\dfrac{2}{x} - \dfrac{\ln(1 + 2x)}{x^2} \right)$

47. Explain what is wrong with the following calculation using l'Hospital's rule.

$$\lim_{x\to 0} \frac{x^2}{x^2 + 3} = \lim_{x\to 0} \frac{2x}{2x} = 1$$

48. Find the following limit, which is the first one given by l'Hospital in his calculus text *Analysis of Infinitely Small Quantities for the Understanding of Curves*, published in 1696. *Source: A History of Mathematics: An Introduction.*

$$\lim_{x\to a} \frac{\sqrt{2a^3 x - x^4} - a\sqrt[3]{a^2 x}}{a - \sqrt[4]{ax^3}}$$

YOUR TURN ANSWERS

1. 36
2. Does not exist
3. 0
4. 9/2
5. 0
6. 0; 0

CHAPTER REVIEW

SUMMARY

We have provided a brief introduction to the topics of sequences, series, and l'Hospital's rule. Geometric sequences are comparatively simple to analyze and arise in various applications, including annuities. We next investigated infinite series, as well as a particular form known as Taylor series. Because Taylor series have an infinite number of terms, it is often more practical to take a small number of terms, creating Taylor polynomials. We then discussed Newton's method, which produces a sequence that approaches a zero of a function. Finally, l'Hospital's rule provides a method for evaluating certain limits.

General Term of a Geometric Series	$a_n = ar^{n-1}$
Sum of the First n Terms of a Geometric Series	$S_n = \dfrac{a(r^n - 1)}{r - 1}$ for $r \neq 1$
Sum of an Infinite Geometric Series	For $-1 < r < 1$, $\displaystyle\sum_{n=1}^{\infty} ar^{n-1} = \dfrac{a}{1 - r}$
Amount of an Annuity	$S = R\left[\dfrac{(1 + i)^n - 1}{i} \right]$ or $S = R \cdot s_{\overline{n}|i}$
Present Value of an Annuity	$P = R\left[\dfrac{1 - (1 + i)^{-n}}{i} \right]$ or $P = R \cdot a_{\overline{n}|i}$
Rule of 70	For a rate of increase r compounded annually, where $0.001 \le r \le 0.05$, $\text{Doubling Time} \approx \dfrac{70}{100r}$ years.

Rule of 72   For a rate of increase r compounded annually, where $0.05 < r \le 0.12$,

$$\text{Doubling Time} \approx \frac{72}{100r} \text{ years.}$$

Taylor Polynomial at 0 $P_n(x) = \sum_{i=0}^{n} \frac{f^{(i)}(0)}{i!} x^i$

Taylor Series at 0 $f(x) = \sum_{i=0}^{\infty} \frac{f^{(i)}(0)}{i!} x^i$

Taylor Series for e^x $e^x = \sum_{i=0}^{\infty} \frac{1}{i!} x^i$ for $-\infty < x < \infty$

Taylor Series for ln (1 + x) $\ln(1 + x) = \sum_{i=1}^{\infty} \frac{(-1)^{i+1}}{i} x^i$ for $-1 < x \le 1$

Taylor Series for $\dfrac{1}{1-x}$ $\dfrac{1}{1-x} = \sum_{i=0}^{\infty} x^i$ for $-1 < x < 1$

Newton's Method   If $f'(c_n) \ne 0$, then

$$c_{n+1} = c_n - \frac{f(c_n)}{f'(c_n)}.$$

L'Hospital's Rule   If $\lim\limits_{x \to a} f(x) = \lim\limits_{x \to a} g(x) = 0$ or $\lim\limits_{x \to a} f(x) = \pm\infty$ and $\lim\limits_{x \to a} g(x) = \pm\infty$, then

$$\lim_{x \to a} \frac{f(x)}{g(x)} = \lim_{x \to a} \frac{f'(x)}{g'(x)}.$$

KEY TERMS

1
sequence
element
term
general term
nth term
geometric sequence
common ratio

2
annuity
ordinary annuity

payment period
term of an annuity
amount of an annuity
sinking fund
present value of an
  annuity
amortization

3
Taylor polynomial
Taylor polynomial of
  degree n

4
infinite series
nth partial sum
sum of an infinite
  series
convergence
divergence

5
interval of convergence
Taylor series

Maclaurin series
doubling time
rule of 70
rule of 72

6
Newton's method

7
indeterminate form
l'Hospital's rule

REVIEW EXERCISES

CONCEPT CHECK

Determine whether each of the following statements is true or false, and explain why.

1. In a geometric sequence, the ratio between any two consecutive terms is a constant.

2. The amounts paid into an annuity form a geometric sequence.

3. A loan is amortized if both the principal and interest are paid by a sequence of equal periodic payments.

4. The Taylor polynomial of degree 4 for f at 0 has the same second derivative as f at 0.

5. The Taylor polynomial of degree 4 for f at 0 has the same fifth derivative as f at 0.

6. The Taylor polynomial of a discontinuous function is continuous.

7. An infinite geometric series converges as long as $-1 \le r \le 1$.

8. If an infinite series doesn't converge, then it diverges.

9. The Taylor series for e^x at 0 converges for all x.

10. The Taylor series for ln (1 + x) at 0 converges for all x.

11. Newton's method converges as long as there is a real root and the function is differentiable.

12. L'Hospital's rule says that to take the derivative of a quotient, divide the derivative of the numerator by the derivative of the denominator.

PRACTICE AND EXPLORATIONS

Find a_4 and a_n for the following geometric sequences. Then find the sum of the first five terms.

13. $a_1 = 5, r = -2$

14. $a_1 = 128, r = 1/2$

15. $a_1 = 27, r = 1/3$

16. $a_1 = 2, r = -5$

Find Taylor polynomials of degree 4 at 0 for the functions defined as follows.

17. $f(x) = e^{2-x}$

18. $f(x) = 5e^{2x}$

19. $f(x) = \sqrt{x + 1}$

20. $f(x) = \sqrt[3]{x + 27}$

21. $f(x) = \ln(2 - x)$

22. $f(x) = \ln(3 + 2x)$

23. $f(x) = (1 + x)^{2/3}$

24. $f(x) = (4 + x)^{3/2}$

Use Taylor polynomials of degree 4 at $x = 0$, found in Exercises 17–24 above, to approximate the quantities in Exercises 25–32. Round to 4 decimal places.

25. $e^{1.93}$

26. $5e^{0.04}$

27. $\sqrt{1.03}$

28. $\sqrt[3]{26.94}$

29. $\ln 2.05$

30. $\ln 3.06$

31. $0.92^{2/3}$

32. $4.02^{3/2}$

Identify the geometric series that converge. Give the sum of each convergent series.

33. $9 - 6 + 4 - 8/3 + \cdots$

34. $2 + 1.4 + 0.98 + 0.686 + \cdots$

35. $3 + 9 + 27 + 81 + \cdots$

36. $4 + 4.8 + 5.76 + 6.912 + \cdots$

37. $\dfrac{2}{5} - \dfrac{2}{25} + \dfrac{2}{125} - \dfrac{2}{625} + \cdots$

38. $36 + 3 + \dfrac{1}{4} + \dfrac{1}{48} + \cdots$

In Exercises 39–40, the nth term of a sequence is given. Calculate the first five partial sums.

39. $a_n = \dfrac{1}{2n - 1}$

40. $a_n = \dfrac{1}{(n + 2)(n + 3)}$

Use the Taylor series given in the text to find the Taylor series for the functions defined as follows. Give the interval of convergence of each series.

41. $f(x) = \dfrac{4}{3 - x}$

42. $f(x) = \dfrac{2x}{1 + 3x}$

43. $f(x) = \dfrac{x^2}{x + 1}$

44. $f(x) = \dfrac{3x^3}{2 - x}$

45. $f(x) = \ln(1 - 2x)$

46. $f(x) = \ln\left(1 + \dfrac{1}{3}x\right)$

47. $f(x) = e^{-2x^2}$

48. $f(x) = e^{-5x}$

49. $f(x) = 2x^3e^{-3x}$

50. $f(x) = x^6e^{-x}$

Use l'Hospital's rule, where applicable, to find each limit.

51. $\lim\limits_{x \to 2} \dfrac{x^3 - x^2 - x - 2}{x^2 - 4}$

52. $\lim\limits_{x \to 0} \dfrac{x^3 - 4x^2 + 6x}{3x}$

53. $\lim\limits_{x \to -5} \dfrac{x^3 - 3x^2 + 4x - 1}{x^2 - 25}$

54. $\lim\limits_{x \to 0} \dfrac{\ln(3x + 1)}{x}$

55. $\lim\limits_{x \to 0} \dfrac{5e^x - 5}{x^3 - 8x^2 + 7x}$

56. $\lim\limits_{x \to 0} \dfrac{\sqrt{5 + x} - \sqrt{5}}{x}$

57. $\lim\limits_{x \to 0} \dfrac{-xe^{2x}}{e^{2x} - 1}$

58. $\lim\limits_{x \to 16} \dfrac{\sqrt{x} - 4}{x - 16}$

59. $\lim\limits_{x \to 0} \dfrac{1 + 2x - (1 + x)^{1/2}}{x^3}$

60. $\lim\limits_{x \to 0} \dfrac{\sqrt{5 + x} - \sqrt{5 - x}}{2x}$

61. $\lim\limits_{x \to \infty} x^2 e^{-\sqrt{x}}$

62. $\lim\limits_{x \to \infty} \dfrac{\sqrt{x}}{\ln(x^3 + 1)}$

In Exercises 63–66, first get a common denominator; then find the limits that exist.

63. $\lim\limits_{x \to 0} \left(\dfrac{e^{3x}}{x^2} - \dfrac{1}{x^2} - \dfrac{3}{x}\right)$

64. $\lim\limits_{x \to 0} \left(\dfrac{2}{x^3} + \dfrac{2}{x^2} + \dfrac{1}{x} - \dfrac{2e^x}{x^3}\right)$

65. $\lim\limits_{x \to 0} \left(\dfrac{\ln(1 - 4x)}{x^2} + \dfrac{4}{x}\right)$

66. $\lim\limits_{x \to 0} \left(\dfrac{1}{x^3} + \dfrac{1}{x^2}\right)$

Use Newton's method to find a solution to the nearest hundredth for each equation in the given interval.

67. $x^3 - 8x^2 + 18x - 12 = 0; \quad [4, 5]$

68. $3x^3 - 4x^2 - 4x - 7 = 0; \quad [2, 3]$

69. $x^4 + 3x^3 - 4x^2 - 21x - 21 = 0; \quad [2, 3]$

70. $x^4 + x^3 - 14x^2 - 15x - 15 = 0; \quad [3, 4]$

Use Newton's method to approximate each radical to the nearest thousandth.

71. $\sqrt{37.6}$

72. $\sqrt{51.7}$

73. $\sqrt[3]{94.7}$

74. $\sqrt[4]{102.6}$

APPLICATIONS
Business and Economics

75. Total Income A mine produced $750,000 of income during its first year. Each year thereafter, income increased by 18%. Find the total income produced in the first 8 years of the mine's life.

76. Sinking Fund In 4 years, Jack McCanna must pay a pledge of $5000 to his church's building fund. He wants to set up a sinking fund to accumulate that amount. What should each semiannual payment into the fund be at 8% compounded semiannually?

77. Annuity Cathy Schneider deposits $491 at the end of each quarter for 9 years. If the account pays 9.4% compounded quarterly, find the final amount in the account.

78. Annuity J. Euclid deposits $1526.38 at the end of each 6-month period in an account paying 7.6% compounded semiannually. How much will be in the account after 5 years?

79. Amortization Diane Antaya borrows $20,000 from the bank to help her expand her business. She agrees to repay the money in equal payments at the end of each year for 9 years. Interest is at 8.9% compounded annually. Find the amount of each payment.

80. Amortization Ross Craycraft wants to expand his pharmacy. To do this, he takes out a bank loan of $49,275 and agrees to repay it at 12.2% compounded monthly over 48 months. Find the amount of each payment necessary to amortize this loan.

House Payments **Find the monthly house payments for the following mortgages.**

81. $156,890 at 7.74% for 25 years

82. $177,110 at 8.45% for 30 years

83. Investment Michael Dew has invested $14,000 in a certificate of deposit that has a 3.25% annual interest rate. Determine the doubling time for this investment using the doubling-time formula. How does this compare with the estimate given by the rule of 70?

84. Investment It is anticipated that a bank stock that Jeff Marsalis has invested $16,000 in will achieve an annual interest rate of 9%. Determine the doubling time for this investment using the doubling-time formula. How does this compare with the estimate given by the rule of 72?

Life Sciences

85. Bacteria At a summer picnic, the number of bacteria in a bowl of potato salad doubles every 20 minutes. Assume that there are 1000 bacteria at the beginning of the picnic. How many bacteria are present after 2 hours, assuming that no one has eaten any of the potato salad?

Social Sciences

86. Crime The number of reported crimes in a city was about 22,700 in a recent year. Due to the creation of a neighborhood crime program, the city hopes the number of crimes decreases each year by 8%. Let x_n denote the number of crimes in the city n years after the neighborhood crime program began. Find a formula for x_n in terms of n. Determine the number of crimes in the city at the end of five years.

EXTENDED APPLICATION

LIVING ASSISTANCE AND SUBSIDIZED HOUSING

M r. Jones receives living assistance, in the form of a monthly stipend from the State of New York. He is also living in subsidized housing. This means that the amount he pays in rent depends on his income. He has entered into contracts with the State of New York and his landlord specifying how his stipend and rent are computed. The unusual aspect of these contracts is that, to a degree, each depends on the other. Thus a single change in one contract leads to a potentially infinite sequence of changes in both contracts.

The relevant portion of the contract between the State of New York and Mr. Jones is:

The State of New York agrees to pay Mr. Jones a monthly stipend of $1000. This figure is arrived at by considering his living expenses. The stipend will be increased or decreased by 30% of any increase or decrease in rent.

Mr. Jones is also living in subsidized housing and has worked out a contract with his landlord that specifies: *The monthly rent is $300. However, if Mr. Jones's income increases during the period of the contract, the monthly rent will be increased by 20% of the change.*

The situation gets complicated shortly after Mr. Jones receives the good news that his stipend from the government is being increased by $100/month to $1100/month. As required, he reports to his landlord that his income has increased, and, as specified in his contract, his rent increases by 20% of $100. Thus his new rent is $300 + $20 = $320.

Since the contract with the State of New York has a housing allowance built in to it, he reports his $20 rent increase to the state, and his monthly stipend of $1100 is increased by 30% of $20 to $1100 + $6 = $1106.

At this point it becomes clear that Mr. Jones is facing a never ending sequence of stipend and rent adjustments. Although it looks like the adjustments are eventually going to be quite small, he knows he must honor both contracts, and this is going to require a lot of round trips and paperwork. On his way back to his landlord with the news that his state stipend had been raised from $1000 to $1100 to $1106, Mr. Jones decided to consult a lawyer.

The lawyer took a look at the contracts and decided to consult a mathematician to see if it is mathematically possible to make sense of an unending sequence of stipend and rent hikes. As we shall see, this is exactly what infinite series are made for.

To help recognize the pattern, notice that the next term in the infinite series for the state stipend is 30% of the last rent increase, that is, $0.3 \times 20 = \$6$. In other words, every time the state decides to increase the stipend by x, the landlord increases the rent by $0.2x$, and the state is obligated to increase the stipend by $0.3(0.2x) = 0.06x$.

The infinite series for the state stipend (in dollars) is

$$\text{Stipend} = 1000 + 100 + 0.06(100) + (0.06)^2(100) + \cdots.$$

After the first term, this is a geometric series with $r = 0.06$; thus, the sum is $\$1000 + \$100/(1 - 0.06) = \$1,106.38$.

The analysis of the rent is similar. Each rent hike of y dollars is followed by a stipend increase of $0.3y$ and a subsequent rent increase $0.2(0.3y) = 0.06y$. Thus, the infinite series for rent (in dollars) is

$$\text{Rent} = 300 + 20 + 0.06(20) + (0.06)^2(20) + \cdots,$$

which converges to $\$300 + \$20/(1 - 0.06) = \$321.28$.

There is a surprising aspect to this problem. The interrelated nature of the contracts seems to demand an infinite series solution;

yet, it can also be solved without using infinite series. How can this be possible?

The key is to anticipate that the original $100 increase in stipend is going to necessitate subsequent increases. So we can express the ultimate stipend as $1000 + $100 + S, where S is yet to be determined. Similarly, the rent will ultimately be $300 + R, where R also needs to be determined. The question becomes, can we find values of S and R such that neither contract is violated?

Mr. Jones's contract with the state requires that his stipend be increased by 30% of the change in his rent, that is $S = 0.3R$. On the other hand, his contract with his landlord requires that his 20% stipend increase of $100 + S$ be included in his rent, or in terms of equations, $0.2(100 + S) = R$. In Exercise 1, you will show that solving these simultaneous equations leads to the same stipend and rent as found with infinite series.

EXERCISES

1. Find values for S and R that satisfy $S = 0.3R$ and $0.2(100 + S) = R$. Show that these solutions give the same stipend and rent as found by summing the infinite series.

2. Suppose that instead of a stipend increase of $100, the state cuts Mr. Jones's stipend by $50. Assuming that Mr. Jones is able to convince his landlord that he should have his rent decreased by 20% of the change, this also leads to an infinite cycle of stipend and rent changes. Express his stipend and rent as infinite series, and find the sum of each series.

3. Eastville is located 12 miles from Westville. The town councils decide to pool resources and build a single fire station to serve the needs of both towns. The negotiations on where to build the fire station start with both towns proposing the fire station be built in their town. The impasse is broken when Eastville proposes to move the site halfway to Westville, i.e., 6 miles to the west. Westville in turn proposes to move the site halfway to the Eastville proposed site, i.e., 3 miles to the east. This sets off an infinite round of negotiations in which each party proposes moving the site halfway towards the other's previous proposal. Give an infinite series expressing the changes in location proposed by Eastville, and give a similar

series for the changes proposed by Westville. Where is the fire station eventually located? (*Hint:* The surest way to recognize a pattern is to work out a few terms, and this calls for simple, but careful, record keeping. Initial separation is 12 miles. Eastville moves 6 miles. Now the separation is 6 miles. Westville moves 3 miles. Separation is 3 miles. Eastville moves 3/2 miles. Separation is . . .)

4. There was enough money leftover after building the fire station in Exercise 3 for a swimming pool. This time, Eastville and Westville approach the negotiations more warily. Eastville starts by suggesting the pool be located just 1/3 of the way towards Westville. From that point on, Westville agrees to split the difference, while at every stage, Eastville proposes moving the pool just 1/3 of the way towards Westville's last proposal. Are the towns able to reach an agreement on the final location of the pool?

5. The sum of the series for the stipend paid to Mr. Jones is approximately $1,106.3829787. Understandably, an accountant for the State of New York would view this as needless precision. To gain an appreciation of how quickly geometric series converge, particularly with a small value of R, like 0.06, use a calculator to answer the following questions. How many terms of the series do you need to add up so that the sum is within one dollar of the final answer? How many terms do you need to add up to be within a dime or a penny of the final answer?

6. Not all series converge as quickly as geometric series. We know from Section 5

$$\ln(2) = 1 - 1/2 + 1/3 - 1/4 + 1/5 \ldots,$$

so the nth term of this series is $(-1)^{n+1}/n$. Use the website WolframAlpha.com to decide how many terms you need to add up so the sum is within 0.01 of $\ln(2)$. To sum a series on WolframAlpha.com, enter the following:

sum <formula for nth term of your series> from $n =$ <first value of n> to <final value of n, and this can even be infinity>.

ANSWERS TO SELECTED EXERCISES

Exercises 1

1. 2, 6, 18, 54 **3.** 1/2, 2, 8, 32 **5.** 3/2, 3, 6, 12, 24

7. $a_5 = 324$; $a_n = 4(3)^{n-1}$ **9.** $a_5 = -1875$; $a_n = -3(-5)^{n-1}$

11. $a_5 = 3/2$; $a_n = 24/2^{n-1}$ **13.** $a_5 = -256$; $a_n = -(-4)^{n-1}$ **15.** $r = 2$; $a_n = 6(2)^{n-1}$ **17.** $r = 2$; $a_n = (3/4)(2)^{n-1}$

19. Not geometric **21.** $r = -2/3$; $a_n = (-5/8)(-2/3)^{n-1}$ **23.** 93 **25.** 33/4 **27.** 33 **29.** 464.4 **31.** 2040

33. 262,143/2 **35.** 183/4 **37.** 511/4 **39. a.** \$3932 **b.** \$2013 **41.** 2^{30} or \$1,073,741,824; $2^{31} - \$1$ or \$2,147,483,647

43. About 41% **45.** About 95 times **47. a.** $1 + 2 + 2^2 + 2^3 + 2^4 + 2^5$ **b.** 63 **c.** $1 + 2 + 2^2 + \cdots + 2^{n-1} = 2^n - 1$

For exercises . . .	1 6	7 22	23 30	31 38	39,42,43, 44–46	40,41, 47,48
Refer to example . . .	1	2	4	5	3	6

Exercises 2

(*Note:* Answers in this section may differ by a few cents, depending on how calculators are used.)

For exercises . . .	1–6,31, 37–40	7–10,32	11–14, 33–36, 41–43	15–24, 44–47	25–30,48, 53,54	49–52	55–58
Refer to example . . .	1	2	3,4	5	6	8	7

1. \$1509.35 **3.** \$278,150.87 **5.** \$833,008.00

7. \$205,785.64 **9.** \$142,836.33 **11.** \$526.95 **13.** \$952.33 **15.** \$39,434.37 **17.** \$17,585.54 **19.** \$1,367,773.96

21. \$111,183.87 **23.** \$97,122.49 **25.** \$476.90 **27.** \$11,942.55 **29.** \$1673.21 **31. a.** \$132,318.77 **b.** \$121,909.27

c. \$10,409.50 **33. a.** \$491.54 **b.** \$533.42 **35.** \$1398.12 **37.** \$112,796.87 **39.** \$209,348.00

41. a. \$1200 **b.** \$3511.58 **c.**

Payment Number	Amount of Deposit	Interest Earned	Total
1	\$3511.58	\$0	\$3511.58
2	\$3511.58	\$105.35	\$7128.51
3	\$3511.58	\$213.86	\$10,853.95
4	\$3511.58	\$325.62	\$14,691.15
5	\$3511.58	\$440.73	\$18,643.46
6	\$3511.58	\$559.30	\$22,714.34
7	\$3511.58	\$681.43	\$26,907.35
8	\$3511.58	\$807.22	\$31,226.15
9	\$3511.58	\$936.78	\$35,674.51
10	\$3511.58	\$1070.24	\$40,256.33
11	\$3511.58	\$1207.69	\$44,975.60
12	\$3511.58	\$1349.27	\$49,836.45
13	\$3511.58	\$1495.09	\$54,843.12
14	\$3511.59	\$1645.29	\$60,000.00

43. a. \$32.49 **b.** \$195.52; \$10.97 **45.** \$12,493.78

47. a. \$623,110.52 **b.** \$456,427.28 **c.** \$563,757.78 **d.** \$392,903.18 **49.** \$1885.00; \$229,612.44 **51.** \$2583.01; \$336,107.59 **53. a.** \$4025.90 **b.** \$2981.93

55.

Payment Number	Amount of Payment	Interest for Period	Portion to Principal	Principal at End of Period
0	—	—	—	\$4000
1	\$1207.68	\$320.00	\$887.68	\$3112.32
2	\$1207.68	\$248.99	\$958.69	\$2153.63
3	\$1207.68	\$172.29	\$1035.39	\$1118.24
4	\$1207.70	\$89.46	\$1118.24	\$0

57.

Payment Number	Amount of Payment	Interest for Period	Portion to Principal	Principal at End of Period
0	—	—	—	—
1	\$183.93	\$62.86	\$121.07	\$7062.93
2	\$183.93	\$61.80	\$122.13	\$6940.80
3	\$183.93	\$60.73	\$123.20	\$6817.60
4	\$183.93	\$59.65	\$124.28	\$6693.32
5	\$183.93	\$58.57	\$125.36	\$6567.96
6	\$183.93	\$57.47	\$126.46	\$6441.50

Exercises 3

1. $1 - 2x + 2^2x^2/2! - 2^3x^3/3! + 2^4x^4/4!$ or $1 - 2x + 2x^2 - (4/3)x^3 + (2/3)x^4$

3. $e + ex + ex^2/2! + ex^3/3! + ex^4/4!$ or $e + ex + ex^2/2 + ex^3/6 + ex^4/24$

5. $3 + x/6 - x^2/216 + x^3/3888 - (5/279{,}936)x^4$

7. $-1 + x/3 + x^2/9 + (5/81)x^3 + (10/243)x^4$ **9.** $1 + x/4 - (3/32)x^2 + (7/128)x^3 - (77/2048)x^4$

11. $-x - x^2/2 - x^3/3 - x^4/4$ **13.** $2x^2 - 2x^4$ **15.** $x - x^2 + x^3/2 - x^4/6$ **17.** $27 - (9/2)x + x^2/8 + x^3/432 + x^4/10{,}368$

19. $1 - x + x^2 - x^3 + x^4$ **21.** 0.9608 **23.** 2.7732 **25.** 2.9866 **27.** -1.0164 **29.** 1.0147 **31.** -0.0305 **33.** 0.0080

35. $P_3(x) = 3 + 6x + 6x^2 + 4x^3$ **37. b.** 4.04167; actual value is 4.04124. **39. a.** $1 + \lambda N + \lambda^2 N^2/2$ **b.** $N = \sqrt{2k/\lambda}$

41. \$4623; \$4623 **43.** \$718; \$718

For exercises . . .	1–20,35–39, 40–44,45,46	21–34,40–44
Refer to example . . .	1,2,4	3,5

Exercises 4

1. Converges to 40 **3.** Diverges **5.** Converges to 81/2 **7.** Converges to 1000/9

9. Converges to 5/2 **11.** Converges to 1/5 **13.** Converges to $e^2/(e + 1)$

15. $S_1 = 1; S_2 = 3/2; S_3 = 11/6; S_4 = 25/12; S_5 = 137/60$

17. $S_1 = 1/7; S_2 = 16/63; S_3 = 239/693; S_4 = 3800/9009; S_5 = 22{,}003/45{,}045$

19. $S_1 = 1/6; S_2 = 1/4; S_3 = 3/10; S_4 = 1/3; S_5 = 5/14$ **21.** 2/9 **23. a.** First 3.12; second 2.90 **b.** 38

25. a. \$2000 **b.** 10 **27.** d **29.** 70 meters **31.** 200 centimeters **33.** $4\sqrt{3}/3$ square meters **35. a.** 10/9 sec **b.** 10/9 sec

For exercises . . .	1–14, 21,22, 24,26–33	15–20	25	34,35,36
Refer to example . . .	2	1	4	3

Exercises 5

1. $6 + 6x + 6x^2 + 6x^3 + \cdots + 6x^n + \cdots; (-1, 1)$

3. $x^2 + x^3 + x^4/2! + x^5/3! + \cdots + x^{n+2}/n! + \cdots; (-\infty, \infty)$

5. $5/2 + (5/2^2)x + (5/2^3)x^2 + (5/2^4)x^3 + \cdots + (5/2^{n+1})x^n + \cdots; (-2, 2)$

7. $8x - 8 \cdot 3x^2 + 8 \cdot 3^2x^3 - 8 \cdot 3^3x^4 + \cdots + (-1)^n \cdot 8 \cdot 3^nx^{n+1} + \cdots; (-1/3, 1/3)$

9. $x^2/4 + x^3/4^2 + x^4/4^3 + x^5/4^4 + \cdots + x^{n+2}/4^{n+1} + \cdots; (-4, 4)$

11. $4x - (4^2/2)x^2 + (4^3/3)x^3 - (4^4/4)x^4 + \cdots + (-1)^n4^{n+1}x^{n+1}/(n + 1) + \cdots; (-1/4, 1/4]$

13. $1 + 4x^2 + (4^2/2!)x^4 + (4^3/3!)x^6 + \cdots + (4^n/n!)x^{2n} + \cdots; (-\infty, \infty)$

15. $x^3 - x^4 + x^5/2! - x^6/3! + \cdots + (-1)^nx^{n+3}/n! + \cdots; (-\infty, \infty)$

17. $2 - 2x^2 + 2x^4 - 2x^6 + \cdots + (-1)^n2x^{2n} + \cdots; (-1, 1)$

19. $1 + x^2/2! + x^4/4! + x^6/6! + \cdots + x^{2n}/(2n)! + \cdots; (-\infty, \infty)$

21. $2x^4 - (2^2/2)x^8 + (2^3/3)x^{12} - (2^4/4)x^{16} + \cdots + (-1)^n 2^{n+1}x^{4n+4}/(n + 1) + \cdots; [-1/\sqrt[4]{2}, 1/\sqrt[4]{2}]$

23. $1 + 2x + 2x^2 + 2x^3 + \cdots + 2x^n + \cdots$ **29.** 0.3461 **31.** 0.1729 **33.** 0.1554 **35.** About 14.94 years; about 14.74 years; a

difference of 0.2 years, or about 10 weeks **37. b.** λ **c.** 0.1391 **39. a.** 6 **b.** 0.5787

For exercises . . .	1–4,23	5–22,24, 37–39	29–34	35,36
Refer to example . . .	2	3	4	5

Exercises 6

1. 1.13 **3.** 3.06 **5.** 2.24 **7.** $-1.13, 2.37$ **9.** -0.58 **11.** 0.44 **13.** 1.25 **15.** 1.56

17. 1.414 **19.** 3.317 **21.** 15.811 **23.** 2.080 **25.** 4.642 **27.** Relative maximum at -1.65; relative minimum at 3.65

29. Relative minima at -0.71 and 1.77; relative maximum at 1.19 **33.** 4.80 years **35.** $i_2 = 0.02075485; i_3 = 0.02075742$

For exercises . . .	1–16,27–30,32–36	17–26
Refer to example . . .	1	2

Exercises 7

1. 4 **3.** 0 **5.** 1 **7.** Does not exist **9.** 1

11. Does not exist **13.** $1/(2\sqrt{2})$ or $\sqrt{2}/4$ **15.** 1/4

17. 1/12 **19.** 53 **21.** 0 **23.** 1/8 **25.** 1/9 **27.** 1

29. Does not exist **31.** 5 **33.** 0 **35.** 0

37. ∞ (does not exist) **39.** 1/5 **41.** 0

43. 1/2 **45.** 1/2 **47.** $\lim_{x \to 0}(x^2 + 3) \neq 0$, so l'Hospital's rule does not apply.

For exercises . . .	1–3,5,6, 8–10,13–24, 27,28,31,32, 43–46	4,7	11,12, 29,30, 47	25,26	33–36	37–42
Refer to example . . .	1,3	2	5	4	6	7

Chapter Review Exercises

For exercises . . .	1, 13–16, 75, 85,86	2,3, 76–82	4 6, 17–32	7,8, 33–40	9,10, 41–50, 83,84	11, 67–74	12, 51–66
Refer to section . . .	1	2	3	4	5	6	7

1. True **2.** False **3.** True **4.** True **5.** False
6. True **7.** False **8.** True **9.** True **10.** False
11. False **12.** False **13.** -40; $a_n = 5(-2)^{n-1}$; 55
15. 1; $a_n = 27(1/3)^{n-1}$; 121/3 **17.** $e^2 - e^2x + (e^2/2!)x^2 - (e^2/3!)x^3 + (e^2/4!)x^4$
19. $1 + x/2 - x^2/8 + x^3/16 - (5/128)x^4$ **21.** $\ln 2 - x/2 - x^2/8 - x^3/24 - x^4/64$
23. $1 + (2/3)x - x^2/9 + (4/81)x^3 - (7/243)x^4$ **25.** 6.8895 **27.** 1.0149 **29.** 0.7178 **31.** 0.9459 **33.** Converges to 27/5
35. Diverges **37.** Converges to 1/3 **39.** $S_1 = 1$; $S_2 = 4/3$; $S_3 = 23/15$; $S_4 = 176/105$; $S_5 = 563/315$
41. $4/3 + (4/3^2)x + (4/3^3)x^2 + (4/3^4)x^3 + \cdots + (4/3^{n+1})x^n + \cdots$; $(-3,3)$
43. $x^2 - x^3 + x^4 - x^5 + \cdots + (-1)^n x^{n+2} + \cdots$; $(-1,1)$
45. $-2x - (2^2/2)x^2 - (2^3/3)x^3 - (2^4/4)x^4 - \cdots - 2^{n+1}x^{n+1}/(n+1) - \cdots$; $[-1/2, 1/2)$
47. $1 - 2x^2 + (2^2/2!)x^4 - (2^3/3!)x^6 + \cdots + (-1)^n(2^n/n!)x^{2n} + \cdots$; $(-\infty, \infty)$
49. $2x^3 - 2 \cdot 3x^4 + (2 \cdot 3^2/2!)x^5 - (2 \cdot 3^3/3!)x^6 + \cdots + (-1)^n(2 \cdot 3^n/n!)x^{n+3} + \cdots$; $(-\infty, \infty)$ **51.** 7/4 **53.** Does not exist
55. 5/7 **57.** $-1/2$ **59.** Does not exist **61.** 0 **63.** 9/2 **65.** -8 **67.** 4.73 **69.** 2.65 **71.** 6.132
73. 4.558 **75.** \$11,495,247 **77.** \$27,320.71 **79.** \$3322.43 **81.** \$1184.01 **83.** About 21.67 years; about 21.54 years; differ by 0.13 years, or about 7 weeks **85.** 64,000 bacteria

CREDITS

Exercise 38: Professor Robert D. Campbell Exercise 27: Copyright © Society of Actuaries. Used by permission.
Exercise 28: Copyright © Society of Actuaries. Used by permission.

Systems of Linear Equations and Matrices

Systems of Linear Equations and Matrices

The synchronized movements of band members marching on a field can be modeled using matrix arithmetic. An exercise in Section 5 in this chapter shows how multiplication by a matrix inverse transforms the original positions of the marchers into their new coordinates as they change direction.

1

any mathematical models require finding the solutions of two or more equations. The solutions must satisfy *all* of the equations in the model. A set of equations related in this way is called a **system of equations**. In this chapter we will discuss systems of equations, introduce the idea of a *matrix*, and then show how matrices are used to solve systems of equations.

Solution of Linear Systems by the Echelon Method

APPLY IT

How much of each ingredient should be used in an animal feed to meet dietary requirements?

APPLY IT

Suppose that an animal feed is made from two ingredients: corn and soybeans. One serving of each ingredient provides the number of grams of protein and fiber shown in the table. For example, the entries in the first column, 3 and 11, indicate that one serving of corn provides 3 g of protein and 11 g of fiber.

Nutritional Content of Ingredients		
	Corn	Soybeans
Protein	3	10
Fiber	11	4

Now suppose we want to know how many servings of corn and soybeans should be used to make a feed that contains 115 g of protein and 95 g of fiber. Let x represent the number of servings of corn used and y the number of servings of soybeans. Each serving of corn provides 3 g of protein, so the amount of protein provided by x servings of corn is $3x$. Similarly, the amount of protein provided by y servings of soybeans is $10y$. Since the total amount of protein is to be 115 g,

$$3x + 10y = 115.$$

The feed must supply 95 g of fiber, so

$$11x + 4y = 95.$$

Solving this problem means finding values of x and y that satisfy this system of equations. Verify that $x = 5$ and $y = 10$ is a solution of the system, since these numbers satisfy both equations. In fact, this is the only solution of this system. Many practical problems lead to such a system of *first-degree equations*.

A **first-degree equation in n unknowns** is any equation of the form

$$a_1x_1 + a_2x_2 + \cdots + a_nx_n = k,$$

where $a_1, a_2, \ldots, a_n$ and k are real numbers and $x_1, x_2, \ldots, x_n$ represent variables.* Each of the two equations from the animal feed problem is a first-degree equation. For example, the first equation

$$3x + 10y = 115$$

---

*a_1 is read "a-sub-one." The notation $a_1, a_2, \ldots, a_n$ represents n real-number coefficients (some of which may be equal), and the notation $x_1, x_2, \ldots, x_n$ represents n different variables, or unknowns.

is a first-degree equation with $n = 2$ where

$$a_1 = 3, \qquad a_2 = 10, \qquad k = 115,$$

and the variables are x and y. We use x_1, x_2, etc., rather than x, y, etc., in the general case because we might have any number of variables. When n is no more than 4, we usually use x, y, z, and w to represent x_1, x_2, x_3, and x_4.

A *solution* of the first-degree equation

$$a_1x_1 + a_2x_2 + \cdots + a_nx_n = k$$

is a sequence of numbers $s_1, s_2, \ldots, s_n$ such that

$$a_1s_1 + a_2s_2 + \cdots + a_ns_n = k.$$

A solution of an equation is usually written in parentheses as $(s_1, s_2, \ldots, s_n)$. For example, $(1, 6, 2)$ is a solution of the equation $3x_1 + 2x_2 - 4x_3 = 7$, since $3(1) + 2(6) - 4(2) = 7$. This is an extension of the idea of an ordered pair. A solution of a first-degree equation in two unknowns is an ordered pair, and the graph of the equation is a straight line. For this reason, all first-degree equations are also called linear equations.

Because the graph of a linear equation in two unknowns is a straight line, there are three possibilities for the solutions of a system of two linear equations in two unknowns.

Types of Solutions for Two Equations in Two Unknowns

1. The two graphs are lines intersecting at a single point. The system has a **unique solution**, and it is given by the coordinates of this point. See Figure 1(a).

2. The graphs are distinct parallel lines. When this is the case, the system is **inconsistent**; that is, there is no solution common to both equations. See Figure 1(b).

3. The graphs are the same line. In this case, the equations are said to be **dependent**, since any solution of one equation is also a solution of the other. There are infinitely many solutions. See Figure 1(c).

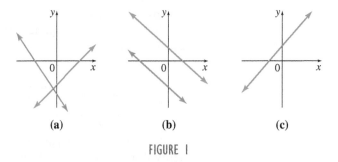

FIGURE 1

In larger systems, with more variables or more equations (or both, as is usually the case), there also may be exactly one solution, no solution, or infinitely many solutions. With more than two variables, the geometrical interpretation becomes more complicated, so we will only consider the geometry of two variables in two unknowns. We will, however, look at the algebra of two equations in three unknowns. In the next section, we will show how to handle any number of equations in any number of unknowns.

By now, you've used the graphing method and the substitution method to find the solution to a pair of equations describing the supply and demand for a commodity. The graphing method does not necessarily give an exact answer, and the substitution method becomes awkward with larger systems. In this section we will demonstrate a method to determine solutions using the addition property of equality to eliminate variables. This method forms the basis of the more general method presented in the next section.

Transformations

To solve a linear system of equations, we use properties of algebra to change, or transform, the system into a simpler *equivalent* system. An **equivalent system** is one that has the same solution(s) as the given system. Algebraic properties are the basis of the following transformations.

Transformations of a System

The following transformations can be applied to a system of equations to get an equivalent system:

1. exchanging any two equations;
2. multiplying both sides of an equation by any nonzero real number;
3. replacing any equation by a nonzero multiple of that equation plus a nonzero multiple of any other equation.

Use of these transformations leads to an equivalent system because each transformation can be reversed or "undone," allowing a return to the original system.

The Echelon Method

A systematic approach for solving systems of equations using the three transformations is called the **echelon method**. The goal of the echelon method is to use the transformations to rewrite the equations of the system until the system has a triangular form.

For a system of two equations in two variables, for example, the system should be transformed into the form

$$x + ay = b$$
$$y = c,$$

where a, b, and c are constants. Then the value for y from the second equation can be substituted into the first equation to find x. This is called **back substitution**. In a similar manner, a system of three equations in three variables should be transformed into the form

$$x + ay + bz = c$$
$$y + dz = e,$$
$$z = f.$$

EXAMPLE 1 Solving a System of Equations with a Unique Solution

Solve the system of equations from the animal feed example that began this section:

$$3x + 10y = 115 \qquad (1)$$
$$11x + 4y = 95. \qquad (2)$$

SOLUTION   We first use transformation 3 to eliminate the x-term from equation (2). We multiply equation (1) by 11 and add the results to -3 times equation (2).

$$
\begin{aligned}
11(3x + 10y) &= 11 \cdot 115 \\
-3(11x + 4y) &= -3 \cdot 95
\end{aligned}
\rightarrow
\begin{aligned}
33x + 110y &= 1265 \\
\underline{-33x - 12y = -285} \\
98y = 980
\end{aligned}
$$

We will indicate this process by the notation $11R_1 + (-3)R_2 \rightarrow R_2$. (R stands for the row.) The new system is

$$3x + 10y = 115 \qquad (1)$$
$$11R_1 + (-3)R_2 \rightarrow R_2 \qquad 98y = 980 \qquad (3)$$

337

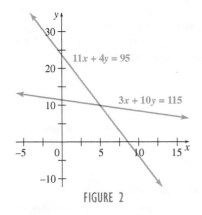

FIGURE 2

YOUR TURN 1

Solve the system

$2x + 3y = 12$

$3x - 4y = 1$.

Now we use transformation 2 to make the coefficient of the first term in each row equal to 1. Here, we must multiply equation (1) by 1/3 and equation (3) by 1/98 to accomplish this.

We get the system

$$\tfrac{1}{3}R_1 \rightarrow R_1 \qquad x + \frac{10}{3}y = \frac{115}{3}$$

$$\tfrac{1}{98}R_2 \rightarrow R_2 \qquad\qquad y = 10.$$

Back-substitution gives

$$x + \frac{10}{3}(10) = \frac{115}{3} \qquad \text{Substitute } y = 10.$$

$$x + \frac{100}{3} = \frac{115}{3}$$

$$x = \frac{115}{3} - \frac{100}{3}$$

$$= \frac{15}{3} = 5.$$

The solution of the system is $(5, 10)$. The graphs of the two equations in Figure 2 suggest that $(5, 10)$ satisfies both equations in the system. **TRY YOUR TURN 1**

The echelon method, as illustrated in Example 1, is a specific case of a procedure known as the *elimination method*. The elimination method allows for any variable to be eliminated. For example, the variable y in Equations (1) and (2) could be eliminated by calculating $2R_1 - 5R_2$. In the echelon method, the goal is to get the system into the specific form described just before Example 1.

EXAMPLE 2 **Solving a System of Equations with No Solution**

Solve the system

$$2x - 3y = 6 \tag{1}$$

$$-4x + 6y = 8. \tag{2}$$

SOLUTION Eliminate x in equation (2) to get the system

$$2x - 3y = 6 \tag{1}$$

$$2R_1 + R_2 \rightarrow R_2 \qquad 0 = 20. \tag{3}$$

In equation (3), both variables have been eliminated, leaving a *false statement*. This means it is impossible to have values of x and y that satisfy both equations, because this leads to a contradiction. To see why this occurs, see Figure 3, where we have shown that the graph of the system consists of two parallel lines. A solution would be a point lying on both lines, which is impossible. We conclude that the system is inconsistent and has no solution.

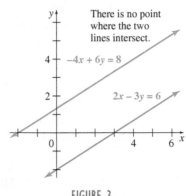

FIGURE 3

EXAMPLE 3 Solving a System of Equations with an Infinite Number of Solutions

Solve the system

$$3x - y = 4 \tag{1}$$
$$-6x + 2y = -8. \tag{2}$$

SOLUTION We use transformation 3 to eliminate x in equation (2), getting the system

$$3x - y = 4 \tag{1}$$
$$2R_1 + R_2 \rightarrow R_2 \qquad 0 = 0. \tag{3}$$

The system becomes

$$\tfrac{1}{3}R_1 \rightarrow R_1 \qquad x - \frac{1}{3}y = \frac{4}{3} \tag{4}$$
$$0 = 0. \tag{3}$$

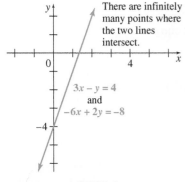

There are infinitely many points where the two lines intersect.

$3x - y = 4$
and
$-6x + 2y = -8$

FIGURE 4

In equation (3), both variables have been eliminated, leaving a *true statement*. If we graph the original equations of the system on the same axes, as shown in Figure 4, we see that the graphs are the same line, and any point on the line will satisfy the system. This indicates that one equation was simply a multiple of the other. This system is dependent and has an infinite number of solutions.

We will express the solutions in terms of y, where y can be any real number. The variable y in this case is called a **parameter**. (We could also let x be the parameter. In this text, we will follow the common practice of letting the rightmost variable be the parameter.) Solving equation (4) for x gives $x = (1/3)y + 4/3 = (y + 4)/3$, and all ordered pairs of the form

$$\left(\frac{y + 4}{3}, y \right)$$

are solutions. For example, if we let $y = 5$, then $x = (5 + 4)/3 = 3$ and one solution is $(3, 5)$. Similarly, letting $y = -10$ and $y = 3$ gives the solutions $(-2, -10)$ and $(7/3, 3)$.

Note that the original two equations are solved not only by the particular solutions like $(3, 5)$, $(-2, -10)$, and $(7/3, 3)$ but also by the general solution $(x, y) = ((y + 4)/3, y)$. For example, substituting this general solution into the first equation gives

$$3\left(\frac{y + 4}{3} \right) - y = y + 4 - y = 4,$$

which verifies that this general solution is indeed a solution.

In some applications, x and y must be nonnegative integers. For instance, in Example 3, if x and y represent the number of male and female workers in a factory, it makes no sense to have $x = 7/3$ or $x = -2$. To make both x and y nonnegative, we solve the inequalities

$$\frac{y + 4}{3} \geq 0 \qquad \text{and} \qquad y \geq 0,$$

yielding

$$y \geq -4 \qquad \text{and} \qquad y \geq 0.$$

To make these last two inequalities true, we require $y \geq 0$, from which $y \geq -4$ automatically follows. Furthermore, to ensure $(y + 4)/3$ is an integer, it is necessary that y be 2 more than a whole-number multiple of 3. Therefore, the possible values of y are 2, 5, 8, 11, and so on, and the corresponding values of x are 2, 3, 4, 5, and so on.

The echelon method can be generalized to systems with more equations and unknowns. Because systems with three or more equations are more complicated, however, we will postpone those to the next section, where we will show a procedure for solving them based on the echelon system. Meanwhile, we summarize the echelon method here. To solve a linear system in n variables, perform the following steps using the three transformations given earlier.

Echelon Method of Solving a Linear System

1. If possible, arrange the equations so that there is an x_1-term in the first equation, an x_2-term in the second equation, and so on.
2. Eliminate the x_1-term in all equations after the first equation.
3. Eliminate the x_2-term in all equations after the second equation.
4. Eliminate the x_3-term in all equations after the third equation.
5. Continue in this way until the last equation has the form $ax_n = k$, for constants a and k, if possible.
6. Multiply each equation by the reciprocal of the coefficient of its first term.
7. Use back-substitution to find the value of each variable.

Applications

The mathematical techniques in this text will be useful to you only if you are able to apply them to practical problems. To do this, always begin by reading the problem carefully. Next, identify what must be found. Let each unknown quantity be represented by a variable. (It is a good idea to *write down* exactly what each variable represents.) Now reread the problem, looking for all necessary data. Write those down, too. Finally, look for one or more sentences that lead to equations or inequalities. The next example illustrates these steps.

EXAMPLE 4   Flight Time

A flight leaves New York at 8 P.M. and arrives in Paris at 9 A.M. (Paris time). This 13-hour difference includes the flight time plus the change in time zones. The return flight leaves Paris at 1 P.M. and arrives in New York at 3 P.M. (New York time). This 2-hour difference includes the flight time *minus* time zones, plus an extra hour due to the fact that flying westward is against the wind. Find the actual flight time eastward and the difference in time zones.

SOLUTION   Let x be the flight time eastward and y be the difference in time zones. For the trip east, the flight time plus the change in time zones is 13 hours, so

$$x + y = 13.$$

For the trip west, the flight time (which is $x + 1$ hours due to the wind) minus the time zone is 2 hours, so

$$(x + 1) - y = 2.$$

Subtract 1 from both sides of this equation, and then solve the system

$$x + y = 13$$
$$x - y = \ 1$$

YOUR TURN 2   Solve Example 4 for the case in which there is a 16-hour time difference on the trip from New York, a 2-hour difference on the return trip, and no wind.

using the echelon method.

$$x + y = 13$$
$$\mathbf{R}_1 + (-1)\mathbf{R}_2 \rightarrow \mathbf{R}_2 \qquad 2y = 12$$

Dividing the last equation by 2 gives $y = 6$. Substituting this into the first equation gives $x + 6 = 13$, so $x = 7$. Therefore, the flight time eastward is 7 hours, and the difference in time zones is 6 hours.   TRY YOUR TURN 2

EXAMPLE 5   Integral Solutions

A restaurant owner orders a replacement set of knives, forks, and spoons. The box arrives containing 40 utensils and weighing 141.3 oz (ignoring the weight of the box). A knife, fork, and spoon weigh 3.9 oz, 3.6 oz, and 3.0 oz, respectively.

(a) How many solutions are there for the number of knives, forks, and spoons in the box?

SOLUTION   Let

$$x = \text{the number of knives;}$$
$$y = \text{the number of forks;}$$
$$z = \text{the number of spoons.}$$

A chart is useful for organizing the information in a problem of this type.

	Number and Weight of Utensils			
	Knives	Forks	Spoons	Total
Number	x	y	z	40
Weight	3.9	3.6	3.0	141.3

Because the box contains 40 utensils,

$$x + y + z = 40.$$

The x knives weigh $3.9x$ ounces, the y forks weigh $3.6y$ ounces, and the z spoons weigh $3.0z$ ounces. Since the total weight is 141.3 oz, we have the system

$$x + \quad y + \quad z = \quad 40$$
$$3.9x + 3.6y + 3.0z = 141.3.$$

Solve using the echelon method.

$$x + \quad y + \quad z = 40$$
$$3.9\mathbf{R}_1 + (-1)\mathbf{R}_2 \rightarrow \mathbf{R}_2 \qquad 0.3y + 0.9z = 14.7$$

We do not have a third equation to solve for z, as we did in Example 4. We could thus let z be any real number, and then use this value of z in the second equation to find a corresponding value of y. These values of y and z could be put into the first equation to find a corresponding value of x. This system, then, has an infinite number of solutions. Letting z be the parameter, solve the second equation for y to get

$$y = \frac{14.7 - 0.9z}{0.3} = 49 - 3z.$$

Substituting this into the first equation, we get

$$x + (49 - 3z) + z = 40.$$

Solving this for x gives

$$x = 2z - 9.$$

Thus, the solutions are $(2z - 9, 49 - 3z, z)$, where z is any real number.

Now that we have solved for x and y in terms of z, let us investigate what values z can take on. This application demands that the solutions be nonnegative integers. The number of forks cannot be negative, so set

$$49 - 3z \geq 0.$$

Solving for z gives

$$z \leq \frac{49}{3} \approx 16.33.$$

Also, the number of knives cannot be negative, so set

$$2z - 9 \geq 0.$$

Solving for z gives

$$z \geq \frac{9}{2} = 4.5.$$

Therefore, the permissible values of z are 5, 6, 7, . . . , 16, for a total of 12 solutions.

YOUR TURN 3 Find the solution with the largest number of spoons.

(b) Find the solution with the smallest number of spoons.

SOLUTION The smallest value of z is $z = 5$, from which we find $x = 2(5) - 9 = 1$ and $y = 49 - 3(5) = 34$. This solution has 1 knife, 34 forks, and 5 spoons.

TRY YOUR TURN 3

EXERCISES

Use the echelon method to solve each system of two equations in two unknowns. Check your answers.

1. $x + y = 5$
$2x - 2y = 2$

2. $4x + y = 9$
$3x - y = 5$

3. $3x - 2y = -3$
$5x - y = 2$

4. $2x + 7y = -8$
$-2x + 3y = -12$

5. $3x + 2y = -6$
$5x - 2y = -10$

6. $-3x + y = 4$
$2x - 2y = -4$

7. $6x - 2y = -4$
$3x + 4y = 8$

8. $4m + 3n = -1$
$2m + 5n = 3$

9. $5p + 11q = -7$
$3p - 8q = 25$

10. $12s - 5t = 9$
$3s - 8t = -18$

11. $6x + 7y = -2$
$7x - 6y = 26$

12. $3a - 8b = 14$
$a - 2b = 2$

13. $3x + 2y = 5$
$6x + 4y = 8$

14. $9x - 5y = 1$
$-18x + 10y = 1$

15. $3x - 2y = -4$
$-6x + 4y = 8$

16. $3x + 5y + 2 = 0$
$9x + 15y + 6 = 0$

17. $x - \dfrac{3y}{2} = \dfrac{5}{2}$
$\dfrac{4x}{3} + \dfrac{2y}{3} = 6$

18. $\dfrac{x}{5} + 3y = 31$
$2x - \dfrac{y}{5} = 8$

19. $\dfrac{x}{2} + y = \dfrac{3}{2}$
$\dfrac{x}{3} + y = \dfrac{1}{3}$

20. $\dfrac{x}{9} + \dfrac{y}{6} = \dfrac{1}{3}$
$2x + \dfrac{8y}{5} = \dfrac{2}{5}$

21. An inconsistent system has _____ solutions.

22. The solution of a system with two dependent equations in two variables is _____.

For each of the following systems of equations in echelon form, tell how many solutions there are in nonnegative integers.

23. $x + 2y + 3z = 90$
$3y + 4z = 36$

24. $x - 7y + 4z = 75$
$2y + 7z = 60$

25. $3x + 2y + 4z = 80$
$y - 3z = 10$

26. $4x + 2y + 3z = 72$
$2y - 3z = 12$

27. Describe what a parameter is and why it is used in systems of equations with an infinite number of solutions.

28. In your own words, describe the echelon method as used to solve a system of two equations in three variables.

Solve each system of equations. Let z be the parameter.

29. $2x + 3y - z = 1$
$3x + 5y + z = 3$

30. $3x + y - z = 0$
$2x - y + 3z = -7$

31. $x + 2y + 3z = 11$
$2x - y + z = 2$

32. $-x + y - z = -7$
$2x + 3y + z = 7$

33. In Exercise 9 in Section 1.3, you were asked to solve the system of least squares line equations

$$nb + (\Sigma x)m = \Sigma y$$
$$(\Sigma x)b + (\Sigma x^2)m = \Sigma xy$$

by the method of substitution. Now solve the system by the echelon method to get

$$m = \frac{n(\Sigma xy) - (\Sigma x)(\Sigma y)}{n(\Sigma x^2) - (\Sigma x)^2}$$

$$b = \frac{\Sigma y - m(\Sigma x)}{n}.$$

34. The examples in this section did not use the first transformation. How might this transformation be used in the echelon method?

APPLICATIONS

Business and Economics

35. Groceries   If 20 lb of rice and 10 lb of potatoes cost $16.20, and 30 lb of rice and 12 lb of potatoes cost $23.04, how much will 10 lb of rice and 50 lb of potatoes cost?

36. Sales   An apparel shop sells skirts for $45 and blouses for $35. Its entire stock is worth $51,750. But sales are slow and only half the skirts and two-thirds of the blouses are sold, for a total of $30,600. How many skirts and blouses are left in the store?

37. Sales   A theater charges $8 for main floor seats and $5 for balcony seats. If all seats are sold, the ticket income is $4200. At one show, 25% of the main floor seats and 40% of the balcony seats were sold and ticket income was $1200. How many seats are on the main floor and how many are in the balcony?

38. Stock   Lorri Morgan has $16,000 invested in Disney and Exxon stock. The Disney stock currently sells for $30 a share and the Exxon stock for $70 a share. Her stockbroker points out that if Disney stock goes up 50% and Exxon stock goes up by $35 a share, her stock will be worth $25,500. Is this possible? If so, tell how many shares of each stock she owns. If not, explain why not.

39. Production   A company produces two models of bicycles, model 201 and model 301. Model 201 requires 2 hours of assembly time and model 301 requires 3 hours of assembly time. The parts for model 201 cost $18 per bike and the parts for model 301 cost $27 per bike. If the company has a total of 34 hours of assembly time and $335 available per day for these two models, how many of each should be made in a day to use up all available time and money? If it is not possible, explain why not.

40. Banking   A bank teller has a total of 70 bills in five-, ten-, and twenty-dollar denominations. The total value of the money is $960.

a. Find the total number of solutions.

b. Find the solution with the smallest number of five-dollar bills.

c. Find the solution with the largest number of five-dollar bills.

41. Production   Felsted Furniture makes dining room furniture. A buffet requires 30 hours for construction and 10 hours for finishing. A chair requires 10 hours for construction and 10 hours for finishing. A table requires 10 hours for construction and 30 hours for finishing. The construction department has 350 hours of labor and the finishing department has 150 hours of labor available each week. How many pieces of each type of furniture should be produced each week if the factory is to run at full capacity?

42. Rug Cleaning Machines   Kelly Karpet Kleaners sells rug cleaning machines. The EZ model weighs 10 lb and comes in a 10-cubic-ft box. The compact model weighs 20 lb and comes in an 8-cubic-ft box. The commercial model weighs 60 lb and comes in a 28-cubic-ft box. Each of their delivery vans has 248 cubic ft of space and can hold a maximum of 440 lb. In order for a van to be fully loaded, how many of each model should it carry?

43. Production   Turley Tailor, Inc. makes long-sleeve, short-sleeve, and sleeveless blouses. A long-sleeve blouse requires 1.5 hours of cutting and 1.2 hours of sewing. A short-sleeve blouse requires 1 hour of cutting and 0.9 hour of sewing. A sleeveless blouse requires 0.5 hour of cutting and 0.6 hour of sewing. There are 380 hours of labor available in the cutting department each day and 330 hours in the sewing department. If the plant is to run at full capacity, how many of each type of blouse should be made each day?

44. Broadway Economics   When Neil Simon opens a new play, he has to decide whether to open the show on Broadway or Off Broadway. For example, in his play *London Suite*, he decided to open it Off Broadway. From information provided by Emanuel Azenberg, his producer, the following equations were developed:

$$43,500x - y = 1,295,000$$
$$27,000x - y = 440,000,$$

where x represents the number of weeks that the show has run and y represents the profit or loss from the show (first equation is for Broadway and second equation is for Off Broadway). *Source: The Mathematics Teacher.*

a. Solve this system of equations to determine when the profit/loss from the show will be equal for each venue. What is the profit at that point?

b. Discuss which venue is favorable for the show.

Life Sciences

45. Birds   The date of the first sighting of robins has been occurring earlier each spring over the past 25 years at the Rocky Mountain Biological Laboratory. Scientists from this laboratory have developed two linear equations that estimate the date of the first sighting of robins:

$$y = 759 - 0.338x$$
$$y = 1637 - 0.779x,$$

where x is the year and y is the estimated number of days into the year when a robin can be expected. *Source: Proceedings of the National Academy of Science.*

a. Compare the date of first sighting in 2000 for each of these equations. (*Hint:* 2000 was a leap year.)

b. Solve this system of equations to find the year in which the two estimates agree.

Physical Sciences

46. Stopping Distance   The stopping distance of a car traveling 25 mph is 61.7 ft, and for a car traveling 35 mph it is 106 ft. The stopping distance in feet can be described by the equation $y = ax^2 + bx$, where x is the speed in mph. *Source: National Traffic Safety Institute.*

a. Find the values of a and b.

b. Use your answers from part a to find the stopping distance for a car traveling 55 mph.

General Interest

47. Basketball   Wilt Chamberlain holds the record for the highest number of points scored in a single NBA basketball game.

Chamberlain scored 100 points for Philadelphia against the New York Knicks on March 2, 1962. This is an amazing feat, considering he scored all of his points without the help of three-point shots. Chamberlain made a total of 64 baskets, consisting of field goals (worth two points) and foul shots (worth one point). Find the number of field goals and the number of foul shots that Chamberlain made. *Source: ESPN.*

48. The 24® Game   The object of the 24® Game, created by Robert Sun, is to combine four numbers, using addition, subtraction, multiplication, and/or division, to get the number 24. For example, the numbers 2, 5, 5, 4 can be combined as $2(5 + 5) + 4 = 24$. For the algebra edition of the game and the game card shown to the right, the object is to find single-digit positive integer values x and y so the four numbers $x + y$, $3x + 2y$, 8, and 9 can be combined to make 24. *Source: Suntex.*

a. Using the game card, write a system of equations that, when solved, can be used to make 24 from the game card. What is the solution to this system, and how can it be used to make 24 on the game card?

b. Repeat part a and develop a second system of equations.

YOUR TURN ANSWERS

1. (3, 2)
2. Flight time is 9 hours, difference in time zones is 7 hours.
3. 23 knives, 1 fork, and 16 spoons

2   Solution of Linear Systems by the Gauss-Jordan Method

APPLY IT   How can an auto manufacturer with more than one factory and several dealers decide how many cars to send to each dealer from each factory? *Questions like this are called transportation problems; they frequently lead to a system of equations that must be satisfied. In Exercise 52 in this section we use a further refinement of the echelon method to answer this question.*

When we use the echelon method, since the variables are in the same order in each equation, we really need to keep track of just the coefficients and the constants. For example, consider the following system of three equations in three unknowns.

$$2x + y - z = 2$$
$$x + 3y + 2z = 1$$
$$x + y + z = 2$$

This system can be written in an abbreviated form as

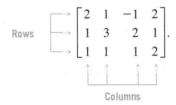

Such a rectangular array of numbers enclosed by brackets is called a **matrix** (plural: **matrices**).* Each number in the array is an **element** or **entry**. To separate the constants in

---

*The word matrix, Latin for "womb," was coined by James Joseph Sylvester (1814–1897) and made popular by his friend Arthur Cayley (1821–1895). Both mathematicians were English, although Sylvester spent much of his life in the United States.

the last column of the matrix from the coefficients of the variables, we use a vertical line, producing the following **augmented matrix**.

$$\begin{bmatrix} 2 & 1 & -1 & | & 2 \\ 1 & 3 & 2 & | & 1 \\ 1 & 1 & 1 & | & 2 \end{bmatrix}$$

The rows of the augmented matrix can be transformed in the same way as the equations of the system, since the matrix is just a shortened form of the system. The following **row operations** on the augmented matrix correspond to the transformations of systems of equations given earlier.

Row Operations

For any augmented matrix of a system of equations, the following operations produce the augmented matrix of an equivalent system:

1. interchanging any two rows;
2. multiplying the elements of a row by any nonzero real number;
3. adding a nonzero multiple of the elements of one row to the corresponding elements of a nonzero multiple of some other row.

In steps 2 and 3, we are replacing a row with a new, modified row, which the old row helped to form, just as we replaced an equation with a new, modified equation in the previous section.

Row operations, like the transformations of systems of equations, are reversible. If they are used to change matrix A to matrix B, then it is possible to use row operations to transform B back into A. In addition to their use in solving equations, row operations are very important in the simplex method.

In the examples in this section, we will use the same notation as in Section 1 to show the row operation used. For example, the notation R_1 indicates row 1 of the previous matrix, and $-3R_1 + R_2$ means that row 1 is multiplied by -3 and added to row 2.

By the first row operation, interchanging two rows, the matrix

$$\begin{bmatrix} 0 & 1 & 2 & | & 3 \\ -2 & -6 & -10 & | & -12 \\ 2 & 1 & -2 & | & -5 \end{bmatrix} \quad \text{becomes} \quad \begin{bmatrix} -2 & -6 & -10 & | & -12 \\ 0 & 1 & 2 & | & 3 \\ 2 & 1 & -2 & | & -5 \end{bmatrix} \quad \begin{array}{l} \text{Interchange } R_1 \\ \text{and } R_2 \end{array}$$

by interchanging the first two rows. Row 3 is left unchanged.

The second row operation, multiplying a row by a number, allows us to change

$$\begin{bmatrix} -2 & -6 & -10 & | & -12 \\ 0 & 1 & 2 & | & 3 \\ 2 & 1 & -2 & | & -5 \end{bmatrix} \quad \text{to} \quad \begin{bmatrix} 1 & 3 & 5 & | & 6 \\ 0 & 1 & 2 & | & 3 \\ 2 & 1 & -2 & | & -5 \end{bmatrix} \quad (-1/2)R_1 \rightarrow R_1$$

by multiplying the elements of row 1 of the original matrix by $-1/2$. Note that rows 2 and 3 are left unchanged.

Using the third row operation, adding a multiple of one row to another, we change

$$\begin{bmatrix} 1 & 3 & 5 & | & 6 \\ 0 & 1 & 2 & | & 3 \\ 2 & 1 & -2 & | & -5 \end{bmatrix} \quad \text{to} \quad \begin{bmatrix} 1 & 3 & 5 & | & 6 \\ 0 & 1 & 2 & | & 3 \\ 0 & -5 & -12 & | & -17 \end{bmatrix} \quad -2R_1 + R_3 \rightarrow R_3$$

by first multiplying each element in row 1 of the original matrix by -2 and then adding the results to the corresponding elements in the third row of that matrix. Work as follows.

$$\begin{bmatrix} 1 & 3 & 5 & | & 6 \\ 0 & 1 & 2 & | & 3 \\ (-2)1 + 2 & (-2)3 + 1 & (-2)5 - 2 & | & (-2)6 - 5 \end{bmatrix} = \begin{bmatrix} 1 & 3 & 5 & | & 6 \\ 0 & 1 & 2 & | & 3 \\ 0 & -5 & -12 & | & -17 \end{bmatrix}$$

Notice that rows 1 and 2 are left unchanged, *even though the elements of row 1 were used to transform row 3.*

The Gauss-Jordan Method

The **Gauss-Jordan method** is an extension of the echelon method of solving systems.* Before the Gauss-Jordan method can be used, the system must be in proper form: the terms with variables should be on the left and the constants on the right in each equation, with the variables in the same order in each equation.

The system is then written as an augmented matrix. Using row operations, the goal is to transform the matrix so that it has zeros above and below a diagonal of 1's on the left of the vertical bar. Once this is accomplished, the final solution can be read directly from the last matrix. The following example illustrates the use of the Gauss-Jordan method to solve a system of equations.

EXAMPLE 1 Gauss-Jordan Method

Solve the system

$$3x - 4y = 1 \tag{1}$$
$$5x + 2y = 19. \tag{2}$$

SOLUTION

**Method I
I's on Diagonal**

The system is already in the proper form to use the Gauss-Jordan method. Our goal is to transform this matrix, if possible, into the form

$$\begin{bmatrix} 1 & 0 & | & m \\ 0 & 1 & | & n \end{bmatrix},$$

where m and n are real numbers. To begin, we change the 3 in the first row to 1 using the second row operation. (Notice that the same notation is used to indicate each transformation, as in the previous section.)

$$\begin{bmatrix} 3 & -4 & | & 1 \\ 5 & 2 & | & 19 \end{bmatrix} \quad \text{Augmented matrix}$$

$$\tfrac{1}{3}R_1 \to R_1 \quad \begin{bmatrix} 1 & -\tfrac{4}{3} & | & \tfrac{1}{3} \\ 5 & 2 & | & 19 \end{bmatrix}$$

Using the third row operation, we change the 5 in row 2 to 0.

$$-5R_1 + R_2 \to R_2 \quad \begin{bmatrix} 1 & -\tfrac{4}{3} & | & \tfrac{1}{3} \\ 0 & \tfrac{26}{3} & | & \tfrac{52}{3} \end{bmatrix}$$

We now change 26/3 in row 2 to 1 to complete the diagonal of 1's.

$$\tfrac{3}{26}R_2 \to R_2 \quad \begin{bmatrix} 1 & -\tfrac{4}{3} & | & \tfrac{1}{3} \\ 0 & 1 & | & 2 \end{bmatrix}$$

*The great German mathematician Carl Friedrich Gauss (1777–1855), sometimes referred to as the "Prince of Mathematicians," originally developed his elimination method for use in finding least squares coefficients. The German geodesist Wilhelm Jordan (1842–1899) improved his method and used it in surveying problems. Gauss's method had been known to the Chinese at least 1800 years earlier and was described in the *Jiuahang Suanshu* (*Nine Chapters on the Mathematical Art*).

The final transformation is to change the $-4/3$ in row 1 to 0.

$$\tfrac{4}{3}R_2 + R_1 \to R_1 \qquad \begin{bmatrix} 1 & 0 & 3 \\ 0 & 1 & 2 \end{bmatrix}$$

The last matrix corresponds to the system

$$x = 3$$
$$y = 2,$$

so we can read the solution directly from the last column of the final matrix. Check that $(3, 2)$ is the solution by substitution in the equations of the original matrix.

Method 2
Fraction-Free

An alternate form of Gauss-Jordan is to first transform the matrix so that it contains zeros above and below the main diagonal. Then, use the second transformation to get the required 1's. When doing calculations by hand, this second method simplifies the calculations by avoiding fractions and decimals. We will use this method when doing calculations by hand throughout the remainder of this chapter.

To begin, we change the 5 in row 2 to 0.

$$\begin{bmatrix} 3 & -4 & 1 \\ 5 & 2 & 19 \end{bmatrix} \quad \text{Augmented matrix}$$

$$5R_1 + (-3)R_2 \to R_2 \qquad \begin{bmatrix} 3 & -4 & 1 \\ 0 & -26 & -52 \end{bmatrix}$$

We change the -4 in row 1 to 0.

$$-4R_2 + 26R_1 \to R_1 \qquad \begin{bmatrix} 78 & 0 & 234 \\ 0 & -26 & -52 \end{bmatrix}$$

Then we change the first nonzero number in each row to 1.

$$\begin{array}{c} \tfrac{1}{78}R_1 \to R_1 \\ -\tfrac{1}{26}R_2 \to R_2 \end{array} \qquad \begin{bmatrix} 1 & 0 & 3 \\ 0 & 1 & 2 \end{bmatrix}$$

The solution is read directly from this last matrix: $x = 3$ and $y = 2$, or $(3, 2)$.

TRY YOUR TURN 1

YOUR TURN 1 Use the Gauss-Jordan method to solve the system

$4x + 5y = 10$
$7x + 8y = 19.$

NOTE If your solution does not check, the most efficient way to find the error is to substitute back through the equations that correspond to each matrix, starting with the last matrix. When you find a system that is not satisfied by your (incorrect) answers, you have probably reached the matrix just before the error occurred. Look for the error in the transformation to the next matrix. For example, if you erroneously wrote the 2 as -2 in the final matrix of the fraction-free method of Example 2, you would find that $(3, -2)$ was not a solution of the system represented by the previous matrix because $-26(-2) \neq -52$, telling you that your error occurred between this matrix and the final one.

When the Gauss-Jordan method is used to solve a system, the final matrix always will have zeros above and below the diagonal of 1's on the left of the vertical bar. To transform the matrix, it is best to work column by column from left to right. Such an orderly method avoids confusion and going around in circles. For each column, first perform the steps that give the zeros. When all columns have zeros in place, multiply each row by the reciprocal of the coefficient of the remaining nonzero number in that row to get the required 1's. With dependent equations or inconsistent systems, it will not be possible to get the complete diagonal of 1's.

We will demonstrate the method in an example with three variables and three equations, after which we will summarize the steps.

EXAMPLE 2 Gauss-Jordan Method

Use the Gauss-Jordan method to solve the system

$$x + 5z = -6 + y$$
$$3x + 3y = 10 + z$$
$$x + 3y + 2z = 5.$$

Method 1
Calculating by Hand

SOLUTION

First, rewrite the system in proper form, as follows.

$$x - y + 5z = -6$$
$$3x + 3y - z = 10$$
$$x + 3y + 2z = 5$$

Begin to find the solution by writing the augmented matrix of the linear system.

$$\begin{bmatrix} 1 & -1 & 5 & | & -6 \\ 3 & 3 & -1 & | & 10 \\ 1 & 3 & 2 & | & 5 \end{bmatrix}$$

Row transformations will be used to rewrite this matrix in the form

$$\begin{bmatrix} 1 & 0 & 0 & | & m \\ 0 & 1 & 0 & | & n \\ 0 & 0 & 1 & | & p \end{bmatrix},$$

where m, n, and p are real numbers (if this form is possible). From this final form of the matrix, the solution can be read: $x = m$, $y = n$, $z = p$, or (m, n, p).

In the first column, we need zeros in the second and third rows. Multiply the first row by -3 and add to the second row to get a zero there. Then multiply the first row by -1 and add to the third row to get that zero.

$$\begin{array}{cc} -3R_1 + R_2 \rightarrow R_2 \\ -1R_1 + R_3 \rightarrow R_3 \end{array} \begin{bmatrix} 1 & -1 & 5 & | & -6 \\ 0 & 6 & -16 & | & 28 \\ 0 & 4 & -3 & | & 11 \end{bmatrix}$$

Now get zeros in the second column in a similar way. We want zeros in the first and third rows. Row 2 will not change.

$$\begin{array}{cc} R_2 + 6R_1 \rightarrow R_1 \\ \\ 2R_2 + (-3)R_3 \rightarrow R_3 \end{array} \begin{bmatrix} 6 & 0 & 14 & | & -8 \\ 0 & 6 & -16 & | & 28 \\ 0 & 0 & -23 & | & 23 \end{bmatrix}$$

In transforming the third row, you may have used the operation $4R_2 + (-6)R_3 \rightarrow R_3$ instead of $2R_2 + (-3)R_3 \rightarrow R_3$. This is perfectly fine; the last row would then have -46 and 46 in place of -23 and 23. To avoid errors, it helps to keep the numbers as small as possible. We observe at this point that all of the numbers can be reduced in size by multiplying each row by an appropriate constant. This next step is not essential, but it simplifies the arithmetic.

$$\begin{array}{cc} \frac{1}{2}R_1 \rightarrow R_1 \\ \frac{1}{2}R_2 \rightarrow R_2 \\ -\frac{1}{23}R_3 \rightarrow R_3 \end{array} \begin{bmatrix} 3 & 0 & 7 & | & -4 \\ 0 & 3 & -8 & | & 14 \\ 0 & 0 & 1 & | & -1 \end{bmatrix}$$

Next, we want zeros in the first and second rows of the third column. Row 3 will not change.

$$\begin{array}{cc} -7R_3 + R_1 \rightarrow R_1 \\ 8R_3 + R_2 \rightarrow R_2 \end{array} \begin{bmatrix} 3 & 0 & 0 & | & 3 \\ 0 & 3 & 0 & | & 6 \\ 0 & 0 & 1 & | & -1 \end{bmatrix}$$

Finally, get 1's in each row by multiplying the row by the reciprocal of (or dividing the row by) the number in the diagonal position.

$$\begin{array}{c} \frac{1}{3}R_1 \rightarrow R_1 \\ \frac{1}{3}R_2 \rightarrow R_2 \end{array} \quad \left[\begin{array}{ccc|c} 1 & 0 & 0 & 1 \\ 0 & 1 & 0 & 2 \\ 0 & 0 & 1 & -1 \end{array}\right]$$

The linear system associated with the final augmented matrix is

$$x = 1$$
$$y = 2$$
$$z = -1,$$

and the solution is $(1, 2, -1)$. Verify that this is the solution to the original system of equations.

CAUTION   Notice that we have performed two or three operations on the same matrix in one step. This is permissible as long as we do not use a row that we are changing as part of another row operation. For example, when we changed row 2 in the first step, we could not use row 2 to transform row 3 in the same step. To avoid difficulty, use *only* row 1 to get zeros in column 1, row 2 to get zeros in column 2, and so on.

Method 2
Graphing Calculator

The row operations of the Gauss-Jordan method can also be done on a graphing calculator. For example, Figure 5 shows the result when the augmented matrix is entered into a TI-84 Plus. Figures 6 and 7 show how row operations can be used to get zeros in rows 2 and 3 of the first column.

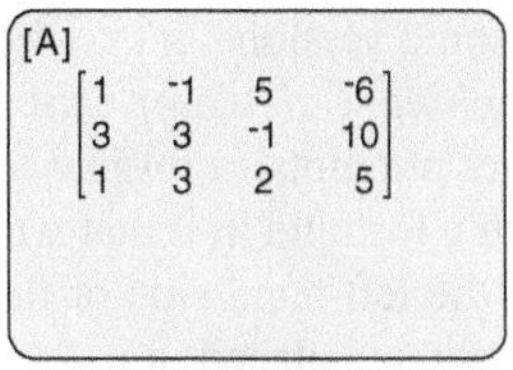

Calculators typically do not allow any multiple of a row to be added to any multiple of another row, such as in the operation $2R_2 + 6R_1 \rightarrow R_1$. They normally allow a multiple of a row to be added only to another unmodified row. To get around this restriction, we can convert the diagonal element to a 1 before changing the other elements in the column to 0, as we did in the first method of Example 1. In this example, we change the 6 in row 2, column 2, to a 1 by dividing by 6. The result is shown in Figure 8. (The right side of the matrix is not visible but can be seen by pressing the right arrow key.) Notice that this operation introduces decimals. Converting to fractions is preferable on calculators that have that option; 1/3 is certainly more concise than 0.3333333333. Figure 9 shows such a conversion on the TI-84 Plus.

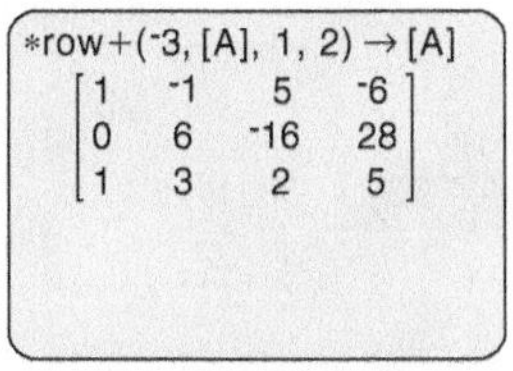

[A]
$$\begin{bmatrix} 1 & \text{-}1 & 5 & \text{-}6 \\ 3 & 3 & \text{-}1 & 10 \\ 1 & 3 & 2 & 5 \end{bmatrix}$$

FIGURE 5

*row+(-3, [A], 1, 2) → [A]
$$\begin{bmatrix} 1 & \text{-}1 & 5 & \text{-}6 \\ 0 & 6 & \text{-}16 & 28 \\ 1 & 3 & 2 & 5 \end{bmatrix}$$

FIGURE 6

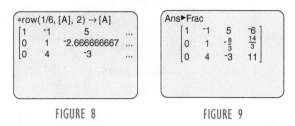

*row(1/6, [A], 2) → [A]
$$\begin{bmatrix} 1 & \text{-}1 & 5 & \cdots \\ 0 & 1 & \text{-}2.666666667 & \cdots \\ 0 & 4 & \text{-}3 & \cdots \end{bmatrix}$$

FIGURE 8

Ans►Frac
$$\begin{bmatrix} 1 & \text{-}1 & 5 & \text{-}6 \\ 0 & 1 & \text{-}\frac{8}{3} & \frac{14}{3} \\ 0 & 4 & \text{-}3 & 11 \end{bmatrix}$$

FIGURE 9

*row+(-1, [A], 1, 3)→[A]
$$\begin{bmatrix} 1 & \text{-}1 & 5 & \text{-}6 \\ 0 & 6 & \text{-}16 & 28 \\ 0 & 4 & \text{-}3 & 11 \end{bmatrix}$$

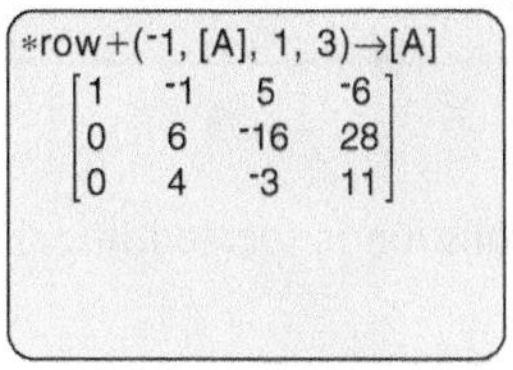

FIGURE 7

When performing row operations without a graphing calculator, it is best to avoid fractions and decimals, because these make the operations more difficult and more prone to error. A calculator, on the other hand, encounters no such difficulties.

Continuing in the same manner, the solution $(1, 2, -1)$ is found as shown in Figure 10.

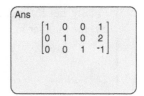

FIGURE 10

Some calculators can do the entire Gauss-Jordan process with a single command; on the TI-84 Plus, for example, this is done with the `rref` command. This is very useful in practice, although it does not show any of the intermediate steps. For more details, see the *Graphing Calculator and Excel Spreadsheet Manual* available with this text.

Method 3
Spreadsheet

The Gauss-Jordan method can be done using a spreadsheet either by using a macro or by developing the pivot steps using formulas with the copy and paste commands. However, spreadsheets also have built-in methods to solve systems of equations. Although these solvers do not usually employ the Gauss-Jordan method for solving systems of equations, they are, nonetheless, efficient and practical to use.

The Solver included with Excel can solve systems of equations that are both linear and nonlinear. The Solver is located in the Tools menu and requires that cells be identified ahead of time for each variable in the problem. It also requires that the left-hand side of each equation be placed in the spreadsheet as a formula. For example, to solve the above problem, we could identify cells A1, B1, and C1 for the variables x, y, and z, respectively. The Solver requires that we place a guess for the answer in these cells. It is convenient to place a zero in each of these cells. The left-hand side of each equation must be placed in a cell. We could choose A3, A4, and A5 to hold each of these formulas. Thus, in cell A3, we would type "=A1 − B1 + 5*C1" and put the other two equations in cells A4 and A5.

We now click on the Tools menu and choose Solver. (In some versions, it may be necessary to install the Solver. For more details, see the *Graphing Calculator and Excel Spreadsheet Manual* available with this text.) Since this solver attempts to find a solution that is best in some way, we are required to identify a cell with a formula in it that we want to optimize. In this case, it is convenient to use the cell with the left-hand side of the first constraint in it, A3. Figure 11 illustrates the Solver box and the items placed in it.

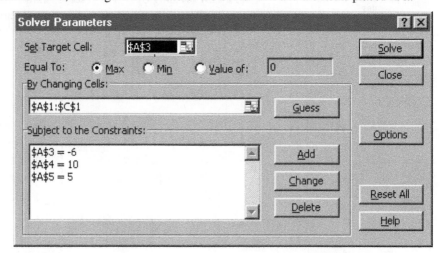

FIGURE 11

YOUR TURN 2 Use the Gauss-Jordan method to solve the system

$$x + 2y + 3z = 2$$
$$2x + 2y - 3z = 27$$
$$3x + 2y + 5z = 10.$$

To obtain a solution, click on Solve. The approximate solution is located in cells A1, B1, and C1, and these correspond to x, y, and z, respectively.

TRY YOUR TURN 2

In summary, the Gauss-Jordan method of solving a linear system requires the following steps.

Gauss-Jordan Method of Solving a Linear System

1. Write each equation so that variable terms are in the same order on the left side of the equal sign and constants are on the right.

2. Write the augmented matrix that corresponds to the system.

3. Use row operations to transform the first column so that all elements except the element in the first row are zero.

4. Use row operations to transform the second column so that all elements except the element in the second row are zero.

5. Use row operations to transform the third column so that all elements except the element in the third row are zero.

6. Continue in this way, when possible, until the last row is written in the form

$$[0 \quad 0 \quad 0 \quad \cdots \quad 0 \quad j \mid k],$$

where j and k are constants with $j \neq 0$. When this is not possible, continue until every row has more zeros on the left than the previous row (except possibly for any rows of all zero at the bottom of the matrix), and the first nonzero entry in each row is the only nonzero entry in its column.

7. Multiply each row by the reciprocal of the nonzero element in that row.

Systems without a Unique Solution

In the previous examples, we were able to get the last row in the form $[0 \quad 0 \quad 0 \quad \cdots \quad 0 \quad j \mid k]$, where j and k are constants with $j \neq 0$. We will now look at examples where this is not the case.

EXAMPLE 3 **Solving a System of Equations with No Solution**

Use the Gauss-Jordan method to solve the system

$$x - 2y = 2$$
$$3x - 6y = 5.$$

SOLUTION Begin by writing the augmented matrix.

$$\begin{bmatrix} 1 & -2 & \mid & 2 \\ 3 & -6 & \mid & 5 \end{bmatrix}$$

To get a zero for the second element in column 1, multiply the numbers in row 1 by -3 and add the results to the corresponding elements in row 2.

$$-3R_1 + R_2 \rightarrow R_2 \quad \begin{bmatrix} 1 & -2 & \mid & 2 \\ 0 & 0 & \mid & -1 \end{bmatrix}$$

This matrix corresponds to the system

$$x - 2y = 2$$
$$0x + 0y = -1.$$

Since the second equation is $0 = -1$, the system is inconsistent and, therefore, has no solution. The row $[0 \quad 0 \mid k]$ for any nonzero k is a signal that the given system is inconsistent.

EXAMPLE 4   **Solving a System of Equations with an Infinite Number of Solutions**

Use the Gauss-Jordan method to solve the system

$$\begin{aligned} x + 2y - z &= 0 \\ 3x - y + z &= 6 \\ -2x - 4y + 2z &= 0. \end{aligned}$$

SOLUTION   The augmented matrix is

$$\left[\begin{array}{ccc|c} 1 & 2 & -1 & 0 \\ 3 & -1 & 1 & 6 \\ -2 & -4 & 2 & 0 \end{array}\right].$$

We first get zeros in the second and third rows of column 1.

$$\begin{array}{c} -3R_1 + R_2 \rightarrow R_2 \\ 2R_1 + R_3 \rightarrow R_3 \end{array} \left[\begin{array}{ccc|c} 1 & 2 & -1 & 0 \\ 0 & -7 & 4 & 6 \\ 0 & 0 & 0 & 0 \end{array}\right]$$

To continue, we get a zero in the first row of column 2 using the second row, as usual.

$$2R_2 + 7R_1 \rightarrow R_1 \quad \left[\begin{array}{ccc|c} 7 & 0 & 1 & 12 \\ 0 & -7 & 4 & 6 \\ 0 & 0 & 0 & 0 \end{array}\right]$$

We cannot get a zero for the first-row, third-column element without changing the form of the first two columns. We must multiply each of the first two rows by the reciprocal of the first nonzero number.

$$\begin{array}{c} \frac{1}{7}R_1 \rightarrow R_1 \\ -\frac{1}{7}R_2 \rightarrow R_2 \end{array} \left[\begin{array}{ccc|c} 1 & 0 & \frac{1}{7} & \frac{12}{7} \\ 0 & 1 & -\frac{4}{7} & -\frac{6}{7} \\ 0 & 0 & 0 & 0 \end{array}\right]$$

To complete the solution, write the equations that correspond to the first two rows of the matrix.

$$x + \frac{1}{7}z = \frac{12}{7}$$

$$y - \frac{4}{7}z = -\frac{6}{7}$$

Because both equations involve z, let z be the parameter. There are an infinite number of solutions, corresponding to the infinite number of values of z. Solve the first equation for x and the second for y to get

$$x = \frac{12 - z}{7} \quad \text{and} \quad y = \frac{4z - 6}{7}.$$

As shown in the previous section, the general solution is written

$$\left(\frac{12 - z}{7}, \frac{4z - 6}{7}, z \right),$$

where z is any real number. For example, $z = 2$ and $z = 12$ lead to the solutions $(10/7, 2/7, 2)$ and $(0, 6, 12)$.

EXAMPLE 5   Solving a System of Equations with an Infinite Number of Solutions

Consider the following system of equations.

$$\begin{aligned} x + 2y + 3z - w &= 4 \\ 2x + 3y \qquad\quad + w &= -3 \\ 3x + 5y + 3z \qquad &= 1 \end{aligned}$$

(a) Set this up as an augmented matrix, and verify that the result after the Gauss-Jordan method is

$$\begin{bmatrix} 1 & 0 & -9 & 5 & -18 \\ 0 & 1 & 6 & -3 & 11 \\ 0 & 0 & 0 & 0 & 0 \end{bmatrix}$$

(b) Find the solution to this system of equations.

SOLUTION   To complete the solution, write the equations that correspond to the first two rows of the matrix.

$$\begin{aligned} x \quad - 9z + 5w &= -18 \\ y + 6z - 3w &= 11 \end{aligned}$$

Because both equations involve both z and w, let z and w be parameters. There are an infinite number of solutions, corresponding to the infinite number of values of z and w. Solve the first equation for x and the second for y to get

YOUR TURN 3 Use the Gauss-Jordan method to solve the system

$$\begin{aligned} 2x - 2y + 3z - 4w &= 6 \\ 3x + 2y + 5z - 3w &= 7 \\ 4x + y + 2z - 2w &= 8. \end{aligned}$$

$$x = -18 + 9z - 5w \qquad \text{and} \qquad y = 11 - 6z + 3w.$$

In an analogous manner to problems with a single parameter, the general solution is written

$$(-18 + 9z - 5w, 11 - 6z + 3w, z, w),$$

where z and w are any real numbers. For example, $z = 1$ and $w = -2$ leads to the solution $(1, -1, 1, -2)$.   **TRY YOUR TURN 3**

Although the examples have used only systems with two equations in two unknowns, three equations in three unknowns, or three equations in four unknowns, the Gauss-Jordan method can be used for any system with n equations and m unknowns. The method becomes tedious with more than three equations in three unknowns; on the other hand, it is very suitable for use with graphing calculators and computers, which can solve fairly large systems quickly. Sophisticated computer programs modify the method to reduce round-off error. Other methods used for special types of large matrices are studied in a course on numerical analysis.

EXAMPLE 6   Soda Sales

A convenience store sells 23 sodas one summer afternoon in 12-, 16-, and 20-oz cups (small, medium, and large). The total volume of soda sold was 376 oz.

(a) Suppose that the prices for a small, medium, and large soda are $1, $1.25, and $1.40, respectively, and that the total sales were $28.45. How many of each size did the store sell?

SOLUTION   As in Example 6 of the previous section, we will organize the information in a table.

Soda Sales	Small	Medium	Large	Total
Number	x	y	z	23
Volume	12	16	20	376
Price	1.00	1.25	1.40	28.45

The three rows of the table lead to three equations: one for the total number of sodas, one for the volume, and one for the price.

$$x + \quad y + \quad z = \quad 23$$
$$12x + \quad 16y + \quad 20z = \quad 376$$
$$1.00x + 1.25y + 1.40z = 28.45$$

Set this up as an augmented matrix, and verify that the result after the Gauss-Jordan method is

$$\begin{bmatrix} 1 & 0 & 0 & | & 6 \\ 0 & 1 & 0 & | & 9 \\ 0 & 0 & 1 & | & 8 \end{bmatrix}.$$

The store sold 6 small, 9 medium, and 8 large sodas.

(b) Suppose the prices for small, medium, and large sodas are changed to $1, $2, and $3, respectively, but all other information is kept the same. How many of each size did the store sell?

SOLUTION Change the third equation to

$$x + 2y + 3z = 28.45$$

and go through the Gauss-Jordan method again. The result is

$$\begin{bmatrix} 1 & 0 & -1 & | & -2 \\ 0 & 1 & 2 & | & 25 \\ 0 & 0 & 0 & | & -19.55 \end{bmatrix}.$$

(If you do the row operations in a different order in this example, you will have different numbers in the last column.) The last row of this matrix says that $0 = -19.55$, so the system is inconsistent and has no solution. (In retrospect, this is clear, because each soda sells for a whole number of dollars, and the total amount of money is not a whole number of dollars. In general, however, it is not easy to tell whether a system of equations has a solution or not by just looking at it.)

(c) Suppose the prices are the same as in part (b), but the total revenue is $48. Now how many of each size did the store sell?

SOLUTION The third equation becomes

$$x + 2y + 3z = 48,$$

and the Gauss-Jordan method leads to

$$\begin{bmatrix} 1 & 0 & -1 & | & -2 \\ 0 & 1 & 2 & | & 25 \\ 0 & 0 & 0 & | & 0 \end{bmatrix}.$$

The system is dependent, similar to Example 4. Let z be the parameter, and solve the first two equations for x and y, yielding

$$x = z - 2 \quad \text{and} \quad y = 25 - 2z.$$

Remember that in this problem, x, y, and z must be nonnegative integers. From the equation for x, we must have

$$z \geq 2,$$

and from the equation for y, we must have

$$25 - 2z \geq 0,$$

from which we find

$$z \leq 12.5.$$

Therefore, we have 11 solutions corresponding to $z = 2, 3, \ldots, 12$.

(d) Give the solutions from part (c) that have the smallest and largest numbers of large sodas.

SOLUTION For the smallest number of large sodas, let $z = 2$, giving $x = 2 - 2 = 0$ and $y = 25 - 2(2) = 21$. There are 0 small, 21 medium, and 2 large sodas.

For the largest number of large sodas, let $z = 12$, giving $x = 12 - 2 = 10$ and $y = 25 - 2(12) = 1$. There are 10 small, 1 medium, and 12 large sodas.

2 EXERCISES

Write the augmented matrix for each system. Do not solve.

1. $3x + y = 6$
  $2x + 5y = 15$

2. $4x - 2y = 8$
  $-7y = -12$

3. $2x + y + z = 3$
  $3x - 4y + 2z = -7$
  $x + y + z = 2$

4. $2x - 5y + 3z = 4$
  $-4x + 2y - 7z = -5$
  $3x - y = 8$

Write the system of equations associated with each augmented matrix.

5. $\begin{bmatrix} 1 & 0 & | & 2 \\ 0 & 1 & | & 3 \end{bmatrix}$

6. $\begin{bmatrix} 1 & 0 & | & 5 \\ 0 & 1 & | & -3 \end{bmatrix}$

7. $\begin{bmatrix} 1 & 0 & 0 & | & 4 \\ 0 & 1 & 0 & | & -5 \\ 0 & 0 & 1 & | & 1 \end{bmatrix}$

8. $\begin{bmatrix} 1 & 0 & 0 & | & 4 \\ 0 & 1 & 0 & | & 2 \\ 0 & 0 & 1 & | & 3 \end{bmatrix}$

9. _____ on a matrix correspond to transformations of a system of equations.

10. Describe in your own words what $2R_1 + R_3 \rightarrow R_3$ means.

Use the indicated row operations to change each matrix.

11. Replace R_2 by $R_1 + (-3)R_2$.

$\begin{bmatrix} 3 & 7 & 4 & | & 10 \\ 1 & 2 & 3 & | & 6 \\ 0 & 4 & 5 & | & 11 \end{bmatrix}$

12. Replace R_3 by $(-1)R_1 + 3R_3$.

$\begin{bmatrix} 3 & 2 & 6 & | & 18 \\ 2 & -2 & 5 & | & 7 \\ 1 & 0 & 5 & | & 20 \end{bmatrix}$

13. Replace R_1 by $(-2)R_2 + R_1$.

$\begin{bmatrix} 1 & 6 & 4 & | & 7 \\ 0 & 3 & 2 & | & 5 \\ 0 & 5 & 3 & | & 7 \end{bmatrix}$

14. Replace R_1 by $R_3 + (-3)R_1$.

$\begin{bmatrix} 1 & 0 & 4 & | & 21 \\ 0 & 6 & 5 & | & 30 \\ 0 & 0 & 12 & | & 15 \end{bmatrix}$

15. Replace R_1 by $\dfrac{1}{3}R_1$.

$\begin{bmatrix} 3 & 0 & 0 & | & 18 \\ 0 & 5 & 0 & | & 9 \\ 0 & 0 & 4 & | & 8 \end{bmatrix}$

16. Replace R_3 by $\dfrac{1}{6}R_3$.

$\begin{bmatrix} 1 & 0 & 0 & | & 30 \\ 0 & 1 & 0 & | & 17 \\ 0 & 0 & 6 & | & 162 \end{bmatrix}$

Use the Gauss-Jordan method to solve each system of equations.

17. $x + y = 5$
  $3x + 2y = 12$

18. $x + 2y = 5$
  $2x + y = -2$

19. $x + y = 7$
  $4x + 3y = 22$

20. $4x - 2y = 3$
  $-2x + 3y = 1$

21. $2x - 3y = 2$
  $4x - 6y = 1$

22. $2x + 3y = 9$
  $4x + 6y = 7$

23. $6x - 3y = 1$
  $-12x + 6y = -2$

24. $x - y = 1$
  $-x + y = -1$

25. $y = x - 3$
  $y = 1 + z$
  $z = 4 - x$

26. $x = 1 - y$
  $2x = z$
  $2z = -2 - y$

27. $2x - 2y = -5$
  $2y + z = 0$
  $2x + z = -7$

28. $x - z = -3$
  $y + z = 9$
  $-2x + 3y + 5z = 33$

29. $4x + 4y - 4z = 24$
  $2x - y + z = -9$
  $x - 2y + 3z = 1$

30. $x + 2y - 7z = -2$
  $-2x - 5y + 2z = 1$
  $3x + 5y + 4z = -9$

31. $3x + 5y - z = 0$
  $4x - y + 2z = 1$
  $7x + 4y + z = 1$

32. $3x - 6y + 3z = 11$
  $2x + y - z = 2$
  $5x - 5y + 2z = 6$

33.
$$5x - 4y + 2z = 6$$
$$5x + 3y - z = 11$$
$$15x - 5y + 3z = 23$$

34.
$$3x + 2y - z = -16$$
$$6x - 4y + 3z = 12$$
$$5x - 2y + 2z = 4$$

35.
$$2x + 3y + z = 9$$
$$4x + 6y + 2z = 18$$
$$-\frac{1}{2}x - \frac{3}{4}y - \frac{1}{4}z = -\frac{9}{4}$$

36.
$$3x - 5y - 2z = -9$$
$$-4x + 3y + z = 11$$
$$8x - 5y + 4z = 6$$

37.
$$x + 2y - w = 3$$
$$2x + 4z + 2w = -6$$
$$x + 2y - z = 6$$
$$2x - y + z + w = -3$$

38.
$$x + 3y - 2z - w = 9$$
$$2x + 4y + 2w = 10$$
$$-3x - 5y + 2z - w = -15$$
$$x - y - 3z + 2w = 6$$

39.
$$x + y - z + 2w = -20$$
$$2x - y + z + w = 11$$
$$3x - 2y + z - 2w = 27$$

40.
$$4x - 3y + z + w = 21$$
$$-2x - y + 2z + 7w = 2$$
$$10x - 5z - 20w = 15$$

41.
$$10.47x + 3.52y + 2.58z - 6.42w = 218.65$$
$$8.62x - 4.93y - 1.75z + 2.83w = 157.03$$
$$4.92x + 6.83y - 2.97z + 2.65w = 462.3$$
$$2.86x + 19.10y - 6.24z - 8.73w = 398.4$$

42.
$$28.6x + 94.5y + 16.0z - 2.94w = 198.3$$
$$16.7x + 44.3y - 27.3z + 8.9w = 254.7$$
$$12.5x - 38.7y + 92.5z + 22.4w = 562.7$$
$$40.1x - 28.3y + 17.5z - 10.2w = 375.4$$

43. On National Public Radio, the "Weekend Edition" program on Sunday, July 29, 2001, posed the following puzzle: Draw a three-by-three square (three boxes across by three boxes down). Put the fraction 3/8 in the first square in the first row. Put the fraction 1/4 in the last square in the second row. The object is to put a fraction in each of the remaining boxes, so the three numbers in each row, each column, and each of the long diagonals add up to 1. Solve this puzzle by letting seven variables represent the seven unknown fractions, writing eight equations for the eight sums, and solving by the Gauss-Jordan method.

APPLICATIONS

Business and Economics

44. Surveys The president of Sam's Supermarkets plans to hire two public relations firms to survey 500 customers by phone, 750 by mail, and 250 by in-person interviews. The Garcia firm has personnel to do 10 phone surveys, 30 mail surveys, and 5 interviews per hour. The Wong firm can handle 20 phone surveys, 10 mail surveys, and 10 interviews per hour. For how many hours should each firm be hired to produce the exact number of surveys needed?

45. Investments Katherine Chong invests $10,000 received from her grandmother in three ways. With one part, she buys U.S. savings bonds at an interest rate of 2.5% per year. She uses the second part, which amounts to twice the first, to buy mutual funds that offer a return of 6% per year. She puts the rest of the money into a money market account paying 4.5% annual interest. The first year her investments bring a return of $470. How much did she invest in each way?

46. Office Technology Pyro-Tech, Inc. is upgrading office technology by purchasing inkjet printers, LCD monitors, and additional memory chips. The total number of pieces of hardware purchased is 46. The cost of each inkjet printer is $109, the cost of each LD monitor is $129, and the cost of each memory chip is $89. The total amount of money spent on new hardware came to $4774. They purchased two times as many memory chips as they did LCD monitors. Determine the number of each that was purchased. *Source: Nathan Borchelt.*

47. Manufacturing Fred's Furniture Factory has 1950 machine hours available each week in the cutting department, 1490 hours in the assembly department, and 2160 in the finishing department. Manufacturing a chair requires 0.2 hours of cutting, 0.3 hours of assembly, and 0.1 hours of finishing. A cabinet requires 0.5 hours of cutting, 0.4 hours of assembly, and 0.6 hours of finishing. A buffet requires 0.3 hours of cutting, 0.1 hours of assembly, and 0.4 hours of finishing. How many chairs, cabinets, and buffets should be produced in order to use all the available production capacity?

48. Manufacturing Nadir, Inc. produces three models of television sets: deluxe, super-deluxe, and ultra. Each deluxe set requires 2 hours of electronics work, 3 hours of assembly time, and 5 hours of finishing time. Each super-deluxe requires 1, 3, and 2 hours of electronics, assembly, and finishing time, respectively. Each ultra requires 2, 2, and 6 hours of the same work, respectively.

a. There are 54 hours available for electronics, 72 hours available for assembly, and 148 hours available for finishing per week. How many of each model should be produced each week if all available time is to be used?

b. Suppose everything is the same as in part a, but a super-deluxe set requires 1, rather than 2, hours of finishing time. How many solutions are there now?

c. Suppose everything is the same as in part b, but the total hours available for finishing changes from 148 hours to 144 hours. Now how many solutions are there?

49. Transportation An electronics company produces three models of stereo speakers, models A, B, and C, and can deliver them by truck, van, or SUV. A truck holds 2 boxes of model A, 2 of model B, and 3 of model C. A van holds 3 boxes of model A, 4 boxes of model B, and 2 boxes of model C. An SUV holds 3 boxes of model A, 5 boxes of model B, and 1 box of model C.

a. If 25 boxes of model A, 33 boxes of model B, and 22 boxes of model C are to be delivered, how many vehicles of each type should be used so that all operate at full capacity?

b. Model C has been discontinued. If 25 boxes of model A and 33 boxes of model B are to be delivered, how many vehicles of each type should be used so that all operate at full capacity?

50. Truck Rental The U-Drive Rent-A-Truck company plans to spend $7 million on 200 new vehicles. Each commercial van will cost $35,000, each small truck $30,000, and each large truck $50,000. Past experience shows that they need twice as many vans as small trucks. How many of each type of vehicle can they buy?

51. Loans To get the necessary funds for a planned expansion, a small company took out three loans totaling $25,000. Company owners were able to get interest rates of 8%, 9%, and 10%. They borrowed $1000 more at 9% than they borrowed at 10%. The total annual interest on the loans was $2190.

a. How much did they borrow at each rate?

b. Suppose we drop the condition that they borrowed $1000 more at 9% than at 10%. What can you say about the amount borrowed at 10%? What is the solution if the amount borrowed at 10% is $5000?

c. Suppose the bank sets a maximum of $10,000 at the lowest interest rate of 8%. Is a solution possible that still meets all of the original conditions?

d. Explain why $10,000 at 8%, $8000 at 9%, and $7000 at 10% is not a feasible solution for part c.

52. APPLY IT Transportation An auto manufacturer sends cars from two plants, I and II, to dealerships A and B located in a midwestern city. Plant I has a total of 28 cars to send, and plant II has 8. Dealer A needs 20 cars, and dealer B needs 16. Transportation costs per car, based on the distance of each dealership from each plant, are $220 from I to A, $300 from I to B, $400 from II to A, and $180 from II to B. The manufacturer wants to limit transportation costs to $10,640. How many cars should be sent from each plant to each of the two dealerships?

53. Transportation A manufacturer purchases a part for use at both of its plants — one at Roseville, California, the other at Akron, Ohio. The part is available in limited quantities from two suppliers. Each supplier has 75 units available. The Roseville plant needs 40 units, and the Akron plant requires 75 units. The first supplier charges $70 per unit delivered to Roseville and $90 per unit delivered to Akron. Corresponding costs from the second supplier are $80 and $120. The manufacturer wants to order a total of 75 units from the first, less expensive supplier, with the remaining 40 units to come from the second supplier. If the company spends $10,750 to purchase the required number of units for the two plants, find the number of units that should be sent from each supplier to each plant.

54. Packaging A company produces three combinations of mixed vegetables that sell in 1-kg packages. Italian style combines 0.3 kg of zucchini, 0.3 of broccoli, and 0.4 of carrots. French style combines 0.6 kg of broccoli and 0.4 of carrots. Oriental style combines 0.2 kg of zucchini, 0.5 of broccoli, and 0.3 of carrots. The company has a stock of 16,200 kg of zucchini, 41,400 kg of broccoli, and 29,400 kg of carrots. How many packages of each style should it prepare to use up existing supplies?

55. Tents L.L. Bean makes three sizes of Ultra Dome tents: two-person, four-person, and six-person models, which cost $129,

$179, and $229, respectively. A two-person tent provides 40 ft^2 of floor space, while a four-person and a six-person model provide 64 ft^2 and 88 ft^2 of floor space, respectively. ***Source: L. L. Bean.*** A recent order by an organization that takes children camping ordered enough tents to hold 200 people and provide 3200 ft^2 of floor space. The total cost was $8950, and we wish to know how many tents of each size were ordered.

a. How many solutions are there to this problem?

b. What is the solution with the most four-person tents?

c. What is the solution with the most two-person tents?

d. Discuss the company's pricing strategy that led to a system of equations that is dependent. Do you think that this is a coincidence or an example of logical thinking?

Life Sciences

56. Animal Breeding An animal breeder can buy four types of food for Vietnamese pot-bellied pigs. Each case of Brand A contains 25 units of fiber, 30 units of protein, and 30 units of fat. Each case of Brand B contains 50 units of fiber, 30 units of protein, and 20 units of fat. Each case of Brand C contains 75 units of fiber, 30 units of protein, and 20 units of fat. Each case of Brand D contains 100 units of fiber, 60 units of protein, and 30 units of fat. How many cases of each should the breeder mix together to obtain a food that provides 1200 units of fiber, 600 units of protein, and 400 units of fat?

57. Dietetics A hospital dietician is planning a special diet for a certain patient. The total amount per meal of food groups A, B, and C must equal 400 grams. The diet should include one-third as much of group A as of group B, and the sum of the amounts of group A and group C should equal twice the amount of group B.

a. How many grams of each food group should be included?

b. Suppose we drop the requirement that the diet include one-third as much of group A as of group B. Describe the set of all possible solutions.

c. Suppose that, in addition to the conditions given in the original problem, foods A and B cost 2 cents per gram and food C costs 3 cents per gram, and that a meal must cost $8. Is a solution possible?

58. Bacterial Food Requirements Three species of bacteria are fed three foods, I, II, and III. A bacterium of the first species consumes 1.3 units each of foods I and II and 2.3 units of food III each day. A bacterium of the second species consumes 1.1 units of food I, 2.4 units of food II, and 3.7 units of food III each day. A bacterium of the third species consumes 8.1 units of I, 2.9 units of II, and 5.1 units of III each day. If 16,000 units of I, 28,000 units of II, and 44,000 units of III are supplied each day, how many of each species can be maintained in this environment?

59. Fish Food Requirements A lake is stocked each spring with three species of fish, A, B, and C. Three foods, I, II, and III, are available in the lake. Each fish of species A requires an average of 1.32 units of food I, 2.9 units of food II, and 1.75 units of food III each day. Species B fish each require 2.1 units of food I, 0.95 unit of food II, and 0.6 unit of food III daily. Species C fish require 0.86, 1.52, and 2.01 units of I, II, and III per day, respectively. If 490 units of food I, 897 units of food II, and

653 units of food III are available daily, how many of each species should be stocked?

 60. Agriculture According to data from a Texas agricultural report, the amount of nitrogen (in lb/acre), phosphate (in lb/acre), and labor (in hr/acre) needed to grow honeydews, yellow onions, and lettuce is given by the following table. *Source: The AMATYC Review.*

	Honeydews	Yellow Onions	Lettuce
Nitrogen	120	150	180
Phosphate	180	80	80
Labor	4.97	4.45	4.65

a. If the farmer has 220 acres, 29,100 lb of nitrogen, 32,600 lb of phosphate, and 480 hours of labor, is it possible to use all resources completely? If so, how many acres should he allot for each crop?

b. Suppose everything is the same as in part a, except that 1061 hours of labor are available. Is it possible to use all resources completely? If so, how many acres should he allot for each crop?

61. Archimedes' Problem Bovinum Archimedes is credited with the authorship of a famous problem involving the number of cattle of the sun god. A simplified version of the problem is stated as follows:

> The sun god had a herd of cattle consisting of bulls and cows, one part of which was white, a second black, a third spotted, and a fourth brown.
> Among the bulls, the number of white ones was one-half plus one-third the number of the black greater than the brown; the number of the black, one-quarter plus one-fifth the number of the spotted greater than the brown; the number of the spotted, one-sixth and one-seventh the number of the white greater than the brown.
> Among the cows, the number of white ones was one-third plus one-quarter of the total black cattle; the number of the black, one-quarter plus one-fifth the total of the spotted cattle; the number of the spotted, one-fifth plus one-sixth the total of the brown cattle; the number of the brown, one-sixth plus one-seventh the total of the white cattle.
> What was the composition of the herd?

Source: 100 Great Problems of Elementary Mathematics.
The problem can be solved by converting the statements into two systems of equations, using X, Y, Z, and T for the number of white, black, spotted, and brown bulls, respectively, and x, y, z, and t for the number of white, black, spotted, and brown cows, respectively. For example, the first statement can be written as $X = (1/2 + 1/3)Y + T$ and then reduced. The result is the following two systems of equations:

$$6X - 5Y = 6T \qquad 12x - 7y = 7Y$$
$$20Y - 9Z = 20T \quad \text{and} \quad 20y - 9z = 9Z$$
$$42Z - 13X = 42T \qquad 30z - 11t = 11T$$
$$-13x + 42t = 13X$$

a. Show that these two systems of equations represent Archimedes' Problem Bovinum.

 b. If it is known that the number of brown bulls, T, is 4,149,387, use the Gauss-Jordan method to first find a solution to the 3×3 system and then use these values and the Gauss-Jordan method to find a solution to the 4×4 system of equations.

62. Health The U.S. National Center for Health Statistics tracks the major causes of death in the United States. After a steady increase, the death rate by cancer has decreased since the early 1990s. The table lists the age-adjusted death rate per 100,000 people for 4 years. *Source: The New York Times 2010 Almanac.*

Year	Rate
1980	183.9
1990	203.3
2000	196.5
2006	187.0

a. If the relationship between the death rate R and the year t is expressed as $R = at^2 + bt + c$, where $t = 0$ corresponds to 1980, use data from 1980, 1990, and 2000 and a linear system of equations to determine the constants a, b, and c.

b. Use the equation from part a to predict the rate in 2006, and compare the result with the actual data.

 c. If the relationship between the death rate R and the year t is expressed as $R = at^3 + bt^2 + ct + d$, where $t = 0$ corresponds to 1980, use all four data points and a linear system of equations to determine the constants a, b, c, and d.

d. Discuss the appropriateness of the functions used in parts a and c to model this data.

Social Sciences

63. Modeling War One of the factors that contribute to the success or failure of a particular army during war is its ability to get new troops ready for service. It is possible to analyze the rate of change in the number of troops of two hypothetical armies with the following simplified model,

Rate of increase (RED ARMY) $= 200,000 - 0.5r - 0.3b$

Rate of increase (BLUE ARMY) $= 350,000 - 0.5r - 0.7b$,

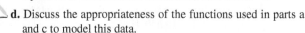

where r is the number of soldiers in the Red Army at a given time and b is the number of soldiers in the Blue Army at a given time. The factors 0.5 and 0.7 represent each army's efficiency of bringing new soldiers to the fight. *Source: Journal of Peace Research.*

a. Solve this system of equations to determine the number of soldiers in each army when the rate of increase for each is zero.

b. Describe what might be going on in a war when the rate of increase is zero.

64. Traffic Control At rush hours, substantial traffic congestion is encountered at the traffic intersections shown in the figure on the next page. (The streets are one-way, as shown by the arrows.)

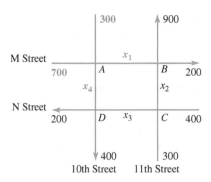

M Street

700   A

x_4

N Street

200   D x_3 C   400

300   900

x_1

B   200

x_2

400   300

10th Street   11th Street

The city wishes to improve the signals at these corners so as to speed the flow of traffic. The traffic engineers first gather data. As the figure shows, 700 cars per hour come down M Street to intersection A, and 300 cars per hour come down 10th Street to intersection A. A total of x_1 of these cars leave A on M Street, and x_4 cars leave A on 10th Street. The number of cars entering A must equal the number leaving, so that

$$x_1 + x_4 = 700 + 300$$

or

$$x_1 + x_4 = 1000.$$

For intersection B, x_1 cars enter on M Street and x_2 on 11th Street. The figure shows that 900 cars leave B on 11th and 200 on M. Thus,

$$x_1 + x_2 = 900 + 200$$

$$x_1 + x_2 = 1100.$$

a. Write two equations representing the traffic entering and leaving intersections C and D.

b. Use the four equations to set up an augmented matrix, and solve the system by the Gauss-Jordan method, using x_4 as the parameter.

c. Based on your solution to part b, what are the largest and smallest possible values for the number of cars leaving intersection A on 10th Street?

d. Answer the question in part c for the other three variables.

e. Verify that you could have discarded any one of the four original equations without changing the solution. What does this tell you about the original problem?

General Interest

65. Snack Food According to the nutrition labels on the package, a single serving of Oreos® has 10 g of fat, 36 g of carbohydrates, 2 g of protein, and 240 calories. The figures for a single serving of Twix® are 14 g, 37 g, 3 g, and 280 calories. The figures for a single serving of trail mix are 20 g, 23 g, 11 g, and 295 calories. How many calories are in each gram of fat, carbohydrate, and protein? *Source: The Mathematics Teacher.**

*For a discussion of some complications that can come up in solving linear systems, read the original article: Szydlik, Stephen D., "The Problem with the Snack Food Problem," *The Mathematics Teacher*, Vol. 103, No. 1, Aug. 2009, p. 18–28.

66. Basketball Kobe Bryant has the second highest single game point total in the NBA. Bryant scored 81 points for the Los Angeles Lakers on January 22, 2006, against the Toronto Raptors. Bryant made a total of 46 baskets, including foul shots (worth one point), field goals (worth two points), and three-point shots (worth three points). The number of field goal shots he made is equal to three times the number of three pointers he made. Find the number of foul shots, field goals, and three pointers Bryant made. *Source: ESPN.*

67. Toys One hundred toys are to be given out to a group of children. A ball costs $2, a doll costs $3, and a car costs $4. A total of $295 was spent on the toys.

a. A ball weighs 12 oz, a doll 16 oz, and a car 18 oz. The total weight of all the toys is 1542 oz. Find how many of each toy there are.

b. Now suppose the weight of a ball, doll, and car are 11, 15, and 19 oz, respectively. If the total weight is still 1542 oz, how many solutions are there now?

c. Keep the weights as in part b, but change the total weight to 1480 oz. How many solutions are there?

d. Give the solution to part c that has the smallest number of cars.

e. Give the solution to part c that has the largest number of cars.

68. Ice Cream Researchers have determined that the amount of sugar contained in ice cream helps to determine the overall "degree of like" that a consumer has toward that particular flavor. They have also determined that too much or too little sugar will have the same negative affect on the "degree of like" and that this relationship follows a quadratic function. In an experiment conducted at Pennsylvania State University, the following condensed table was obtained. *Source: Journal of Food Science.*

Percentage of Sugar	Degree of Like
8	5.4
13	6.3
18	5.6

a. Use this information and the Gauss-Jordan method to determine the coefficients a, b, c, of the quadratic equation

$$y = ax^2 + bx + c,$$

where y is the "degree of like" and x is the percentage of sugar in the ice cream mix.

b. Repeat part a by using the quadratic regression feature on a graphing calculator. Compare your answers.

69. Lights Out The Tiger Electronics' game, Lights Out, consists of five rows of five lighted buttons. When a button is pushed, it changes the on/off status of it and the status of all of its vertical and horizontal neighbors. For any given situation where some of the lights are on and some are off, the goal of the game is to push buttons until all of the lights are turned off. It turns out that for any given array of lights, solving a system of equations can be used to develop a strategy for turning the lights out. The following system of equations can be used to solve the problem for a simplified version of the game with 2 rows of 2 buttons where all of the lights are initially turned on:

$$x_{11} + x_{12} + x_{21} = 1$$
$$x_{11} + x_{12} + x_{22} = 1$$
$$x_{11} + x_{21} + x_{22} = 1$$
$$x_{12} + x_{21} + x_{22} = 1,$$

where $x_{ij} = 1$ if the light in row i, column j, is on and $x_{ij} = 0$ when it is off. The order in which the buttons are pushed does not matter, so we are only seeking which buttons should be pushed. *Source: Mathematics Magazine.*

a. Solve this system of equations and determine a strategy to turn the lights out. (*Hint:* While doing row operations, if an odd number is found, immediately replace this value with a 1; if an even number is found, then immediately replace that

number with a zero. This is called modulo 2 arithmetic, and it is necessary in problems dealing with on/off switches.)

b. Resolve the equation with the right side changed to $(0, 1, 1, 0)$.

70. Baseball Ichiro Suzuki holds the American League record for the most hits in a single baseball season. In 2004, Suzuki had a total of 262 hits for the Seattle Mariners. He hit three fewer triples than home runs, and he hit three times as many doubles as home runs. Suzuki also hit 45 times as many singles as triples. Find the number of singles, doubles, triples, and home runs hit by Suzuki during the season. *Source: Baseball Almanac.*

YOUR TURN ANSWERS

1. $(5, -2)$
2. $(7, 2, -3)$
3. $(17/9 + w/3, -4/9 - 2w/3, 4/9 + 2w/3, w)$

3 Addition and Subtraction of Matrices

APPLY IT

A company sends monthly shipments to its warehouses in several cities. How might the company keep track of the shipments to each warehouse most efficiently?

In the previous section, matrices were used to store information about systems of linear equations. In this section, we begin to study calculations with matrices, which we will use in Examples 1, 5, and 7 to answer the question posed above.

The use of matrices has gained increasing importance in the fields of management, natural science, and social science because matrices provide a convenient way to organize data, as Example 1 demonstrates.

EXAMPLE 1 Furniture Shipments

The EZ Life Company manufactures sofas and armchairs in three models, A, B, and C. The company has regional warehouses in New York, Chicago, and San Francisco. In its August shipment, the company sends 10 model-A sofas, 12 model-B sofas, 5 model-C sofas, 15 model-A chairs, 20 model-B chairs, and 8 model-C chairs to each warehouse. Use a matrix to organize this information.

APPLY IT **SOLUTION** To organize this data, we might tabulate the data in a chart.

Number of Furniture Pieces

		Model		
		A	B	C
Furniture Type	Sofas	10	12	5
	Chairs	15	20	8

With the understanding that the numbers in each row refer to the furniture type (sofa, chair) and the numbers in each column refer to the model (A, B, C), the same information can be given by a matrix, as follows.

$$M = \begin{bmatrix} 10 & 12 & 5 \\ 15 & 20 & 8 \end{bmatrix}$$

Matrices often are named with capital letters, as in Example 1. Matrices are classified by **size**; that is, by the number of rows and columns they contain. For example, matrix M above has two rows and three columns. This matrix is a 2 × 3 (read "2 by 3") matrix. By definition, a matrix with m rows and n columns is an $m \times n$ matrix. The number of rows is always given first.

EXAMPLE 2   Matrix Size

(a) The matrix $\begin{bmatrix} -3 & 5 \\ 2 & 0 \\ 5 & -1 \end{bmatrix}$ is a 3 × 2 matrix.

(b) $\begin{bmatrix} 0.5 & 8 & 0.9 \\ 0 & 5.1 & -3 \\ -4 & 0 & 5 \end{bmatrix}$ is a 3 × 3 matrix.

(c) $\begin{bmatrix} 1 & 6 & 5 & -2 & 5 \end{bmatrix}$ is a 1 × 5 matrix.

(d) $\begin{bmatrix} 3 \\ -5 \\ 0 \\ 2 \end{bmatrix}$ is a 4 × 1 matrix.

A matrix with the same number of rows as columns is called a **square matrix**. The matrix in Example 2(b) is a square matrix.

A matrix containing only one row is called a **row matrix** or a **row vector**. The matrix in Example 2(c) is a row matrix, as are

$$\begin{bmatrix} 5 & 8 \end{bmatrix}, \qquad \begin{bmatrix} 6 & -9 & 2 \end{bmatrix}, \qquad \text{and} \qquad \begin{bmatrix} -4 & 0 & 0 & 0 \end{bmatrix}.$$

A matrix of only one column, as in Example 2(d), is a **column matrix** or a **column vector**.

Equality for matrices is defined as follows.

Matrix Equality

Two matrices are equal if they are the same size and if each pair of corresponding elements is equal.

By this definition,

$$\begin{bmatrix} 2 & 1 \\ 3 & -5 \end{bmatrix} \qquad \text{and} \qquad \begin{bmatrix} 1 & 2 \\ -5 & 3 \end{bmatrix}$$

are not equal (even though they contain the same elements and are the same size) since the corresponding elements differ.

EXAMPLE 3   Matrix Equality

(a) From the definition of matrix equality given above, the only way that the statement

$$\begin{bmatrix} 2 & 1 \\ p & q \end{bmatrix} = \begin{bmatrix} x & y \\ -1 & 0 \end{bmatrix}$$

can be true is if $2 = x$, $1 = y$, $p = -1$, and $q = 0$.

(b) The statement

$$\begin{bmatrix} x \\ y \end{bmatrix} = \begin{bmatrix} 1 \\ -3 \\ 0 \end{bmatrix}$$

can never be true, since the two matrices are different sizes. (One is 2 × 1 and the other is 3 × 1.)

Addition

The matrix given in Example 1,

$$M = \begin{bmatrix} 10 & 12 & 5 \\ 15 & 20 & 8 \end{bmatrix},$$

shows the August shipment from the EZ Life plant to each of its warehouses. If matrix N below gives the September shipment to the New York warehouse, what is the total shipment of each item of furniture to the New York warehouse for these two months?

$$N = \begin{bmatrix} 45 & 35 & 20 \\ 65 & 40 & 35 \end{bmatrix}$$

If 10 model-A sofas were shipped in August and 45 in September, then altogether $10 + 45 = 55$ model-A sofas were shipped in the two months. The other corresponding entries can be added in a similar way to get a new matrix Q, which represents the total shipment for the two months.

$$Q = \begin{bmatrix} 55 & 47 & 25 \\ 80 & 60 & 43 \end{bmatrix}$$

It is convenient to refer to Q as the sum of M and N.

The way these two matrices were added illustrates the following definition of addition of matrices.

Adding Matrices
The sum of two $m \times n$ matrices X and Y is the $m \times n$ matrix $X + Y$ in which each element is the sum of the corresponding elements of X and Y.

CAUTION | It is important to remember that only matrices that are the same size can be added.

EXAMPLE 4 Adding Matrices

Find each sum, if possible.

SOLUTION

YOUR TURN 1 Find each sum, if possible.

(a) $\begin{bmatrix} 3 & 4 & 5 & 6 \\ 1 & 2 & 3 & 4 \end{bmatrix} + \begin{bmatrix} 1 & -2 & 4 \\ -2 & -4 & 8 \end{bmatrix}$

(b) $\begin{bmatrix} 3 & 4 & 5 \\ 1 & 2 & 3 \end{bmatrix} + \begin{bmatrix} 1 & -2 & 4 \\ -2 & -4 & 8 \end{bmatrix}$

(a) $\begin{bmatrix} 5 & -6 \\ 8 & 9 \end{bmatrix} + \begin{bmatrix} -4 & 6 \\ 8 & -3 \end{bmatrix} = \begin{bmatrix} 5 + (-4) & -6 + 6 \\ 8 + 8 & 9 + (-3) \end{bmatrix} = \begin{bmatrix} 1 & 0 \\ 16 & 6 \end{bmatrix}$

(b) The matrices

$$A = \begin{bmatrix} 5 & -8 \\ 6 & 2 \end{bmatrix} \quad \text{and} \quad B = \begin{bmatrix} 3 & -9 & 1 \\ 4 & 2 & -5 \end{bmatrix}$$

are different sizes. Therefore, the sum $A + B$ does not exist.   TRY YOUR TURN 1

EXAMPLE 5 Furniture Shipments

The September shipments from the EZ Life Company to the New York, San Francisco, and Chicago warehouses are given in matrices N, S, and C below.

$$N = \begin{bmatrix} 45 & 35 & 20 \\ 65 & 40 & 35 \end{bmatrix} \quad S = \begin{bmatrix} 30 & 32 & 28 \\ 43 & 47 & 30 \end{bmatrix} \quad C = \begin{bmatrix} 22 & 25 & 38 \\ 31 & 34 & 35 \end{bmatrix}$$

What was the total amount shipped to the three warehouses in September?

APPLY IT

SOLUTION The total of the September shipments is represented by the sum of the three matrices N, S, and C.

$$N + S + C = \begin{bmatrix} 45 & 35 & 20 \\ 65 & 40 & 35 \end{bmatrix} + \begin{bmatrix} 30 & 32 & 28 \\ 43 & 47 & 30 \end{bmatrix} + \begin{bmatrix} 22 & 25 & 38 \\ 31 & 34 & 35 \end{bmatrix}$$

$$= \begin{bmatrix} 97 & 92 & 86 \\ 139 & 121 & 100 \end{bmatrix}$$

For example, this sum shows that the total number of model-C sofas shipped to the three warehouses in September was 86.

Subtraction Subtraction of matrices is defined similarly to addition.

Subtracting Matrices

The difference of two $m \times n$ matrices X and Y is the $m \times n$ matrix $X - Y$ in which each element is found by subtracting the corresponding elements of X and Y.

EXAMPLE 6   Subtracting Matrices

Subtract each pair of matrices, if possible.

SOLUTION

(a) $\begin{bmatrix} 8 & 6 & -4 \\ -2 & 7 & 5 \end{bmatrix} - \begin{bmatrix} 3 & 5 & -8 \\ -4 & 2 & 9 \end{bmatrix} = \begin{bmatrix} 8-3 & 6-5 & -4-(-8) \\ -2-(-4) & 7-2 & 5-9 \end{bmatrix} = \begin{bmatrix} 5 & 1 & 4 \\ 2 & 5 & -4 \end{bmatrix}.$

(b) The matrices

$$\begin{bmatrix} -2 & 5 \\ 0 & 1 \end{bmatrix} \quad \text{and} \quad \begin{bmatrix} 3 \\ 5 \end{bmatrix}$$

YOUR TURN 2 Calculate
$\begin{bmatrix} 3 & 4 & 5 \\ 1 & 2 & 3 \end{bmatrix} - \begin{bmatrix} 1 & -2 & 4 \\ -2 & -4 & 8 \end{bmatrix}.$

are different sizes and cannot be subtracted. **TRY YOUR TURN 2**

EXAMPLE 7   Furniture Shipments

APPLY IT

During September the Chicago warehouse of the EZ Life Company shipped out the following numbers of each model.

$$K = \begin{bmatrix} 5 & 10 & 8 \\ 11 & 14 & 15 \end{bmatrix}$$

What was the Chicago warehouse inventory on October 1, taking into account only the number of items received and sent out during the month?

Method 1
Calculating by Hand

[A]-[B]
$\begin{bmatrix} 17 & 15 & 30 \\ 20 & 20 & 20 \end{bmatrix}$

FIGURE 12

SOLUTION The number of each kind of item received during September is given by matrix C from Example 5; the number of each model sent out during September is given by matrix K. The October 1 inventory will be represented by the matrix $C - K$:

$$\begin{bmatrix} 22 & 25 & 38 \\ 31 & 34 & 35 \end{bmatrix} - \begin{bmatrix} 5 & 10 & 8 \\ 11 & 14 & 15 \end{bmatrix} = \begin{bmatrix} 17 & 15 & 30 \\ 20 & 20 & 20 \end{bmatrix}.$$

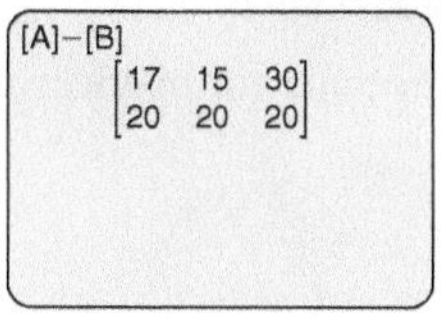

Method 2
Graphing Calculator

Matrix operations are easily performed on a graphing calculator. Figure 12 shows the previous operation; the matrices A and B were already entered into the calculator.

TECHNOLOGY NOTE Spreadsheet programs are designed to effectively organize data that can be represented in rows and columns. Accordingly, matrix operations are also easily performed on spreadsheets. See the *Graphing Calculator and Excel Spreadsheet Manual* available with this text for details.

3 EXERCISES

Decide whether each statement is true or false. If false, tell why.

1. $\begin{bmatrix} 1 & 3 \\ 5 & 7 \end{bmatrix} = \begin{bmatrix} 1 & 5 \\ 3 & 7 \end{bmatrix}$

2. $\begin{bmatrix} 1 \\ 2 \\ 3 \end{bmatrix} = \begin{bmatrix} 1 & 2 & 3 \end{bmatrix}$

3. $\begin{bmatrix} x \\ y \end{bmatrix} = \begin{bmatrix} -2 \\ 8 \end{bmatrix}$ if $x = -2$ and $y = 8$.

4. $\begin{bmatrix} 3 & 5 & 2 & 8 \\ 1 & -1 & 4 & 0 \end{bmatrix}$ is a 4×2 matrix.

5. $\begin{bmatrix} 1 & 9 & -4 \\ 3 & 7 & 2 \\ -1 & 1 & 0 \end{bmatrix}$ is a square matrix.

6. $\begin{bmatrix} 2 & 4 & -1 \\ 3 & 7 & 5 \\ 0 & 0 & 0 \end{bmatrix} = \begin{bmatrix} 2 & 4 & -1 \\ 3 & 7 & 5 \end{bmatrix}$

Find the size of each matrix. Identify any square, column, or row matrices.

7. $\begin{bmatrix} -4 & 8 \\ 2 & 3 \end{bmatrix}$

8. $\begin{bmatrix} 2 & -3 & 7 \\ 1 & 0 & 4 \end{bmatrix}$

9. $\begin{bmatrix} -6 & 8 & 0 & 0 \\ 4 & 1 & 9 & 2 \\ 3 & -5 & 7 & 1 \end{bmatrix}$

10. $\begin{bmatrix} 8 & -2 & 4 & 6 & 3 \end{bmatrix}$

11. $\begin{bmatrix} -7 \\ 5 \end{bmatrix}$

12. $\begin{bmatrix} -9 \end{bmatrix}$

13. The sum of an $n \times m$ matrix and an $m \times n$ matrix, where $m \neq n$, is _____.

14. If A is a 5×2 matrix and $A + K = A$, what do you know about K?

Find the values of the variables in each equation.

15. $\begin{bmatrix} 3 & 4 \\ -8 & 1 \end{bmatrix} = \begin{bmatrix} 3 & x \\ y & z \end{bmatrix}$

16. $\begin{bmatrix} -5 \\ y \end{bmatrix} = \begin{bmatrix} -5 \\ 8 \end{bmatrix}$

17. $\begin{bmatrix} s - 4 & t + 2 \\ -5 & 7 \end{bmatrix} = \begin{bmatrix} 6 & 2 \\ -5 & r \end{bmatrix}$

18. $\begin{bmatrix} 9 & 7 \\ r & 0 \end{bmatrix} = \begin{bmatrix} m - 3 & n + 5 \\ 8 & 0 \end{bmatrix}$

19. $\begin{bmatrix} a + 2 & 3b & 4c \\ d & 7f & 8 \end{bmatrix} + \begin{bmatrix} -7 & 2b & 6 \\ -3d & -6 & -2 \end{bmatrix} = \begin{bmatrix} 15 & 25 & 6 \\ -8 & 1 & 6 \end{bmatrix}$

20. $\begin{bmatrix} a + 2 & 3z + 1 & 5m \\ 4k & 0 & 3 \end{bmatrix} + \begin{bmatrix} 3a & 2z & 5m \\ 2k & 5 & 6 \end{bmatrix} = \begin{bmatrix} 10 & -14 & 80 \\ 10 & 5 & 9 \end{bmatrix}$

Perform the indicated operations, where possible.

21. $\begin{bmatrix} 2 & 4 & 5 & -7 \\ 6 & -3 & 12 & 0 \end{bmatrix} + \begin{bmatrix} 8 & 0 & -10 & 1 \\ -2 & 8 & -9 & 11 \end{bmatrix}$

22. $\begin{bmatrix} 1 & 5 \\ 2 & -3 \\ 3 & 7 \end{bmatrix} + \begin{bmatrix} 2 & 3 \\ 8 & 5 \\ -1 & 9 \end{bmatrix}$

23. $\begin{bmatrix} 1 & 3 & -2 \\ 4 & 7 & 1 \end{bmatrix} + \begin{bmatrix} 3 & 0 \\ 6 & 4 \\ -5 & 2 \end{bmatrix}$

24. $\begin{bmatrix} 8 & 0 & -3 \\ 1 & 19 & -5 \end{bmatrix} - \begin{bmatrix} 1 & -5 & 2 \\ 3 & 9 & -8 \end{bmatrix}$

25. $\begin{bmatrix} 2 & 8 & 12 & 0 \\ 7 & 4 & -1 & 5 \\ 1 & 2 & 0 & 10 \end{bmatrix} - \begin{bmatrix} 1 & 3 & 6 & 9 \\ 2 & -3 & -3 & 4 \\ 8 & 0 & -2 & 17 \end{bmatrix}$

26. $\begin{bmatrix} 2 & 1 \\ 5 & -3 \\ -7 & 2 \\ 9 & 0 \end{bmatrix} + \begin{bmatrix} 1 & -8 & 0 \\ 5 & 3 & 2 \\ -6 & 7 & -5 \\ 2 & -1 & 0 \end{bmatrix}$

27. $\begin{bmatrix} 2 & 3 \\ -2 & 4 \end{bmatrix} + \begin{bmatrix} 4 & 3 \\ 7 & 8 \end{bmatrix} - \begin{bmatrix} 3 & 2 \\ 1 & 4 \end{bmatrix}$

28. $\begin{bmatrix} 4 & 3 \\ 1 & 2 \end{bmatrix} - \begin{bmatrix} 1 & 1 \\ 1 & 0 \end{bmatrix} + \begin{bmatrix} 1 & 1 \\ 1 & 4 \end{bmatrix}$

29. $\begin{bmatrix} 2 & -1 \\ 0 & 13 \end{bmatrix} - \begin{bmatrix} 4 & 8 \\ -5 & 7 \end{bmatrix} + \begin{bmatrix} 12 & 7 \\ 5 & 3 \end{bmatrix}$

30. $\begin{bmatrix} 5 & 8 \\ -3 & 1 \end{bmatrix} + \begin{bmatrix} 0 & 1 \\ -2 & -2 \end{bmatrix} + \begin{bmatrix} -5 & -8 \\ 6 & 1 \end{bmatrix}$

31. $\begin{bmatrix} -4x + 2y & -3x + y \\ 6x - 3y & 2x - 5y \end{bmatrix} + \begin{bmatrix} -8x + 6y & 2x \\ 3y - 5x & 6x + 4y \end{bmatrix}$

32. $\begin{bmatrix} 4k - 8y \\ 6z - 3x \\ 2k + 5a \\ -4m + 2n \end{bmatrix} - \begin{bmatrix} 5k + 6y \\ 2z + 5x \\ 4k + 6a \\ 4m - 2n \end{bmatrix}$

33. For matrices $X = \begin{bmatrix} x & y \\ z & w \end{bmatrix}$ and $0 = \begin{bmatrix} 0 & 0 \\ 0 & 0 \end{bmatrix}$, find the matrix $0 - X$.

Using matrices $O = \begin{bmatrix} 0 & 0 \\ 0 & 0 \end{bmatrix}$, $P = \begin{bmatrix} m & n \\ p & q \end{bmatrix}$, $T = \begin{bmatrix} r & s \\ t & u \end{bmatrix}$, and $X = \begin{bmatrix} x & y \\ z & w \end{bmatrix}$, verify the statements in Exercises 34–37.

34. $X + T = T + X$ (commutative property of addition of matrices)

35. $X + (T + P) = (X + T) + P$ (associative property of addition of matrices)

36. $X - X = O$ (inverse property of addition of matrices)

37. $P + O = P$ (identity property of addition of matrices)

38. Which of the above properties are valid for matrices that are not square?

APPLICATIONS

Business and Economics

39. Management   A toy company has plants in Boston, Chicago, and Seattle that manufacture toy phones and calculators. The following matrix gives the production costs (in dollars) for each item at the Boston plant:

	Phones	Calculators
Material	4.27	6.94
Labor	3.45	3.65

a. In Chicago, a phone costs $4.05 for material and $3.27 for labor; a calculator costs $7.01 for material and $3.51 for labor. In Seattle, material costs are $4.40 for a phone and $6.90 for a calculator; labor costs are $3.54 for a phone and $3.76 for a calculator. Write the production cost matrices for Chicago and Seattle.

b. Suppose labor costs increase by $0.11 per item in Chicago and material costs there increase by $0.37 for a phone and $0.42 for a calculator. What is the new production cost matrix for Chicago?

40. Management There are three convenience stores in Folsom. This week, store I sold 88 loaves of bread, 48 qt of milk, 16 jars of peanut butter, and 112 lb of cold cuts. Store II sold 105 loaves of bread, 72 qt of milk, 21 jars of peanut butter, and 147 lb of cold cuts. Store III sold 60 loaves of bread, 40 qt of milk, no peanut butter, and 50 lb of cold cuts.

a. Use a 4×3 matrix to express the sales information for the three stores.

b. During the following week, sales on these products at store I increased by 25%; sales at store II increased by 1/3; and sales at store III increased by 10%. Write the sales matrix for that week.

c. Write a matrix that represents total sales over the two-week period.

Life Sciences

41. Dietetics A dietician prepares a diet specifying the amounts a patient should eat of four basic food groups: group I, meats; group II, fruits and vegetables; group III, breads and starches; group IV, milk products. Amounts are given in "exchanges" that represent 1 oz (meat), 1/2 cup (fruits and vegetables), 1 slice (bread), 8 oz (milk), or other suitable measurements.

a. The number of "exchanges" for breakfast for each of the four food groups, respectively, are 2, 1, 2, and 1; for lunch, 3, 2, 2, and 1; and for dinner, 4, 3, 2, and 1. Write a 3×4 matrix using this information.

b. The amounts of fat, carbohydrates, and protein (in appropriate units) in each food group, respectively, are as follows.

  Fat: 5, 0, 0, 10

  Carbohydrates: 0, 10, 15, 12

  Protein: 7, 1, 2, 8

Use this information to write a 4×3 matrix.

c. There are 8 calories per exchange of fat, 4 calories per exchange of carbohydrates, and 5 calories per exchange of protein. Summarize this data in a 3×1 matrix.

42. Animal Growth At the beginning of a laboratory experiment, five baby rats measured 5.6, 6.4, 6.9, 7.6, and 6.1 cm in length, and weighed 144, 138, 149, 152, and 146 g, respectively.

a. Write a 2×5 matrix using this information.

b. At the end of two weeks, their lengths (in centimeters) were 10.2, 11.4, 11.4, 12.7, and 10.8 and their weights (in grams) were 196, 196, 225, 250, and 230. Write a 2×5 matrix with this information.

c. Use matrix subtraction and the matrices found in parts a and b to write a matrix that gives the amount of change in length and weight for each rat.

d. During the third week, the rats grew by the amounts shown in the matrix below.

$$\begin{array}{c} \text{Length} \\ \text{Weight} \end{array} \begin{bmatrix} 1.8 & 1.5 & 2.3 & 1.8 & 2.0 \\ 25 & 22 & 29 & 33 & 20 \end{bmatrix}$$

What were their lengths and weights at the end of this week?

43. Testing Medication A drug company is testing 200 patients to see if Painfree (a new headache medicine) is effective. Half the patients receive Painfree and half receive a placebo. The data on the first 50 patients is summarized in this matrix:

$$\begin{array}{c} \\ \text{Painfree} \\ \text{Placebo} \end{array} \begin{array}{cc} \multicolumn{2}{c}{\text{Pain Relief Obtained}} \\ \text{Yes} \quad \text{No} \\ \begin{bmatrix} 22 & 3 \\ 8 & 17 \end{bmatrix} \end{array}.$$

a. Of those who took the placebo, how many got relief?

b. Of those who took the new medication, how many got no relief?

c. The test was repeated on three more groups of 50 patients each, with the results summarized by these matrices.

$$\begin{bmatrix} 21 & 4 \\ 6 & 19 \end{bmatrix} \quad \begin{bmatrix} 19 & 6 \\ 10 & 15 \end{bmatrix} \quad \begin{bmatrix} 23 & 2 \\ 3 & 22 \end{bmatrix}$$

Find the total results for all 200 patients.

d. On the basis of these results, does it appear that Painfree is effective?

44. Motorcycle Helmets The following table shows the percentage of motorcyclists in various regions of the country who used helmets compliant with federal safety regulations and the percentage who used helmets that were noncompliant in two recent years. *Source: NHTSA.*

2008	Compliant	Noncompliant
Northeast	45	8
Midwest	67	16
South	61	14
West	71	5

2009	Compliant	Noncompliant
Northeast	61	15
Midwest	67	8
South	65	6
West	83	4

a. Write two matrices for the 2008 and 2009 helmet usage.

b. Use the two matrices from part a to write a matrix showing the change in helmet usage from 2008 to 2009.

c. Analyze the results from part b and discuss the extent to which changes from 2008 to 2009 differ from one region to another.

45. Life Expectancy The following table gives the life expectancy of African American males and females and white American males and females at the beginning of each decade since 1970. *Source: The New York Times 2010 Almanac.*

Year	African American Male	African American Female	White American Male	White American Female
1970	60.0	68.3	68.0	75.6
1980	63.8	72.5	70.7	78.1
1990	64.5	73.6	72.7	79.4
2000	68.3	75.2	74.9	80.1

a. Write a matrix for the life expectancy of African Americans.

b. Write a matrix for the life expectancy of white Americans.

c. Use the matrices from parts a and b to write a matrix showing the difference between the two groups.

d. Analyze the results from part c and discuss any noticeable trends.

46. Educational Attainment The table below gives the educational attainment of the U.S. population 25 years and older since 1970. *Source: U. S. Census Bureau.*

Year	Male Percentage with 4 Years of High School or More	Male Percentage with 4 Years of College or More	Female Percentage with 4 Years of High School or More	Female Percentage with 4 Years of College or More
1970	55.0	14.1	55.4	8.2
1980	69.2	20.9	68.1	13.6
1990	77.7	24.4	77.5	18.4
2000	84.2	27.8	84.0	23.6
2008	85.9	30.1	87.2	28.8

a. Write a matrix for the educational attainment of males.

b. Write a matrix for the educational attainment of females.

c. Use the matrices from parts a and b to write a matrix showing the difference in educational attainment between males and females since 1970.

47. Educational Attainment The following table gives the educational attainment of African Americans and Hispanic Americans 25 years and older since 1980. *Source: U. S. Census Bureau.*

a. Write a matrix for the educational attainment of African Americans.

b. Write a matrix for the educational attainment of Hispanic Americans.

Year	African American Percentage with 4 Years of High School or More	African American Percentage with 4 Years of College or More	Hispanic American Percentage with 4 Years of High School or More	Hispanic American Percentage with 4 Years of College or More
1980	51.2	7.9	45.3	7.9
1985	59.8	11.1	47.9	8.5
1990	66.2	11.3	50.8	9.2
1995	73.8	13.2	53.4	9.3
2000	78.5	16.5	57.0	10.6
2008	83.0	19.6	62.3	13.3

c. Use the matrices from parts a and b to write a matrix showing the difference in educational attainment between African and Hispanic Americans.

General Interest

48. Animal Interactions When two kittens named Cauchy and Cliché were introduced into a household with Jamie (an older cat) and Musk (a dog), the interactions among animals were complicated. The two kittens liked each other and Jamie, but didn't like Musk. Musk liked everybody, but Jamie didn't like any of the other animals.

a. Write a 4 × 4 matrix in which rows (and columns) 1, 2, 3, and 4 refer to Musk, Jamie, Cauchy, and Cliché. Make an element a 1 if the animal for that row likes the animal for that column, and otherwise make the element a 0. Assume every animal likes herself.

b. Within a few days, Cauchy and Cliché decided that they liked Musk after all. Write a 4 × 4 matrix, as you did in part a, representing the new situation.

Courtesy of Raymond N. Greenwell

YOUR TURN ANSWERS

1. (a) Does not exist (b) $\begin{bmatrix} 4 & 2 & 9 \\ -1 & -2 & 11 \end{bmatrix}$

2. $\begin{bmatrix} 2 & 6 & 1 \\ 3 & 6 & -5 \end{bmatrix}$

4 Multiplication of Matrices

APPLY IT   **What is a contractor's total cost for materials required for various types of model homes?**
Matrix multiplication will be used to answer this question in Example 6.

We begin by defining the product of a real number and a matrix. In work with matrices, a real number is called a **scalar**.

Product of a Matrix and a Scalar
The product of a scalar k and a matrix X is the matrix kX, each of whose elements is k times the corresponding element of X.

EXAMPLE 1   Scalar Product of a Matrix

Calculate $-5A$, where $A = \begin{bmatrix} 3 & 4 \\ 0 & -1 \end{bmatrix}$.

SOLUTION

$$(-5)\begin{bmatrix} 3 & 4 \\ 0 & -1 \end{bmatrix} = \begin{bmatrix} -15 & -20 \\ 0 & 5 \end{bmatrix}.$$

Finding the product of two matrices is more involved, but such multiplication is important in solving practical problems. To understand the reasoning behind matrix multiplication, it may be helpful to consider another example concerning EZ Life Company discussed in the previous section. Suppose sofas and chairs of the same model are often sold as sets. Matrix W shows the number of sets of each model in each warehouse.

$$\begin{array}{c} \\ \text{New York} \\ \text{Chicago} \\ \text{San Francisco} \end{array} \begin{array}{ccc} A & B & C \\ \begin{bmatrix} 10 & 7 & 3 \\ 5 & 9 & 6 \\ 4 & 8 & 2 \end{bmatrix} \end{array} = W$$

If the selling price of a model-A set is $1000, of a model-B set $1200, and of a model-C set $1400, the total value of the sets in the New York warehouse is found as follows.

		Value of Furniture		
Type	Number of Sets		Price of Set	Total
A	10	×	$1000	= $10,000
B	7	×	$1200	= $8400
C	3	×	$1400	= $4200
	(Total for New York)			$22,600

The total value of the three kinds of sets in New York is $22,600.

The work done in the table above is summarized as follows:

$$10(\$1000) + 7(\$1200) + 3(\$1400) = \$22,600.$$

In the same way, we find that the Chicago sets have a total value of

$$5(\$1000) + 9(\$1200) + 6(\$1400) = \$24,200,$$

and in San Francisco, the total value of the sets is

$$4(\$1000) + 8(\$1200) + 2(\$1400) = \$16,400.$$

The selling prices can be written as a column matrix P, and the total value in each location as another column matrix, V.

$$\begin{bmatrix} 1000 \\ 1200 \\ 1400 \end{bmatrix} = P \qquad \begin{bmatrix} 22,600 \\ 24,200 \\ 16,400 \end{bmatrix} = V$$

Look at the elements of W and P below; multiplying the first, second, and third elements of the first row of W by the first, second, and third elements, respectively, of the column matrix P and then adding these products gives the first element in V. Doing the same thing with the second row of W gives the second element of V; the third row of W leads to the third element of V, suggesting that it is reasonable to write the product of matrices

$$W = \begin{bmatrix} 10 & 7 & 3 \\ 5 & 9 & 6 \\ 4 & 8 & 2 \end{bmatrix} \qquad \text{and} \qquad P = \begin{bmatrix} 1000 \\ 1200 \\ 1400 \end{bmatrix}$$

as

$$WP = \begin{bmatrix} 10 & 7 & 3 \\ 5 & 9 & 6 \\ 4 & 8 & 2 \end{bmatrix} \begin{bmatrix} 1000 \\ 1200 \\ 1400 \end{bmatrix} = \begin{bmatrix} 22,600 \\ 24,200 \\ 16,400 \end{bmatrix} = V.$$

The product was found by multiplying the elements of *rows* of the matrix on the left and the corresponding elements of the *column* of the matrix on the right, and then finding the sum of these separate products. Notice that the product of a 3×3 matrix and a 3×1 matrix is a 3×1 matrix. Notice also that each element of the product of two matrices is a sum of products. This is exactly what you do when you go to the store and buy 8 candy bars at \$0.80 each, 4 bottles of water at \$1.25 each, and so forth, and calculate the total as $8 \times 0.80 + 4 \times 1.25 + \cdots$.

The product AB of an $m \times n$ matrix A and an $n \times k$ matrix B is found as follows. Multiply each element of the first row of A by the corresponding element of the *first column* of B. The sum of these n products is the *first-row, first-column* element of AB. Similarly, the sum of the products found by multiplying the elements of the *first row* of A by the corresponding elements of the *second column* of B gives the *first-row, second-column* element of AB, and so on.

Product of Two Matrices

Let A be an $m \times n$ matrix and let B be an $n \times k$ matrix. To find the element in the ith row and jth column of the **product matrix** AB, multiply each element in the ith row of A by the corresponding element in the jth column of B, and then add these products. The product matrix AB is an $m \times k$ matrix.

EXAMPLE 2 Matrix Product

Find the product AB of matrices

$$A = \begin{bmatrix} 2 & 3 & -1 \\ 4 & 2 & 2 \end{bmatrix} \qquad \text{and} \qquad B = \begin{bmatrix} 1 \\ 8 \\ 6 \end{bmatrix}.$$

SOLUTION Since A is 2×3 and B is 3×1, we can find the product matrix AB.

Step 1 Multiply the elements of the first row of A and the corresponding elements of the column of B.

$$\begin{bmatrix} 2 & 3 & -1 \\ 4 & 2 & 2 \end{bmatrix} \begin{bmatrix} 1 \\ 8 \\ 6 \end{bmatrix} \qquad 2 \cdot 1 + 3 \cdot 8 + (-1) \cdot 6 = 20$$

Thus, 20 is the first-row entry of the product matrix AB.

Step 2 Multiply the elements of the second row of A and the corresponding elements of B.

$$\begin{bmatrix} 2 & 3 & -1 \\ 4 & 2 & 2 \end{bmatrix}\begin{bmatrix} 1 \\ 8 \\ 6 \end{bmatrix} \quad \mathbf{4 \cdot 1 + 2 \cdot 8 + 2 \cdot 6} = 32$$

The second-row entry of the product matrix AB is 32.

Step 3 Write the product as a column matrix using the two entries found above.

$$AB = \begin{bmatrix} 2 & 3 & -1 \\ 4 & 2 & 2 \end{bmatrix}\begin{bmatrix} 1 \\ 8 \\ 6 \end{bmatrix} = \begin{bmatrix} 20 \\ 32 \end{bmatrix}$$

Note that the product of a 2×3 matrix and a 3×1 matrix is a 2×1 matrix.

EXAMPLE 3   Matrix Product

Find the product CD of matrices

$$C = \begin{bmatrix} -3 & 4 & 2 \\ 5 & 0 & 4 \end{bmatrix} \quad \text{and} \quad D = \begin{bmatrix} -6 & 4 \\ 2 & 3 \\ 3 & -2 \end{bmatrix}.$$

SOLUTION   Since C is 2×3 and D is 3×2, we can find the product matrix CD.

Step 1
$$\begin{bmatrix} -3 & 4 & 2 \\ 5 & 0 & 4 \end{bmatrix}\begin{bmatrix} -6 & 4 \\ 2 & 3 \\ 3 & -2 \end{bmatrix} \quad \mathbf{(-3) \cdot (-6) + 4 \cdot 2 + 2 \cdot 3} = 32$$

Step 2
$$\begin{bmatrix} -3 & 4 & 2 \\ 5 & 0 & 4 \end{bmatrix}\begin{bmatrix} -6 & 4 \\ 2 & 3 \\ 3 & -2 \end{bmatrix} \quad \mathbf{(-3) \cdot 4 + 4 \cdot 3 + 2 \cdot (-2)} = -4$$

Step 3
$$\begin{bmatrix} -3 & 4 & 2 \\ 5 & 0 & 4 \end{bmatrix}\begin{bmatrix} -6 & 4 \\ 2 & 3 \\ 3 & -2 \end{bmatrix} \quad \mathbf{5 \cdot (-6) + 0 \cdot 2 + 4 \cdot 3} = -18$$

Step 4
$$\begin{bmatrix} -3 & 4 & 2 \\ 5 & 0 & 4 \end{bmatrix}\begin{bmatrix} -6 & 4 \\ 2 & 3 \\ 3 & -2 \end{bmatrix} \quad \mathbf{5 \cdot 4 + 0 \cdot 3 + 4 \cdot (-2)} = 12$$

Step 5 The product is

YOUR TURN 1 Calculate the product AB where $A = \begin{bmatrix} 3 & 4 \\ 1 & 2 \end{bmatrix}$ and $B = \begin{bmatrix} 1 & -2 \\ -2 & -4 \end{bmatrix}$.

$$CD = \begin{bmatrix} -3 & 4 & 2 \\ 5 & 0 & 4 \end{bmatrix}\begin{bmatrix} -6 & 4 \\ 2 & 3 \\ 3 & -2 \end{bmatrix} = \begin{bmatrix} 32 & -4 \\ -18 & 12 \end{bmatrix}.$$

Here the product of a 2×3 matrix and a 3×2 matrix is a 2×2 matrix.

TRY YOUR TURN 1

NOTE   One way to avoid errors in matrix multiplication is to lower the first matrix so it is below and to the left of the second matrix, and then write the product in the space between the two matrices. For example, to multiply the matrices in Example 2, we could rewrite the product as shown on the following page.

$$\downarrow$$
$$\begin{bmatrix} -6 & 4 \\ 2 & 3 \\ 3 & -2 \end{bmatrix}$$
$$\rightarrow \begin{bmatrix} -3 & 4 & 2 \\ 5 & 0 & 4 \end{bmatrix} \begin{bmatrix} & * & \end{bmatrix}$$

To find the entry where the * is, for example, multiply the row and the column indicated by the arrows: $5 \cdot (-6) + 0 \cdot 2 + 4 \cdot 3 = -18$.

As the definition of matrix multiplication shows,

> the product AB of two matrices A and B can be found only if the number of columns of A is the same as the number of rows of B.

The final product will have as many rows as A and as many columns as B.

EXAMPLE 4   Matrix Product

Suppose matrix A is 2×2 and matrix B is 2×4. Can the products AB and BA be calculated? If so, what is the size of each product?

SOLUTION   The following diagram helps decide the answers to these questions.

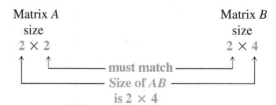

The product of A and B can be found because A has two columns and B has two rows. The size of the product is 2×4.

Matrix B Matrix A
size   size
2×4 2×2

do not match

The product BA cannot be found because B has 4 columns and A has 2 rows.

EXAMPLE 5   Comparing Matrix Products *AB* and *BA*

Find AB and BA, given

$$A = \begin{bmatrix} 1 & -3 \\ 7 & 2 \\ -2 & 5 \end{bmatrix} \quad \text{and} \quad B = \begin{bmatrix} 1 & 0 & -1 \\ 3 & 1 & 4 \end{bmatrix}.$$

SOLUTION

$$AB = \begin{bmatrix} 1 & -3 \\ 7 & 2 \\ -2 & 5 \end{bmatrix} \begin{bmatrix} 1 & 0 & -1 \\ 3 & 1 & 4 \end{bmatrix}$$

$$= \begin{bmatrix} -8 & -3 & -13 \\ 13 & 2 & 1 \\ 13 & 5 & 22 \end{bmatrix}$$

YOUR TURN 2 Calculate each product AB and BA, if possible, where $A = \begin{bmatrix} 3 & 5 & -1 \\ 2 & 4 & -2 \end{bmatrix}$ and $B = \begin{bmatrix} 3 & -4 \\ -5 & -3 \end{bmatrix}$.

$$BA = \begin{bmatrix} 1 & 0 & -1 \\ 3 & 1 & 4 \end{bmatrix} \begin{bmatrix} 1 & -3 \\ 7 & 2 \\ -2 & 5 \end{bmatrix}$$

$$= \begin{bmatrix} 3 & -8 \\ 2 & 13 \end{bmatrix}$$

Matrix multiplication is easily performed on a graphing calculator. Figure 13 in the margin below shows the results. The matrices A and B were already entered into the calculator.

TRY YOUR TURN 2

TECHNOLOGY NOTE | Matrix multiplication can also be easily done with a spreadsheet. See the *Graphing Calculator and Excel Spreadsheet Manual* available with this textbook for details.

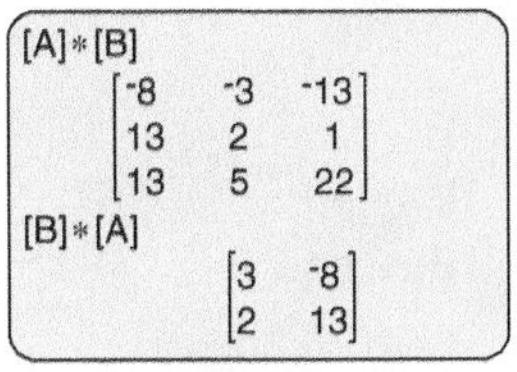

[A]*[B]
$$\begin{bmatrix} -8 & -3 & -13 \\ 13 & 2 & 1 \\ 13 & 5 & 22 \end{bmatrix}$$
[B]*[A]
$$\begin{bmatrix} 3 & -8 \\ 2 & 13 \end{bmatrix}$$

FIGURE 13

Notice in Example 5 that $AB \neq BA$; matrices AB and BA aren't even the same size. In Example 4, we showed that they may not both exist. This means that matrix multiplication is *not* commutative. Even if both A and B are square matrices, in general, matrices AB and BA are not equal. (See Exercise 31.) Of course, there may be special cases in which they are equal, but this is not true in general.

CAUTION Since matrix multiplication is not commutative, always be careful to multiply matrices in the correct order.

Matrix multiplication *is* associative, however. For example, if

$$C = \begin{bmatrix} 3 & 2 \\ 0 & -4 \\ -1 & 1 \end{bmatrix},$$

then $(AB)C = A(BC)$, where A and B are the matrices given in Example 5. (Verify this.) Also, there is a distributive property of matrices such that, for appropriate matrices A, B, and C,

$$A(B + C) = AB + AC.$$

(See Exercises 32 and 33.) Other properties of matrix multiplication involving scalars are included in the exercises. Multiplicative inverses and multiplicative identities are defined in the next section.

EXAMPLE 6 **Home Construction**

A contractor builds three kinds of houses, models A, B, and C, with a choice of two styles, Spanish and contemporary. Matrix P shows the number of each kind of house planned for a new 100-home subdivision. The amounts for each of the exterior materials depend primarily on the style of the house. These amounts are shown in matrix Q. (Concrete is in cubic yards, lumber in units of 1000 board feet, brick in 1000s, and shingles in units of 100 ft^2.) Matrix R gives the cost in dollars for each kind of material.

$$
\begin{array}{c}
 & \overset{\text{Spanish}\quad\text{Contemporary}}{} \\
\begin{array}{c}\text{Model A}\\ \text{Model B}\\ \text{Model C}\end{array}
\begin{bmatrix} 0 & 30 \\ 10 & 20 \\ 20 & 20 \end{bmatrix} = P
\end{array}
$$

$$
\begin{array}{c}
 & \overset{\text{Concrete}\quad\text{Lumber}\quad\text{Brick}\quad\text{Shingles}}{} \\
\begin{array}{c}\text{Spanish}\\ \text{Contemporary}\end{array}
\begin{bmatrix} 10 & 2 & 0 & 2 \\ 50 & 1 & 20 & 2 \end{bmatrix} = Q
\end{array}
$$

$$
\begin{array}{c}
 & \overset{\text{Cost per Unit}}{} \\
\begin{array}{c}\text{Concrete}\\ \text{Lumber}\\ \text{Brick}\\ \text{Shingles}\end{array}
\begin{bmatrix} 20 \\ 180 \\ 60 \\ 25 \end{bmatrix} = R
\end{array}
$$

(a) What is the total cost of these materials for each model?

SOLUTION To find the cost for each model, first find PQ, which shows the amount of each material needed for each model.

$$
PQ = \begin{bmatrix} 0 & 30 \\ 10 & 20 \\ 20 & 20 \end{bmatrix} \begin{bmatrix} 10 & 2 & 0 & 2 \\ 50 & 1 & 20 & 2 \end{bmatrix}
$$

$$
= \begin{array}{c}
\overset{\text{Concrete}\quad\text{Lumber}\quad\text{Brick}\quad\text{Shingles}}{}\\
\begin{bmatrix} 1500 & 30 & 600 & 60 \\ 1100 & 40 & 400 & 60 \\ 1200 & 60 & 400 & 80 \end{bmatrix}
\end{array}
\begin{array}{c}\text{Model A}\\ \text{Model B}\\ \text{Model C}\end{array}
$$

Now multiply PQ and R, the cost matrix, to get the total cost of the exterior materials for each model.

$$
\begin{bmatrix} 1500 & 30 & 600 & 60 \\ 1100 & 40 & 400 & 60 \\ 1200 & 60 & 400 & 80 \end{bmatrix}
\begin{bmatrix} 20 \\ 180 \\ 60 \\ 25 \end{bmatrix} =
\begin{array}{c}
\overset{\text{Cost}}{}\\
\begin{bmatrix} 72,900 \\ 54,700 \\ 60,800 \end{bmatrix}
\end{array}
\begin{array}{c}\text{Model A}\\ \text{Model B}\\ \text{Model C}\end{array}
$$

The total cost of materials is $72,900 for model A, $54,700 for model B, and $60,800 for model C.

(b) How much of each of the four kinds of material must be ordered?

SOLUTION The totals of the columns of matrix PQ will give a matrix whose elements represent the total amounts of each material needed for the subdivision. Call this matrix T, and write it as a row matrix.

$$
T = \begin{bmatrix} 3800 & 130 & 1400 & 200 \end{bmatrix}
$$

Thus, 3800 yd^3 of concrete, 130,000 board feet of lumber, 1,400,000 bricks, and 20,000 ft^2 of shingles are needed.

(c) What is the total cost for exterior materials?

SOLUTION For the total cost of all the exterior materials, find the product of matrix T, the matrix showing the total amount of each material, and matrix R, the cost matrix. (To multiply these and get a 1×1 matrix representing total cost, we need a 1×4 matrix multiplied by a 4×1 matrix. This is why T was written as a row matrix in (b) above.)

$$TR = \begin{bmatrix} 3800 & 130 & 1400 & 200 \end{bmatrix} \begin{bmatrix} 20 \\ 180 \\ 60 \\ 25 \end{bmatrix} = \begin{bmatrix} 188{,}400 \end{bmatrix}$$

The total cost for exterior materials is $188,400.

(d) Suppose the contractor builds the same number of homes in five subdivisions. Calculate the total amount of each exterior material for each model for all five subdivisions.

SOLUTION   Multiply PQ by the scalar 5, as follows.

$$5(PQ) = 5\begin{bmatrix} 1500 & 30 & 600 & 60 \\ 1100 & 40 & 400 & 60 \\ 1200 & 60 & 400 & 80 \end{bmatrix} = \begin{bmatrix} 7500 & 150 & 3000 & 300 \\ 5500 & 200 & 2000 & 300 \\ 6000 & 300 & 2000 & 400 \end{bmatrix}$$

The total amount of concrete needed for model A homes, for example, is 7500 yd^3.

Meaning of a Matrix Product
It is helpful to use a notation that keeps track of the quantities a matrix represents. We will use the notation

meaning of the rows/meaning of the columns,

that is, writing the meaning of the rows first, followed by the meaning of the columns. In Example 6, we would use the notation models/styles for matrix P, styles/materials for matrix Q, and materials/cost for matrix R. In multiplying PQ, we are multiplying models/styles by styles/materials. The result is models/materials. Notice that styles, the common quantity in both P and Q, was eliminated in the product PQ. By this method, the product $(PQ)R$ represents models/cost.

In practical problems this notation helps us decide in which order to multiply matrices so that the results are meaningful. In Example 6(c) either RT or TR can be calculated. Since T represents subdivisions/materials and R represents materials/cost, the product TR gives subdivisions/cost, while the product RT is meaningless.

4 EXERCISES

Let $A = \begin{bmatrix} -2 & 4 \\ 0 & 3 \end{bmatrix}$ and $B = \begin{bmatrix} -6 & 2 \\ 4 & 0 \end{bmatrix}$. **Find each value.**

1. $2A$ **2.** $-3B$ **3.** $-6A$

4. $5B$ **5.** $-4A + 5B$ **6.** $7B - 3A$

In Exercises 7–12, the sizes of two matrices A and B are given. Find the sizes of the product AB and the product BA, whenever these products exist.

7. A is 2×2, and B is 2×2.   **8.** A is 3×3, and B is 3×3.

9. A is 3×4, and B is 4×4.   **10.** A is 4×3, and B is 3×6.

11. A is 4×2, and B is 3×4.   **12.** A is 3×2, and B is 1×3.

13. To find the product matrix AB, the number of _____ of A must be the same as the number of _____ of B.

14. The product matrix AB has the same number of _____ as A and the same number of _____ as B.

Find each matrix product, if possible.

15. $\begin{bmatrix} 2 & -1 \\ 5 & 8 \end{bmatrix} \begin{bmatrix} 3 \\ -2 \end{bmatrix}$ **16.** $\begin{bmatrix} -1 & 5 \\ 7 & 0 \end{bmatrix} \begin{bmatrix} 6 \\ 2 \end{bmatrix}$

17. $\begin{bmatrix} 2 & -1 & 7 \\ -3 & 0 & -4 \end{bmatrix} \begin{bmatrix} 5 \\ 10 \\ 2 \end{bmatrix}$ **18.** $\begin{bmatrix} 5 & 2 \\ 7 & 6 \\ 1 & 0 \end{bmatrix} \begin{bmatrix} 1 & 4 & 0 \\ 2 & -1 & 2 \end{bmatrix}$

19. $\begin{bmatrix} 2 & -1 \\ 3 & 6 \end{bmatrix} \begin{bmatrix} -1 & 0 & 4 \\ 5 & -2 & 0 \end{bmatrix}$ **20.** $\begin{bmatrix} 6 & 0 & -4 \\ 1 & 2 & 5 \\ 10 & -1 & 3 \end{bmatrix} \begin{bmatrix} 1 \\ 2 \\ 0 \end{bmatrix}$

21. $\begin{bmatrix} 2 & 2 & -1 \\ 3 & 0 & 1 \end{bmatrix} \begin{bmatrix} 0 & 2 \\ -1 & 4 \\ 0 & 2 \end{bmatrix}$ **22.** $\begin{bmatrix} -3 & 1 & 0 \\ 6 & 0 & 8 \end{bmatrix} \begin{bmatrix} 3 \\ -1 \\ -2 \end{bmatrix}$

23. $\begin{bmatrix} 1 & 2 \\ 3 & 4 \end{bmatrix}\begin{bmatrix} -1 & 5 \\ 7 & 0 \end{bmatrix}$

24. $\begin{bmatrix} 2 & 8 \\ -7 & 5 \end{bmatrix}\begin{bmatrix} 1 & 0 \\ 0 & 1 \end{bmatrix}$

25. $\begin{bmatrix} -2 & -3 & 7 \\ 1 & 5 & 6 \end{bmatrix}\begin{bmatrix} 1 \\ 2 \\ 3 \end{bmatrix}$

26. $\begin{bmatrix} 2 \\ -9 \\ 12 \end{bmatrix}\begin{bmatrix} 1 & 0 & -1 \end{bmatrix}$

27. $\left(\begin{bmatrix} 2 & 1 \\ -3 & -6 \\ 4 & 0 \end{bmatrix}\begin{bmatrix} 1 & -2 \\ 2 & -1 \end{bmatrix}\right)\begin{bmatrix} 3 \\ 1 \end{bmatrix}$

28. $\begin{bmatrix} 2 & 1 \\ -3 & -6 \\ 4 & 0 \end{bmatrix}\left(\begin{bmatrix} 1 & -2 \\ 2 & -1 \end{bmatrix}\begin{bmatrix} 3 \\ 1 \end{bmatrix}\right)$

29. $\begin{bmatrix} 2 & -2 \\ 1 & -1 \end{bmatrix}\left(\begin{bmatrix} 4 & 3 \\ 1 & 2 \end{bmatrix}+\begin{bmatrix} 7 & 0 \\ -1 & 5 \end{bmatrix}\right)$

30. $\begin{bmatrix} 2 & -2 \\ 1 & -1 \end{bmatrix}\begin{bmatrix} 4 & 3 \\ 1 & 2 \end{bmatrix}+\begin{bmatrix} 2 & -2 \\ 1 & -1 \end{bmatrix}\begin{bmatrix} 7 & 0 \\ -1 & 5 \end{bmatrix}$

31. Let $A = \begin{bmatrix} -2 & 4 \\ 1 & 3 \end{bmatrix}$ and $B = \begin{bmatrix} -2 & 1 \\ 3 & 6 \end{bmatrix}$.

  a. Find AB.

  b. Find BA.

  c. Did you get the same answer in parts a and b?

  d. In general, for matrices A and B such that AB and BA both exist, does AB always equal BA?

Given matrices $P = \begin{bmatrix} m & n \\ p & q \end{bmatrix}$, $X = \begin{bmatrix} x & y \\ z & w \end{bmatrix}$, and $T = \begin{bmatrix} r & s \\ t & u \end{bmatrix}$, verify that the statements in Exercises 32–35 are true. The statements are valid for any matrices whenever matrix multiplication and addition can be carried out. This, of course, depends on the size of the matrices.

32. $(PX)T = P(XT)$ (associative property: see Exercises 27 and 28)

33. $P(X + T) = PX + PT$ (distributive property: see Exercises 29 and 30)

34. $k(X + T) = kX + kT$ for any real number k.

35. $(k + h)P = kP + hP$ for any real numbers k and h.

36. Let I be the matrix $I = \begin{bmatrix} 1 & 0 \\ 0 & 1 \end{bmatrix}$, and let matrices P, X, and T be defined as for Exercises 32–35.

  a. Find IP, PI, and IX.

  b. Without calculating, guess what the matrix IT might be.

  c. Suggest a reason for naming a matrix such as I an *identity matrix*.

37. Show that the system of linear equations

$$2x_1 + 3x_2 + x_3 = 5$$
$$x_1 - 4x_2 + 5x_3 = 8$$

can be written as the matrix equation

$$\begin{bmatrix} 2 & 3 & 1 \\ 1 & -4 & 5 \end{bmatrix}\begin{bmatrix} x_1 \\ x_2 \\ x_3 \end{bmatrix} = \begin{bmatrix} 5 \\ 8 \end{bmatrix}.$$

38. Let $A = \begin{bmatrix} 1 & 2 \\ -3 & 5 \end{bmatrix}$, $X = \begin{bmatrix} x_1 \\ x_2 \end{bmatrix}$, and $B = \begin{bmatrix} -4 \\ 12 \end{bmatrix}$. Show that the equation $AX = B$ represents a linear system of two equations in two unknowns. Solve the system and substitute into the matrix equation to check your results.

Use a computer or graphing calculator and the following matrices to find the matrix products and sums in Exercises 39–41.

$$A = \begin{bmatrix} 2 & 3 & -1 & 5 & 10 \\ 2 & 8 & 7 & 4 & 3 \\ -1 & -4 & -12 & 6 & 8 \\ 2 & 5 & 7 & 1 & 4 \end{bmatrix}$$

$$B = \begin{bmatrix} 9 & 3 & 7 & -6 \\ -1 & 0 & 4 & 2 \\ -10 & -7 & 6 & 9 \\ 8 & 4 & 2 & -1 \\ 2 & -5 & 3 & 7 \end{bmatrix}$$

$$C = \begin{bmatrix} -6 & 8 & 2 & 4 & -3 \\ 1 & 9 & 7 & -12 & 5 \\ 15 & 2 & -8 & 10 & 11 \\ 4 & 7 & 9 & 6 & -2 \\ 1 & 3 & 8 & 23 & 4 \end{bmatrix}$$

$$D = \begin{bmatrix} 5 & -3 & 7 & 9 & 2 \\ 6 & 8 & -5 & 2 & 1 \\ 3 & 7 & -4 & 2 & 11 \\ 5 & -3 & 9 & 4 & -1 \\ 0 & 3 & 2 & 5 & 1 \end{bmatrix}$$

39. a. Find AC. **b.** Find CA. **c.** Does $AC = CA$?

40. a. Find CD. **b.** Find DC. **c.** Does $CD = DC$?

41. a. Find $C + D$. **b.** Find $(C + D)B$. **c.** Find CB.

  d. Find DB. **e.** Find $CB + DB$.

  f. Does $(C + D)B = CB + DB$?

42. Which property of matrices does Exercise 41 illustrate?

APPLICATIONS

Business and Economics

43. Cost Analysis The four departments of Spangler Enterprises need to order the following amounts of the same products.

	Paper	Tape	Binders	Memo Pads	Pens
Department 1	10	4	3	5	6
Department 2	7	2	2	3	8
Department 3	4	5	1	0	10
Department 4	0	3	4	5	5

The unit price (in dollars) of each product is given below for two suppliers.

	Supplier A	Supplier B
Paper	2	3
Tape	1	1
Binders	4	3
Memo Pads	3	3
Pens	1	2

a. Use matrix multiplication to get a matrix showing the comparative costs for each department for the products from the two suppliers.

b. Find the total cost over all departments to buy products from each supplier. From which supplier should the company make the purchase?

44. Cost Analysis The Mundo Candy Company makes three types of chocolate candy: Cheery Cherry, Mucho Mocha, and Almond Delight. The company produces its products in San Diego, Mexico City, and Managua using two main ingredients: chocolate and sugar.

a. Each kilogram of Cheery Cherry requires 0.5 kg of sugar and 0.2 kg of chocolate; each kilogram of Mucho Mocha requires 0.4 kg of sugar and 0.3 kg of chocolate; and each kilogram of Almond Delight requires 0.3 kg of sugar and 0.3 kg of chocolate. Put this information into a 2×3 matrix called A, labeling the rows and columns.

b. The cost of 1 kg of sugar is $4 in San Diego, $2 in Mexico City, and $1 in Managua. The cost of 1 kg of chocolate is $3 in San Diego, $5 in Mexico City, and $7 in Managua. Put this information into a matrix called C in such a way that when you multiply it with your matrix from part a, you get a matrix representing the ingredient cost of producing each type of candy in each city.

c. Only one of the two products AC and CA is meaningful. Determine which one it is, calculate the product, and describe what the entries represent.

d. From your answer to part c, what is the combined sugar-and-chocolate cost to produce 1 kg of Mucho Mocha in Managua?

e. Mundo Candy needs to quickly produce a special shipment of 100 kg of Cheery Cherry, 200 kg of Mucho Mocha, and 500 kg of Almond Delight, and it decides to select one factory to fill the entire order. Use matrix multiplication to determine in which city the total sugar-and-chocolate cost to produce the order is the smallest.

45. Management In Exercise 39 from Section 2.3, consider the matrices $\begin{bmatrix} 4.27 & 6.94 \\ 3.45 & 3.65 \end{bmatrix}$, $\begin{bmatrix} 4.05 & 7.01 \\ 3.27 & 3.51 \end{bmatrix}$, and $\begin{bmatrix} 4.40 & 6.90 \\ 3.54 & 3.76 \end{bmatrix}$ for the production costs at the Boston, Chicago, and Seattle plants, respectively.

a. Assume each plant makes the same number of each item. Write a matrix that expresses the average production costs for all three plants.

b. In part b of Exercise 39 in Section 2.3, cost increases for the Chicago plant resulted in a new production cost matrix $\begin{bmatrix} 4.42 & 7.43 \\ 3.38 & 3.62 \end{bmatrix}$. Following those cost increases the Boston plant was closed and production divided evenly between the Chicago and Seattle plants. What is the matrix that now expresses the average production cost for the entire country?

46. House Construction Consider the matrices P, Q, and R given in Example 6.

a. Find and interpret the matrix product QR.

b. Verify that $P(QR)$ is equal to $(PQ)R$ calculated in Example 5.

47. Shoe Sales Sal's Shoes and Fred's Footwear both have outlets in California and Arizona. Sal's sells shoes for $80, sandals for $40, and boots for $120. Fred's prices are $60, $30, and $150 for shoes, sandals, and boots, respectively. Half of all sales in California stores are shoes, 1/4 are sandals, and 1/4 are boots. In Arizona the fractions are 1/5 shoes, 1/5 sandals, and 3/5 boots.

a. Write a 2×3 matrix called P representing prices for the two stores and three types of footwear.

b. Write a 3×2 matrix called F representing the fraction of each type of footwear sold in each state.

c. Only one of the two products PF and FP is meaningful. Determine which one it is, calculate the product, and describe what the entries represent.

d. From your answer to part c, what is the average price for a pair of footwear at an outlet of Fred's in Arizona?

48. Management In Exercise 40 from Section 2.3, consider the matrix

$$\begin{bmatrix} 88 & 105 & 60 \\ 48 & 72 & 40 \\ 16 & 21 & 0 \\ 112 & 147 & 50 \end{bmatrix}$$

expressing the sales information for the three stores.

a. Write a 3×1 matrix expressing the factors by which sales in each store should be multiplied to reflect the fact that sales increased during the following week by 25%, 1/3, and 10% in stores I, II, and III, respectively, as described in part b of Exercise 40 from Section 2.3.

b. Multiply the matrix expressing sales information by the matrix found in part a of this exercise to find the sales for all three stores in the second week.

Life Sciences

49. Dietetics In Exercise 41 from Section 2.3, label the matrices

$$\begin{bmatrix} 2 & 1 & 2 & 1 \\ 3 & 2 & 2 & 1 \\ 4 & 3 & 2 & 1 \end{bmatrix}, \quad \begin{bmatrix} 5 & 0 & 7 \\ 0 & 10 & 1 \\ 0 & 15 & 2 \\ 10 & 12 & 8 \end{bmatrix}, \quad \text{and} \quad \begin{bmatrix} 8 \\ 4 \\ 5 \end{bmatrix}$$

found in parts a, b, and c, respectively, X, Y, and Z.

a. Find the product matrix XY. What do the entries of this matrix represent?

b. Find the product matrix YZ. What do the entries represent?

c. Find the products $(XY)Z$ and $X(YZ)$ and verify that they are equal. What do the entries represent?

50. Motorcycle Helmets In Exercise 44 from Section 2.3, you constructed matrices that represented usage of motorcycle helmets for 2008 and 2009. Use matrix operations to combine these two matrices to form one matrix that represents the average of the two years.

51. Life Expectancy In Exercise 45 from Section 2.3, you constructed matrices that represent the life expectancy of African American and white American males and females. Use matrix operations to combine these two matrices to form one matrix that represents the combined life expectancy of both races at the beginning of each decade since 1970. Use the fact that of the combined African and white American population, African Americans are about one-sixth of the total and white Americans about five-sixths. (*Hint:* Multiply the matrix for African Americans by 1/6 and the matrix for the white Americans by 5/6, and then add the results.)

52. Northern Spotted Owl Population In an attempt to save the endangered northern spotted owl, the U.S. Fish and Wildlife Service imposed strict guidelines for the use of 12 million acres of Pacific Northwest forest. This decision led to a national debate between the logging industry and environmentalists. Mathematical ecologists have created a mathematical model to analyze population dynamics of the northern spotted owl by dividing the female owl population into three categories: juvenile (up to 1 year old), subadult (1 to 2 years), and adult (over 2 years old). By analyzing these three subgroups, it is possible to use the number of females in each subgroup at time n to estimate the number of females in each group at any time $n + 1$ with the following matrix equation:

$$\begin{bmatrix} j_{n+1} \\ s_{n+1} \\ a_{n+1} \end{bmatrix} = \begin{bmatrix} 0 & 0 & 0.33 \\ 0.18 & 0 & 0 \\ 0 & 0.71 & 0.94 \end{bmatrix} \begin{bmatrix} j_n \\ s_n \\ a_n \end{bmatrix},$$

where j_n is the number of juveniles, s_n is the number of subadults, and a_n is the number of adults at time n. *Source: Conservation Biology.*

a. If there are currently 4000 female northern spotted owls made up of 900 juveniles, 500 subadults, and 2600 adults, use a graphing calculator or spreadsheet and matrix operations to determine the total number of female owls for each of the next 5 years. (*Hint:* Round each answer to the nearest whole number after each matrix multiplication.)

John and Karen Hollingsworth/U.S. Fish and Wildlife Service

b. With advanced techniques from linear algebra, it is possible to show that in the long run, the following holds.

$$\begin{bmatrix} j_{n+1} \\ s_{n+1} \\ a_{n+1} \end{bmatrix} \approx 0.98359 \begin{bmatrix} j_n \\ s_n \\ a_n \end{bmatrix}$$

What can we conclude about the long-term survival of the northern spotted owl?

c. Notice that only 18 percent of the juveniles become subadults. Assuming that, through better habitat management, this number could be increased to 40 percent, rework part a. Discuss possible reasons why only 18 percent of the juveniles become subadults. Under the new assumption, what can you conclude about the long-term survival of the northern spotted owl?

Social Sciences

53. World Population The 2010 birth and death rates per million for several regions and the world population (in millions) by region are given in the following tables. *Source: U. S. Census Bureau.*

	Births	Deaths
Africa	0.0346	0.0118
Asia	0.0174	0.0073
Latin America	0.0189·	0.0059
North America	0.0135	0.0083
Europe	0.0099	0.0103

	Population (millions)				
Year	Africa	Asia	Latin America	North America	Europe
1970	361	2038	286	227	460
1980	473	2494	362	252	484
1990	627	2978	443	278	499
2000	803	3435	524	314	511
2010	1013	3824	591	344	522

a. Write the information in each table as a matrix.

b. Use the matrices from part a to find the total number (in millions) of births and deaths in each year (assuming birth and death rates for all years are close to these in 2010).

c. Using the results of part b, compare the number of births in 1970 and in 2010. Also compare the birth rates from part a. Which gives better information?

d. Using the results of part b, compare the number of deaths in 1980 and in 2010. Discuss how this comparison differs from a comparison of death rates from part a.

YOUR TURN ANSWERS

1. $\begin{bmatrix} -5 & -22 \\ -3 & -10 \end{bmatrix}$ **2.** *AB* does not exist; $BA = \begin{bmatrix} 1 & -1 & 5 \\ -21 & -37 & 11 \end{bmatrix}$

5 Matrix Inverses

APPLY IT   One top leader needs to get an important message to one of her agents. How can she encrypt the message to ensure secrecy?
This question is answered in Example 7.

In this section, we introduce the idea of a matrix inverse, which is comparable to the reciprocal of a real number. This will allow us to solve a matrix equation.

The real number 1 is the *multiplicative* identity for real numbers: for any real number a, we have $a \cdot 1 = 1 \cdot a = a$. In this section, we define a *multiplicative identity matrix I* that has properties similar to those of the number 1. We then use the definition of matrix I to find the *multiplicative inverse* of any square matrix that has an inverse.

If I is to be the identity matrix, both of the products AI and IA must equal A. This means that an identity matrix exists only for square matrices. The 2×2 **identity matrix** that satisfies these conditions is

$$I = \begin{bmatrix} 1 & 0 \\ 0 & 1 \end{bmatrix}.$$

To check that I, as defined above, is really the 2×2 identity, let

$$A = \begin{bmatrix} a & b \\ c & d \end{bmatrix}.$$

Then AI and IA should both equal A.

$$AI = \begin{bmatrix} a & b \\ c & d \end{bmatrix} \begin{bmatrix} 1 & 0 \\ 0 & 1 \end{bmatrix} = \begin{bmatrix} a(1) + b(0) & a(0) + b(1) \\ c(1) + d(0) & c(0) + d(1) \end{bmatrix} = \begin{bmatrix} a & b \\ c & d \end{bmatrix} = A$$

$$IA = \begin{bmatrix} 1 & 0 \\ 0 & 1 \end{bmatrix} \begin{bmatrix} a & b \\ c & d \end{bmatrix} = \begin{bmatrix} 1(a) + 0(c) & 1(b) + 0(d) \\ 0(a) + 1(c) & 0(b) + 1(d) \end{bmatrix} = \begin{bmatrix} a & b \\ c & d \end{bmatrix} = A$$

This verifies that I has been defined correctly.

It is easy to verify that the identity matrix I is unique. Suppose there is another identity; call it J. Then IJ must equal I, because J is an identity, and IJ must also equal J, because I is an identity. Thus $I = J$.

The identity matrices for 3×3 matrices and 4×4 matrices, respectively, are

$$I = \begin{bmatrix} 1 & 0 & 0 \\ 0 & 1 & 0 \\ 0 & 0 & 1 \end{bmatrix} \quad \text{and} \quad I = \begin{bmatrix} 1 & 0 & 0 & 0 \\ 0 & 1 & 0 & 0 \\ 0 & 0 & 1 & 0 \\ 0 & 0 & 0 & 1 \end{bmatrix}.$$

By generalizing, we can find an $n \times n$ identity matrix for any value of n.

Recall that the multiplicative inverse of the nonzero real number a is $1/a$. The product of a and its multiplicative inverse $1/a$ is 1. Given a matrix A, can a **multiplicative inverse matrix A^{-1}** (read "A-inverse") that will satisfy both

$$AA^{-1} = I \quad \text{and} \quad A^{-1}A = I$$

be found? For a given matrix, we often can find an inverse matrix by using the row operations of Section 2.

NOTE A^{-1} does not mean $1/A$; here, A^{-1} is just the notation for the multiplicative inverse of matrix A. Also, only square matrices can have inverses because both $A^{-1}A$ and AA^{-1} must exist and be equal to an identity matrix of the same size.

EXAMPLE 1 Inverse Matrices

Verify that the matrices $A = \begin{bmatrix} 1 & 3 \\ 2 & 5 \end{bmatrix}$ and $B = \begin{bmatrix} -5 & 3 \\ 2 & -1 \end{bmatrix}$ are inverses of each other.

SOLUTION Multiply A times B as in the previous section:

$$AB = \begin{bmatrix} 1 & 3 \\ 2 & 5 \end{bmatrix}\begin{bmatrix} -5 & 3 \\ 2 & -1 \end{bmatrix} = \begin{bmatrix} 1 & 0 \\ 0 & 1 \end{bmatrix}.$$

Similarly,

$$BA = \begin{bmatrix} -5 & 3 \\ 2 & -1 \end{bmatrix}\begin{bmatrix} 1 & 3 \\ 2 & 5 \end{bmatrix} = \begin{bmatrix} 1 & 0 \\ 0 & 1 \end{bmatrix}.$$

Since $AB = BA = I$, A and B are inverses of each other.

If an inverse exists, it is unique. That is, any given square matrix has no more than one inverse. The proof of this is left to Exercise 50 in this section.

As an example, let us find the inverse of

$$A = \begin{bmatrix} 1 & 3 \\ -1 & 2 \end{bmatrix}.$$

Let the unknown inverse matrix be

$$A^{-1} = \begin{bmatrix} x & y \\ z & w \end{bmatrix}.$$

By the definition of matrix inverse, $AA^{-1} = I$, or

$$AA^{-1} = \begin{bmatrix} 1 & 3 \\ -1 & 2 \end{bmatrix}\begin{bmatrix} x & y \\ z & w \end{bmatrix} = \begin{bmatrix} 1 & 0 \\ 0 & 1 \end{bmatrix}.$$

By matrix multiplication,

$$\begin{bmatrix} x + 3z & y + 3w \\ -x + 2z & -y + 2w \end{bmatrix} = \begin{bmatrix} 1 & 0 \\ 0 & 1 \end{bmatrix}.$$

Setting corresponding elements equal gives the system of equations

$$x \quad\quad + 3z \quad\quad = 1 \tag{1}$$
$$y \quad\quad + 3w = 0 \tag{2}$$
$$-x \quad + 2z \quad\quad = 0 \tag{3}$$
$$-y \quad\quad + 2w = 1. \tag{4}$$

Since equations (1) and (3) involve only x and z, while equations (2) and (4) involve only y and w, these four equations lead to two systems of equations,

$$\begin{array}{ll} x + 3z = 1 \\ -x + 2z = 0 \end{array} \quad \text{and} \quad \begin{array}{ll} y + 3w = 0 \\ -y + 2w = 1. \end{array}$$

Writing the two systems as augmented matrices gives

$$\begin{bmatrix} 1 & 3 & | & 1 \\ -1 & 2 & | & 0 \end{bmatrix} \quad \text{and} \quad \begin{bmatrix} 1 & 3 & | & 0 \\ -1 & 2 & | & 1 \end{bmatrix}.$$

Systems of Linear Equations and Matrices

Each of these systems can be solved by the Gauss-Jordan method. Notice, however, that the elements to the left of the vertical bar are identical. The two systems can be combined into the single matrix

$$\begin{bmatrix} 1 & 3 & | & 1 & 0 \\ -1 & 2 & | & 0 & 1 \end{bmatrix}.$$

This is of the form $[A|I]$. It is solved simultaneously as follows.

$R_1 + R_2 \rightarrow R_2$ $\begin{bmatrix} 1 & 3 & | & 1 & 0 \\ 0 & 5 & | & 1 & 1 \end{bmatrix}$ Get 0 in the second-row, first-column position.

$-3R_2 + 5R_1 \rightarrow R_1$ $\begin{bmatrix} 5 & 0 & | & 2 & -3 \\ 0 & 5 & | & 1 & 1 \end{bmatrix}$ Get 0 in the first-row, second-column position.

$\frac{1}{5}R_1 \rightarrow R_1$ $\begin{bmatrix} 1 & 0 & | & \frac{2}{5} & -\frac{3}{5} \\ 0 & 1 & | & \frac{1}{5} & \frac{1}{5} \end{bmatrix}$ Get 1's down the diagonal.

The numbers in the first column to the right of the vertical bar give the values of x and z. The second column gives the values of y and w. That is,

$$\begin{bmatrix} 1 & 0 & | & x & y \\ 0 & 1 & | & z & w \end{bmatrix} = \begin{bmatrix} 1 & 0 & | & \frac{2}{5} & -\frac{3}{5} \\ 0 & 1 & | & \frac{1}{5} & \frac{1}{5} \end{bmatrix}$$

so that

$$A^{-1} = \begin{bmatrix} x & y \\ z & w \end{bmatrix} = \begin{bmatrix} \frac{2}{5} & -\frac{3}{5} \\ \frac{1}{5} & \frac{1}{5} \end{bmatrix}.$$

To check, multiply A by A^{-1}. The result should be I.

$$AA^{-1} = \begin{bmatrix} 1 & 3 \\ -1 & 2 \end{bmatrix}\begin{bmatrix} \frac{2}{5} & -\frac{3}{5} \\ \frac{1}{5} & \frac{1}{5} \end{bmatrix} = \begin{bmatrix} \frac{2}{5}+\frac{3}{5} & -\frac{3}{5}+\frac{3}{5} \\ -\frac{2}{5}+\frac{2}{5} & \frac{3}{5}+\frac{2}{5} \end{bmatrix} = \begin{bmatrix} 1 & 0 \\ 0 & 1 \end{bmatrix} = I$$

Verify that $A^{-1}A = I$, also.

Finding a Multiplicative Inverse Matrix
To obtain A^{-1} for any $n \times n$ matrix A for which A^{-1} exists, follow these steps.

1. Form the augmented matrix $[A|I]$, where I is the $n \times n$ identity matrix.
2. Perform row operations on $[A|I]$ to get a matrix of the form $[I|B]$, if this is possible.
3. Matrix B is A^{-1}.

EXAMPLE 2 Inverse Matrix

Find A^{-1} if $A = \begin{bmatrix} 1 & 0 & 1 \\ 2 & -2 & -1 \\ 3 & 0 & 0 \end{bmatrix}$.

**Method 1
Calculating by Hand**

SOLUTION Write the augmented matrix $[A | I]$.

$$[A|I] = \begin{bmatrix} 1 & 0 & 1 & | & 1 & 0 & 0 \\ 2 & -2 & -1 & | & 0 & 1 & 0 \\ 3 & 0 & 0 & | & 0 & 0 & 1 \end{bmatrix}$$

Begin by selecting the row operation that produces a zero for the first element in row 2.

$-2R_1 + R_2 \rightarrow R_2$
$-3R_1 + R_3 \rightarrow R_3$ $\begin{bmatrix} 1 & 0 & 1 & | & 1 & 0 & 0 \\ 0 & -2 & -3 & | & -2 & 1 & 0 \\ 0 & 0 & -3 & | & -3 & 0 & 1 \end{bmatrix}$ Get 0's in the first column.

379

Column 2 already has zeros in the required positions, so work on column 3.

$$\begin{array}{c} R_3 + 3R_1 \to R_1 \\ R_3 + (-1)R_2 \to R_2 \\ \end{array} \left[\begin{array}{ccc|ccc} 3 & 0 & 0 & 0 & 0 & 1 \\ 0 & 2 & 0 & -1 & -1 & 1 \\ 0 & 0 & -3 & -3 & 0 & 1 \end{array}\right] \quad \text{Get 0's in the third column.}$$

Now get 1's down the main diagonal.

$$\begin{array}{c} \frac{1}{3}R_1 \to R_1 \\ \frac{1}{2}R_2 \to R_2 \\ -\frac{1}{3}R_3 \to R_3 \end{array} \left[\begin{array}{ccc|ccc} 1 & 0 & 0 & 0 & 0 & \frac{1}{3} \\ 0 & 1 & 0 & -\frac{1}{2} & -\frac{1}{2} & \frac{1}{2} \\ 0 & 0 & 1 & 1 & 0 & -\frac{1}{3} \end{array}\right] \quad \text{Get 1's down the diagonal.}$$

From the last transformation, the desired inverse is

$$A^{-1} = \begin{bmatrix} 0 & 0 & \frac{1}{3} \\ -\frac{1}{2} & -\frac{1}{2} & \frac{1}{2} \\ 1 & 0 & -\frac{1}{3} \end{bmatrix}.$$

YOUR TURN 1 Find A^{-1} if

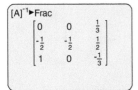

$$A = \begin{bmatrix} 2 & 3 & 1 \\ 1 & -2 & -1 \\ 3 & 3 & 2 \end{bmatrix}.$$

Confirm this by forming the products $A^{-1}A$ and AA^{-1}, both of which should equal I.

⌇ **Method 2**
Graphing Calculator

The inverse of A can also be found with a graphing calculator, as shown in Figure 14 in the margin below. (The matrix A had previously been entered into the calculator.) The entire answer can be viewed by pressing the right and left arrow keys on the calculator.

TRY YOUR TURN 1

▦ **TECHNOLOGY NOTE**

Spreadsheets also have the capability of calculating the inverse of a matrix with a simple command. See the *Graphing Calculator and Excel Spreadsheet Manual* available with this text for details.

```
[A]⁻¹▶Frac
 ⌈ 0     0     1/3 ⌉
 │ -1/2  -1/2  1/2 │
 ⌊ 1     0     -1/3⌋
```

FIGURE 14

EXAMPLE 3   **Inverse Matrix**

Find A^{-1} if $A = \begin{bmatrix} 2 & -4 \\ 1 & -2 \end{bmatrix}$.

SOLUTION   Using row operations to transform the first column of the augmented matrix

$$\left[\begin{array}{cc|cc} 2 & -4 & 1 & 0 \\ 1 & -2 & 0 & 1 \end{array}\right]$$

gives the following results.

$$R_1 + (-2)R_2 \to R_2 \quad \left[\begin{array}{cc|cc} 2 & -4 & 1 & 0 \\ 0 & 0 & 1 & -2 \end{array}\right]$$

Because the last row has all zeros to the left of the vertical bar, there is no way to complete the process of finding the inverse matrix. What is wrong? Just as the real number 0 has no multiplicative inverse, some matrices do not have inverses. Matrix A is an example of a matrix that has no inverse: there is no matrix A^{-1} such that $AA^{-1} = A^{-1}A = I$.

Solving Systems of Equations with Inverses

We used matrices to solve systems of linear equations by the Gauss-Jordan method in Section 2. Another way to use matrices to solve linear systems is to write the system as a matrix equation $AX = B$, where A is the matrix of the coefficients of the variables of the system, X is the matrix of the variables, and B is the matrix of the constants. Matrix A is called the **coefficient matrix**.

To solve the matrix equation $AX = B$, first see if A^{-1} exists. Assuming A^{-1} exists and using the facts that $A^{-1}A = I$ and $IX = X$ gives

$$AX = B$$
$$A^{-1}(AX) = A^{-1}B \quad \text{Multiply both sides by } A^{-1}.$$
$$(A^{-1}A)X = A^{-1}B \quad \text{Associative property}$$
$$IX = A^{-1}B \quad \text{Multiplicative inverse property}$$
$$X = A^{-1}B. \quad \text{Identity property}$$

CAUTION When multiplying by matrices on both sides of a matrix equation, be careful to multiply in the same order on both sides of the equation, since multiplication of matrices is not commutative (unlike multiplication of real numbers).

The work thus far leads to the following method of solving a system of equations written as a matrix equation.

Solving a System $AX = B$ Using Matrix Inverses

To solve a system of equations $AX = B$, where A is the square matrix of coefficients and A^{-1} exists, X is the matrix of variables, and B is the matrix of constants, first find A^{-1}. Then $X = A^{-1}B$.

This method is most practical in solving several systems that have the same coefficient matrix but different constants, as in Example 5 in this section. Then just one inverse matrix must be found.

EXAMPLE 4 Inverse Matrices and Systems of Equations

Use the inverse of the coefficient matrix to solve the linear system

$$2x - 3y = 4$$
$$x + 5y = 2.$$

SOLUTION To represent the system as a matrix equation, use the coefficient matrix of the system together with the matrix of variables and the matrix of constants:

$$A = \begin{bmatrix} 2 & -3 \\ 1 & 5 \end{bmatrix}, \qquad X = \begin{bmatrix} x \\ y \end{bmatrix}, \qquad \text{and} \qquad B = \begin{bmatrix} 4 \\ 2 \end{bmatrix}.$$

The system can now be written in matrix form as the equation $AX = B$ since

$$AX = \begin{bmatrix} 2 & -3 \\ 1 & 5 \end{bmatrix} \begin{bmatrix} x \\ y \end{bmatrix} = \begin{bmatrix} 2x - 3y \\ x + 5y \end{bmatrix} = \begin{bmatrix} 4 \\ 2 \end{bmatrix} = B.$$

To solve the system, first find A^{-1}. Do this by using row operations on matrix $[A|I]$ to get

$$\begin{bmatrix} 1 & 0 & \frac{5}{13} & \frac{3}{13} \\ 0 & 1 & -\frac{1}{13} & \frac{2}{13} \end{bmatrix}.$$

From this result,

$$A^{-1} = \begin{bmatrix} \frac{5}{13} & \frac{3}{13} \\ -\frac{1}{13} & \frac{2}{13} \end{bmatrix}.$$

Next, find the product $A^{-1}B$.

$$A^{-1}B = \begin{bmatrix} \frac{5}{13} & \frac{3}{13} \\ -\frac{1}{13} & \frac{2}{13} \end{bmatrix} \begin{bmatrix} 4 \\ 2 \end{bmatrix} = \begin{bmatrix} 2 \\ 0 \end{bmatrix}.$$

YOUR TURN 2 Use the inverse of the coefficient matrix to solve the linear system
$$5x + 4y = 23$$
$$4x - 3y = 6.$$

Since $X = A^{-1}B$,

$$X = \begin{bmatrix} x \\ y \end{bmatrix} = \begin{bmatrix} 2 \\ 0 \end{bmatrix}.$$

The solution of the system is $(2, 0)$.   TRY YOUR TURN 2

EXAMPLE 5 Fertilizer

Three brands of fertilizer are available that provide nitrogen, phosphoric acid, and soluble potash to the soil. One bag of each brand provides the following units of each nutrient.

		Brand		
		Fertifun	Big Grow	Soakem
Nutrient	*Nitrogen*	1	2	3
	Phosphoric Acid	3	1	2
	Potash	2	0	1

For ideal growth, the soil on a Michigan farm needs 18 units of nitrogen, 23 units of phosphoric acid, and 13 units of potash per acre. The corresponding numbers for a California farm are 31, 24, and 11, and for a Kansas farm are 20, 19, and 15. How many bags of each brand of fertilizer should be used per acre for ideal growth on each farm?

SOLUTION   Rather than solve three separate systems, we consider the single system

$$x + 2y + 3z = a$$
$$3x + y + 2z = b$$
$$2x + z = c,$$

where a, b, and c represent the units of nitrogen, phosphoric acid, and potash needed for the different farms. The system of equations is then of the form $AX = B$, where

$$A = \begin{bmatrix} 1 & 2 & 3 \\ 3 & 1 & 2 \\ 2 & 0 & 1 \end{bmatrix} \quad \text{and} \quad X = \begin{bmatrix} x \\ y \\ z \end{bmatrix}.$$

B has different values for the different farms. We find A^{-1} first, then use it to solve all three systems.

To find A^{-1}, we start with the matrix

$$[A|I] = \begin{bmatrix} 1 & 2 & 3 & | & 1 & 0 & 0 \\ 3 & 1 & 2 & | & 0 & 1 & 0 \\ 2 & 0 & 1 & | & 0 & 0 & 1 \end{bmatrix}$$

and use row operations to get $\left[I|A^{-1}\right]$. The result is

$$A^{-1} = \begin{bmatrix} -\frac{1}{3} & \frac{2}{3} & -\frac{1}{3} \\ -\frac{1}{3} & \frac{5}{3} & -\frac{7}{3} \\ \frac{2}{3} & -\frac{4}{3} & \frac{5}{3} \end{bmatrix}.$$

Now we can solve each of the three systems by using $X = A^{-1}B$.

For the Michigan farm, $B = \begin{bmatrix} 18 \\ 23 \\ 13 \end{bmatrix}$, and

$$X = \begin{bmatrix} -\frac{1}{3} & \frac{2}{3} & -\frac{1}{3} \\ -\frac{1}{3} & \frac{5}{3} & -\frac{7}{3} \\ \frac{2}{3} & -\frac{4}{3} & \frac{5}{3} \end{bmatrix} \begin{bmatrix} 18 \\ 23 \\ 13 \end{bmatrix} = \begin{bmatrix} 5 \\ 2 \\ 3 \end{bmatrix}.$$

Therefore, $x = 5$, $y = 2$, and $z = 3$. Buy 5 bags of Fertifun, 2 bags of Big Grow, and 3 bags of Soakem.

For the California farm, $B = \begin{bmatrix} 31 \\ 24 \\ 11 \end{bmatrix}$, and

$$X = \begin{bmatrix} -\frac{1}{3} & \frac{2}{3} & -\frac{1}{3} \\ -\frac{1}{3} & \frac{5}{3} & -\frac{7}{3} \\ \frac{2}{3} & -\frac{4}{3} & \frac{5}{3} \end{bmatrix} \begin{bmatrix} 31 \\ 24 \\ 11 \end{bmatrix} = \begin{bmatrix} 2 \\ 4 \\ 7 \end{bmatrix}.$$

Buy 2 bags of Fertifun, 4 bags of Big Grow, and 7 bags of Soakem.

For the Kansas farm, $B = \begin{bmatrix} 20 \\ 19 \\ 15 \end{bmatrix}$. Verify that this leads to $x = 1$, $y = -10$, and $z = 13$. We cannot have a negative number of bags, so this solution is impossible. In buying enough bags to meet all of the nutrient requirements, the farmer must purchase an excess of some nutrients. In the next two chapters, we will study a method of solving such problems at a minimum cost.

In Example 5, using the matrix inverse method of solving the systems involved considerably less work than using row operations for each of the three systems.

EXAMPLE 6 **Solving an Inconsistent System of Equations**

Use the inverse of the coefficient matrix to solve the system

$$2x - 4y = 13$$
$$x - 2y = 1.$$

SOLUTION We saw in Example 3 that the coefficient matrix $\begin{bmatrix} 2 & -4 \\ 1 & -2 \end{bmatrix}$ does not have an inverse. This means that the given system either has no solution or has an infinite number of solutions. Verify that this system is inconsistent and has no solution.

NOTE If a matrix has no inverse, then a corresponding system of equations might have either no solutions or an infinite number of solutions, and we instead use the echelon or Gauss-Jordan method. In Example 3, we saw that the matrix $\begin{bmatrix} 2 & -4 \\ 1 & -2 \end{bmatrix}$ had no inverse. The reason is that the first row of this matrix is double the second row. The system

$$2x - 4y = 2$$
$$x - 2y = 1$$

has an infinite number of solutions because the first equation is double the second equation. The system

$$2x - 4y = 13$$
$$x - 2y = 1$$

has no solutions because the left side of the first equation is double the left side of the second equation, but the right side is not.

EXAMPLE 7 **Cryptography**

Throughout the Cold War and as the Internet has grown and developed, the need for sophisticated methods of coding and decoding messages has increased. Although there are many methods of encrypting messages, one fairly sophisticated method uses matrix operations. This method first assigns a number to each letter of the alphabet. The simplest way to do this is to assign the number 1 to A, 2 to B, and so on, with the number 27 used to represent a space between words.

APPLY IT

For example, the message *math is cool* can be divided into groups of three letters and spaces each and then converted into numbers as follows

$$\begin{bmatrix} m \\ a \\ t \end{bmatrix} = \begin{bmatrix} 13 \\ 1 \\ 20 \end{bmatrix}.$$

The entire message would then consist of four 3×1 columns of numbers:

$$\begin{bmatrix} 13 \\ 1 \\ 20 \end{bmatrix}, \quad \begin{bmatrix} 8 \\ 27 \\ 9 \end{bmatrix}, \quad \begin{bmatrix} 19 \\ 27 \\ 3 \end{bmatrix}, \quad \begin{bmatrix} 15 \\ 15 \\ 12 \end{bmatrix}.$$

This code is easy to break, so we further complicate the code by choosing a matrix that has an inverse (in this case a 3×3 matrix) and calculate the products of the matrix and each of the column vectors above.

If we choose the coding matrix

$$A = \begin{bmatrix} 1 & 3 & 4 \\ 2 & 1 & 3 \\ 4 & 2 & 1 \end{bmatrix},$$

then the products of A with each of the column vectors above produce a new set of vectors

$$\begin{bmatrix} 96 \\ 87 \\ 74 \end{bmatrix}, \quad \begin{bmatrix} 125 \\ 70 \\ 95 \end{bmatrix}, \quad \begin{bmatrix} 112 \\ 74 \\ 133 \end{bmatrix}, \quad \begin{bmatrix} 108 \\ 81 \\ 102 \end{bmatrix}.$$

This set of vectors represents our coded message, and it will be transmitted as 96, 87, 74, 125 and so on.

When the intended person receives the message, it is divided into groups of three numbers, and each group is formed into a column matrix. The message is easily decoded if the receiver knows the inverse of the original matrix. The inverse of matrix A is

$$A^{-1} = \begin{bmatrix} -0.2 & 0.2 & 0.2 \\ 0.4 & -0.6 & 0.2 \\ 0 & 0.4 & -0.2 \end{bmatrix}.$$

Thus, the message is decoded by taking the product of the inverse matrix with each column vector of the received message. For example,

$$A^{-1} \begin{bmatrix} 96 \\ 87 \\ 74 \end{bmatrix} = \begin{bmatrix} 13 \\ 1 \\ 20 \end{bmatrix}.$$

YOUR TURN 3 Use the matrix A and its inverse A^{-1} in Example 7 to do the following.

a) Encode the message "Behold".
b) Decode the message 96, 87, 74, 141, 117, 114.

Unless the original matrix or its inverse is known, this type of code can be difficult to break. In fact, very large matrices can be used to encrypt data. It is interesting to note that many mathematicians are employed by the National Security Agency to develop encryption methods that are virtually unbreakable.   **TRY YOUR TURN 3**

5   EXERCISES

Decide whether the given matrices are inverses of each other. (Check to see if their product is the identity matrix *I*.)

1. $\begin{bmatrix} 2 & 1 \\ 5 & 3 \end{bmatrix}$ and $\begin{bmatrix} 3 & -1 \\ -5 & 2 \end{bmatrix}$ **2.** $\begin{bmatrix} 1 & -4 \\ 2 & -7 \end{bmatrix}$ and $\begin{bmatrix} -7 & 4 \\ -2 & 1 \end{bmatrix}$

3. $\begin{bmatrix} 2 & 6 \\ 2 & 4 \end{bmatrix}$ and $\begin{bmatrix} -1 & 2 \\ 2 & -4 \end{bmatrix}$ **4.** $\begin{bmatrix} -1 & 2 \\ 3 & -5 \end{bmatrix}$ and $\begin{bmatrix} -5 & -2 \\ -3 & -1 \end{bmatrix}$

5. $\begin{bmatrix} 2 & 0 & 1 \\ 1 & 1 & 2 \\ 0 & 1 & 0 \end{bmatrix}$ and $\begin{bmatrix} 1 & 1 & -1 \\ 0 & 1 & 0 \\ -1 & -2 & 2 \end{bmatrix}$

6. $\begin{bmatrix} 0 & 1 & 0 \\ 0 & 0 & -2 \\ 1 & -1 & 0 \end{bmatrix}$ and $\begin{bmatrix} 1 & 0 & 1 \\ 1 & 0 & 0 \\ 0 & -1 & 0 \end{bmatrix}$

7. $\begin{bmatrix} 1 & 3 & 3 \\ 1 & 4 & 3 \\ 1 & 3 & 4 \end{bmatrix}$ and $\begin{bmatrix} 7 & -3 & -3 \\ -1 & 1 & 0 \\ -1 & 0 & 1 \end{bmatrix}$

8. $\begin{bmatrix} 1 & 0 & 0 \\ -1 & -2 & 3 \\ 0 & 1 & 0 \end{bmatrix}$ and $\begin{bmatrix} 1 & 0 & 0 \\ 0 & 0 & 1 \\ \frac{1}{3} & \frac{1}{3} & \frac{2}{3} \end{bmatrix}$

9. Does a matrix with a row of all zeros have an inverse? Why?

 10. Matrix A has A^{-1} as its inverse. What does $(A^{-1})^{-1}$ equal? (*Hint:* Experiment with a few matrices to see what you get.)

Find the inverse, if it exists, for each matrix.

11. $\begin{bmatrix} 1 & -1 \\ 2 & 0 \end{bmatrix}$ 　　**12.** $\begin{bmatrix} 1 & 1 \\ 2 & 3 \end{bmatrix}$

13. $\begin{bmatrix} 3 & -1 \\ -5 & 2 \end{bmatrix}$ 　　**14.** $\begin{bmatrix} -3 & -8 \\ 1 & 3 \end{bmatrix}$

15. $\begin{bmatrix} 1 & -3 \\ -2 & 6 \end{bmatrix}$ 　　**16.** $\begin{bmatrix} 5 & 10 \\ -3 & -6 \end{bmatrix}$

17. $\begin{bmatrix} 1 & 0 & 0 \\ 0 & -1 & 0 \\ 1 & 0 & 1 \end{bmatrix}$ 　　**18.** $\begin{bmatrix} 1 & 3 & 0 \\ 0 & 2 & -1 \\ 1 & 0 & 2 \end{bmatrix}$

19. $\begin{bmatrix} -1 & -1 & -1 \\ 4 & 5 & 0 \\ 0 & 1 & -3 \end{bmatrix}$ 　　**20.** $\begin{bmatrix} 2 & 1 & 0 \\ 0 & 3 & 1 \\ 4 & -1 & -3 \end{bmatrix}$

21. $\begin{bmatrix} 1 & 2 & 3 \\ -3 & -2 & -1 \\ -1 & 0 & 1 \end{bmatrix}$ 　　**22.** $\begin{bmatrix} 2 & 0 & 4 \\ 1 & 0 & -1 \\ 3 & 0 & -2 \end{bmatrix}$

23. $\begin{bmatrix} 1 & 3 & -2 \\ 2 & 7 & -3 \\ 3 & 8 & -5 \end{bmatrix}$ 　　**24.** $\begin{bmatrix} 4 & 1 & -4 \\ 2 & 1 & -1 \\ -2 & -4 & 5 \end{bmatrix}$

25. $\begin{bmatrix} 1 & -2 & 3 & 0 \\ 0 & 1 & -1 & 1 \\ -2 & 2 & -2 & 4 \\ 0 & 2 & -3 & 1 \end{bmatrix}$ 　**26.** $\begin{bmatrix} 1 & 1 & 0 & 2 \\ 2 & -1 & 1 & -1 \\ 3 & 3 & 2 & -2 \\ 1 & 2 & 1 & 0 \end{bmatrix}$

Solve each system of equations by using the inverse of the coefficient matrix if it exists and by the echelon method if the inverse doesn't exist.

27. $2x + 5y = 15$
$\quad\;\; x + 4y = 9$

28. $-x + 2y = 15$
$\quad\;\; -2x - y = 20$

29. $2x + y = 5$
$\quad\;\; 5x + 3y = 13$

30. $-x - 2y = 8$
$\quad\;\; 3x + 4y = 24$

31. $3x - 2y = 3$
$\quad\;\; 7x - 5y = 0$

32. $3x - 6y = 1$
$\quad\;\; -5x + 9y = -1$

33. $-x - 8y = 12$
$\quad\;\; 3x + 24y = -36$

34. $2x + 7y = 14$
$\quad\;\; 4x + 14y = 28$

Solve each system of equations by using the inverse of the coefficient matrix if it exists and by the Gauss-Jordan method if the inverse doesn't exist. (The inverses for the first four problems were found in Exercises 19, 20, 23, and 24.)

35. $-x - y - z = 1$
$\quad\;\; 4x + 5y \quad\;\; = -2$
$\quad\;\;\quad\;\; y - 3z = 3$

36. $2x + y \quad\;\; = 1$
$\quad\;\;\quad\;\; 3y + z = 8$
$\quad\;\; 4x - y - 3z = 8$

37. $x + 3y - 2z = 4$
$\quad\;\; 2x + 7y - 3z = 8$
$\quad\;\; 3x + 8y - 5z = -4$

38. $4x + y - 4z = 17$
$\quad\;\; 2x + y - z = 12$
$\quad\;\; -2x - 4y + 5z = 17$

39. $2x - 2y = 5$
$\quad\;\; 4y + 8z = 7$
$\quad\;\; x + 2z = 1$

40. $x + 2z = -1$
$\quad\;\; y - z = 5$
$\quad\;\; x + 2y = 7$

Solve each system of equations by using the inverse of the coefficient matrix. (The inverses were found in Exercises 25 and 26.)

41. $x - 2y + 3z \quad\;\; = 4$
$\quad\;\;\quad\;\; y - z + w = -8$
$\quad\;\; -2x + 2y - 2z + 4w = 12$
$\quad\;\;\quad\;\; 2y - 3z + w = -4$

42. $x + y \quad\;\; + 2w = 3$
$\quad\;\; 2x - y + z - w = 3$
$\quad\;\; 3x + 3y + 2z - 2w = 5$
$\quad\;\; x + 2y + z \quad\;\; = 3$

Let $A = \begin{bmatrix} a & b \\ c & d \end{bmatrix}$ and $0 = \begin{bmatrix} 0 & 0 \\ 0 & 0 \end{bmatrix}$ in Exercises 43–48.

43. Show that $IA = A$. 　　**44.** Show that $AI = A$.

45. Show that $A \cdot O = O$. 　　**46.** Find A^{-1}.
　　　　　　　　　　　　　　(Assume $ad - bc \neq 0$.)

47. Show that $A^{-1}A = I$. 　　**48.** Show that $AA^{-1} = I$.

49. Using the definition and properties listed in this section, show that for square matrices A and B of the same size, if $AB = O$ and if A^{-1} exists, then $B = O$, where O is a matrix whose elements are all zeros.

50. Prove that, if it exists, the inverse of a matrix is unique. (*Hint:* Assume there are two inverses B and C for some matrix A, so that $AB = BA = I$ and $AC = CA = I$. Multiply the first equation by C and the second by B.)

Use matrices C and D in Exercises 51–55.

$$C = \begin{bmatrix} -6 & 8 & 2 & 4 & -3 \\ 1 & 9 & 7 & -12 & 5 \\ 15 & 2 & -8 & 10 & 11 \\ 4 & 7 & 9 & 6 & -2 \\ 1 & 3 & 8 & 23 & 4 \end{bmatrix}, \; D = \begin{bmatrix} 5 & -3 & 7 & 9 & 2 \\ 6 & 8 & -5 & 2 & 1 \\ 3 & 7 & -4 & 2 & 11 \\ 5 & -3 & 9 & 4 & -1 \\ 0 & 3 & 2 & 5 & 1 \end{bmatrix}$$

51. Find C^{-1}. 　　**52.** Find $(CD)^{-1}$.

53. Find D^{-1}. 　　**54.** Is $C^{-1}D^{-1} = (CD)^{-1}$?

55. Is $D^{-1}C^{-1} = (CD)^{-1}$?

Solve the matrix equation $AX = B$ for X by finding A^{-1}, given A and B as follows.

56. $A = \begin{bmatrix} 2 & -5 & 7 \\ 4 & -3 & 2 \\ 15 & 2 & 6 \end{bmatrix}, \; B = \begin{bmatrix} -2 \\ 5 \\ 8 \end{bmatrix}$

57. $A = \begin{bmatrix} 2 & 5 & 7 & 9 \\ 1 & 3 & -4 & 6 \\ -1 & 0 & 5 & 8 \\ 2 & -2 & 4 & 10 \end{bmatrix}, \; B = \begin{bmatrix} 3 \\ 7 \\ -1 \\ 5 \end{bmatrix}$

58. $A = \begin{bmatrix} 3 & 2 & -1 & -2 & 6 \\ -5 & 17 & 4 & 3 & 15 \\ 7 & 9 & -3 & -7 & 12 \\ 9 & -2 & 1 & 4 & 8 \\ 1 & 21 & 9 & -7 & 25 \end{bmatrix}, \; B = \begin{bmatrix} -2 \\ 5 \\ 3 \\ -8 \\ 25 \end{bmatrix}$

APPLICATIONS

Business and Economics

Solve each exercise by using the inverse of the coefficient matrix to solve a system of equations.

59. Analysis of Orders The Bread Box Bakery sells three types of cakes, each requiring the amounts of the basic ingredients shown in the following matrix.

$$\begin{array}{c} \\ \\ \text{Ingredient} \end{array} \begin{array}{c} \\ \text{Flour (in cups)} \\ \text{Sugar (in cups)} \\ \text{Eggs} \end{array} \overset{\begin{array}{ccc} \text{Type of Cake} \\ \text{I} & \text{II} & \text{III} \end{array}}{\begin{bmatrix} 2 & 4 & 2 \\ 2 & 1 & 2 \\ 2 & 1 & 3 \end{bmatrix}}$$

To fill its daily orders for these three kinds of cake, the bakery uses 72 cups of flour, 48 cups of sugar, and 60 eggs.

a. Write a 3×1 matrix for the amounts used daily.

b. Let the number of daily orders for cakes be a 3×1 matrix X with entries x_1, x_2, and x_3. Write a matrix equation that can be solved for X, using the given matrix and the matrix from part a.

c. Solve the equation from part b to find the number of daily orders for each type of cake.

60. Production Requirements An electronics company produces transistors, resistors, and computer chips. Each transistor requires 3 units of copper, 1 unit of zinc, and 2 units of glass. Each resistor requires 3, 2, and 1 units of the three materials, and each computer chip requires 2, 1, and 2 units of these materials, respectively. How many of each product can be made with the following amounts of materials?

a. 810 units of copper, 410 units of zinc, and 490 units of glass

b. 765 units of copper, 385 units of zinc, and 470 units of glass

c. 1010 units of copper, 500 units of zinc, and 610 units of glass

61. Investments An investment firm recommends that a client invest in AAA-, A-, and B-rated bonds. The average yield on AAA bonds is 6%, on A bonds 6.5%, and on B bonds 8%. The client wants to invest twice as much in AAA bonds as in B bonds. How much should be invested in each type of bond under the following conditions?

a. The total investment is $25,000, and the investor wants an annual return of $1650 on the three investments.

b. The values in part a are changed to $30,000 and $1985, respectively.

c. The values in part a are changed to $40,000 and $2660, respectively.

62. Production Pretzels cost $4 per lb, dried fruit $5 per lb, and nuts $9 per lb. The three ingredients are to be combined in a trail mix containing twice the weight of pretzels as dried fruit. How many pounds of each should be used to produce the following amounts at the given cost?

a. 140 lb at $6 per lb

b. 100 lb at $7.60 per lb

c. 125 lb at $6.20 per lb

Life Sciences

63. Vitamins Greg Tobin mixes together three types of vitamin tablets. Each Super Vim tablet contains, among other things, 15 mg of niacin and 12 I.U. of vitamin E. The figures for a Multitab tablet are 20 mg and 15 I.U., and for a Mighty Mix are 25 mg and 35 I.U. How many of each tablet are there if the total number of tablets, total amount of niacin, and total amount of vitamin E are as follows?

a. 225 tablets, 4750 mg of niacin, and 5225 I.U. of vitamin E

b. 185 tablets, 3625 mg of niacin, and 3750 I.U. of vitamin E

c. 230 tablets, 4450 mg of niacin, and 4210 I.U. of vitamin E

General Interest

64. Encryption Use the matrices presented in Example 7 of this section to do the following:

a. Encode the message, "All is fair in love and war."

b. Decode the message 138, 81, 102, 101, 67, 109, 162, 124, 173, 210, 150, 165.

65. Encryption Use the methods presented in Example 7 along with the given matrix B to do the following.

$$B = \begin{bmatrix} 2 & 4 & 6 \\ -1 & -4 & -3 \\ 0 & 1 & -1 \end{bmatrix}$$

a. Encode the message, "To be or not to be."

b. Find the inverse of B.

c. Use the inverse of B to decode the message 116, -60, -15, 294, -197, -2, 148, -92, -9, 96, -64, 4, 264, -182, -2.

66. Music During a marching band's half-time show, the band members generally line up in such a way that a common shape is recognized by the fans. For example, as illustrated in the figure, a band might form a letter T, where an **x** represents a member of the band. As the music is played, the band will either create a new shape or rotate the original shape. In doing this, each member of the band will need to move from one point on the field to another. For larger bands, keeping track of who goes where can be a daunting task. However, it is possible to use matrix inverses to make the process a bit easier. The entire process is calculated by knowing how three band members, all of whom cannot be in a straight line, will move from the current position to a new position. For example, in the figure, we can see that there are band members at $(50, 0)$, $(50, 15)$, and $(45, 20)$. We will assume that these three band members move to $(40, 10)$, $(55, 10)$, and $(60, 15)$, respectively. *Source: The College Mathematics Journal.*

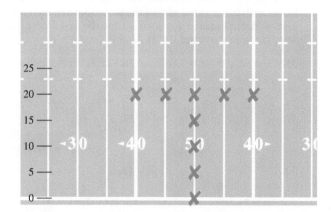

a. Find the inverse of $B = \begin{bmatrix} 50 & 50 & 45 \\ 0 & 15 & 20 \\ 1 & 1 & 1 \end{bmatrix}$.

b. Find $A = \begin{bmatrix} 40 & 55 & 60 \\ 10 & 10 & 15 \\ 1 & 1 & 1 \end{bmatrix} B^{-1}$.

c. Use the result of part b to find the new position of the other band members. What is the shape of the new position? (*Hint:* Multiply the matrix A by a 3×1 column vector with

the first two components equal to the original position of each band member and the third component equal to 1. The new position of the band member is in the first two components of the product.)

1. $\begin{bmatrix} 1/8 & 3/8 & 1/8 \\ 5/8 & -1/8 & -3/8 \\ -9/8 & -3/8 & 7/8 \end{bmatrix}$ **2.** (3, 2) **3. a.** 49, 33, 26, 67, 54, 88 **b.** matrix

6 Input-Output Models

APPLY IT

What production levels are needed to keep an economy going and to supply demands from outside the economy?

A *method for solving such questions is developed in this section and applied in Examples 3 and 4.*

Wassily Leontief (1906–1999) developed an interesting and powerful application of matrix theory to economics and was recognized for this contribution with the Nobel prize in economics in 1973. His matrix models for studying the interdependencies in an economy are called *input-output* models. In practice these models are very complicated, with many variables. Only simple examples with a few variables are discussed here.

Input-output models are concerned with the production and flow of goods (and perhaps services). In an economy with n basic commodities, or sectors, the production of each commodity uses some (perhaps all) of the commodities in the economy as inputs. For example, oil is needed to run the machinery that plants and harvests the wheat, and wheat is used to feed the people who drill and refine the oil. The amounts of each commodity used in the production of one unit of each commodity can be written as an $n \times n$ matrix A, called the **technological matrix** or **input-output matrix** of the economy.

EXAMPLE 1 Input-Output Matrix

Suppose a simplified economy involves just three commodity categories: agriculture, manufacturing, and transportation, all in appropriate units. Production of 1 unit of agriculture requires 1/2 unit of manufacturing and 1/4 unit of transportation; production of 1 unit of manufacturing requires 1/4 unit of agriculture and 1/4 unit of transportation; and production of 1 unit of transportation requires 1/3 unit of agriculture and 1/4 unit of manufacturing. Give the input-output matrix for this economy.

SOLUTION

$$
\begin{array}{c}
 \\
\text{Agriculture} \\
\text{Manufacturing} \\
\text{Transportation}
\end{array}
\begin{array}{ccc}
\text{Agriculture} & \text{Manufacturing} & \text{Transportation} \\
\begin{bmatrix} 0 & \frac{1}{4} & \frac{1}{3} \\ \frac{1}{2} & 0 & \frac{1}{4} \\ \frac{1}{4} & \frac{1}{4} & 0 \end{bmatrix} & = A
\end{array}
$$

The first column of the input-output matrix represents the amount of each of the three commodities consumed in the production of 1 unit of agriculture. The second column gives the amounts required to produce 1 unit of manufacturing, and the last column gives the amounts required to produce 1 unit of transportation. (Although it is perhaps unrealistic that production of a unit of each commodity requires none of that commodity, the simpler matrix involved is useful for our purposes.)

NOTE Notice that for each commodity produced, the various units needed are put in a column. Each column corresponds to a commodity produced, and the rows correspond to what is needed to produce the commodity.

Systems of Linear Equations and Matrices

Another matrix used with the input-output matrix is the matrix giving the amount of each commodity produced, called the **production matrix**, or the matrix of gross output. In an economy producing n commodities, the production matrix can be represented by a column matrix X with entries $x_1, x_2, x_3, \ldots, x_n$.

EXAMPLE 2 Production Matrix

In Example 1, suppose the production matrix is

$$X = \begin{bmatrix} 60 \\ 52 \\ 48 \end{bmatrix}.$$

Then 60 units of agriculture, 52 units of manufacturing, and 48 units of transportation are produced. Because 1/4 unit of agriculture is used for each unit of manufacturing produced, $1/4 \times 52 = 13$ units of agriculture must be used in the "production" of manufacturing. Similarly, $1/3 \times 48 = 16$ units of agriculture will be used in the "production" of transportation. Thus, $13 + 16 = 29$ units of agriculture are used for production in the economy. Look again at the matrices A and X. Since X gives the number of units of each commodity produced and A gives the amount (in units) of each commodity used to produce 1 unit of each of the various commodities, the matrix product AX gives the amount of each commodity used in the production process.

$$AX = \begin{bmatrix} 0 & \frac{1}{4} & \frac{1}{3} \\ \frac{1}{2} & 0 & \frac{1}{4} \\ \frac{1}{4} & \frac{1}{4} & 0 \end{bmatrix} \begin{bmatrix} 60 \\ 52 \\ 48 \end{bmatrix} = \begin{bmatrix} 29 \\ 42 \\ 28 \end{bmatrix}$$

From this result, 29 units of agriculture, 42 units of manufacturing, and 28 units of transportation are used to produce 60 units of agriculture, 52 units of manufacturing, and 48 units of transportation.

The matrix product AX represents the amount of each commodity used in the production process. The remainder (if any) must be enough to satisfy the demand for the various commodities from outside the production system. In an n-commodity economy, this demand can be represented by a **demand matrix** D with entries $d_1, d_2, \ldots, d_n$. If no production is to remain unused, the difference between the production matrix X and the amount AX used in the production process must equal the demand D, or

$$D = X - AX.$$

In Example 2,

$$D = \begin{bmatrix} 60 \\ 52 \\ 48 \end{bmatrix} - \begin{bmatrix} 29 \\ 42 \\ 28 \end{bmatrix} = \begin{bmatrix} 31 \\ 10 \\ 20 \end{bmatrix},$$

so production of 60 units of agriculture, 52 units of manufacturing, and 48 units of transportation would satisfy a demand of 31, 10, and 20 units of each commodity, respectively.

In practice, A and D usually are known and X must be found. That is, we need to decide what amounts of production are needed to satisfy the required demands. Matrix algebra can be used to solve the equation $D = X - AX$ for X.

$$D = X - AX$$
$$D = IX - AX \qquad \text{Identity property}$$
$$D = (I - A)X \qquad \text{Distributive property}$$

If the matrix $I - A$ has an inverse, then

$$X = (I - A)^{-1}D.$$

FOR REVIEW
Recall that I is the identity matrix, a square matrix in which each element on the main diagonal is 1 and all other elements are 0.

TECHNOLOGY NOTE If the production matrix is large or complicated, we could use a graphing calculator. On the TI-84 Plus, for example, we would enter the command (identity(3) $-$ [A])$^{-1}$*[D] for a 3×3 matrix A.

TECHNOLOGY NOTE It is also practical to do these calculations on a spreadsheet. For more details, see the *Graphing Calculator and Excel Spreadsheet Manual* available with this text.

EXAMPLE 3   Demand Matrix

Suppose, in the three-commodity economy from Examples 1 and 2, there is a demand for 516 units of agriculture, 258 units of manufacturing, and 129 units of transportation. What should production of each commodity be?

SOLUTION   The demand matrix is

$$D = \begin{bmatrix} 516 \\ 258 \\ 129 \end{bmatrix}.$$

To find the production matrix X, first calculate $I - A$.

$$I - A = \begin{bmatrix} 1 & 0 & 0 \\ 0 & 1 & 0 \\ 0 & 0 & 1 \end{bmatrix} - \begin{bmatrix} 0 & \frac{1}{4} & \frac{1}{3} \\ \frac{1}{2} & 0 & \frac{1}{4} \\ \frac{1}{4} & \frac{1}{4} & 0 \end{bmatrix} = \begin{bmatrix} 1 & -\frac{1}{4} & -\frac{1}{3} \\ -\frac{1}{2} & 1 & -\frac{1}{4} \\ -\frac{1}{4} & -\frac{1}{4} & 1 \end{bmatrix}$$

Use row operations to find the inverse of $I - A$ (the entries are rounded to three decimal places).

$$(I - A)^{-1} = \begin{bmatrix} 1.395 & 0.496 & 0.589 \\ 0.837 & 1.364 & 0.620 \\ 0.558 & 0.465 & 1.302 \end{bmatrix}$$

Since $X = (I - A)^{-1}D$,

$$X = \begin{bmatrix} 1.395 & 0.496 & 0.589 \\ 0.837 & 1.364 & 0.620 \\ 0.558 & 0.465 & 1.302 \end{bmatrix} \begin{bmatrix} 516 \\ 258 \\ 129 \end{bmatrix} = \begin{bmatrix} 924 \\ 864 \\ 576 \end{bmatrix}.$$

(Each entry in X has been rounded to the nearest whole number.)

The last result shows that production of 924 units of agriculture, 864 units of manufacturing, and 576 units of transportation are required to satisfy demands of 516, 258, and 129 units, respectively.

The entries in the matrix $(I - A)^{-1}$ are often called *multipliers*, and they have important economic interpretations. For example, every \$1 increase in total agricultural demand will result in an increase in agricultural production by about \$1.40, an increase in manufacturing production by about \$0.84, and an increase in transportation production by about \$0.56. Similarly, every \$3 increase in total manufacturing demand will result in an increase of about $3(0.50) = 1.50$, $3(1.36) = 4.08$, and $3(0.47) = 1.41$ dollars in agricultural production, manufacturing production, and transportation production, respectively.

YOUR TURN 1 Find the production of each commodity for the economy in Example 3 if there is a demand for 322 units of agriculture, 447 units of manufacturing, and 133 units of transportation.

TRY YOUR TURN 1

EXAMPLE 4   Wheat and Oil Production

An economy depends on two basic products, wheat and oil. To produce 1 metric ton of wheat requires 0.25 metric tons of wheat and 0.33 metric tons of oil. Production of 1 metric ton of oil consumes 0.08 metric tons of wheat and 0.11 metric tons of oil.

(a) Find the production that will satisfy a demand for 500 metric tons of wheat and 1000 metric tons of oil.

SOLUTION The input-output matrix is

$$A = \begin{bmatrix} 0.25 & 0.08 \\ 0.33 & 0.11 \end{bmatrix}.$$

Also,

$$I - A = \begin{bmatrix} 0.75 & -0.08 \\ -0.33 & 0.89 \end{bmatrix}.$$

Next, calculate $(I - A)^{-1}$.

$$(I - A)^{-1} = \begin{bmatrix} 1.3882 & 0.1248 \\ 0.5147 & 1.1699 \end{bmatrix} \quad \text{(rounded)}$$

To find the production matrix X, use the equation $X = (I - A)^{-1}D$, with

$$D = \begin{bmatrix} 500 \\ 1000 \end{bmatrix}.$$

The production matrix is

$$X = \begin{bmatrix} 1.3882 & 0.1248 \\ 0.5147 & 1.1699 \end{bmatrix} \begin{bmatrix} 500 \\ 1000 \end{bmatrix} \approx \begin{bmatrix} 819 \\ 1427 \end{bmatrix}.$$

Production of 819 metric tons of wheat and 1427 metric tons of oil is required to satisfy the indicated demand.

(b) Suppose the demand for wheat goes up from 500 to 600 metric tons. Find the increased production in wheat and oil that will be required to meet the new demand.

SOLUTION One way to solve this problem is using the multipliers for wheat, found in the first column of $(I - A)^{-1}$ from part (a). The element in the first row, 1.3882, is used to find the increased production in wheat, while the item in the second row, 0.5147, is used to find the increased production in oil. Since the increase in demand for wheat is 100 metric tons, the increased production in wheat must be $100(1.3882) \approx 139$ metric tons. Similarly, the increased production in oil is $100(0.5147) \approx 51$ metric tons.

Alternatively, we could have found the new production in wheat and oil with the equation $X = (I - A)^{-1}D$, giving

$$X = \begin{bmatrix} 1.3882 & 0.1248 \\ 0.5147 & 1.1699 \end{bmatrix} \begin{bmatrix} 600 \\ 1000 \end{bmatrix} \approx \begin{bmatrix} 958 \\ 1479 \end{bmatrix}.$$

We find the increased production by subtracting the answers found in part (a) from these answers. The increased production in wheat is $958 - 819 = 139$ metric tons, and the increased production in oil is $1479 - 1427 = 52$ metric tons. The slight difference here from the previous answer of 51 metric tons is due to rounding.

Closed Models

The input-output model discussed above is referred to as an **open model**, since it allows for a surplus from the production equal to D. In the **closed model**, all the production is consumed internally in the production process, so that $X = AX$. There is nothing left over to satisfy any outside demands from other parts of the economy or from other economies. In this case, the sum of each column in the input-output matrix equals 1.

To solve the closed model, set $D = O$ in the equation derived earlier, where O is a **zero matrix,** a matrix whose elements are all zeros.

$$(I - A)X = D = O$$

FOR REVIEW
Parameters were discussed in the first section of this chapter. As mentioned there, parameters are required when a system has infinitely many solutions.

The system of equations that corresponds to $(I - A)X = O$ does not have a single unique solution, but it can be solved in terms of a parameter. (It can be shown that if the columns of a matrix A sum to 1, then the equation $(I - A)X = O$ has an infinite number of solutions.)

EXAMPLE 5 Closed Input-Output Model

Use matrix A below to find the production of each commodity in a closed model.

$$A = \begin{bmatrix} \frac{1}{2} & \frac{1}{4} & \frac{1}{3} \\ 0 & \frac{1}{4} & \frac{1}{3} \\ \frac{1}{2} & \frac{1}{2} & \frac{1}{3} \end{bmatrix}$$

SOLUTION Find the value of $I - A$, then set $(I - A)X = O$ to find X.

$$I - A = \begin{bmatrix} \frac{1}{2} & -\frac{1}{4} & -\frac{1}{3} \\ 0 & \frac{3}{4} & -\frac{1}{3} \\ -\frac{1}{2} & -\frac{1}{2} & \frac{2}{3} \end{bmatrix}$$

$$(I - A)X = \begin{bmatrix} \frac{1}{2} & -\frac{1}{4} & -\frac{1}{3} \\ 0 & \frac{3}{4} & -\frac{1}{3} \\ -\frac{1}{2} & -\frac{1}{2} & \frac{2}{3} \end{bmatrix} \begin{bmatrix} x_1 \\ x_2 \\ x_3 \end{bmatrix} = \begin{bmatrix} 0 \\ 0 \\ 0 \end{bmatrix}$$

Multiply to get

$$\begin{bmatrix} \frac{1}{2}x_1 - \frac{1}{4}x_2 - \frac{1}{3}x_3 \\ 0x_1 + \frac{3}{4}x_2 - \frac{1}{3}x_3 \\ -\frac{1}{2}x_1 - \frac{1}{2}x_2 + \frac{2}{3}x_3 \end{bmatrix} = \begin{bmatrix} 0 \\ 0 \\ 0 \end{bmatrix}.$$

The last matrix equation corresponds to the following system.

$$\frac{1}{2}x_1 - \frac{1}{4}x_2 - \frac{1}{3}x_3 = 0$$
$$\frac{3}{4}x_2 - \frac{1}{3}x_3 = 0$$
$$-\frac{1}{2}x_1 - \frac{1}{2}x_2 + \frac{2}{3}x_3 = 0$$

YOUR TURN 2 Change the last column of matrix A in Example 5 to $\begin{bmatrix} \frac{1}{6} \\ \frac{1}{6} \\ \frac{2}{3} \end{bmatrix}$ and find the solution corresponding to $x_3 = 9$.

Solving the system with x_3 as the parameter gives the solution of the system

$$\left(\tfrac{8}{9}x_3, \tfrac{4}{9}x_3, x_3\right).$$

For example, if $x_3 = 9$ (a choice that eliminates fractions in the answer), then $x_1 = 8$ and $x_2 = 4$, so the production of the three commodities should be in the ratio 8:4:9.

TRY YOUR TURN 2

Finding a Production Matrix

To obtain the production matrix, X, for an open input-output model, follow these steps:

1. Form the $n \times n$ input-output matrix, A, by placing in each column the amount of the various commodities required to produce 1 unit of a particular commodity.

2. Calculate $I - A$, where I is the $n \times n$ identity matrix.

3. Find the inverse, $(I - A)^{-1}$.

4. Multiply the inverse on the right by the demand matrix, D, to obtain $X = (I - A)^{-1}D$.

To obtain a production matrix, X, for a closed input-output model, solve the system $(I - A)X = O$.

Production matrices for actual economies are much larger than those shown in this section. An analysis of the U.S. economy in 1997 has close to 500 commodity categories. *Source: U.S. Bureau of Economic Analysis.* Such matrices require large human and computer resources for their analysis. Some of the exercises at the end of this section use actual data in which categories have been combined to simplify the work.

6 EXERCISES

Find the production matrix for the following input-output and demand matrices using the open model.

1. $A = \begin{bmatrix} 0.8 & 0.2 \\ 0.2 & 0.7 \end{bmatrix}$, $D = \begin{bmatrix} 2 \\ 3 \end{bmatrix}$

2. $A = \begin{bmatrix} 0.2 & 0.04 \\ 0.6 & 0.05 \end{bmatrix}$, $D = \begin{bmatrix} 3 \\ 10 \end{bmatrix}$

3. $A = \begin{bmatrix} 0.1 & 0.03 \\ 0.07 & 0.6 \end{bmatrix}$, $D = \begin{bmatrix} 5 \\ 10 \end{bmatrix}$

4. $A = \begin{bmatrix} 0.02 & 0.03 \\ 0.06 & 0.08 \end{bmatrix}$, $D = \begin{bmatrix} 100 \\ 200 \end{bmatrix}$

5. $A = \begin{bmatrix} 0.8 & 0 & 0.1 \\ 0.1 & 0.5 & 0.2 \\ 0 & 0 & 0.7 \end{bmatrix}$, $D = \begin{bmatrix} 1 \\ 6 \\ 3 \end{bmatrix}$

6. $A = \begin{bmatrix} 0.1 & 0.5 & 0 \\ 0 & 0.3 & 0.4 \\ 0.1 & 0.2 & 0.1 \end{bmatrix}$, $D = \begin{bmatrix} 10 \\ 4 \\ 2 \end{bmatrix}$

Find the ratios of products A, B, and C using a closed model.

7.
	A	B	C
A	0.3	0.1	0.8
B	0.5	0.6	0.1
C	0.2	0.3	0.1

8.
	A	B	C
A	0.3	0.2	0.3
B	0.1	0.5	0.4
C	0.6	0.3	0.3

Use a graphing calculator or computer to find the production matrix X, given the following input-output and demand matrices.

9. $A = \begin{bmatrix} 0.25 & 0.25 & 0.25 & 0.05 \\ 0.01 & 0.02 & 0.01 & 0.1 \\ 0.3 & 0.3 & 0.01 & 0.1 \\ 0.2 & 0.01 & 0.3 & 0.01 \end{bmatrix}$, $D = \begin{bmatrix} 2930 \\ 3570 \\ 2300 \\ 580 \end{bmatrix}$

10. $A = \begin{bmatrix} 0.01 & 0.2 & 0.01 & 0.2 \\ 0.5 & 0.02 & 0.03 & 0.02 \\ 0.09 & 0.05 & 0.02 & 0.03 \\ 0.3 & 0.2 & 0.2 & 0.01 \end{bmatrix}$, $D = \begin{bmatrix} 5000 \\ 1000 \\ 4000 \\ 500 \end{bmatrix}$

APPLICATIONS

Business and Economics

Input-Output Open Model In Exercises 11 and 12, refer to Example 4.

11. If the demand is changed to 925 metric tons of wheat and 1250 metric tons of oil, how many units of each commodity should be produced?

12. Change the technological matrix so that production of 1 metric ton of wheat requires 1/5 metric ton of oil (and no wheat), and production of 1 metric ton of oil requires 1/3 metric ton of wheat (and no oil). To satisfy the same demand matrix, how many units of each commodity should be produced?

Input-Output Open Model In Exercises 13–16, refer to Example 3.

13. If the demand is changed to 607 units of each commodity, how many units of each commodity should be produced?

14. Suppose 1/3 unit of manufacturing (no agriculture or transportation) is required to produce 1 unit of agriculture, 1/4 unit of transportation is required to produce 1 unit of manufacturing, and 1/2 unit of agriculture is required to produce 1 unit of transportation. How many units of each commodity should be produced to satisfy a demand of 1000 units of each commodity?

15. Suppose 1/4 unit of manufacturing and 1/2 unit of transportation are required to produce 1 unit of agriculture, 1/2 unit of agriculture and 1/4 unit of transportation to produce 1 unit of manufacturing, and 1/4 unit of agriculture and 1/4 unit of manufacturing to produce 1 unit of transportation. How many units of each commodity should be produced to satisfy a demand of 1000 units for each commodity?

16. If the input-output matrix is changed so that 1/4 unit of manufacturing and 1/2 unit of transportation are required to produce 1 unit of agriculture, 1/2 unit of agriculture and 1/4 unit of transportation are required to produce 1 unit of manufacturing, and 1/4 unit each of agriculture and manufacturing are required to produce 1 unit of transportation, find the number of units of each commodity that should be produced to satisfy a demand for 500 units of each commodity.

Input-Output Open Model

17. A primitive economy depends on two basic goods, yams and pork. Production of 1 bushel of yams requires 1/4 bushel of yams and 1/2 of a pig. To produce 1 pig requires 1/6 bushel of yams. Find the amount of each commodity that should be produced to get the following.

a. 1 bushel of yams and 1 pig

b. 100 bushels of yams and 70 pigs

18. A simple economy depends on three commodities: oil, corn, and coffee. Production of 1 unit of oil requires 0.2 unit of oil, 0.4 unit of corn, and no units of coffee. To produce 1 unit of corn requires 0.4 unit of oil, 0.2 unit of corn, and 0.1 unit of coffee. To produce 1 unit of coffee requires 0.2 unit of oil, 0.1 unit of corn, and 0.2 unit of coffee. Find the production required to meet a demand of 1000 units each of oil, corn, and coffee.

19. In his work *Input-Output Economics*, Leontief provides an example of a simplified economy with just three sectors: agriculture, manufacturing, and households (i.e., the sector of the economy that produces labor). It has the following input-output matrix: ***Source: Input-Output Economics.***

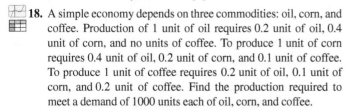

	Agriculture	Manufacturing	Households
Agriculture	0.25	0.40	0.133
Manufacturing	0.14	0.12	0.100
Households	0.80	3.60	0.133

He also gives the demand matrix

$$D = \begin{bmatrix} 35 \\ 38 \\ 40 \end{bmatrix}.$$

Find the amount of each commodity that should be produced.

20. A much-simplified version of Leontief's 42-sector analysis of the 1947 American economy has the following input-output matrix. ***Source: Input-Output Economics.***

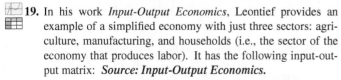

	Agriculture	Manufacturing	Households
Agriculture	0.245	0.102	0.051
Manufacturing	0.099	0.291	0.279
Households	0.433	0.372	0.011

The demand matrix (in billions of dollars) is

$$D = \begin{bmatrix} 2.88 \\ 31.45 \\ 30.91 \end{bmatrix}.$$

Find the amount of each commodity that should be produced.

21. An analysis of the 1958 Israeli economy is simplified here by grouping the economy into three sectors, with the following input-output matrix. ***Source: Input-Output Economics.***

	Agriculture	Manufacturing	Energy
Agriculture	0.293	0	0
Manufacturing	0.014	0.207	0.017
Energy	0.044	0.010	0.216

The demand (in thousands of Israeli pounds) as measured by exports is

$$D = \begin{bmatrix} 138,213 \\ 17,597 \\ 1786 \end{bmatrix}.$$

Find the amount of each commodity that should be produced.

22. The 1981 Chinese economy can be simplified to three sectors: agriculture, industry and construction, and transportation and commerce. The input-output matrix is given below. ***Source: Input-Output Tables of China, 1981.***

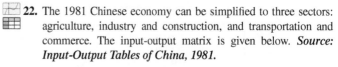

	Agriculture	Industry/ Constr.	Trans./ Commerce
Agriculture	0.158	0.156	0.009
Industry/Constr.	0.136	0.432	0.071
Trans./Commerce	0.013	0.041	0.011

The demand (in 100,000 RMB, the unit of money in China) is

$$D = \begin{bmatrix} 106,674 \\ 144,739 \\ 26,725 \end{bmatrix}.$$

a. Find the amount of each commodity that should be produced.

b. Interpret the economic value of an increase in demand of 1 RMB in agricultural exports.

23. Washington The 1987 economy of the state of Washington has been simplified to four sectors: natural resources, manufacturing, trade and services, and personal consumption. The input-output matrix is given below. ***Source: University of Washington.***

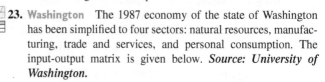

	Natural Resources	Manufacturing	Trade & Services	Personal Consumption
Natural Resources	0.1045	0.0428	0.0029	0.0031
Manufacturing	0.0826	0.1087	0.0584	0.0321
Trade & Services	0.0867	0.1019	0.2032	0.3555
Personal Consumption	0.6253	0.3448	0.6106	0.0798

Suppose the demand (in millions of dollars) is

$$D = \begin{bmatrix} 450 \\ 300 \\ 125 \\ 100 \end{bmatrix}.$$

Find the amount of each commodity that should be produced.

24. Washington In addition to solving the previous input-output model, most models of this nature also include an employment equation. For the previous model, the employment equation is added and a new system of equations is obtained as follows. ***Source: University of Washington.***

$$\begin{bmatrix} x_1 \\ x_2 \\ x_3 \\ x_4 \\ N \end{bmatrix} = (I - B)^{-1}C,$$

where x_1, x_2, x_3, x_4 represent the amount, in millions of dollars, that must be produced to satisfy internal and external demands of the four sectors; N is the total workforce required for a particular set of demands; and

$$B = \begin{bmatrix} 0.1045 & 0.0428 & 0.0029 & 0.0031 & 0 \\ 0.0826 & 0.1087 & 0.0584 & 0.0321 & 0 \\ 0.0867 & 0.1019 & 0.2032 & 0.3555 & 0 \\ 0.6253 & 0.3448 & 0.6106 & 0.0798 & 0 \\ 21.6 & 6.6 & 20.2 & 0 & 0 \end{bmatrix}.$$

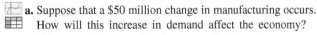 **a.** Suppose that a \$50 million change in manufacturing occurs. How will this increase in demand affect the economy?

$$(Hint: \text{Find } (I - B)^{-1}C, \text{ where } C = \begin{bmatrix} 0 \\ 50 \\ 0 \\ 0 \\ 0 \end{bmatrix}.)$$

b. Interpret the meaning of the bottom row in the matrix $(I - B)^{-1}$.

25. Community Links The use of input-output analysis can also be used to model how changes in one city can affect cities that are connected with it in some way. For example, if a large manufacturing company shuts down in one city, it is very likely that the economic welfare of all of the cities around it will suffer. Consider three Pennsylvania communities: Sharon, Farrell, and Hermitage. Due to their proximity to each other, residents of these three communities regularly spend time and money in the other communities. Suppose that we have gathered information in the form of an input-output matrix. *Source: Thayer Watkins.*

$$A = \begin{array}{c} \\ S \\ F \\ H \end{array} \begin{array}{ccc} S & F & H \\ \begin{bmatrix} 0.2 & 0.1 & 0.1 \\ 0.1 & 0.1 & 0 \\ 0.5 & 0.6 & 0.7 \end{bmatrix} \end{array}$$

This matrix can be thought of as the likelihood that a person from a particular community will spend money in each of the communities.

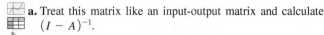 **a.** Treat this matrix like an input-output matrix and calculate $(I - A)^{-1}$.

b. Interpret the entries of this inverse matrix.

Input-Output Closed Model

26. Use the input-output matrix

$$\begin{array}{c} \\ \text{Yams} \\ \text{Pigs} \end{array} \begin{array}{cc} \text{Yams} & \text{Pigs} \\ \begin{bmatrix} \frac{1}{4} & \frac{1}{2} \\ \frac{3}{4} & \frac{1}{2} \end{bmatrix} \end{array}$$

and the closed model to find the ratio of yams to pigs produced.

27. Use the input-output matrix

$$\begin{array}{c} \\ \text{Steel} \\ \text{Coal} \end{array} \begin{array}{cc} \text{Steel} & \text{Coal} \\ \begin{bmatrix} \frac{3}{4} & \frac{1}{3} \\ \frac{1}{4} & \frac{2}{3} \end{bmatrix} \end{array}$$

and the closed model to find the ratio of coal to steel produced.

28. Suppose that production of 1 unit of agriculture requires 1/3 unit of agriculture, 1/3 unit of manufacturing, and 1/3 unit of transportation. To produce 1 unit of manufacturing requires 1/2 unit of agriculture, 1/4 unit of manufacturing, and 1/4 unit of transportation. To produce 1 unit of transportation requires 0 units of agriculture, 1/4 unit of manufacturing, and 3/4 unit of transportation. Find the ratio of the three commodities in the closed model.

29. Suppose that production of 1 unit of mining requires 1/5 unit of mining, 2/5 unit of manufacturing, and 2/5 unit of communication. To produce 1 unit of manufacturing requires 3/5 unit of mining, 1/5 unit of manufacturing, and 1/5 unit of communication. To produce 1 unit of communication requires 0 units of mining, 4/5 unit of manufacturing, and 1/5 unit of communication. Find the ratio of the three commodities in the closed model.

YOUR TURN ANSWERS

1. 749 units of agriculture, 962 units of manufacturing, and 561 units of transportation

2. (4, 2, 9)

CHAPTER REVIEW

SUMMARY

In this chapter we extended our study of linear functions to include finding solutions of systems of linear equations. Techniques such as the echelon method and the Gauss-Jordan method were developed and used to solve systems of linear equations. We introduced matrices, which are used to store mathematical information. We saw that matrices can be combined using addition, subtraction, scalar multiplication, and matrix multiplication. Two special matrices, the zero matrix and the identity matrix, were also introduced.

- The zero matrix O is a matrix whose elements are all zero.
- The identity matrix I is an $n \times n$ matrix consisting of 1's along the diagonal and 0's elsewhere.

We then developed the concept of a multiplicative inverse of a matrix and used such inverses to solve systems of equations. We concluded the chapter by introducing the Leontief input-output models, which are used to study interdependencies in an economy.

Row Operations For any augmented matrix of a system of equations, the following operations produce the augmented matrix of an equivalent system:

1. interchanging any two rows;
2. multiplying the elements of a row by a nonzero real number;
3. adding a nonzero multiple of the elements of one row to the corresponding elements of a nonzero multiple of some other row.

The Gauss-Jordan Method
1. Write each equation so that variable terms are in the same order on the left side of the equal sign and constants are on the right.
2. Write the augmented matrix that corresponds to the system.
3. Use row operations to transform the first column so that all elements except the element in the first row are zero.
4. Use row operations to transform the second column so that all elements except the element in the second row are zero.
5. Use row operations to transform the third column so that all elements except the element in the third row are zero.
6. Continue in this way, when possible, until the last row is written in the form

$$[0\ 0\ 0\ \cdots\ 0\ j\ |\ k],$$

where j and k are constants with $j \neq 0$. When this is not possible, continue until every row has more zeros on the left than the previous row (except possibly for any rows of all zero at the bottom of the matrix), and the first nonzero entry in each row is the only nonzero entry in its column.
7. Multiply each row by the reciprocal of the nonzero element in that row.

Adding Matrices The sum of two $m \times n$ matrices X and Y is the $m \times n$ matrix $X + Y$ in which each element is the sum of the corresponding elements of X and Y.

Subtracting Matrices The difference of two $m \times n$ matrices X and Y is the $m \times n$ matrix $X - Y$ in which each element is found by subtracting the corresponding elements of X and Y.

Product of a Matrix and a Scalar The product of a scalar k and a matrix X is the matrix kX, each of whose elements is k times the corresponding element of X.

Product of Two Matrices Let A be an $m \times n$ matrix and let B be an $n \times k$ matrix. To find the element in the ith row and jth column of the product AB, multiply each element in the ith row of A by the corresponding element in the jth column of B, and then add these products. The product matrix AB is an $m \times k$ matrix.

Solving a System $AX = B$ Using Matrix Inverses To solve a system of equations $AX = B$, where A is a square matrix of coefficients, X is the matrix of variables, and B is the matrix of constants, first find A^{-1}. Then, $X = A^{-1}B$.

Finding a Production Matrix
1. Form the input-output matrix, A.
2. Calculate $I - A$, where I is the $n \times n$ identity matrix.
3. Find the inverse, $(I - A)^{-1}$.
4. Multiply the inverse on the right by the demand matrix, D, to obtain $X = (I - A)^{-1}D$.

To obtain a production matrix, X, for a closed input-output model, solve the system $(I - A)X = O$.

KEY TERMS

To understand the concepts presented in this chapter, you should know the meaning and use of the following terms.
For easy reference, the section in the chapter where a word (or expression) was first used is provided.

system of equations

1
first-degree equation in n unknowns

unique solution
inconsistent system
dependent equations
equivalent system

echelon method
back-substitution
parameter

2
matrix (matrices)
element (entry)
augmented matrix

row operations

Gauss-Jordan method

3

size

square matrix

row matrix (row vector)

column matrix (column vector)

4

scalar

product matrix

5

identity matrix

multiplicative inverse matrix

coefficient matrix

6

input-output (technological)

  matrix

production matrix

demand matrix

open model

closed model

zero matrix

REVIEW EXERCISES

CONCEPT CHECK

Determine whether each of the following statements is true or false, and explain why.

1. If a system of equations has three equations and four unknowns, then it could have a unique solution.

2. If $A = \begin{bmatrix} 2 & 3 \\ 1 & -1 \end{bmatrix}$ and $B = \begin{bmatrix} 3 & 4 \\ 7 & 4 \\ 1 & 0 \end{bmatrix}$, then $A + B = \begin{bmatrix} 5 & 7 \\ 8 & 3 \\ 1 & 0 \end{bmatrix}$.

3. If a system of equations has three equations and three unknowns, then it may have a unique solution, an infinite number of solutions, or no solutions.

4. The only solution to the system of equations

$$2x + 3y = 7$$
$$5x - 4y = 6$$

is $x = 2$ and $y = 1$.

5. If A is a 2×3 matrix and B is a 3×4 matrix, then $A + B$ is a 2×4 matrix.

6. If A is an $n \times k$ matrix and B is a $k \times m$ matrix, then AB is an $n \times m$ matrix.

7. If A is a 4×4 matrix and B is a 4×4 matrix, then $AB = BA$.

8. A 3×4 matrix could have an inverse.

9. It is not possible to find a matrix A such that $OA = AO = I$, where O is a 5×5 zero matrix and I is a 5×5 identity matrix.

10. When solving a system of equations by the Gauss-Jordan method, we can add a nonzero multiple of the elements of one column to the corresponding elements of some nonzero multiple of some other column.

11. Every square matrix has an inverse.

12. If A, B, and C are matrices such that $AB = C$, then $B = \dfrac{C}{A}$.

13. A system of three equations in three unknowns might have exactly five positive integer solutions.

14. If A and B are matrices such that $A = B^{-1}$, then $AB = BA$.

15. If A, B, and C are matrices such that $AB = CB$, then $A = C$.

16. The difference between an open and a closed input-output model is that in a closed model, the demand matrix D is a zero matrix.

PRACTICE AND EXPLORATIONS

17. What is true about the number of solutions to a system of m linear equations in n unknowns if $m = n$? If $m < n$? If $m > n$?

18. Suppose someone says that a more reasonable way to multiply two matrices than the method presented in the text is to multiply corresponding elements. For example, the result of

$$\begin{bmatrix} 1 & 2 \\ 3 & 4 \end{bmatrix} \cdot \begin{bmatrix} 3 & 5 \\ 7 & 11 \end{bmatrix} \quad \text{should be} \quad \begin{bmatrix} 3 & 10 \\ 21 & 44 \end{bmatrix},$$

according to this person. How would you respond?

Solve each system by the echelon method.

19. $2x - 3y = 14$
    $3x + 2y = -5$

20. $\dfrac{x}{2} + \dfrac{y}{4} = 3$
    $\dfrac{x}{4} - \dfrac{y}{2} = 4$

21. $2x - 3y + z = -5$
    $5x + 5y + 3z = 14$

22. $2x + 3y + 4z = 5$
    $3x + 4y + 5z = 6$

Solve each system by the Gauss-Jordan method.

23. $2x + 4y = -6$
    $-3x - 5y = 12$

24. $x - 4y = 10$
    $5x + 3y = 119$

25. $x - y + 3z = 13$
    $4x + y + 2z = 17$
    $3x + 2y + 2z = 1$

26. $x + 2y + 3z = 9$
    $x - 2y = 4$
    $3x + 2z = 12$

27. $3x - 6y + 9z = 12$
    $-x + 2y - 3z = -4$
    $x + y + 2z = 7$

28. $x - 2z = 5$
    $3x + 2y = 8$
    $-x + 2z = 10$

Find the size of each matrix, find the values of any variables, and identify any square, row, or column matrices.

29. $\begin{bmatrix} 2 & 3 \\ 5 & q \end{bmatrix} = \begin{bmatrix} a & b \\ c & 9 \end{bmatrix}$

30. $\begin{bmatrix} 2 & x \\ y & 6 \\ 5 & z \end{bmatrix} = \begin{bmatrix} a & -1 \\ 4 & 6 \\ p & 7 \end{bmatrix}$

31. $\begin{bmatrix} 2m & 4 & 3z & -12 \end{bmatrix} = \begin{bmatrix} 12 & k+1 & -9 & r-3 \end{bmatrix}$

32. $\begin{bmatrix} a+5 & 3b & 6 \\ 4c & 2+d & -3 \\ -1 & 4p & q-1 \end{bmatrix} = \begin{bmatrix} -7 & b+2 & 2k-3 \\ 3 & 2d-1 & 4l \\ m & 12 & 8 \end{bmatrix}$

Given the matrices

$$A = \begin{bmatrix} 4 & 10 \\ -2 & -3 \\ 6 & 9 \end{bmatrix}, \quad B = \begin{bmatrix} 2 & 3 & -2 \\ 2 & 4 & 0 \\ 0 & 1 & 2 \end{bmatrix}, \quad C = \begin{bmatrix} 5 & 0 \\ -1 & 3 \\ 4 & 7 \end{bmatrix},$$

$$D = \begin{bmatrix} 6 \\ 1 \\ 0 \end{bmatrix}, \quad E = \begin{bmatrix} 1 & 3 & -4 \end{bmatrix},$$

$$F = \begin{bmatrix} -1 & 4 \\ 3 & 7 \end{bmatrix}, \quad G = \begin{bmatrix} -2 & 0 \\ 1 & 5 \end{bmatrix},$$

find each of the following, if it exists.

33. $A + C$ **34.** $2G - 4F$ **35.** $3C + 2A$

36. $B - C$ **37.** $2A - 5C$ **38.** AG

39. AC **40.** DE **41.** ED

42. BD **43.** EC **44.** F^{-1}

45. B^{-1} **46.** $(A + C)^{-1}$

Find the inverse of each matrix that has an inverse.

47. $\begin{bmatrix} 1 & 3 \\ 2 & 7 \end{bmatrix}$ **48.** $\begin{bmatrix} -4 & 2 \\ 0 & 3 \end{bmatrix}$

49. $\begin{bmatrix} 3 & -6 \\ -4 & 8 \end{bmatrix}$ **50.** $\begin{bmatrix} 6 & 4 \\ 3 & 2 \end{bmatrix}$

51. $\begin{bmatrix} 2 & -1 & 0 \\ 1 & 0 & 1 \\ 1 & -2 & 0 \end{bmatrix}$ **52.** $\begin{bmatrix} 2 & 0 & 4 \\ 1 & -1 & 0 \\ 0 & 1 & -2 \end{bmatrix}$

53. $\begin{bmatrix} 1 & 3 & 6 \\ 4 & 0 & 9 \\ 5 & 15 & 30 \end{bmatrix}$ **54.** $\begin{bmatrix} 2 & -3 & 4 \\ 1 & 5 & 7 \\ -4 & 6 & -8 \end{bmatrix}$

Solve the matrix equation $AX = B$ for **X** using the given matrices.

55. $A = \begin{bmatrix} 5 & 1 \\ -2 & -2 \end{bmatrix}, \quad B = \begin{bmatrix} -8 \\ 24 \end{bmatrix}$

56. $A = \begin{bmatrix} 1 & 2 \\ 2 & 4 \end{bmatrix}, \quad B = \begin{bmatrix} 5 \\ 10 \end{bmatrix}$

57. $A = \begin{bmatrix} 1 & 0 & 2 \\ -1 & 1 & 0 \\ 3 & 0 & 4 \end{bmatrix}, \quad B = \begin{bmatrix} 8 \\ 4 \\ -6 \end{bmatrix}$

58. $A = \begin{bmatrix} 2 & 4 & 0 \\ 1 & -2 & 0 \\ 0 & 0 & 3 \end{bmatrix}, \quad B = \begin{bmatrix} 72 \\ -24 \\ 48 \end{bmatrix}$

Solve each system of equations by inverses.

59. $x + 2y = 4$
$\quad 2x - 3y = 1$

60. $5x + 10y = 80$
$\quad 3x - 2y = 120$

61. $x + y + z = 1$
$\quad 2x + y \quad\;\; = -2$
$\quad\quad\; + 3y + z = 2$

62. $x - 4y + 2z = -1$
$\quad -2x + y - 3z = -9$
$\quad 3x + 5y - 2z = 7$

Find each production matrix, given the following input-output and demand matrices.

63. $A = \begin{bmatrix} 0.01 & 0.05 \\ 0.04 & 0.03 \end{bmatrix}, \quad D = \begin{bmatrix} 200 \\ 300 \end{bmatrix}$

64. $A = \begin{bmatrix} 0.2 & 0.1 & 0.3 \\ 0.1 & 0 & 0.2 \\ 0 & 0 & 0.4 \end{bmatrix}, \quad D = \begin{bmatrix} 500 \\ 200 \\ 100 \end{bmatrix}$

65. The following system of equations is given.

$$x + 2y + z = 7$$
$$2x - y - z = 2$$
$$3x - 3y + 2z = -5$$

  a. Solve by the echelon method.

  b. Solve by the Gauss-Jordan method. Compare with the echelon method.

  c. Write the system as a matrix equation, $AX = B$.

  d. Find the inverse of matrix A from part c.

  e. Solve the system using A^{-1} from part d.

APPLICATIONS

Business and Economics

In Exercises 66–69, write a system of equations and solve.

66. Scheduling Production An office supply manufacturer makes two kinds of paper clips, standard and extra large. To make 1000 standard paper clips requires 1/4 hour on a cutting machine and 1/2 hour on a machine that shapes the clips. One thousand extra large paper clips require 1/3 hour on each machine. The manager of paper clip production has 4 hours per day available on the cutting machine and 6 hours per day on the shaping machine. How many of each kind of clip can he make?

67. Production Requirements The Waputi Indians make woven blankets, rugs, and skirts. Each blanket requires 24 hours for spinning the yarn, 4 hours for dyeing the yarn, and 15 hours for weaving. Rugs require 30, 5, and 18 hours and skirts 12, 3, and 9 hours, respectively. If there are 306, 59, and 201 hours available for spinning, dyeing, and weaving, respectively, how many of each item can be made? (*Hint:* Simplify the equations you write, if possible, before solving the system.)

68. Distribution An oil refinery in Tulsa sells 50% of its production to a Chicago distributor, 20% to a Dallas distributor, and 30% to an Atlanta distributor. Another refinery in New Orleans sells 40% of its production to the Chicago distributor, 40% to the Dallas distributor, and 20% to the Atlanta distributor. A third refinery in Ardmore sells the same distributors 30%, 40%, and 30% of its production. The three distributors received 219,000, 192,000, and 144,000 gal of oil, respectively. How many gallons of oil were produced at each of the three plants?

69. Stock Reports The New York Stock Exchange reports in daily newspapers give the dividend, price-to-earnings ratio, sales (in hundreds of shares), last price, and change in price for each company. Write the following stock reports as a 4 × 5 matrix: American Telephone & Telegraph: 1.33, 17.6, 152,000, 26.75,

+1.88; General Electric: 1.00, 20.0, 238,200, 32.36, −1.50; Sara Lee: 0.79, 25.4, 39,110, 16.51, −0.89; Walt Disney Company: 0.27, 21.2, 122,500, 28.60, +0.75.

70. Filling Orders A printer has three orders for pamphlets that require three kinds of paper, as shown in the following matrix.

		Order	
	I	II	III
High-grade	10	5	8
Paper Medium-grade	12	0	4
Coated	0	10	5

The printer has on hand 3170 sheets of high-grade paper, 2360 sheets of medium-grade paper, and 1800 sheets of coated paper. All the paper must be used in preparing the order.

a. Write a 3×1 matrix for the amounts of paper on hand.

b. Write a matrix of variables to represent the number of pamphlets that must be printed in each of the three orders.

c. Write a matrix equation using the given matrix and your matrices from parts a and b.

d. Solve the equation from part c.

71. Input-Output An economy depends on two commodities, goats and cheese. It takes 2/3 of a unit of goats to produce 1 unit of cheese and 1/2 unit of cheese to produce 1 unit of goats.

a. Write the input-output matrix for this economy.

b. Find the production required to satisfy a demand of 400 units of cheese and 800 units of goats.

72. Nebraska The 1970 economy of the state of Nebraska has been condensed to six sectors: livestock, crops, food products, mining and manufacturing, households, and other. The input-output matrix is given below. *Source: University of Nebraska Lincoln.*

$$\begin{bmatrix} 0.178 & 0.018 & 0.411 & 0 & 0.005 & 0 \\ 0.143 & 0.018 & 0.088 & 0 & 0.001 & 0 \\ 0.089 & 0 & 0.035 & 0 & 0.060 & 0.003 \\ 0.001 & 0.010 & 0.012 & 0.063 & 0.007 & 0.014 \\ 0.141 & 0.252 & 0.088 & 0.089 & 0.402 & 0.124 \\ 0.188 & 0.156 & 0.103 & 0.255 & 0.008 & 0.474 \end{bmatrix}$$

a. Find the matrix $(I - A)^{-1}$ and interpret the value in row 2, column 1 of this matrix.

b. Suppose the demand (in millions of dollars) is

$$D = \begin{bmatrix} 1980 \\ 650 \\ 1750 \\ 1000 \\ 2500 \\ 3750 \end{bmatrix}.$$

Find the dollar amount of each commodity that should be produced.

Life Sciences

73. Animal Activity The activities of a grazing animal can be classified roughly into three categories: grazing, moving, and resting. Suppose horses spend 8 hours grazing, 8 moving, and 8 resting; cattle spend 10 grazing, 5 moving, and 9 resting; sheep spend 7 grazing, 10 moving, and 7 resting; and goats spend 8 grazing, 9 moving, and 7 resting. Write this information as a 4×3 matrix.

74. CAT Scans Computer Aided Tomography (CAT) scanners take X-rays of a part of the body from different directions, and put the information together to create a picture of a cross section of the body. The amount by which the energy of the X-ray decreases, measured in linear-attenuation units, tells whether the X-ray has passed through healthy tissue, tumorous tissue, or bone, based on the following table. *Source: The Mathematics Teacher.*

Type of Tissue	Linear-Attenuation Values
Healthy tissue	0.1625–0.2977
Tumorous tissue	0.2679–0.3930
Bone	0.3857–0.5108

The part of the body to be scanned is divided into cells. If an X-ray passes through more than one cell, the total linear-attenuation value is the sum of the values for the cells. For example, in the figure, let a, b, and c be the values for cells A, B, and C. The attenuation value for beam 1 is $a + b$ and for beam 2 is $a + c$.

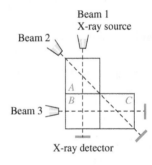

a. Find the attenuation value for beam 3.

b. Suppose that the attenuation values are 0.8, 0.55, and 0.65 for beams 1, 2, and 3, respectively. Set up and solve the system of three equations for a, b, and c. What can you conclude about cells A, B, and C?

c. Find the inverse of the coefficient matrix from part b to find a, b, and c for the following three cases, and make conclusions about cells A, B, and C for each.

Patient	Linear-Attenuation Values		
	Beam 1	Beam 2	Beam 3
X	0.54	0.40	0.52
Y	0.65	0.80	0.75
Z	0.51	0.49	0.44

75. CAT Scans (Refer to Exercise 74.) Four X-ray beams are aimed at four cells, as shown in the following figure. *Source: The Mathematics Teacher.*

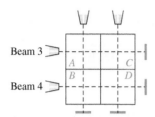

Beam 1 Beam 2

a. Suppose the attenuation values for beams 1, 2, 3, and 4 are 0.60, 0.75, 0.65, and 0.70, respectively. Do we have enough information to determine the values of a, b, c, and d? Explain.

b. Suppose we have the data from part a, as well as the following values for d. Find the values for a, b, and c, and draw conclusions about cells A, B, C, and D in each case.

(i) 0.33   **(ii)** 0.43

c. Two X-ray beams are added, as shown in the figure. In addition to the data in part a, we now have attenuation values for beams 5 and 6 of 0.85 and 0.50. Find the values for a, b, c, and d, and make conclusions about cells A, B, C, and D. 109

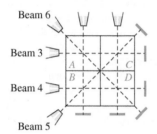

Beam 1 Beam 2

d. Six X-ray beams are not necessary because four appropriately chosen beams are sufficient. Give two examples of four beams (chosen from beams 1–6 in part c) that will give the solution. (*Note:* There are 12 possible solutions.)

e. Discuss what properties the four beams selected in part d must have in order to provide a unique solution.

76. Hockey In a recent study, the number of head and neck injuries among hockey players wearing full face shields and half face shields were compared. The following table provides the rates per 1000 athlete-exposures for specific injuries that caused a player wearing either shield to miss one or more events. *Source: JAMA.*

	Half Shield	Full Shield
Head and Face Injuries (excluding Concussions)	3.54	1.41
Concussions	1.53	1.57
Neck Injuries	0.34	0.29
Other	7.53	6.21

If an equal number of players in a large league wear each type of shield and the total number of athlete-exposures for the league in a season is 8000, use matrix operations to estimate the total number of injuries of each type.

Photos/Thinkstock

Physical Sciences

77. Roof Trusses Linear systems occur in the design of roof trusses for new homes and buildings. The simplest type of roof truss is a triangle. The truss shown in the figure below is used to frame roofs of small buildings. If a 100-lb force is applied at the peak of the truss, then the forces or weights W_1 and W_2 exerted parallel to each rafter of the truss are determined by the following linear system of equations.

$$\frac{\sqrt{3}}{2}(W_1 + W_2) = 100$$

$$W_1 - W_2 = 0$$

Solve the system to find W_1 and W_2. *Source: Structural Analysis.*

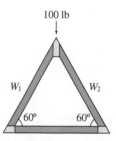

100 lb

W_1 W_2

60°   60°

78. Roof Trusses (Refer to Exercise 77.) Use the following system of equations to determine the force or weights W_1 and W_2 exerted on each rafter for the truss shown in the figure.

$$\frac{1}{2}W_1 + \frac{\sqrt{2}}{2}W_2 = 150$$

$$\frac{\sqrt{3}}{2}W_1 - \frac{\sqrt{2}}{2}W_2 = 0$$

150 lb

W_1 W_2

30°   45°

79. Carbon Dioxide Determining the amount of carbon dioxide in the atmosphere is important because carbon dioxide is known to be a greenhouse gas. Carbon dioxide concentrations (in parts per million) have been measured at Mauna Loa, Hawaii, for more than 40 years. The concentrations have increased quadratically. The table lists readings for 3 years. *Source: Scripps Institution of Oceanography.*

Year	CO$_2$
1960	317
1980	339
2004	377

a. If the relationship between the carbon dioxide concentration C and the year t is expressed as $C = at^2 + bt + c$, where $t = 0$ corresponds to 1960, use a linear system of equations to determine the constants a, b, and c.

b. Predict the year when the amount of carbon dioxide in the atmosphere will double from its 1960 level. (*Hint:* This requires solving a quadratic equation. For review on how to do this, see Section R.4.)

80. Chemistry When carbon monoxide (CO) reacts with oxygen (O$_2$), carbon dioxide (CO$_2$) is formed. This can be written as CO + (1/2)O$_2$ = CO$_2$ and as a matrix equation. If we form a 2×1 column matrix by letting the first element be the number of carbon atoms and the second element be the number of oxygen atoms, then CO would have the column matrix *Source: Journal of Chemical Education.*

$$\begin{bmatrix} 1 \\ 1 \end{bmatrix}.$$

Similarly, O$_2$ and CO$_2$ would have the column matrices $\begin{bmatrix} 0 \\ 2 \end{bmatrix}$ and $\begin{bmatrix} 1 \\ 2 \end{bmatrix}$, respectively.

a. Use the Gauss-Jordan method to find numbers x and y (known as *stoichiometric numbers*) that solve the system of equations

$$\begin{bmatrix} 1 \\ 1 \end{bmatrix} x + \begin{bmatrix} 0 \\ 2 \end{bmatrix} y = \begin{bmatrix} 1 \\ 2 \end{bmatrix}.$$

Compare your answers to the equation written above.

b. Repeat the process for xCO$_2$ + yH$_2$ + zCO = H$_2$O, where H$_2$ is hydrogen, and H$_2$O is water. In words, what does this mean?

General Interest

81. Students Suppose 20% of the boys and 30% of the girls in a high school like tennis, and 60% of the boys and 90% of the girls like math. If 500 students like tennis and 1500 like math, how many boys and girls are in the school? Find all possible solutions.

82. Baseball In the 2009 Major League Baseball season, slugger Ichiro Suzuki had a total of 225 hits. The number of singles he hit was 11 more than four times the combined total of doubles and home runs. The number of doubles he hit was 1 more than twice the combined total of triples and home runs. The number of singles and home runs together was 15 more than five times the combined total of doubles and triples. Find the number of singles, doubles, triples, and home runs that Suzuki hit during the season. *Source: Baseball-Reference.com.*

83. Cookies Regular Nabisco Oreo cookies are made of two chocolate cookie wafers surrounding a single layer of vanilla cream. The claim on the package states that a single serving is 34 g, which is three cookies. Nabisco Double Stuf cookies are made of the same two chocolate cookie wafers surrounding a double layer of vanilla cream. The claim on this package states that a single serving is 29 g, which is two Double Stuf cookies. If the Double Stuf cookies truly have a double layer of vanilla cream, find the weight of a single chocolate wafer and the weight of a single layer of vanilla cream.

EXTENDED APPLICATION

CONTAGION

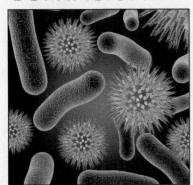

Tischenko Irina/Shutterstock

Suppose that three people have contracted a contagious disease. *Source: Finite Mathematics with Applications to Business, Life Sciences, and Social Sciences.* A second group of five people may have been in contact with the three infected persons. A third group of six people may have been in contact with the second group. We can form a 3×5 matrix P with rows representing the first group of three and columns representing the second group of five. We enter a one in the corresponding position if a person in the first group has contact with a person in the second group. These direct contacts are called *first-order contacts*. Similarly, we form a 5×6 matrix Q representing the first-order contacts between the second and third group. For example, suppose

$$P = \begin{bmatrix} 1 & 0 & 0 & 1 & 0 \\ 0 & 0 & 1 & 1 & 0 \\ 1 & 1 & 0 & 0 & 0 \end{bmatrix} \text{ and }$$

$$Q = \begin{bmatrix} 1 & 1 & 0 & 1 & 1 & 1 \\ 0 & 0 & 0 & 0 & 1 & 0 \\ 0 & 0 & 0 & 0 & 0 & 0 \\ 0 & 1 & 0 & 1 & 0 & 0 \\ 1 & 0 & 0 & 0 & 1 & 0 \end{bmatrix}.$$

From matrix P we see that the first person in the first group had contact with the first and fourth persons in the second group. Also, none of the first group had contact with the last person in the second group.

A *second-order contact* is an indirect contact between persons in the first and third groups through some person in the second group. The product matrix PQ indicates these contacts. Verify that the second-row, fourth-column entry of PQ is 1. That is, there is one second-order contact between the second person in group one and the fourth person in group three. Let a_{ij} denote the element in the ith row and jth column of the matrix PQ. By looking at the products that form a_{24} below, we see that the common contact was with the fourth individual in group two. (The p_{ij} are entries in P, and the q_{ij} are entries in Q.)

$$\begin{aligned} a_{24} &= p_{21}q_{14} + p_{22}q_{24} + p_{23}q_{34} + p_{24}q_{44} + p_{25}q_{54} \\ &= 0 \cdot 1 + 0 \cdot 0 + 1 \cdot 0 + 1 \cdot 1 + 0 \cdot 0 \\ &= 1 \end{aligned}$$

The second person in group 1 and the fourth person in group 3 both had contact with the fourth person in group 2.

This idea could be extended to third-, fourth-, and larger-order contacts. It indicates a way to use matrices to trace the spread of a contagious disease. It could also pertain to the dispersal of ideas or anything that might pass from one individual to another.

EXERCISES

1. Find the second-order contact matrix PQ mentioned in the text.

2. How many second-order contacts were there between the second contagious person and the third person in the third group?

3. Is there anyone in the third group who has had no contacts at all with the first group?

4. The totals of the columns in PQ give the total number of second-order contacts per person, while the column totals in P and Q give the total number of first-order contacts per person. Which person(s) in the third group had the most contacts, counting first- and second-order contacts?

5. Go to the website WolframAlpha.com and enter: "multiply matrices." Study how matrix multiplication can be performed by Wolfram|Alpha. Try Exercise 1 with Wolfram|Alpha and discuss how it compares with Microsoft Excel and with your graphing calculator.

DIRECTIONS FOR GROUP PROJECT

Assume that your group (3–5 students) is trying to map the spread of a new disease. Suppose also that the information given above has been obtained from interviews with the first three people that were hospitalized with symptoms of the disease and their contacts. Using the questions above as a guide, prepare a presentation for a public meeting that describes the method of obtaining the data, the data itself, and addresses the spirit of each question. Formulate a strategy for how to handle the spread of this disease to other people. The presentation should be mathematically sound, grammatically correct, and professionally crafted. Use presentation software, such as Microsoft PowerPoint, to present your findings.

LEARNING OBJECTIVES

1: Solution of Linear Systems by the Echelon Method

1. Apply system transformation operations on matrices
2. Solve linear systems using the echelon method
3. Solve application problems

2: Solution of Linear Systems by the Gauss-Jordan Method

1. Perform row operations on matrices
2. Solve linear systems by the Gauss-Jordan method
3. Solve application problems

3: Addition and Subtraction of Matrices

1. Identify the size of a matrix
2. Add and subtract matrices
3. Solve application problems

4: Multiplication of Matrices

1. Multiply a matrix by a constant value
2. Find the product two matrices
3. Simplify matrix expressions
4. Solve application problems

5: Matrix Inverses

1. Determine if two matrices are inverses of each other
2. Find the inverse of a matrix (if it exists)
3. Solve a system by using the inverse
4. Solve application problems

6: Input-Output Models

1. Find the production matrix for an input-output model
2. Find the demand matrix for an input-output model
3. Solve application problems

ANSWERS TO SELECTED EXERCISES

Answers to selected writing exercises are provided.

Exercises 1

1. $(3, 2)$ **3.** $(1, 3)$ **5.** $(-2, 0)$ **7.** $(0, 2)$ **9.** $(3, -2)$ **11.** $(2, -2)$
13. No solution **15.** $((2y - 4)/3, y)$ **17.** $(4, 1)$ **19.** $(7, -2)$ **21.** No **23.** 4 **25.** 3 **29.** $(8z - 4, 3 - 5z, z)$
31. $(3 - z, 4 - z, z)$ **35.** \$27 **37.** 400 main floor, 200 balcony **39.** Not possible; inconsistent system **41.** Either 10 buffets, 5 chairs, and no tables, or 11 buffets, 1 chair, and 1 table **43.** $z + 80$ long-sleeve blouses, $260 - 2z$ short-sleeve blouses, and z sleeveless blouses with $0 \leq z \leq 130$. **45. a.** March 23, March 19 **b.** 1991 **47.** 36 field goals, 28 foul shots

Exercises 2

1. $\begin{bmatrix} 3 & 1 & | & 6 \\ 2 & 5 & | & 15 \end{bmatrix}$ **3.** $\begin{bmatrix} 2 & 1 & 1 & | & 3 \\ 3 & -4 & 2 & | & -7 \\ 1 & 1 & 1 & | & 2 \end{bmatrix}$ **5.** $x = 2, y = 3$ **7.** $x = 4, y = -5, z = 1$ **9.** Row operations

11. $\begin{bmatrix} 3 & 7 & 4 & | & 10 \\ 0 & 1 & -5 & | & -8 \\ 0 & 4 & 5 & | & 11 \end{bmatrix}$ **13.** $\begin{bmatrix} 1 & 0 & 0 & | & -3 \\ 0 & 3 & 2 & | & 5 \\ 0 & 5 & 3 & | & 7 \end{bmatrix}$ **15.** $\begin{bmatrix} 1 & 0 & 0 & | & 6 \\ 0 & 5 & 0 & | & 9 \\ 0 & 0 & 4 & | & 8 \end{bmatrix}$ **17.** $(2, 3)$ **19.** $(1, 6)$ **21.** No solution

23. $((3y + 1)/6, y)$ **25.** $(4, 1, 0)$ **27.** No solution **29.** $(-1, 23, 16)$ **31.** $((-9z + 5)/23, (10z - 3)/23, z)$
33. $((-2z + 62)/35, (3z + 5)/7, z)$ **35.** $((9 - 3y - z)/2, y, z)$ **37.** $(0, 2, -2, 1)$; the answers are given in the order x, y, z, w.
39. $(-w - 3, -4w - 19, -3w - 2, w)$ **41.** $(28.9436, 36.6326, 9.6390, 37.1036)$ **43.** row 1: 3/8, 1/6, 11/24; row 2: 5/12, 1/3, 1/4; row 3: 5/24, 1/2, 7/24 **45.** \$2000 in U.S. Savings bonds, \$4000 in mutual funds, \$4000 in money market **47.** 2000 chairs, 1600 cabinets, and 2500 buffets. **49. a.** 5 trucks, 2 vans, and 3 SUVs. **b.** Use 2 trucks, 6 vans, and 1 SUV, or use 5 trucks, 2 vans, and 3 SUVs. **51. a.** \$12,000 at 8%, \$7000 at 9%, and \$6000 at 10% **b.** The amount borrowed at 10% must be less than or equal to \$9500. If $z = \$5000$, they borrowed \$11,000 at 8% and \$9000 at 9%. **c.** No solution. **d.** The total annual interest would be \$2220, not \$2190, as specified as one of the conditions. **53.** The first supplier should send 40 units to Roseville and 35 units to Akron. The second supplier should send 0 units to Roseville and 40 units to Akron **55. a.** 26 **b.** 0 two-person, 50 four-person, and 0 six-person tents **c.** 25 two-person, 0 four-person, and 25 six-person tents **57. a.** 400/9 g of group A, 400/3 g of group B, and 2000/9 g of group C. **b.** For any positive number z of grams of group C, there should be z grams less than 800/3 g of group A

and 400/3 g of group B.   **c.** No   **59.** About 244 fish of species A, 39 fish of species B, and 101 fish of species C.   **61. b.** 7,206,360 white cows, 4,893,246 black cows, 3,515,820 spotted cows, and 5,439,213 brown cows   **63. a.** $r = 175,000$, $b = 375,000$
65. 8.15, 4.23, 3.15   **67. a.** 24 balls, 57 dolls, and 19 cars   **b.** None   **c.** 48   **d.** 5 balls, 95 dolls, and 0 cars   **e.** 52 balls, 1 doll, and 47 cars   **69. a.** (1, 1, 1, 1); the strategy required to turn all the lights out is to push every button one time.   **b.** (0, 1, 1, 0); the strategy required to turn all the lights out is to push the button in the first row, second column, and push the button in the second row, first column.

Exercises 3

For exercises . . .	1–6,15–20	7–14	21–32	39,40,43	41,48	42	44–46
Refer to example . . .	3	2	4,6	5	1	5,7	7

1. False; not all corresponding elements are equal.
3. True   **5.** True   **7.** 2×2; square   **9.** 3×4 **11.** 2×1; column   **13.** Undefined   **15.** $x = 4$, $y = -8$, $z = 1$
17. $s = 10$, $t = 0$, $r = 7$ **19.** $a = 20$, $b = 5$, $c = 0$, $d = 4$, $f = 1$

21. $\begin{bmatrix} 10 & 4 & -5 & -6 \\ 4 & 5 & 3 & 11 \end{bmatrix}$ **23.** Not possible   **25.** $\begin{bmatrix} 1 & 5 & 6 & -9 \\ 5 & 7 & 2 & 1 \\ -7 & 2 & 2 & -7 \end{bmatrix}$ **27.** $\begin{bmatrix} 3 & 4 \\ 4 & 8 \end{bmatrix}$ **29.** $\begin{bmatrix} 10 & -2 \\ 10 & 9 \end{bmatrix}$

31. $\begin{bmatrix} -12x + 8y & -x + y \\ x & 8x - y \end{bmatrix}$ **33.** $\begin{bmatrix} -x & -y \\ -z & -w \end{bmatrix}$ **39. a.** Chicago: $\begin{bmatrix} 4.05 & 7.01 \\ 3.27 & 3.51 \end{bmatrix}$, Seattle: $\begin{bmatrix} 4.40 & 6.90 \\ 3.54 & 3.76 \end{bmatrix}$ **b.** $\begin{bmatrix} 4.42 & 7.43 \\ 3.38 & 3.62 \end{bmatrix}$

41. a. $\begin{bmatrix} 2 & 1 & 2 & 1 \\ 3 & 2 & 2 & 1 \\ 4 & 3 & 2 & 1 \end{bmatrix}$ **b.** $\begin{bmatrix} 5 & 0 & 7 \\ 0 & 10 & 1 \\ 0 & 15 & 2 \\ 10 & 12 & 8 \end{bmatrix}$ **c.** $\begin{bmatrix} 8 \\ 4 \\ 5 \end{bmatrix}$ **43. a.** 8   **b.** 3   **c.** $\begin{bmatrix} 85 & 15 \\ 27 & 73 \end{bmatrix}$ **d.** Yes

45. a. $\begin{bmatrix} 60.0 & 68.3 \\ 63.8 & 72.5 \\ 64.5 & 73.6 \\ 68.3 & 75.2 \end{bmatrix}$ **b.** $\begin{bmatrix} 68.0 & 75.6 \\ 70.7 & 78.1 \\ 72.7 & 79.4 \\ 74.9 & 80.1 \end{bmatrix}$ **c.** $\begin{bmatrix} -8.0 & -7.3 \\ -6.9 & -5.6 \\ -8.2 & -5.8 \\ -6.6 & -4.9 \end{bmatrix}$ **47. a.** $\begin{bmatrix} 51.2 & 7.9 \\ 59.8 & 11.1 \\ 66.2 & 11.3 \\ 73.8 & 13.2 \\ 78.5 & 16.5 \\ 83.0 & 19.6 \end{bmatrix}$ **b.** $\begin{bmatrix} 45.3 & 7.9 \\ 47.9 & 8.5 \\ 50.8 & 9.2 \\ 53.4 & 9.3 \\ 57.0 & 10.6 \\ 62.3 & 13.3 \end{bmatrix}$ **c.** $\begin{bmatrix} 5.9 & 0 \\ 11.9 & 2.6 \\ 15.4 & 2.1 \\ 20.4 & 3.9 \\ 21.5 & 5.9 \\ 20.7 & 6.3 \end{bmatrix}$

Exercises 4

For exercises . . .	1–6,49,50	7–12	15–31,51	43–48
Refer to example . . .	1	4	2,3,5	6

1. $\begin{bmatrix} -4 & 8 \\ 0 & 6 \end{bmatrix}$ **3.** $\begin{bmatrix} 12 & -24 \\ 0 & -18 \end{bmatrix}$ **5.** $\begin{bmatrix} -22 & -6 \\ 20 & -12 \end{bmatrix}$ **7.** 2×2; 2×2

9. 3×4; BA does not exist.   **11.** AB does not exist; 3×2 **13.** columns; rows   **15.** $\begin{bmatrix} 8 \\ -1 \end{bmatrix}$ **17.** $\begin{bmatrix} 14 \\ -23 \end{bmatrix}$ **19.** $\begin{bmatrix} -7 & 2 & 8 \\ 27 & -12 & 12 \end{bmatrix}$

21. $\begin{bmatrix} -2 & 10 \\ 0 & 8 \end{bmatrix}$ **23.** $\begin{bmatrix} 13 & 5 \\ 25 & 15 \end{bmatrix}$ **25.** $\begin{bmatrix} 13 \\ 29 \end{bmatrix}$ **27.** $\begin{bmatrix} 7 \\ -33 \\ 4 \end{bmatrix}$ **29.** $\begin{bmatrix} 22 & -8 \\ 11 & -4 \end{bmatrix}$ **31. a.** $\begin{bmatrix} 16 & 22 \\ 7 & 19 \end{bmatrix}$ **b.** $\begin{bmatrix} 5 & -5 \\ 0 & 30 \end{bmatrix}$ **c.** No   **d.** No

39. a. $\begin{bmatrix} 6 & 106 & 158 & 222 & 28 \\ 120 & 139 & 64 & 75 & 115 \\ -146 & -2 & 184 & 144 & -129 \\ 106 & 94 & 24 & 116 & 110 \end{bmatrix}$ **b.** Does not exist   **c.** No   **41. a.** $\begin{bmatrix} -1 & 5 & 9 & 13 & -1 \\ 7 & 17 & 2 & -10 & 6 \\ 18 & 9 & -12 & 12 & 22 \\ 9 & 4 & 18 & 10 & -3 \\ 1 & 6 & 10 & 28 & 5 \end{bmatrix}$

b. $\begin{bmatrix} -2 & -9 & 90 & 77 \\ -42 & -63 & 127 & 62 \\ 413 & 76 & 180 & -56 \\ -29 & -44 & 198 & 85 \\ 137 & 20 & 162 & 103 \end{bmatrix}$ **c.** $\begin{bmatrix} -56 & -1 & 1 & 45 \\ -156 & -119 & 76 & 122 \\ 315 & 86 & 118 & -91 \\ -17 & -17 & 116 & 51 \\ 118 & 19 & 125 & 77 \end{bmatrix}$ **d.** $\begin{bmatrix} 54 & -8 & 89 & 32 \\ 114 & 56 & 51 & -60 \\ 98 & -10 & 62 & 35 \\ -12 & -27 & 82 & 34 \\ 19 & 1 & 37 & 26 \end{bmatrix}$ **e.** $\begin{bmatrix} -2 & -9 & 90 & 77 \\ -42 & -63 & 127 & 62 \\ 413 & 76 & 180 & -56 \\ -29 & -44 & 198 & 85 \\ 137 & 20 & 162 & 103 \end{bmatrix}$

f. Yes   **43. a.**

	A	B
Dept. 1	57	70
Dept. 2	41	54
Dept. 3	27	40
Dept. 4	39	40

b. Supplier A: \$164; Supplier B: \$204; Supplier A   **45. a.** $\begin{bmatrix} 4.24 & 6.95 \\ 3.42 & 3.64 \end{bmatrix}$ **b.** $\begin{bmatrix} 4.41 & 7.17 \\ 3.46 & 3.69 \end{bmatrix}$

47. a. $\begin{bmatrix} 80 & 40 & 120 \\ 60 & 30 & 150 \end{bmatrix}$ **b.** $\begin{bmatrix} 1/2 & 1/5 \\ 1/4 & 1/5 \\ 1/4 & 3/5 \end{bmatrix}$ **c.** $PF = \begin{bmatrix} 80 & 96 \\ 75 & 108 \end{bmatrix}$; the rows give the average price per pair of footwear sold by each store, and the columns give the state.   **d.** \$108

49. a. $\begin{bmatrix} 20 & 52 & 27 \\ 25 & 62 & 35 \\ 30 & 72 & 43 \end{bmatrix}$; the rows give the amounts of fat, carbohydrates, and protein, respectively, in each of the daily meals.

b. $\begin{bmatrix} 75 \\ 45 \\ 70 \\ 168 \end{bmatrix}$; the rows give the number of calories in one exchange of each of the food groups.   **c.** The rows give the number of calories in each meal.

51. $\begin{bmatrix} 66.7 & 74.4 \\ 69.6 & 77.2 \\ 71.3 & 78.4 \\ 73.8 & 79.3 \end{bmatrix}$ **53. a.** $\begin{bmatrix} 0.0346 & 0.0118 \\ 0.0174 & 0.0073 \\ 0.0189 & 0.0059 \\ 0.0135 & 0.0083 \\ 0.0099 & 0.0103 \end{bmatrix}$; $\begin{bmatrix} 361 & 2038 & 286 & 227 & 460 \\ 473 & 2494 & 362 & 252 & 484 \\ 627 & 2978 & 443 & 278 & 499 \\ 803 & 3435 & 524 & 314 & 511 \\ 1013 & 3824 & 591 & 344 & 522 \end{bmatrix}$ **b.**

	Births	Deaths
1970	60.98	27.45
1980	74.80	33.00
1990	90.58	39.20
2000	106.75	45.51
2010	122.57	51.59

Exercises 5

1. Yes   **3.** No   **5.** No   **7.** Yes   **9.** No; the row of all zeros makes it impossible to get all the 1's in the diagonal of the identity matrix, no matter what matrix is used as an inverse.

For exercises …	1–8	11–26,51–55	27–42,56–58	59–63	64,65
Refer to example …	1	2,3	4,6	5	7

11. $\begin{bmatrix} 0 & 1/2 \\ -1 & 1/2 \end{bmatrix}$ **13.** $\begin{bmatrix} 2 & 1 \\ 5 & 3 \end{bmatrix}$ **15.** No inverse   **17.** $\begin{bmatrix} 1 & 0 & 0 \\ 0 & -1 & 0 \\ -1 & 0 & 1 \end{bmatrix}$ **19.** $\begin{bmatrix} 15 & 4 & -5 \\ -12 & -3 & 4 \\ -4 & -1 & 1 \end{bmatrix}$ **21.** No inverse

23. $\begin{bmatrix} -11/2 & -1/2 & 5/2 \\ 1/2 & 1/2 & -1/2 \\ -5/2 & 1/2 & 1/2 \end{bmatrix}$ **25.** $\begin{bmatrix} 1/2 & 1/2 & -1/4 & 1/2 \\ -1 & 4 & -1/2 & -2 \\ -1/2 & 5/2 & -1/4 & -3/2 \\ 1/2 & -1/2 & 1/4 & 1/2 \end{bmatrix}$ **27.** $(5, 1)$ **29.** $(2, 1)$ **31.** $(15, 21)$

33. No inverse, $(-8y - 12, y)$ **35.** $(-8, 6, 1)$ **37.** $(-36, 8, -8)$ **39.** No inverse, no solution for system

41. $(-7, -34, -19, 7)$

51. $\begin{bmatrix} -0.0447 & -0.0230 & 0.0292 & 0.0895 & -0.0402 \\ 0.0921 & 0.0150 & 0.0321 & 0.0209 & -0.0276 \\ -0.0678 & 0.0315 & -0.0404 & 0.0326 & 0.0373 \\ 0.0171 & -0.0248 & 0.0069 & -0.0003 & 0.0246 \\ -0.0208 & 0.0740 & 0.0096 & -0.1018 & 0.0646 \end{bmatrix}$

53. $\begin{bmatrix} 0.0394 & 0.0880 & 0.0033 & 0.0530 & -0.1499 \\ -0.1492 & 0.0289 & 0.0187 & 0.1033 & 0.1668 \\ -0.1330 & -0.0543 & 0.0356 & 0.1768 & 0.1055 \\ 0.1407 & 0.0175 & -0.0453 & -0.1344 & 0.0655 \\ 0.0102 & -0.0653 & 0.0993 & 0.0085 & -0.0388 \end{bmatrix}$ **55.** Yes

57. $\begin{bmatrix} 1.51482 \\ 0.053479 \\ -0.637242 \\ 0.462629 \end{bmatrix}$ **59. a.** $\begin{bmatrix} 72 \\ 48 \\ 60 \end{bmatrix}$ **b.** $\begin{bmatrix} 2 & 4 & 2 \\ 2 & 1 & 2 \\ 2 & 1 & 3 \end{bmatrix} \begin{bmatrix} x_1 \\ x_2 \\ x_3 \end{bmatrix} = \begin{bmatrix} 72 \\ 48 \\ 60 \end{bmatrix}$ **c.** 8 type I, 8 type II, and 12 type III

61. a. \$10,000 at 6%, \$10,000 at 6.5%, and \$5000 at 8%   **b.** \$14,000 at 6%, \$9000 at 6.5%, and \$7000 at 8%   **c.** \$24,000 at 6%, \$4000 at 6.5%, and \$12,000 at 8%   **63. a.** 50 Super Vim, 75 Multitab, and 100 Mighty Mix   **b.** 75 Super Vim, 50 Multitab, and 60 Mighty Mix   **c.** 80 Super Vim, 100 Multitab, and 50 Mighty Mix   **65. a.** 262, -161, -12, 186, -103, -22, 264, -168, -9, 208, -134, -5, 224, -152, 5, 92, -50, -3 **b.** $\begin{bmatrix} 1.75 & 2.5 & 3 \\ -0.25 & -0.5 & 0 \\ -0.25 & -0.5 & -1 \end{bmatrix}$ **c.** happy birthday

Exercises 6

For exercises ...	1–6,9–12,17–25	7,8,26–29	13–16
Refer to example ...	4	5	3,4

1. $\begin{bmatrix} 60 \\ 50 \end{bmatrix}$ **3.** $\begin{bmatrix} 6.43 \\ 26.12 \end{bmatrix}$ **5.** $\begin{bmatrix} 10 \\ 18 \\ 10 \end{bmatrix}$ **7.** $33:47:23$ **9.** $\begin{bmatrix} 7697 \\ 4205 \\ 6345 \\ 4106 \end{bmatrix}$ (rounded)   **11.** About 1440 metric tons of wheat and 1938 metric tons of oil.   **13.** About 1506 units of agriculture, 1713 units of manufacturing, and 1412 units of transportation.   **15.** About 3077 units of agriculture, about 2564 units of manufacturing, and about 3179 units of transportation   **17. a.** 7/4 bushels of yams and $15/8 \approx 2$ pigs   **b.** 167.5 bushels of yams and $153.75 \approx 154$ pigs   **19.** About 848 units of agriculture, about 516 units of manufacturing, and about 2970 units of households   **21.** About 195 million pounds of agriculture, about 26 million pounds of manufacturing, and about 13.6 million pounds of energy   **23.** In millions of dollars, the amounts are about 532 for natural resources, about 481 for manufacturing, about 805 for trade and services, and about 1185 for personal consumption.

25. a. $\begin{bmatrix} 1.67 & 0.56 & 0.56 \\ 0.19 & 1.17 & 0.06 \\ 3.15 & 3.27 & 4.38 \end{bmatrix}$ **b.** These multipliers imply that if the demand for one community's output increases by \$1, then the output in the other community will increase by the amount in the row and column of that matrix. For example, if the demand for Hermitage's output increases by \$1, then output from Sharon will increase by \$0.56, Farrell by \$0.06, and Hermitage by \$4.38.   **27.** 3 units of coal to every 4 units of steel   **29.** 6 units of mining to every 8 units of manufacturing and 5 units of communication

Review Exercises

For exercises ...	1,3,10,13, 17,23–28, 67,68,74, 75,79,80,82	2,5,29–33, 36,69,73	4,19–22, 66,77,78, 81,83	6,7,18,34, 35,37–43, 76	8,9,11,12, 14,15, 44–62,70, 74	16,63,64, 71,72
Refer to section ...	2	3	1	4	5	6

1. False   **2.** False   **3.** True   **4.** True   **5.** False   **6.** True   **7.** False   **8.** False   **9.** True   **10.** False   **11.** False   **12.** False
13. True   **14.** True   **15.** False   **16.** True   **19.** $(1, -4)$ **21.** $((34 - 28z)/50, (53 - z)/25, z)$ **23.** $(-9, 3)$ **25.** $(7, -9, -1)$
27. $(6 - 7z/3, 1 + z/3, z)$ **29.** 2×2 (square); $a = 2, b = 3, c = 5, q = 9$ **31.** 1×4 (row); $m = 6, k = 3, z = -3, r = -9$

33. $\begin{bmatrix} 9 & 10 \\ -3 & 0 \\ 10 & 16 \end{bmatrix}$ **35.** $\begin{bmatrix} 23 & 20 \\ -7 & 3 \\ 24 & 39 \end{bmatrix}$ **37.** $\begin{bmatrix} -17 & 20 \\ 1 & -21 \\ -8 & -17 \end{bmatrix}$ **39.** Not possible   **41.** $[9]$ **43.** $[-14 \; -19]$ **45.** No inverse

47. $\begin{bmatrix} 7 & -3 \\ -2 & 1 \end{bmatrix}$ **49.** No inverse   **51.** $\begin{bmatrix} 2/3 & 0 & -1/3 \\ 1/3 & 0 & -2/3 \\ -2/3 & 1 & 1/3 \end{bmatrix}$ **53.** No inverse   **55.** $X = \begin{bmatrix} 1 \\ -13 \end{bmatrix}$ **57.** $X = \begin{bmatrix} -22 \\ -18 \\ 15 \end{bmatrix}$

59. $(2, 1)$ **61.** $(-1, 0, 2)$ **63.** $\begin{bmatrix} 218.1 \\ 318.3 \end{bmatrix}$ **65. a.** $(2, 3, -1)$ **b.** $(2, 3, -1)$ **c.** $\begin{bmatrix} 1 & 2 & 1 \\ 2 & -1 & -1 \\ 3 & -3 & 2 \end{bmatrix}\begin{bmatrix} x \\ y \\ z \end{bmatrix} = \begin{bmatrix} 7 \\ 2 \\ -5 \end{bmatrix}$

d. $\begin{bmatrix} 5/22 & 7/22 & 1/22 \\ 7/22 & 1/22 & -3/22 \\ 3/22 & -9/22 & 5/22 \end{bmatrix}$ **e.** $(2, 3, -1)$ **67.** 5 blankets, 3 rugs, 8 skirts   **69.** $\begin{bmatrix} 1.33 & 17.6 & 152,000 & 26.75 & +1.88 \\ 1.00 & 20.0 & 238,200 & 32.36 & -1.50 \\ 0.79 & 25.4 & 39,110 & 16.51 & -0.89 \\ 0.27 & 21.2 & 122,500 & 28.60 & +0.75 \end{bmatrix}$

71. a. $\begin{matrix} & c & g \\ c & \\ g \end{matrix}\begin{bmatrix} 0 & 1/2 \\ 2/3 & 0 \end{bmatrix}$ **b.** 1200 units of cheese; 1600 units of goats   **73.** $\begin{bmatrix} 8 & 8 & 8 \\ 10 & 5 & 9 \\ 7 & 10 & 7 \\ 8 & 9 & 7 \end{bmatrix}$ **75. a.** No   **b. (i)** 0.23, 0.37, 0.42; A is healthy; B and D are tumorous; C is bone.   **(ii)** 0.33, 0.27, 0.32; A and C are tumorous, B could be healthy or tumorous, D is bone.   **c.** 0.2, 0.4, 0.45, 0.3; A is healthy; B and C are bone; D is tumorous.
d. One example is to choose beams 1, 2, 3, and 6.   **77.** $W_1 = W_2 = 100\sqrt{3}/3 \approx 58$ lb   **79. a.** $C = 0.010985t^2 + 0.8803t + 317$
b. 2095   **81.** There are y girls and $2500 - 1.5y$ boys, where y is any even integer between 0 and 1666.   **83.** A chocolate wafer weighs 4.08 g, and a single layer of vanilla cream weighs 3.17 g.

TEXT CREDITS

Exercise 46: Reprinted by permission of Suntex International, Inc.
Exercise 48: Professor Nathan Borchelt, Clayton State University

SOURCES

Section 1

1. Exercise 44 from Goetz, Albert, "Basic Economics: Calculating Against Theatrical Disaster," *The Mathematics Teacher*, Vol. 89, No. 1, Jan. 1996, pp. 30–32.
2. Exercise 45 from Inouye, David, Billy Barr, Kenneth Armitage, and Brian Inouye, "Climate Change Is Affecting Altitudinal Migrants and Hibernating Species," *Proceedings of the National Academy of Science*, Vol. 97, No. 4, Feb. 15, 2000, pp. 1630–1633.
3. Exercise 46 from *National Traffic Safety Institute Student Workbook*, 1993, p. 7.
4. Exercise 47 from "Kobe's 81-Point Game Second Only to Wilt," http://sports.espn.go.com.
5. Exercise 48 from Suntex Int. Inc., Easton, PA, http://www.24game.com. Copied with permission. 24® is a registered trademark of Suntex International Inc., all rights reserved.

Section 2

1. Exercise 46 was provided by Prof. Nathan Borchelt, Clayton State University.
2. Exercise 55 from L. L. Bean, http://www.llbean.com.
3. Exercise 60 from Paredes, Miguel, Mohammad Fatehi, and Richard Hinthorn, "The Transformation of an Inconsistent Linear System into a Consistent System," *The AMATYC Review*, Vol. 13, No. 2, Spring 1992.
4. Exercise 61 from Dorrie, Heinrich, *100 Great Problems of Elementary Mathematics, Their History and Solution*, New York: Dover Publications, 1965, pp. 3–7.
5. Exercise 62 from *The New York Times 2010 Almanac*, p. 392.
6. Exercise 63 from Bellany, Ian, "Modeling War," *Journal of Peace Research*, Vol. 36, No. 6, 1999, pp. 729–739.
7. Exercise 65 from Szydlik, Stephen D., "The Problem with the Snack Food Problem," *The Mathematics Teacher*, Vol. 103, No. 1, Aug. 2009, pp. 18–28.
8. Exercise 66 from "Kobe's 81-Point Game Second Only to Wilt," http://sports.espn.go.com.
9. Exercise 68 from Guinard, J., C. Zoumas-Morse, L. Mori, B. Uatoni, D. Panyam, and A. Kilar, "Sugar and Fat Effects on Sensory Properties of Ice Cream," *Journal of Food Science*, Vol. 62, No. 4, Sept./Oct. 1997, pp. 1087–1094.
10. Exercise 69 from Anderson, Marlow and Todd Feil, "Turning Lights Out with Linear Algebra," *Mathematics Magazine*, Vol. 71, No. 4, 1998, pp. 300–303.
11. Exercise 70 from http://www.baseball-almanac.com.

Section 3

1. Exercise 44 from *Traffic Safety Facts Research Note*, NHTSA, December 2009.
2. Exercise 45 from *The New York Times 2010 Almanac*, p. 394.
3. Exercise 46 from U.S. Census Bureau Educational Attainment, Table A-2, http://www.census.gov/population/www/socdemo/educ-attn.html.
4. Exercise 47 from U.S. Census Bureau Educational Attainment, Table A-2, http://www.census.gov/population/www/socdemo/educ-attn.html.

Section 4

1. Exercise 52 from David I. Schneider, University of Maryland, based on the article "A Dynamic Analysis of Northern Spotted Owl Viability in a Fragmented Forest Landscape," by Lamberson, R., R. McKelvey, B. Noon, and C. Voss, *Conservation Biology*, Vol. 6, No. 4, Dec. 1992, pp. 505–512.
2. Exercise 53 from http://www.census.gov/ipc/www/idb/region.php and https://www.census.gov/ipc/prod/wp02/tabA-01.xls

Section 5

1. Exercise 66 from Isaksen, Daniel, "Linear Algebra on the Gridiron," *The College Mathematics Journal*, Vol. 26, No. 5, Nov. 1995, pp. 358–360.

Section 6

1. Page 102 from http://www.bea.gov/industry/.
2. Exercise 19 from Leontief, Wassily, Input-Output Economics, 2nd ed., Oxford University Press, 1966, pp. 20–27.
3. Exercise 20 from Ibid, pp. 6–9.
4. Exercise 21 from Ibid. pp. 174–177
5. Exercise 22 from *Input-Output Tables of China, 1981*, China Statistical Information and Consultancy Service Centre, 1987, pp. 17–19.

6. Exercise 23 and 24 from Chase, Robert, Philip Bourque, and Richard Conway Jr., "The 1987 Washington State Input-Output Study," Report to the Graduate School of Business Administration, University of Washington, Sept. 1993.
7. Exercise 25 from an example created by Thayer Watkins, Department of Economics, San Jose State University, www.sjsu.edu/faculty/watkins/inputoutput.htm.

Review Exercises

1. Exercise 72 from Lamphear, F. Charles and Theodore Roesler, "1970 Nebraska Input-Output Tables," *Nebraska Economic and Business Report No. 10*, Bureau of Business Research, University of Nebraska-Lincoln, 1971.
2. Exercises 74 and 75 are based on the article "Medical Applications of Linear Equations" by David Jabon, Gail Nord, Bryce W. Wilson, and Penny Coffman, *The Mathematics Teacher*, Vol. 89, No. 5, May 1996, p. 398.
3. Exercise 76 from Benson, Brian, Nicholas Nohtadi, Sarah Rose, and Willem Meeuwisse, "Head and Neck Injuries Among Ice Hockey Players Wearing Full Face Shields vs. Half Face Shields," *JAMA*, Vol. 282, No. 24, Dec. 22/29, 1999, pp. 2328–2332.
4. Exercise 77 from Hibbeler, R., *Structural Analysis*, Prentice-Hall, 1995.
5. Exercise 79 from Atmospheric Carbon Dioxide Record from Mauna Loa, Scripps Institution of Oceanography http://cdiac.esd.ornl.gov/ftp/trends/co2/maunaloa.co2.
6. Exercise 80 from Alberty, Robert, "Chemical Equations Are Actually Matrix Equations," *Journal of Chemical Education*, Vol. 68, No. 12, Dec. 1991, p. 984.
7. Exercise 82 from http://www.baseball-reference.com.

Extended Application

1. Page 110 from Grossman, Stanley, "First and Second Order Contact to a Contagious Disease." *Finite Mathematics with Applications to Business, Life Sciences, and Social Sciences*, WCB/McGraw-Hill, 1993.

Linear Programming: The Graphical Method

From Chapter 3 of *Finite Math,* Tenth Edition. Margaret L. Lial, Raymond N. Greenwell, Nathan P. Ritchey.Copyright © 2012 by Pearson Education, Inc. All rights reserved.

Linear Programming: The Graphical Method

An oil refinery turns crude oil into many different products, including gasoline and fuel oil. Efficient management requires matching the output of each product to the demand and the available shipping capacity. In an exercise in Section 3, we explore the use of linear programming to allocate refinery production for maximum profit.

M any realistic problems involve inequalities—a factory can manufacture *no more than* 12 items on a shift, or a medical researcher must interview *at least* a hundred patients to be sure that a new treatment for a disease is better than the old treatment. *Linear inequalities* of the form $ax + by \le c$ (or with $\ge$, $<$, or $>$ instead of $\le$) can be used in a process called *linear programming* to *optimize* (find the maximum or minimum value of a quantity) for a given situation.

In this chapter we introduce some *linear programming* problems that can be solved by graphical methods.

1 Graphing Linear Inequalities

APPLY IT How can a company determine the feasible number of units of each product to manufacture in order to meet all production requirements? *We will answer this question in Example 6 by graphing a set of inequalities.*

As mentioned earlier, a linear inequality is defined as follows.

Linear Inequality
A **linear inequality** in two variables has the form

$$ax + by \le c$$
$$ax + by < c,$$
$$ax + by \ge c,$$
or $\quad ax + by > c,$

for real numbers a, b, and c, with a and b not both 0.

EXAMPLE 1   Graphing an Inequality

Graph the linear inequality $2x - 3y \le 12$.

SOLUTION   Because of the "=" portion of $\le$, the points of the line $2x - 3y = 12$ satisfy the linear inequality $2x - 3y \le 12$ and are part of its graph. Find the intercepts by first letting $x = 0$ and then letting $y = 0$; use these points to get the graph of $2x - 3y = 12$ shown in Figure 1.

FOR REVIEW

One way to sketch a line is to first let $x = 0$ to find the y-intercept, then let $y = 0$ to find the x-intercept. For example, given $2x - 3y = 12$, letting $x = 0$ yields $-3y = 12$, so $y = -4$, and the corresponding point is $(0, -4)$. Letting $y = 0$ yields $2x = 12$, so $x = 6$ and the point is $(6, 0)$. Plot these two points, as in Figure 1, then use a straightedge to draw a line through them.

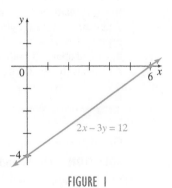

FIGURE 1

409

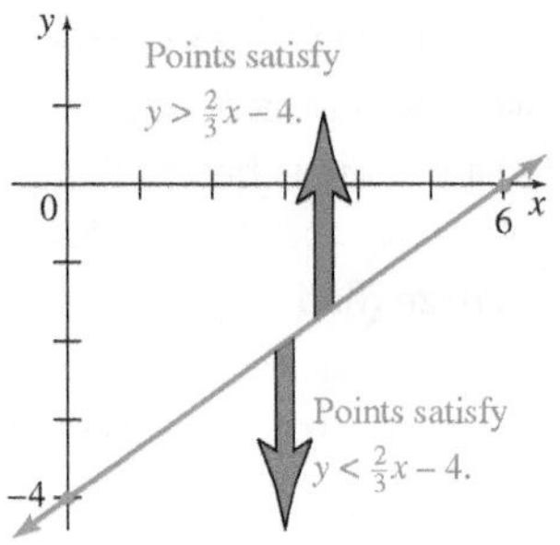

The points on the line satisfy "$2x - 3y$ *equals* 12." To locate the points satisfying "$2x - 3y$ *is less than* or equal to 12," first solve $2x - 3y \leq 12$ for y.

$$2x - 3y \leq 12$$

$$-3y \leq -2x + 12 \qquad \text{Subtract } 2x.$$

$$y \geq \frac{2}{3}x - 4 \qquad \text{Multiply by } -\frac{1}{3}.$$

(Recall that multiplying both sides of an inequality by a negative number reverses the direction of the inequality symbol.)

As shown in Figure 2, the points *above* the line $2x - 3y = 12$ satisfy

$$y > \frac{2}{3}x - 4,$$

while those below the line satisfy

$$y < \frac{2}{3}x - 4.$$

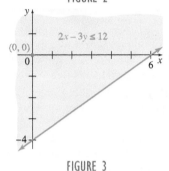

FIGURE 2

In summary, the inequality $2x - 3y \leq 12$ is satisfied by all points *on or above* the line $2x - 3y = 12$. Indicate the points above the line by shading, as in Figure 3. The line and shaded region in Figure 3 make up the graph of the linear inequality $2x - 3y \leq 12$. ▪

FIGURE 3

> **CAUTION** In this chapter, be sure to use a straightedge to draw lines and to plot the points with care. A sloppily drawn line could give a deceptive picture of the region being considered.

In Example 1, the line $2x - 3y = 12$, which separates the points in the solution from the points that are not in the solution, is called the **boundary**.

There is an alternative way to find the correct region to shade or to check the method shown above. Choose as a test point any point not on the boundary line. For example, in Example 1 we could choose the point $(0, 0)$, which is not on the line $2x - 3y = 12$. Substitute 0 for x and 0 for y in the given inequality.

$$2x - 3y \leq 12$$

$$2(0) - 3(0) \leq 12$$

$$0 \leq 12 \qquad \text{True}$$

Since the result $0 \leq 12$ is true, the test point $(0, 0)$ belongs on the side of the boundary where all points satisfy $2x - 3y < 12$. For this reason, we shade the side containing $(0, 0)$, as in Figure 3. Choosing a point on the other side of the line, such as $(4, -3)$, would produce a false result when the values $x = 4$ and $y = -3$ were substituted into the given inequality. In such a case, we would shade the side of the line *not including* the test point.

> **NOTE** Many of the inequalities in this chapter are of the form $ax + by \leq c$ or $ax + by \geq c$. These are most easily graphed by changing the $\leq$ or $\geq$ to $=$ and then plotting the two intercepts by letting $x = 0$ and $y = 0$, as in Example 1. Shade the appropriate side of the line as described above. If both $a > 0$ and $b > 0$ the shaded region for $ax + by \leq c$ is *below* the line, while the shaded region for $ax + by \geq c$ is *above* the line.

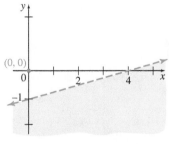

FIGURE 4

EXAMPLE 2 Graphing an Inequality

Graph $x - 4y > 4$.

SOLUTION The boundary here is the line $x - 4y = 4$. Since the points on this line do not satisfy $x - 4y > 4$, the line is drawn dashed, as in Figure 4. To decide whether to shade the region above the line or the region below the line, we will choose a test point not on the boundary line. Choosing $(0, 0)$, we replace x with 0 and y with 0:

$$x - 4y > 4$$
$$0 - 4(0) > 4$$
$$0 > 4. \quad \text{False}$$

The correct half-plane is the one that does *not* contain $(0, 0)$; the region below the boundary line is shaded, as shown in Figure 4.   **TRY YOUR TURN 1**

> **CAUTION**   Be careful. If the point $(0, 0)$ is on the boundary line, it cannot be used as a test point.

As the examples above suggest, the graph of a linear inequality is represented by a shaded region in the plane, perhaps including the line that is the boundary of the region. Each shaded region is an example of a **half-plane**, a region on one side of a line. For example, in Figure 5 line r divides the plane into half-planes P and Q. The points on r belong neither to P nor to Q. Line r is the boundary of each half-plane.

YOUR TURN 1

Graph $3x + 2y \le 18$.

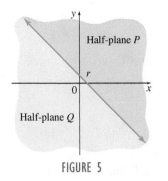

FIGURE 5

⬡ **TECHNOLOGY NOTE**

Graphing calculators can shade regions on the plane. TI calculators have a DRAW menu that includes an option to shade above or below a line. For instance, to graph the inequality in Example 2, first solve the equation for y, then use your calculator to graph the line $y = (1/4)x - 1$. Then the command Shade(-10, $(1/4)$X $- 1$) produces Figure 6(a).

The TI-84 Plus calculator offers another way to graph the region above or below a line. Press the Y= key. Note the slanted line to the left of Y_1, Y_2, and so on. Use the left arrow key to move the cursor to that position for Y_1. Press ENTER until you see the symbol ◣. This indicates that the calculator will shade below the line whose equation is entered in Y_1. (The symbol ◥ operates similarly to shade above a line.) We used this method to get the graph in Figure 6(b). For more details, see the *Graphing Calculator and Excel Spreadsheet Manual* available with this text.

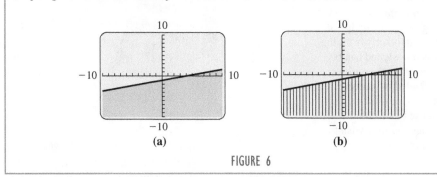

(a)   **(b)**

FIGURE 6

The steps in graphing a linear inequality are summarized below.

Graphing a Linear Inequality

1. Draw the graph of the boundary line. Make the line solid if the inequality involves $\le$ or $\ge$; make the line dashed if the inequality involves $<$ or $>$.

2. Decide which half-plane to shade. Use either of the following methods.

   a. Solve the inequality for y; shade the region above the line if the inequality is of the form $y >$ or $y \ge$; shade the region below the line if the inequality is of the form $y <$ or $y \le$.

   b. Choose any point not on the line as a test point. Shade the half-plane that includes the test point if the test point satisfies the original inequality; otherwise, shade the half-plane on the other side of the boundary line.

Systems of Inequalities

Realistic problems often involve many inequalities. For example, a manufacturing problem might produce inequalities resulting from production requirements as well as inequalities about cost requirements. A collection of at least two inequalities is called a **system of inequalities**. The solution of a system of inequalities is made up of all those points that satisfy all the inequalities of the system at the same time. To graph the solution of a system of inequalities, graph all the inequalities on the same axes and identify, by heavy shading or direction arrows, the region common to all graphs. The next example shows how this is done.

EXAMPLE 3 Graphing a System of Inequalities

Graph the system

$$y < -3x + 12$$
$$x < 2y.$$

SOLUTION The graph of the first inequality has the line $y = -3x + 12$ as its boundary. Because of the $<$ symbol, we use a dotted line and shade *below* the line. The second inequality should first be solved for y to get $y > (1/2)x$ to see that the graph is the region *above* the dotted boundary line $y = (1/2)x$.

The heavily shaded region in Figure 7(a) shows all the points that satisfy both inequalities of the system. Since the points on the boundary lines are not in the solution, the boundary lines are dashed.

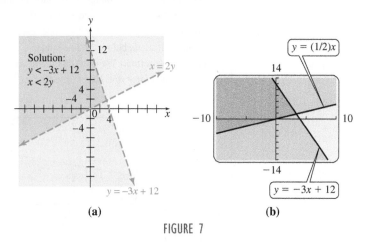

(a)   (b)

FIGURE 7

TECHNOLOGY NOTE A calculator graph of the system in Example 3 is shown in Figure 7(b). You can graph this system on a TI-84 Plus using Shade(Y_2, Y_1).

A region consisting of the overlapping parts of two or more graphs of inequalities in a system, such as the heavily shaded region in Figure 7, is sometimes called the **region of feasible solutions** or the **feasible region**, since it is made up of all the points that satisfy (are feasible for) all inequalities of the system.

EXAMPLE 4 Graphing a Feasible Region

Graph the feasible region for the system

$$y \leq -2x + 8$$
$$-2 \leq x \leq 1.$$

SOLUTION The boundary line of the first inequality is $y = -2x + 8$. Because of the $\leq$ symbol, we use a solid line and shade *below* the line.

YOUR TURN 2 Graph the feasible region for the system

$$3x - 4y \geq 12$$
$$x + y \geq 0.$$

The second inequality is a compound inequality, indicating $-2 \leq x$ *and* $x \leq 1$. Recall that the graph $x = -2$ is the vertical line through $(-2, 0)$ and that the graph $x = 1$ is the vertical line through $(1, 0)$. For $-2 \leq x$, we draw a vertical line and shade the region to the right. For $x \leq 1$, we draw a vertical line and shade the region to the left.

The shaded region in Figure 8 shows all the points that satisfy the system of inequalities.   **TRY YOUR TURN 2**

EXAMPLE 5   Graphing a Feasible Region

Graph the feasible region for the system

$$2x - 5y \leq 10$$
$$x + 2y \leq 8$$
$$x \geq 0$$
$$y \geq 0.$$

SOLUTION   On the same axes, graph each inequality by graphing the boundary and choosing the appropriate half-plane. Then find the feasible region by locating the overlap of all the half-planes. This feasible region is shaded in Figure 9. The inequalities $x \geq 0$ and $y \geq 0$ restrict the feasible region to the first quadrant.

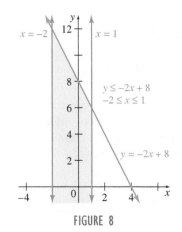

FIGURE 8

The feasible region in Example 5 is **bounded**, since the region is enclosed by boundary lines on all sides. On the other hand, the feasible regions in Examples 3 and 4 are **unbounded.**

Applications
As shown in Section 3 of this chapter, many realistic problems lead to systems of linear inequalities. The next example is typical of such problems.

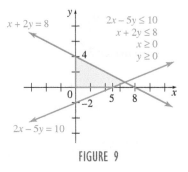

FIGURE 9

EXAMPLE 6   Manufacturing

Happy Ice Cream Cone Company makes cake cones and sugar cones, both of which must be processed in the mixing department and the baking department. Manufacturing one batch of cake cones requires 1 hour in the mixing department and 2 hours in the baking department, and producing one batch of sugar cones requires 2 hours in the mixing department and 1 hour in the baking department. Each department is operated for at most 12 hours per day.

APPLY IT

(a) Write a system of inequalities that expresses these restrictions.

SOLUTION   Let x represent the number of batches of cake cones made and y represent the number of batches of sugar cones made. Then, make a table that summarizes the given information.

Production Requirements for Ice Cream Cones				
	Cake	Sugar		Total
Number of Units Made	x	y		
Hours in Mixing Dept.	1	2	$\leq$	12
Hours in Baking Dept.	2	1	$\leq$	12

Since the departments operate at most 12 hours per day, we put the total number of hours as ≤ 12. Putting the inequality ($\leq$ or $\geq$) next to the number in the chart may help you remember which way to write the inequality.

In the mixing department, x batches of cake cones require a total of $1 \cdot x = x$ hours, and y batches of sugar cones require $2 \cdot y = 2y$ hours. Since the mixing department can operate no more than 12 hours per day,

$$x + 2y \leq 12. \quad \text{Mixing department}$$

413

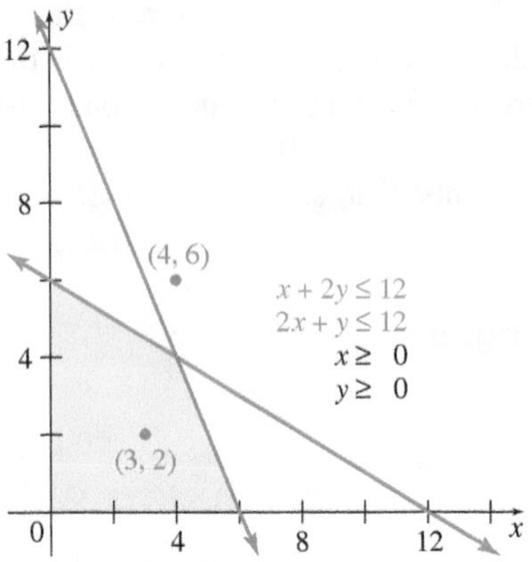

$x + 2y \le 12$
$2x + y \le 12$
$x \ge 0$
$y \ge 0$

FIGURE 10

We translated "no more than" as "less than or equal to." Notice how this inequality corresponds to the row in the table for the mixing department. Similarly, the row corresponding to the baking department gives

$$2x + y \le 12. \qquad \text{Baking department}$$

Since it is not possible to produce a negative number of cake cones or sugar cones,

$$x \ge 0 \qquad \text{and} \qquad y \ge 0.$$

(b) Graph the feasible region.

SOLUTION The feasible region for this system of inequalities is shown in Figure 10.

(c) Using the graph from part (b), can 3 batches of cake cones and 2 batches of sugar cones be manufactured in one day? Can 4 batches of cake cones and 6 batches of sugar cones be manufactured in one day?

SOLUTION Three batches of cake cones and two batches of sugar cones correspond to the point (3, 2). Since (3, 2) is in the feasible region in Figure 10, it is possible to manufacture these quantities in one day. However, since (4, 6) is *not* in the feasible region in Figure 10, it is *not* possible to manufacture 4 batches of cake cones and 6 batches of sugar cones in one day.

The following steps summarize the process of finding the feasible region.

1. Form a table that summarizes the information.

2. Convert the table into a set of linear inequalities.

3. Graph each linear inequality.

4. Graph the region that is common to all the regions graphed in step 3.

EXERCISES

Graph each linear inequality.

1. $x + y \le 2$

2. $y \le x + 1$

3. $x \ge 2 - y$

4. $y \ge x - 3$

5. $4x - y < 6$

6. $4y + x > 6$

7. $4x + y < 8$

8. $2x - y > 2$

9. $x + 3y \ge -2$

10. $2x + 3y \le 6$

11. $x \le 3y$

12. $2x \ge y$

13. $x + y \le 0$

14. $3x + 2y \ge 0$

15. $y < x$

16. $y > 5x$

17. $x < 4$

18. $y > 5$

19. $y \le -2$

20. $x \ge -4$

Graph the feasible region for each system of inequalities. Tell whether each region is bounded or unbounded.

21.
$x + y \le 1$
$x - y \ge 2$

22. $4x - y < 6$
$3x + y < 9$

23. $x + 3y \le 6$
$2x + 4y \ge 7$

24. $-x - y < 5$
$2x - y < 4$

25. $x + y \le 7$
$x - y \le -4$
$4x + y \ge 0$

26. $3x - 2y \ge 6$
$x + y \le -5$
$y \le -6$

27. $-2 < x < 3$
$-1 \le y \le 5$
$2x + y < 6$

28. $1 < x < 4$
$y > 2$
$x > y$

29. $y - 2x \le 4$
$y \ge 2 - x$
$x \ge 0$
$y \ge 0$

30. $2x + 3y \le 12$
$2x + 3y > 3$
$3x + y < 4$
$x \ge 0$
$y \ge 0$

31. $3x + 4y > 12$
$2x - 3y < 6$
$0 \le y \le 2$
$x \ge 0$

32. $0 \le x \le 9$
$x - 2y \ge 4$
$3x + 5y \le 30$
$y \ge 0$

Use a graphing calculator to graph the following.

33. $2x - 6y > 12$

34. $4x - 3y < 12$

35. $3x - 4y < 6$
$2x + 5y > 15$

36. $6x - 4y > 8$
$2x + 5y < 5$

414

37. The regions A through G in the figure can be described by the inequalities

$$x + 3y \; ? \; 6$$
$$x + y \; ? \; 3$$
$$x - 2y \; ? \; 2$$
$$x \geq 0$$
$$y \geq 0,$$

where ? can be either $\leq$ or $\geq$. For each region, tell what the ? should be in the three inequalities. For example, for region A, the ? should be $\geq$, $\leq$, and $\leq$, because region A is described by the inequalities

$$x + 3y \geq 6$$
$$x + y \leq 3$$
$$x - 2y \leq 2$$
$$x \geq 0$$
$$y \geq 0.$$

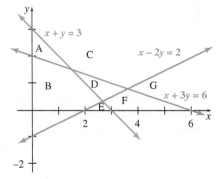

APPLICATIONS

Business and Economics

38. Production Scheduling   A small pottery shop makes two kinds of planters, glazed and unglazed. The glazed type requires 1/2 hour to throw on the wheel and 1 hour in the kiln. The unglazed type takes 1 hour to throw on the wheel and 6 hours in the kiln. The wheel is available for at most 8 hours per day, and the kiln for at most 20 hours per day.

a. Complete the following table.

	Glazed	Unglazed	Total
Number Made	x	y	
Time on Wheel			
Time in Kiln			

b. Set up a system of inequalities and graph the feasible region.

c. Using your graph from part b, can 5 glazed and 2 unglazed planters be made? Can 10 glazed and 2 unglazed planters be made?

39. Time Management   Carmella and Walt produce handmade shawls and afghans. They spin the yarn, dye it, and then weave it. A shawl requires 1 hour of spinning, 1 hour of dyeing, and 1 hour of weaving. An afghan needs 2 hours of spinning, 1 hour of dyeing, and 4 hours of weaving. Together, they spend at most 8 hours spinning, 6 hours dyeing, and 14 hours weaving.

a. Complete the following table.

	Shawls	Afghans	Total
Number Made	x	y	
Spinning Time			
Dyeing Time			
Weaving Time			

b. Set up a system of inequalities and graph the feasible region.

c. Using your graph from part b, can 3 shawls and 2 afghans be made? Can 4 shawls and 3 afghans be made?

For Exercises 40–45, perform the following steps.

a. Write a system of inequalities to express the conditions of the problem.

b. Graph the feasible region of the system.

40. Transportation   Southwestern Oil supplies two distributors located in the Northwest. One distributor needs at least 3000 barrels of oil, and the other needs at least 5000 barrels. Southwestern can send out at most 10,000 barrels. Let $x =$ the number of barrels of oil sent to distributor 1 and $y =$ the number sent to distributor 2.

41. Finance   The loan department in a bank will use at most $30 million for commercial and home loans. The bank's policy is to allocate at least four times as much money to home loans as to commercial loans. The bank's return is 6% on a home loan and 8% on a commercial loan. The manager of the loan department wants to earn a return of at least $1.6 million on these loans. Let $x =$ the amount (in millions) for home loans and $y =$ the amount (in millions) for commercial loans.

42. Transportation   The California Almond Growers have at most 2400 boxes of almonds to be shipped from their plant in Sacramento to Des Moines and San Antonio. The Des Moines market needs at least 1000 boxes, while the San Antonio market must have at least 800 boxes. Let $x =$ the number of boxes to be shipped to Des Moines and $y =$ the number of boxes to be shipped to San Antonio.

Nefall/Fotolia

43. Management   The Gillette Company produces two popular battery-operated razors, the M3Power™ and the Fusion Power™. Because of demand, the number of M3Power™ razors is never more than one-half the number of Fusion Power™ razors. The factory's production cannot exceed 800 razors per day. Let $x =$ the number of M3Power™ razors and $y =$ the number of Fusion Power™ razors produced per day.

44. Production Scheduling   A cement manufacturer produces at least 3.2 million barrels of cement annually. He is told by the Environmental Protection Agency (EPA) that his operation emits 2.5 lb of dust for each barrel produced. The EPA has ruled that annual emissions must be reduced to no more than 1.8 million lb. To do this, the manufacturer plans to replace the present dust collectors with two types of electronic precipitators. One type would reduce emissions to 0.5 lb per barrel and operating costs would be 16¢ per barrel. The other would reduce the dust to 0.3 lb per barrel and operating costs would be 20¢ per barrel. The manufacturer does not want to spend more than 0.8 million dollars in operating costs on the precipitators. He needs to know how many barrels he could produce with each type. Let x = the number of barrels (in millions) produced with the first type and y = the number of barrels (in millions) produced with the second type.

Life Sciences

45. Nutrition A dietician is planning a snack package of fruit and nuts. Each ounce of fruit will supply 1 unit of protein, 2 units

of carbohydrates, and 1 unit of fat. Each ounce of nuts will supply 1 unit of protein, 1 unit of carbohydrates, and 1 unit of fat. Every package must provide at least 7 units of protein, at least 10 units of carbohydrates, and no more than 9 units of fat. Let x = the ounces of fruit and y = the ounces of nuts to be used in each package.

YOUR TURN ANSWERS

1. 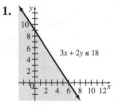   **2.**

---

2 Solving Linear Programming Problems Graphically

Many mathematical models designed to solve problems in business, biology, and economics involve finding an optimum value (maximum or minimum) of a function, subject to certain restrictions. In a **linear programming** problem, we must find the maximum or minimum value of a function, called the **objective function**, and satisfy a set of restrictions, or **constraints**, given by linear inequalities. When only two variables are involved, the solution to a linear programming problem can be found by first graphing the set of constraints, then finding the feasible region as discussed in the previous section. This method is explained in the following example.

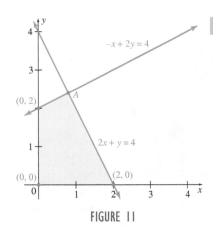

FIGURE 11

EXAMPLE 1 **Maximization**

Find the maximum value of the objective function $z = 3x + 4y$, subject to the following constraints.

$$2x + y \leq 4$$
$$-x + 2y \leq 4$$
$$x \geq 0$$
$$y \geq 0$$

SOLUTION The feasible region is graphed in Figure 11. We can find the coordinates of point A, $(4/5, 12/5)$, by solving the system

$$2x + y = 4$$
$$-x + 2y = 4.$$

Every point in the feasible region satisfies all the constraints; however, we want to find those points that produce the maximum possible value of the objective function. To see how to find this maximum value, change the graph of Figure 11 by adding lines that represent the objective function $z = 3x + 4y$ for various sample values of z. By choosing the values 0, 5, 10, and 15 for z, the objective function becomes (in turn)

$$0 = 3x + 4y, \quad 5 = 3x + 4y, \quad 10 = 3x + 4y, \quad \text{and} \quad 15 = 3x + 4y.$$

Two equations in two unknowns can be solved by using row operations to eliminate one variable. For example, to solve the system

$$2x + y = 4$$
$$-x + 2y = 4,$$

we could take the first equation plus 2 times the second to eliminate x. (This is equivalent to $R_1 + 2R_2 \rightarrow R_2$ in the Gauss-Jordan method.) The result is $5y = 12$, so $y = 12/5$. We can then substitute this value of y into either equation and solve for x. For example, substitution into the first equation yields

$$2x + \frac{12}{5} = 4$$
$$2x = \frac{8}{5}$$
$$x = \frac{4}{5}.$$

We instead could have subtracted the original second equation from twice the first equation to eliminate y, yielding $5x = 4$, or $x = 4/5$, and then substitute into either equation and solve for y.

These four lines (known as **isoprofit lines**) are graphed in Figure 12. (Why are the lines parallel?) The figure shows that z cannot take on the value 15 because the graph for $z = 15$ is entirely outside the feasible region. The maximum possible value of z will be obtained from a line parallel to the others and between the lines representing the objective function when $z = 10$ and $z = 15$. The value of z will be as large as possible and all constraints will be satisfied if this line just touches the feasible region. This occurs at point A. We find that A has coordinates $(4/5, 12/5)$. (See the review in the margin.) The value of z at this point is

$$z = 3x + 4y = 3\left(\frac{4}{5}\right) + 4\left(\frac{12}{5}\right) = \frac{60}{5} = 12.$$

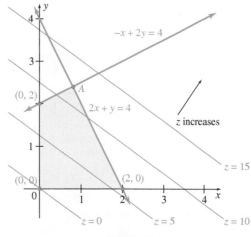

FIGURE 12

The maximum possible value of z is 12. Of all the points in the feasible region, A leads to the largest possible value of z.

TECHNOLOGY NOTE A graphing calculator can be useful for finding the coordinates of intersection points such as point A. We do this by solving each equation for y, graphing each line, and then using the capability of the calculator to find the coordinates of the point of intersection.

Points such as A in Example 1 are called corner points. A **corner point** is a point in the feasible region where the boundary lines of two constraints cross. Since corner points occur where two straight lines cross, the coordinates of a corner point are the solution of a system of two linear equations. As we saw in Example 1, corner points play a key role in the solution of linear programming problems. We will make this explicit after the following example.

EXAMPLE 2 **Minimization**

Solve the following linear programming problem.

$$\text{Minimize} \quad z = 2x + 4y$$
$$\text{subject to:} \quad x + 2y \geq 10$$
$$3x + y \geq 10$$
$$x \geq 0$$
$$y \geq 0.$$

SOLUTION Figure 13 on the next page shows the feasible region and the lines that result when z in the objective function is replaced by 0, 10, 20, 40, and 50. The line representing the objective function touches the region of feasible solutions when $z = 20$. Two corner points, $(2, 4)$ and $(10, 0)$, lie on this line; both $(2, 4)$ and $(10, 0)$, as well as all the points on the boundary line between them, give the same optimum value of z. There are infinitely many equally good values of x and y that will give the same minimum value of the objective function $z = 2x + 4y$. This minimum value is 20.

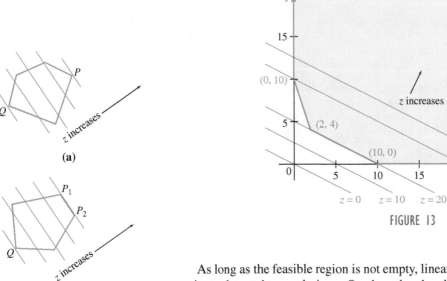

FIGURE 13

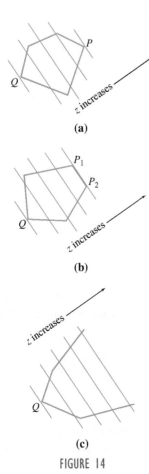

As long as the feasible region is not empty, linear programming problems with bounded regions always have solutions. On the other hand, the feasible region in Example 2 is unbounded, and no solution will *maximize* the value of the objective function because z can be made as large as you like.

Some general conclusions can be drawn from the method of solution used in Examples 1 and 2. Imagine a line sliding across a region. Figure 14 shows various feasible regions and the position of the line $ax + by = z$ for various values of z. We assume here that as the line slides from the lower left to the upper right, the value of z increases. In Figure 14(a), the objective function takes on its minimum value at corner point Q and its maximum value at P. The minimum is again at Q in part (b), but the maximum occurs at P_1 or P_2, or any point on the line segment connecting them. Finally, in part (c), the minimum value occurs at Q, but the objective function has no maximum value because the feasible region is unbounded. As long as the objective function increases as x and y increase, the objective function will have no maximum over an unbounded region.

The preceding discussion suggests the truth of the **corner point theorem**.

Corner Point Theorem

If an optimum value (either a maximum or a minimum) of the objective function exists, it will occur at one or more of the corner points of the feasible region.

This theorem simplifies the job of finding an optimum value. First, we graph the feasible region and find all corner points. Then we test each corner point in the objective function. Finally, we identify the corner point producing the optimum solution. For unbounded regions, we must decide whether the required optimum can be found (see Example 2).

With the theorem, we can solve the problem in Example 1 by first identifying the four corner points in Figure 11: $(0, 0)$, $(0, 2)$, $(4/5, 12/5)$, and $(2, 0)$. Then we substitute each of the four points into the objective function $z = 3x + 4y$ to identify the corner point that produces the maximum value of z.

Values of the Objective Function at Corner Points	
Corner Point	Value of $z = 3x + 4y$
$(0, 0)$	$3(0) + 4(0) = 0$
$(0, 2)$	$3(0) + 4(2) = 8$
$\left(\frac{4}{5}, \frac{12}{5}\right)$	$3\left(\frac{4}{5}\right) + 4\left(\frac{12}{5}\right) = 12$ Maximum
$(2, 0)$	$3(2) + 4(0) = 6$

From these results, the corner point $(4/5, 12/5)$ yields the maximum value of 12. This is the same as the result found earlier.

The following summary gives the steps to use in solving a linear programming problem by the graphical method.

NOTE
As the corner point theorem states and Example 2 illustrates, the optimal value of a linear programming problem may occur at more than one corner point. When the optimal solution occurs at two corner points, every point on the line segment between the two points is also an optimal solution.

Solving a Linear Programming Problem

1. Write the objective function and all necessary constraints.
2. Graph the feasible region.
3. Identify all corner points.
4. Find the value of the objective function at each corner point.
5. For a bounded region, the solution is given by the corner point producing the optimum value of the objective function.
6. For an unbounded region, check that a solution actually exists. If it does, it will occur at a corner point.

When asked to solve a linear programming problem, give the maximum or minimum value, as well any points where that value occurs.

EXAMPLE 3 **Maximization and Minimization**

Sketch the feasible region for the following set of constraints, and then find the maximum and minimum values of the objective function $z = x + 10y$.

$$x + 4y \geq 12$$
$$x - 2y \leq 0$$
$$2y - x \leq 6$$
$$x \leq 6$$

SOLUTION The graph in Figure 15 shows that the feasible region is bounded. Use the corner points from the graph to find the maximum and minimum values of the objective function.

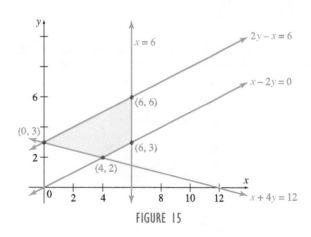

FIGURE 15

419

Values of the Objective Function at Corner Points		
Corner Point	Value of $z = x + 10y$	
$(0, 3)$	$0 + 10(3) = 30$	
$(4, 2)$	$4 + 10(2) = 24$	Minimum
$(6, 3)$	$6 + 10(3) = 36$	
$(6, 6)$	$6 + 10(6) = 66$	Maximum

YOUR TURN 1 Find the maximum and minimum values of the objective function $z = 3x + 4y$ on the region bounded by

$$2x + y \geq 5$$
$$x + 5y \geq 16$$
$$2x + y \leq 14$$
$$-x + 4y \leq 20$$

The minimum value of $z = x + 10y$ is 24 at the corner point $(4, 2)$. The maximum value is 66 at $(6, 6)$. **TRY YOUR TURN 1**

To verify that the minimum or maximum is correct in a linear programming problem, you might want to add the graph of the line $z = 0$ to the graph of the feasible region. For instance, in Example 3, the result of adding the line $x + 10y = 0$ is shown in Figure 16. Now imagine moving a straightedge through the feasible region parallel to this line. It appears that the first place the line touches the feasible region is at $(4, 2)$, where we found the minimum. Similarly, the last place the line touches is at $(6, 6)$, where we found the maximum. In Figure 16, these parallel lines, labeled $z = 24$ and $z = 66$, are also shown.

NOTE
The graphical method is very difficult for a problem with three variables (where the feasible region is three dimensional) and impossible with four or more variables.

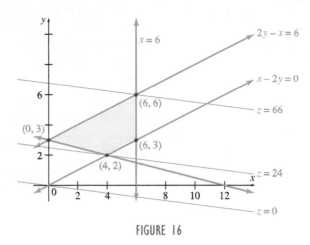

FIGURE 16

2   EXERCISES

The following graphs show regions of feasible solutions. Use these regions to find maximum and minimum values of the given objective functions.

1. **a.** $z = 3x + 2y$
   b. $z = x + 4y$

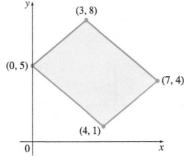

2. **a.** $z = x + 4y$
   b. $z = 5x + 2y$

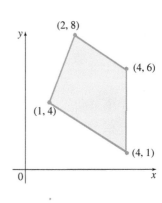

3. a. $z = 0.40x + 0.75y$

  b. $z = 1.50x + 0.25y$

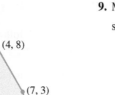

(0, 12)

(4, 8)

(7, 3)

(0, 0)

0

(8, 0) x

9. Maximize $z = 5x + 2y$

  subject to: $4x - y \leq 16$

  $2x + y \geq 11$

  $x \geq 3$

  $y \leq 8.$

10. Maximize $z = 10x + 8y$

  subject to: $2x + 3y \leq 100$

  $5x + 4y \leq 200$

  $x \geq 10$

  $0 \leq y \leq 20.$

4. a. $z = 0.35x + 1.25y$

  b. $z = 1.5x + 0.5y$

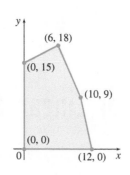

(6, 18)

(0, 15)

(10, 9)

(0, 0)

0

(12, 0) x

11. Maximize $z = 10x + 10y$

  subject to: $5x + 8y \geq 200$

  $25x - 10y \geq 250$

  $x + y \leq 150$

  $x \geq 0$

  $y \geq 0.$

5. a. $z = 4x + 2y$

  b. $z = 2x + 3y$

  c. $z = 2x + 4y$

  d. $z = x + 4y$

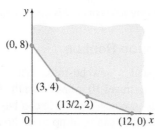

(0, 8)

(3, 4)

(13/2, 2)

0

(12, 0) x

12. Maximize $z = 4x + 5y$

  subject to: $10x - 5y \leq 100$

  $20x + 10y \geq 150$

  $x + y \geq 12$

  $x \geq 0$

  $y \geq 0.$

6. a. $z = 4x + y$

  b. $z = 5x + 6y$

  c. $z = x + 2y$

  d. $z = x + 6y$

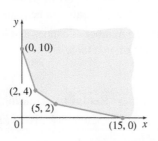

(0, 10)

(2, 4)

(5, 2)

0

(15, 0) x

13. Maximize $z = 3x + 6y$

  subject to: $2x - 3y \leq 12$

  $x + y \leq 5$

  $3x + 4y \geq 24$

  $x \geq 0$

  $y \geq 0.$

14. Maximize $z = 4x + 6y$

  subject to: $3 \leq x + y \leq 10$

  $x - y \geq 3$

  $x \geq 0$

  $y \geq 0.$

Use graphical methods to solve each linear programming problem.

7. Minimize $z = 4x + 7y$

  subject to: $x - y \geq 1$

  $3x + 2y \geq 18$

  $x \geq 0$

  $y \geq 0.$

8. Minimize $z = x + 3y$

  subject to: $x + y \leq 10$

  $5x + 2y \geq 20$

  $-x + 2y \geq 0$

  $x \geq 0$

  $y \geq 0.$

15. Find values of $x \geq 0$ and $y \geq 0$ that maximize $z = 10x + 12y$ subject to each set of constraints.

  a. $x + y \leq 20$ **b.** $3x + y \leq 15$ **c.** $2x + 5y \geq 22$

  $x + 3y \leq 24$ $x + 2y \leq 18$ $4x + 3y \leq 28$

  $2x + 2y \leq 17$

16. Find values of $x \geq 0$ and $y \geq 0$ that minimize $z = 3x + 2y$ subject to each set of constraints.

  a. $10x + 7y \leq 42$ **b.** $6x + 5y \geq 25$ **c.** $x + 2y \geq 10$

  $4x + 10y \geq 35$ $2x + 6y \geq 15$ $2x + y \geq 12$

  $x - y \leq 8$

17. You are given the following linear programming problem:*

Maximize $\qquad z = c_1x_1 + c_2x_2$

subject to: $\qquad 2x_1 + \quad x_2 \le 11$

$\qquad\qquad\quad -x_1 + \ 2x_2 \le \ 2$

$\qquad\qquad\qquad x_1 \ge 0, x_2 \ge \ 0.$

If $c_2 > 0$, determine the range of c_1/c_2 for which $(x_1, x_2) = (4, 3)$ is an optimal solution. (Choose one of the following.) *Source: Society of Actuaries.*

a. $[-2, 1/2]$ **b.** $[-1/2, 2]$ **c.** $[-11, -1]$

d. $[1, 11]$ **e.** $[-11, 11]$

*The notation x_1 and x_2 used in this exercise is the same as x and y.

YOUR TURN ANSWERS

1. Maximum of 36 at (4,6); minimum of 15 at (1,3)

3 Applications of Linear Programming

APPLY IT   **How many canoes and kayaks should a business purchase, given a limited budget and limited storage?**

We will use linear programming to answer this question in Example 1.

EXAMPLE 1   Canoe Rentals

Andrew Crowley plans to start a new business called River Explorers, which will rent canoes and kayaks to people to travel 10 miles down the Clarion River in Cook Forest State Park. He has $45,000 to purchase new boats. He can buy the canoes for $600 each and the kayaks for $750 each. His facility can hold up to 65 boats. The canoes will rent for $25 a day, and the kayaks will rent for $30 a day. How many canoes and how many kayaks should he buy to earn the most revenue if all boats can be rented each day?

 APPLY IT   **SOLUTION**   Let x represent the number of canoes and let y represent the number of kayaks. Summarize the given information in a table.

	Rental Information			
	Canoes	Kayaks		Total
Number of Boats	x	y	$\le$	65
Cost of Each	$600	$750	$\le$	$45,000
Revenue	$25	$30		

The constraints, imposed by the number of boats and the cost, correspond to the rows in the table as follows.

$$x + y \le 65$$

$$600x + 750y \le 45,000$$

Dividing both sides of the second constraint by 150 gives the equivalent inequality

$$4x + 5y \le 300.$$

Since the number of boats cannot be negative, $x \ge 0$ and $y \ge 0$. The objective function to be maximized gives the amount of revenue. If the variable z represents the total revenue, the objective function is

$$z = 25x + 30y.$$

In summary, the mathematical model for the given linear programming problem is as follows:

$$\text{Maximize} \qquad z = 25x + 30y \qquad\qquad (1)$$
$$\text{subject to:} \qquad x + y \le 65 \qquad\qquad (2)$$
$$4x + 5y \le 300 \qquad\qquad (3)$$
$$x \ge 0 \qquad\qquad (4)$$
$$y \ge 0. \qquad\qquad (5)$$

Using the methods described in the previous section, graph the feasible region for the system of inequalities (2)–(5), as in Figure 17. Three of the corner points can be identified from the graph as (0, 0), (65, 0), and (0, 60). The fourth corner point, labeled Q in the figure, can be found by solving the system of equations

$$x + y = 65$$
$$4x + 5y = 300.$$

Solve this system to find that Q is the point (25, 40). Now test these four points in the objective function to determine the maximum value of z. The results are shown in the table.

YOUR TURN 1 Solve Example 1 with everything the same except the revenue for a kayak changed to $35 a day.

YOUR TURN 2 Suppose that in Example 6 in Sec. 1, the company earns $20 in profit for each batch of cake cones and $30 for each batch of sugar cones. How many batches of each should the company make to maximize profit?

Values of the Objective Function at Corner Points	
Corner Point	**Value of $z = 25x + 30y$**
(0, 0)	$25(0) + 30(0) = 0$
(65, 0)	$25(65) + 30(0) = 1625$
(0, 60)	$25(0) + 30(60) = 1800$
(25, 40)	$25(25) + 30(40) = 1825$ Maximum

The objective function, which represents revenue, is maximized when $x = 25$ and $y = 40$. He should buy 25 canoes and 40 kayaks for a maximum revenue of $1825 a day.

TRY YOUR TURN 1 AND 2

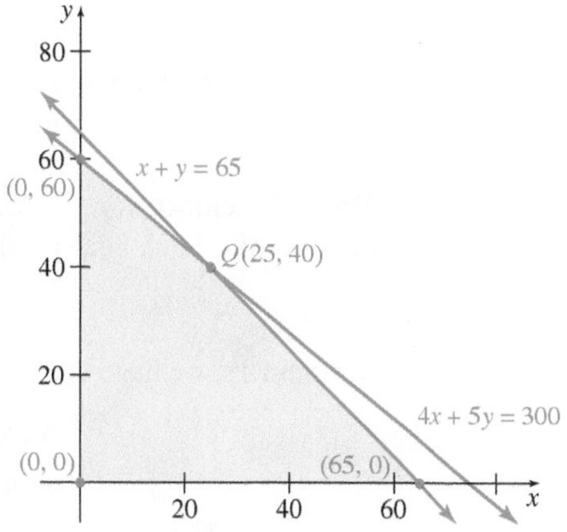

FIGURE 17

Fortunately, the answer to the linear programming problem in Example 1 is a point with integer coordinates, as the number of each type of boat must be an integer. Unfortunately, there is no guarantee that this will always happen at a corner point. When the solution to a linear programming problem is restricted to integers, it is an *integer programming* problem, which is more difficult to solve than a linear programming problem. The feasible region for an integer programming problem consists only of those points with integer coordinates that satisfy the constraints. In this text, all problems in which fractional solutions are meaningless are contrived to have integer solutions.

EXAMPLE 2 Farm Animals

Ondrejschaumann/Dreamstime

A 4-H member raises only goats and pigs. She wants to raise no more than 16 animals, including no more than 10 goats. She spends $25 to raise a goat and $75 to raise a pig, and she has $900 available for this project. Each goat produces $12 in profit and each pig $40 in profit. How many goats and how many pigs should she raise to maximize total profit?

SOLUTION   First, set up a table that shows the information given in the problem.

4-H Animal Information				
	Goats	**Pigs**		**Total**
Number Raised	x	y	$\leq$	16
Goat Limit	x		$\leq$	10
Cost to Raise	$25	$75	$\leq$	$900
Profit (each)	$12	$40		

Use the table to write the necessary constraints. Since the total number of animals cannot exceed 16, the first constraint is

$$x + y \leq 16.$$

"No more than 10 goats" means

$$x \leq 10.$$

The cost to raise x goats at $25 per goat is $25x$ dollars, while the cost for y pigs at $75 each is $75y$ dollars. Since only $900 is available,

$$25x + 75y \leq 900.$$

Dividing both sides by 25 gives the equivalent inequality

$$x + 3y \leq 36.$$

The number of goats and pigs cannot be negative, so

$$x \geq 0 \quad \text{and} \quad y \geq 0.$$

The 4-H member wants to know how many goats and pigs to raise in order to produce maximum profit. Each goat yields $12 profit and each pig $40. If z represents total profit, then

$$z = 12x + 40y.$$

In summary, we have the following linear programming problem:

$$\begin{aligned}
\text{Maximize} \quad & z = 12x + 40y \\
\text{subject to:} \quad & x + \ y \leq 16 \\
& x + 3y \leq 36 \\
& x \leq 10 \\
& x \geq \ 0 \\
& y \geq \ 0.
\end{aligned}$$

A graph of the feasible region is shown in Figure 18. The corner points $(0, 12)$, $(0, 0)$, and $(10, 0)$ can be read directly from the graph. The coordinates of each of the other corner points can be found by solving a system of linear equations.

Test each corner point in the objective function to find the maximum profit.

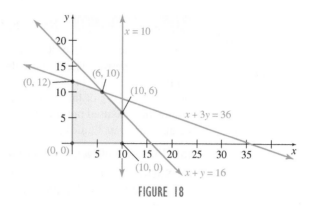

FIGURE 18

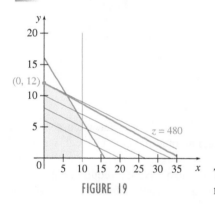

FIGURE 19

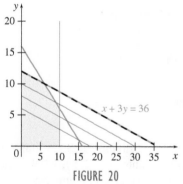

FIGURE 20

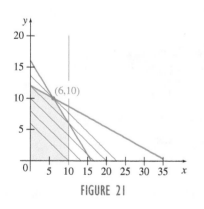

FIGURE 21

Values of the Objective Function at Corner Points		
Corner Point	**Value of $z = 12x + 40y$**	
$(0, 12)$	$12(0) + 40(12) = 480$	Maximum
$(6, 10)$	$12(6) + 40(10) = 472$	
$(10, 6)$	$12(10) + 40(6) = 360$	
$(10, 0)$	$12(10) + 40(0) = 120$	
$(0, 0)$	$12(0) + 40(0) = 0$	

The maximum of 480 occurs at $(0, 12)$. Thus, 12 pigs and no goats will produce a maximum profit of $480. **TRY YOUR TURN 3**

In the maximization problem in Example 2, since the profit for a single pig is $40 and the profit for a single goat is only $12, it is more profitable to raise only pigs and no goats. However, if the profit from raising pigs begins to decrease (or the profit from goats begins to increase), it will eventually be more profitable to raise both goats and pigs. In fact, if the profit from raising pigs decreases to a number below $36, then the previous solution is no longer optimal.

To see why this is true, in Figure 19 we have graphed the original objective function ($z = 12x + 40y$) for various values of z, as we did in Example 1 of the previous section. Notice that each of these objective lines has slope $m = -12/40 = -3/10$. When $z = 480$, the line touches only one feasible point, $(0, 12)$, which is where the maximum profit occurs.

If the profit from raising pigs decreases from $40 to $$p$, where p is a value slightly below 40, the objective function lines will have the equation $z = 12x + py$ for various values of z, and the slope of the lines becomes $m = -12/p$. Eventually, as p becomes smaller, the slope of these objective lines will be equal to the slope of the line $x + 3y = 36$ (that is, $-1/3$), corresponding to the second constraint. This occurs when $-12/p = -1/3$, or $p = 36$, as illustrated by the overlapping blue and dotted lines in Figure 20. In this case, the optimal solution occurs at every point on the line segment that joins $(0, 12)$ and $(6, 10)$.

Once the profit from raising pigs decreases to below $36, the slopes of the sample objective function lines become more negative (steeper) and the optimal solution changes, as indicated in Figure 21. As z increases, the last feasible point that the lines touch is $(6, 10)$. For profits from raising pigs that are slightly below $36, the optimal solution will occur when $x = 6$ and $y = 10$. In other words, the maximum profit will occur when she raises both goats and pigs.

425

Linear Programming: The Graphical Method

EXAMPLE 3 Nutrition

Certain animals in a rescue shelter must have at least 30 g of protein and at least 20 g of fat per feeding period. These nutrients come from food A, which costs 18 cents per unit and supplies 2 g of protein and 4 g of fat; and food B, which costs 12 cents per unit and has 6 g of protein and 2 g of fat. Food B is bought under a long-term contract requiring that at least 2 units of B be used per serving. Another contract requires that the amount of food B used be no more than 3 times the amount of food A used.

(a) How much of each food must be bought to produce the minimum cost per serving?

SOLUTION Let x represent the required amount of food A and y the amount of food B. Use the given information to prepare the following table.

Rescue Animal Nutrition Information				
	Food A	Food B		Total
Number of Units	x	y		
Grams of Protein	2	6	$\geq$	30
Grams of Fat	4	2	$\geq$	20
Long-Term Contract		y	$\geq$	2
Cost	18¢	12¢		

Since the animals must have *at least* 30 g of protein and 20 g of fat, we use $\geq$ in the inequality. If the animals needed *at most* a certain amount of some nutrient, we would use $\leq$. The long-term contract requires that $y \geq 2$.

In addition to the information in the table, we also have the requirement that the amount of food B used be no more than 3 times the amount of food A used. We can write this as $y \leq 3x$.

The linear programming problem can be stated as follows.

Minimize $z = 0.18x + 0.12y$

subject to: $2x + 6y \geq 30$ Protein

$4x + 2y \geq 20$ Fat

$2 \leq y \leq 3x$ Contracts

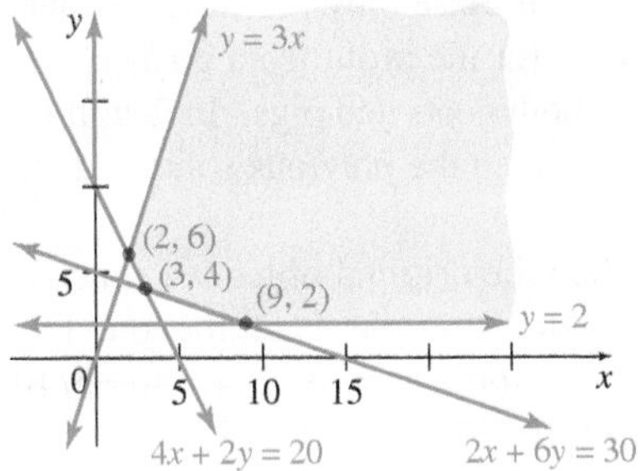

$x \geq 0$.

(The usual constraint $y \geq 0$ is redundant because of the constraint $y \geq 2$.) A graph of the feasible region is shown in Figure 22. The corner points are $(2, 6)$, $(3, 4)$, and $(9, 2)$. Test each corner point in the objective function to find the minimum cost.

FIGURE 22

Values of the Objective Function at Corner Points	
Corner Point	Value of $z = 0.18x + 0.12y$
$(2, 6)$	$0.18(2) + 0.12(6) = 1.08$
$(3, 4)$	$0.18(3) + 0.12(4) = 1.02$ Minimum
$(9, 2)$	$0.18(9) + 0.12(2) = 1.86$

The minimum of 1.02 occurs at $(3, 4)$. Thus, 3 units of food A and 4 units of food B will produce a minimum cost of $1.02 per serving.

(b) The rescue shelter manager notices that although the long-term contract states that at least 2 units of food B be used per serving, the solution uses 4 units of food B, which is 2 units more than the minimum amount required. Can a more economical solution be found that only uses 2 units of food B?

SOLUTION The solution found in part (a) is the most economical solution, even though it exceeds the requirement for using at least 2 units of food B. Notice from Figure 22 that the four lines representing the four constraints do not meet at a single point, so any solution in the feasible region will have to exceed at least one constraint. The rescue shelter manager might use this information to negotiate a better deal with the distributor of food B by making a guarantee to use at least 4 units of food B per serving in the future.

The notion that some constraints are not met exactly is related to the concepts of *surplus* and *slack variables*, which will be explored in the next chapter.

The feasible region in Figure 22 is an *unbounded* feasible region—the region extends indefinitely to the upper right. With this region it would not be possible to *maximize* the objective function, because the total cost of the food could always be increased by encouraging the animals to eat more.

3 EXERCISES

Write Exercises 1–6 as linear inequalities. Identify all variables used. (Note: Not all of the given information is used in Exercises 5 and 6.)

1. Product A requires 3 hours on a machine, while product B needs 5 hours on the same machine. The machine is available for at most 60 hours per week.

2. A cow requires a third of an acre of pasture and a sheep needs a quarter acre. A rancher wants to use at least 120 acres of pasture.

3. Jessica Corpo needs at least 1500 units of calcium supplements per day. Her calcium carbonate supplement provides 600 units, and her calcium citrate supplement supplies 250 units.

4. Pauline Wong spends 3 hours selling a small computer and 5 hours selling a larger model. She works no more than 45 hours per week.

5. Coffee costing $8 per lb is to be mixed with coffee costing $10 per lb to get at least 40 lb of a blended coffee.

6. A tank in an oil refinery holds 120 gal. The tank contains a mixture of light oil worth $1.25 per gal and heavy oil worth $0.80 per gal.

APPLICATIONS

Business and Economics

7. Transportation The Miers Company produces small engines for several manufacturers. The company receives orders from two assembly plants for their Top-flight engine. Plant I needs at least 45 engines, and plant II needs at least 32 engines. The company can send at most 120 engines to these two assembly plants. It costs $30 per engine to ship to plant I and $40 per engine to ship to plant II. Plant I gives Miers $20 in rebates toward its products for each engine they buy, while plant II gives similar $15 rebates. Miers estimates that they need at least $1500 in rebates to cover products they plan to buy from the two plants. How many engines should be shipped to each plant to minimize shipping costs? What is the minimum cost?

8. Transportation A manufacturer of refrigerators must ship at least 100 refrigerators to its two West Coast warehouses. Each warehouse holds a maximum of 100 refrigerators. Warehouse A holds 25 refrigerators already, and warehouse B has 20 on hand. It costs $12 to ship a refrigerator to warehouse A and $10 to ship one to warehouse B. Union rules require that at least 300 workers be hired. Shipping a refrigerator to warehouse A requires 4 workers, while shipping a refrigerator to warehouse B requires 2 workers. How many refrigerators should be shipped to each warehouse to minimize costs? What is the minimum cost?

9. Insurance Premiums A company is considering two insurance plans with the types of coverage and premiums shown in the following table.

	Policy A	Policy B
Fire/Theft	$10,000	$15,000
Liability	$180,000	$120,000
Premium	$50	$40

(For example, this means that $50 buys one unit of plan A, consisting of $10,000 fire and theft insurance and $180,000 of liability insurance.)

a. The company wants at least $300,000 fire/theft insurance and at least $3,000,000 liability insurance from these plans. How many units should be purchased from each plan to minimize the cost of the premiums? What is the minimum premium?

b. Suppose the premium for policy A is reduced to $25. Now how many units should be purchased from each plan to minimize the cost of the premiums? What is the minimum premium?

10. Profit The Muro Manufacturing Company makes two kinds of plasma screen television sets. It produces the Flexscan set that sells for $350 profit and the Panoramic I that sells for $500 profit. On the assembly line, the Flexscan requires 5 hours, and the Panoramic I takes 7 hours. The cabinet shop spends 1 hour on the cabinet for the Flexscan and 2 hours on the cabinet for the Panoramic I. Both sets require 4 hours for testing and packing. On a particular production run, the Muro Company has available 3600 work-hours on the assembly line, 900 work-hours in the cabinet shop, and 2600 work-hours in the testing and packing department.

a. How many sets of each type should it produce to make a maximum profit? What is the maximum profit?

b. Suppose the profit on the Flexscan goes up to $450. Now how many sets of each type should it produce to make a maximum profit? What is the maximum profit?

c. The solutions from parts a and b leave some unused time in either the assembly line, the cabinet shop, or the testing and packing department. Identify any unused time in each solution. Is it possible to have a solution that leaves no excess time? Explain.

11. Revenue A machine shop manufactures two types of bolts. The bolts require time on each of the three groups of machines, but the time required on each group differs, as shown in the table below.

	Type I	Type II
Machine 1	0.2 min	0.2 min
Machine 2	0.6 min	0.2 min
Machine 3	0.04 min	0.08 min

Production schedules are made up one day at a time. In a day, 300, 720, and 100 minutes are available, respectively, on these machines. Type I bolts sell for 15¢ and type II bolts for 20¢.

a. How many of each type of bolt should be manufactured per day to maximize revenue?

b. What is the maximum revenue?

c. Suppose the selling price of type I bolts began to increase. Beyond what amount would this price have to increase before a different number of each type of bolts should be produced to maximize revenue?

12. Revenue The manufacturing process requires that oil refineries must manufacture at least 2 gal of gasoline for every gallon of fuel oil. To meet the winter demand for fuel oil, at least 3 million gal a day must be produced. The demand for gasoline is no more than 6.4 million gal per day. It takes 15 minutes to ship each million gal of gasoline and 1 hour to ship each million gal of fuel oil out of the warehouse. No more than 4 hours and 39 minutes are available for shipping.

a. If the refinery sells gasoline for $2.50 per gal and fuel oil for $2 per gal, how much of each should be produced to maximize revenue?

b. Find the maximum revenue.

c. Suppose the price for fuel oil begins to increase. Beyond what amount would this price have to increase before a different amount of gasoline and fuel oil should be produced to maximize revenue?

13. Revenue A candy company has 150 kg of chocolate-covered nuts and 90 kg of chocolate-covered raisins to be sold as two different mixes. One mix will contain half nuts and half raisins and will sell for $7 per kg. The other mix will contain 3/4 nuts and 1/4 raisins and will sell for $9.50 per kg.

a. How many kilograms of each mix should the company prepare for the maximum revenue? Find the maximum revenue.

b. The company raises the price of the second mix to $11 per kg. Now how many kilograms of each mix should the company prepare for the maximum revenue? Find the maximum revenue.

14. Profit A small country can grow only two crops for export, coffee and cocoa. The country has 500,000 hectares of land available for the crops. Long-term contracts require that at least 100,000 hectares be devoted to coffee and at least 200,000 hectares to cocoa. Cocoa must be processed locally, and production bottlenecks limit cocoa to 270,000 hectares. Coffee requires two workers per hectare, with cocoa requiring five. No more than 1,750,000 people are available for working with these crops. Coffee produces a profit of $220 per hectare and cocoa a profit of $550 per hectare. How many hectares should the country devote to each crop in order to maximize profit? Find the maximum profit.

15. Blending The Mostpure Milk Company gets milk from two dairies and then blends the milk to get the desired amount of butterfat for the company's premier product. Milk from dairy I costs $2.40 per gal, and milk from dairy II costs $0.80 per gal. At most $144 is available for purchasing milk. Dairy I can supply at most 50 gal of milk averaging 3.7% butterfat. Dairy II can supply at most 80 gal of milk averaging 3.2% butterfat.

a. How much milk from each dairy should Mostpure use to get at most 100 gal of milk with the maximum total amount of butterfat? What is the maximum amount of butterfat?

b. The solution from part a leaves both dairy I and dairy II with excess capacity. Calculate the amount of additional milk each dairy could produce. Is there any way all this capacity could be used while still meeting the other constraints? Explain.

16. Transportation A flash drive manufacturer has 370 boxes of a particular drive in warehouse I and 290 boxes of the same drive in warehouse II. A computer store in San Jose orders 350 boxes of the drive, and another store in Memphis orders 300 boxes. The shipping costs per box to these stores from the two warehouses are shown in the following table.

		Destination	
		San Jose	Memphis
Warehouse	I	$2.50	$2.20
	II	$2.30	$2.10

How many boxes should be shipped to each city from each warehouse to minimize shipping costs? What is the minimum cost? (*Hint:* Use $x, 350 - x, y,$ and $300 - y$ as the variables.)

17. Finance A pension fund manager decides to invest a total of at most $30 million in U.S. Treasury bonds paying 4% annual interest and in mutual funds paying 8% annual interest. He plans to invest at least $5 million in bonds and at least $10 million in mutual funds. Bonds have an initial fee of $100 per million dollars, while the fee for mutual funds is $200 per million. The fund manager is allowed to spend no more than $5000 on fees. How much should be invested in each to maximize annual interest? What is the maximum annual interest?

Manufacturing (Note: Exercises 18–20 are from qualification examinations for Certified Public Accountants.) *Source: American Institute of Certified Public Accountants.* The Random Company manufactures two products, Zeta and Beta. Each product must pass through two processing operations. All materials are introduced at the start of Process No. 1. There are no work-in-process inventories. Random may produce either one product exclusively or various combinations of both products subject to the following constraints:

	Process No. 1	Process No. 2	Contribution Margin (per unit)
Hours Required to Produce One Unit:			
Zeta	1 hr	1 hr	$4.00
Beta	2 hr	3 hr	$5.25
Total Capacity (in hours per day)	1000 hr	1275 hr	

A shortage of technical labor has limited Beta production to 400 units per day. There are no constraints on the production of Zeta other than the hour constraints in the above schedule. Assume that all relationships between capacity and production are linear.

18. Given the objective to maximize total contribution margin, what is the production constraint for Process No. 1? (Choose one of the following.)

    a. Zeta + Beta ≤ 1000   **b.** Zeta + 2 Beta ≤ 1000

    c. Zeta + Beta ≥ 1000   **d.** Zeta + 2 Beta ≥ 1000

19. Given the objective to maximize total contribution margin, what is the labor constraint for production of Beta? (Choose one of the following.)

    a. Beta ≤ 400   **b.** Beta ≥ 400

    c. Beta ≤ 425   **d.** Beta ≥ 425

20. What is the objective function of the data presented? (Choose one of the following.)

    a. Zeta + 2 Beta = $9.25

    b. $4.00 Zeta + 3($5.25)Beta = Total Contribution Margin

    c. $4.00 Zeta + $5.25 Beta = Total Contribution Margin

    d. 2($4.00) Zeta + 3($5.25) Beta = Total Contribution Margin

Life Sciences

21. Health Care Glen Spencer takes vitamin pills. Each day he must have at least 480 IU of vitamin A, 5 mg of vitamin B_1, and 100 mg of vitamin C. He can choose between pill 1, which contains 240 IU of vitamin A, 1 mg of vitamin B_1, and 10 mg of vitamin C, and pill 2, which contains 60 IU of vitamin A, 1 mg of vitamin B_1, and 35 mg of vitamin C. Pill 1 costs 15¢, and pill 2 costs 30¢.

    a. How many of each pill should he buy in order to minimize his cost? What is the minimum cost?

    b. For the solution in part a, Glen is receiving more than he needs of at least one vitamin. Identify that vitamin, and tell how much surplus he is receiving. Is there any way he can avoid receiving that surplus while still meeting the other constraints and minimizing the cost? Explain.

22. Predator Food Requirements A certain predator requires at least 10 units of protein and 8 units of fat per day. One prey of species I provides 5 units of protein and 2 units of fat; one prey of species II provides 3 units of protein and 4 units of fat. Capturing and digesting each species-II prey requires 3 units of energy, and capturing and digesting each species-I prey requires 2 units of energy. How many of each prey would meet the predator's daily food requirements with the least expenditure of energy? Are the answers reasonable? How could they be interpreted?

23. Nutrition A dietician is planning a snack package of fruit and nuts. Each ounce of fruit will supply zero units of protein, 2 units of carbohydrates, and 1 unit of fat, and will contain 20 calories. Each ounce of nuts will supply 3 units of protein, 1 unit of carbohydrate, and 2 units of fat, and will contain 30 calories. Every package must provide at least 6 units of protein, at least 10 units of carbohydrates, and no more than 9 units of fat. Find the number of ounces of fruit and number of ounces of nuts that will meet the requirement with the least number of calories. What is the least number of calories?

24. Health Care Ms. Oliveras was given the following advice. She should supplement her daily diet with at least 6000 USP units of vitamin A, at least 195 mg of vitamin C, and at least 600 USP units of vitamin D. Ms. Oliveras finds that Mason's Pharmacy carries Brand X vitamin pills at 5¢ each and Brand Y vitamins at 4¢ each. Each Brand X pill contains 3000 USP units of A, 45 mg of C, and 75 USP units of D, while Brand Y pills contain 1000 USP units of A, 50 mg of C, and 200 USP units of D.

    a. What combination of vitamin pills should she buy to obtain the least possible cost? What is the least possible cost per day?

    b. For the solution in part a, Ms. Oliveras is receiving more than she needs of at least one vitamin. Identify that vitamin, and tell how much surplus she is receiving. Is there any way she can avoid receiving that surplus while still meeting the other constraints and minimizing the cost? Explain.

Social Sciences

25. Anthropology An anthropology article presents a hypothetical situation that could be described by a linear programming model. Suppose a population gathers plants and animals for survival. They need at least 360 units of energy, 300 units of protein, and 8 hides during some time period. One unit of plants provides 30 units of energy, 10 units of protein, and no hides. One animal provides 20 units of energy, 25 units of protein, and 1 hide. Only 25 units of plants and 25 animals are available. It costs the population 30 hours of labor to gather one unit of a plant and 15 hours for an animal. Find how many units of plants and how many animals should be gathered to meet the requirements with a minimum number of hours of labor. *Source: Annual Review of Anthropology.*

General Interest

 26. Construction   In a small town in South Carolina, zoning rules require that the window space (in square feet) in a house be at least one-sixth of the space used up by solid walls. The cost to build windows is $10 per ft^2, while the cost to build solid walls is $20 per ft^2. The total amount available for building walls and windows is no more than $12,000. The estimated

monthly cost to heat the house is $0.32 for each square foot of windows and $0.20 for each square foot of solid walls. Find the maximum total area (windows plus walls) if no more than $160 per month is available to pay for heat.

27. Farming   An agricultural advisor looks at the results of Example 2 and claims that it cannot possibly be correct. After all, the 4-H member is able to raise 16 animals, and she is only raising 12 animals. Surely she can earn more profit by raising all 16 animals. How would you respond?

▬ YOUR TURN ANSWERS

1. He should buy 60 kayaks and no canoes for a maximum revenue of $2100 a day.

2. Make 4 batches of each for a maximum profit of $200.

3. 14 pigs and no goats produces a maximum profit of $560.

CHAPTER REVIEW

SUMMARY

In this chapter, we introduced linear programming, which attempts to solve maximization and minimization problems with linear constraints. Linear programming models can be used to analyze a wide range of applications from many disciplines. The corner point theorem assures us that the optimal solution to a linear program, if it exists, must occur at one or more of the corner points of the feasible

region. Linear programs can be solved using the graphical method, which graphs the region described by the linear constraints and then locates the corner point corresponding to the optimal solution value. The graphical method, however, is restricted to problems with two or three variables.

Graphing a Linear Inequality   1. Draw the graph of the boundary line. Make the line solid if the inequality involves $\leq$ or $\geq$; make the line dashed if the inequality involves $<$ or $>$.

2. Decide which half-plane to shade. Use either of the following methods.

    a. Solve the inequality for y; shade the region above the line if the inequality is of the form of $y >$ or $y \geq$; shade the region below the line if the inequality is of the form of $y <$ or $y \leq$.

    b. Choose any point not on the line as a test point. Shade the half-plane that includes the test point if the test point satisfies the original inequality; otherwise, shade the half-plane on the other side of the boundary line.

Corner Point Theorem   If an optimum value (either a maximum or a minimum) of the objective function exists, it will occur at one or more of the corner points of the feasible region.

Solving a Linear Programming Problem   1. Write the objective function and all necessary constraints.

2. Graph the feasible region.

3. Identify all corner points.

4. Find the value of the objective function at each corner point.

5. For a bounded region, the solution is given by the corner point(s) producing the optimum value of the objective function.

6. For an unbounded region, check that a solution actually exists. If it does, it will occur at one or more corner points.

KEY TERMS

To understand the concepts presented in this chapter, you should know the meaning and use of the following terms.

I
linear inequality
boundary
half-plane
system of inequalities

region of feasible solutions
feasible region
bounded
unbounded

2
linear programming
objective function
constraints

isoprofit line
corner point

REVIEW EXERCISES

CONCEPT CHECK

Determine whether each of the following statements is true or false, and explain why.

1. The graphical method can be used to solve a linear programming problem with four variables.

2. For the inequality $5x + 4y \geq 20$, the test point $(3, 4)$ suggests that the correct half-plane to shade includes this point.

3. Let x represent the number of acres of wheat planted and y represent the number of acres of corn planted. The inequality $x \leq 2y$ implies that the number of acres of wheat planted will be at least twice the number of acres of corn planted.

4. For the variables in Exercise 3, assume that we have a total of 60 hours to plant the wheat and corn and that it takes 2 hours per acre to prepare a wheat field and 1 hour per acre to prepare a corn field. The inequality $2x + y \geq 60$ represents the constraint on the amount of time available for planting.

5. For the variables in Exercise 3, assume that we make a profit of $14 for each acre of corn and $10 for each acre of wheat. The objective function that can be used to maximize profit is $14x + 10y$.

6. The point $(2, 3)$ is a corner point of the linear programming problem

$$\text{Maximize} \quad z = 7x + 4y$$
$$\text{subject to:} \quad 3x + 8y \leq 30$$
$$4x + 2y \leq 15$$
$$x \geq 0, y \geq 0.$$

7. The point $(2, 3)$ is in the feasible region of the linear programming problem in Exercise 6.

8. The optimal solution to the linear programming problem in Exercise 6 occurs at point $(2, 3)$.

9. It is possible to find a point that lies on both sides of a linear inequality.

10. Every linear programming problem with a feasible region that is not empty either has a solution or is unbounded.

11. Solutions to linear programming problems may include fractions.

12. The inequality $4^2x + 5^2y \leq 7^2$ is a linear constraint.

13. The optimal solution to a linear programming problem can occur at a point that is not a corner point.

PRACTICE AND EXPLORATIONS

14. How many constraints are we limited to in the graphical method?

Graph each linear inequality.

15. $y \geq 2x + 3$

16. $5x - 2y \leq 10$

17. $2x + 6y \leq 8$

18. $2x - 6y \geq 18$

19. $y \geq x$

20. $y \geq -2$

Graph the solution of each system of inequalities. Find all corner points and tell whether each region is bounded or unbounded.

21. $x + y \leq 6$
    $2x - y \geq 3$

22. $3x + 2y \geq 12$
    $4x - 5y \leq 20$

23. $-4 \leq x \leq 2$
    $-1 \leq y \leq 3$
    $x + y \leq 4$

24. $2 \leq x \leq 5$
    $1 \leq y \leq 7$
    $x - y \leq 3$

25. $x + 2y \leq 4$
    $5x - 6y \leq 12$
    $x \geq 0$
    $y \geq 0$

26. $x + 2y \leq 4$
    $2x - 3y \leq 6$
    $x \geq 0$
    $y \geq 0$

Use the given regions to find the maximum and minimum values of the objective function $z = 2x + 4y$.

27.

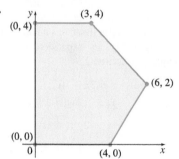

28.

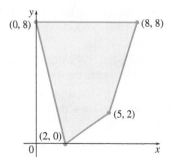

Use the graphical method to solve each linear programming problem.

29. Maximize $\quad z = 2x + 4y$

subject to: $\quad 3x + 2y \le 12$

$\qquad\qquad 5x + \;\; y \ge 5$

$\qquad\qquad\qquad x \ge 0$

$\qquad\qquad\qquad y \ge 0.$

30. Minimize $\quad z = 5x + 3y$

subject to: $\quad 8x + \;\; 5y \ge 40$

$\qquad\qquad 4x + 10y \ge 40$

$\qquad\qquad\qquad x \ge 0$

$\qquad\qquad\qquad y \ge 0.$

31. Minimize $\quad z = 4x + 2y$

subject to: $\quad x + \;\; y \le 50$

$\qquad\qquad 2x + \;\; y \ge 20$

$\qquad\qquad x + 2y \ge 30$

$\qquad\qquad\qquad x \ge 0$

$\qquad\qquad\qquad y \ge 0.$

32. Maximize $\quad z = 8x + 4y$

subject to: $\quad 3x + 12y \le 36$

$\qquad\qquad x + \;\; y \le 4$

$\qquad\qquad\qquad x \ge 0$

$\qquad\qquad\qquad y \ge 0.$

33. Why must the solution to a linear programming problem always occur at a corner point of the feasible region?

34. Is there necessarily a unique point in the feasible region where the maximum or minimum occurs? Why or why not?

35. It is not necessary to check all corner points in a linear programming problem. This exercise illustrates an alternative procedure, which is essentially an expansion of the ideas illustrated in Example 1 of Section 2.

$$\text{Maximize} \quad z = 3x + 4y$$

$$\text{subject to:} \quad 2x + \;\; y \le 4$$

$$-x + 2y \le 4$$

$$x \ge 0$$

$$y \ge 0.$$

a. Sketch the feasible region, and add the line $z = 8$. (*Note:* 8 is chosen because the numbers work out simply, but the chosen value of z is arbitrary.)

b. Draw a line parallel to the line $z = 8$ that is as far from the origin as possible but still touches the feasible region.

c. The line you drew in part b should go through the point $(4/5, 12/5)$. Explain how you know the maximum must be located at this point.

36. Use the method described in the previous exercise to solve Exercise 32.

APPLICATIONS

Business and Economics

37. **Time Management** A bakery makes both cakes and cookies. Each batch of cakes requires 2 hours in the oven and 3 hours in the decorating room. Each batch of cookies needs $1\frac{1}{2}$ hours in the oven and $\frac{2}{3}$ hour in the decorating room. The oven is available no more than 15 hours per day, and the decorating room can be used no more than 13 hours per day. Set up a system of inequalities, and then graph the solution of the system.

38. **Cost Analysis** DeMarco's pizza shop makes two specialty pizzas, the Mighty Meaty and the Very Veggie. The Mighty Meaty is topped with 5 different meat toppings and 2 different cheeses. The Very Veggie has 6 different vegetable toppings and 4 different cheeses. The shop sells at least 4 Mighty Meaty and 6 Very Veggie pizzas every day. The cost of the toppings for each Mighty Meaty is $3, and the cost of the vegetable toppings is $2 for each Very Veggie. No more than $60 per day can be spent on these toppings. The cheese used for the Mighty Meaty is $2 per pizza, and the cheese for the Very Veggie is $4 per pizza. No more than $80 per day can be spent on cheese. Set up a system of inequalities, and then graph the solution of the system.

39. **Profit** Refer to Exercise 37.

a. How many batches of cakes and cookies should the bakery in Exercise 37 make in order to maximize profits if cookies produce a profit of $20 per batch and cakes produce a profit of $30 per batch?

b. How much would the profit from selling cookies have to increase before it becomes more profitable to sell only cookies?

40. **Revenue** How many pizzas of each kind should the pizza shop in Exercise 38 make in order to maximize revenue if the Mighty Meaty sells for $15 and the Very Veggie sells for $12?

41. **Planting** In Karla's garden shop, she makes two kinds of mixtures for planting. A package of gardening mixture requires 2 lb of soil, 1 lb of peat moss, and 1 lb of fertilizer. A package of potting mixture requires 1 lb of soil, 2 lb of peat moss, and 3 lb of fertilizer. She has 16 lb of soil, 11 lb of peat moss, and 15 lb of fertilizer. If a package of gardening mixture sells for $3 and a package of potting mixture for $5, how many of each should she make in order to maximize her income? What is the maximum income?

42. **Construction** A contractor builds boathouses in two basic models, the Atlantic and the Pacific. Each Atlantic model requires 1000 ft of framing lumber, 3000 ft^3 of concrete, and $2000 for advertising. Each Pacific model requires 2000 ft of framing lumber, 3000 ft^3 of concrete, and $3000 for advertising. Contracts call for using at least 8000 ft of framing lumber, 18,000 ft^3 of concrete, and $15,000 worth of advertising. If the construction cost for each Atlantic model is $30,000 and the construction cost for each Pacific model is $40,000, how many of each model should be built to minimize construction costs?

43. **Steel** A steel company produces two types of alloys. A run of type I requires 3000 lb of molybdenum and 2000 tons of iron ore pellets as well as $2000 in advertising. A run of type II requires 3000 lb of molybdenum and 1000 tons of iron ore

Jordache/Shutterstock

pellets as well as $3000 in advertising. Total costs are $15,000 on a run of type I and $6000 on a run of type II. Because of various contracts, the company must use at least 18,000 lb of molybdenum and 7000 tons of iron ore pellets and spend at least $14,000 on advertising. How much of each type should be produced to minimize costs?

Life Sciences

44. Nutrition   A dietician in a hospital is to arrange a special diet containing two foods, Health Trough and Power Gunk. Each ounce of Health Trough contains 30 mg of calcium, 10 mg of iron, 10 IU of vitamin A, and 8 mg of cholesterol. Each ounce of Power Gunk contains 10 mg of calcium, 10 mg of iron, 30 IU of vitamin A, and 4 mg of cholesterol. If the minimum daily requirements are 360 mg of calcium, 160 mg of iron, and 240 IU of vitamin A, how many ounces of each food should be used to meet the minimum requirements and at the same time minimize the cholesterol intake? Also, what is the minimum cholesterol intake?

Social Sciences

45. Anthropology   A simplified model of the Mountain Fur economy of central Africa has been proposed. In this model, two crops can be grown, millet and wheat, which produce 400 lb and 800 lb per acre, respectively. Millet requires 36 days to harvest one acre, while wheat requires only 8 days. There are 2 acres of land and 48 days of harvest labor available. How many acres should be devoted to each crop to maximize the pounds of grain harvested? *Source: Themes in Economic Anthropology.*

General Interest

46. Studying   Jim Pringle is trying to allocate his study time this weekend. He can spend time working with either his math tutor or his accounting tutor to prepare for exams in both classes the following Monday. His math tutor charges $20 per hour, and his accounting tutor charges $40 per hour. He has $220 to spend on tutoring. Each hour that he spends working with his math tutor requires 1 aspirin and 1 hour of sleep to recover, while each hour he spends with his accounting tutor requires 1/2 aspirin and 3 hours of sleep. The maximum dosage of aspirin that he can safely take during his study time is 8 tablets, and he can only afford 15 hours of sleep this weekend. He expects that each hour with his math tutor will increase his score on the math exam by 3 points, while each hour with his accounting tutor will increase his score on the accounting exam by 5 points. How many hours should he spend with each tutor in order to maximize the number of points he will get on the two tests combined?

EXTENDED APPLICATION

SENSITIVITY ANALYSIS

In Section 3 of this chapter we used the graphical method to solve linear programming problems. A quick analysis of the strengths and weaknesses of the process of modeling real-life problems using these techniques reveals two apparent problems. First, most real-life problems require far more than two variables to adequately capture the essence of the problem. Second, our world is so dynamic that the values used to model a problem today can quickly change, leaving the current solution irrelevant or even infeasible.

Recall that in Example 2 of Section 3, a linear programming problem was developed to determine the optimal number of goats and pigs to raise for a 4-H project. The linear program was written as

$$\text{Maximize} \quad z = 12x + 40y$$
$$\text{Subject to:} \quad x + y \leq 16$$
$$x + 3y \leq 36$$
$$x \leq 10$$
$$x \geq 0, y \geq 0,$$

where x is the number of goats and y is the number of pigs.

A graph of the feasible region, with corner points illustrated, is shown in Figure 23 on the next page. We determined that a maximum profit of $480 occurs when 12 pigs and no goats are raised. This is no surprise given that the profit from a pig is $40 and the profit for a goat is just $12. In fact, we saw in that example that if the profit from raising a pig decreases to $36, then it would become profitable to raise goats, too.

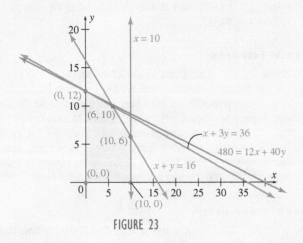

FIGURE 23

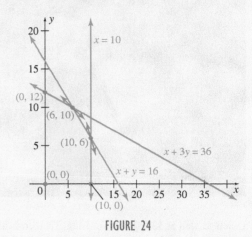

FIGURE 24

CHANGES IN OBJECTIVE FUNCTION COEFFICIENTS

Suppose that the 4-H member, whom we will call Sarah, now wonders what the profit from raising a goat would have to become so that it would become profitable for her to raise both pigs and goats.

Mathematically, we replace the $12 in the objective function with the variable $12 + c$, where c is the change in profit for raising a goat. That is, $z = (12 + c)x + 40y$. Now, for any particular profit z, we can think of this equation as a line, which we called an *isoprofit line* in Section 2. With $c = 0$ and $z = 480$, the isoprofit line is $480 = 12x + 40y$, which is plotted in green in Figure 23. Solving for y helps us to see that the line represented by this equation has slope $-\dfrac{12 + c}{40}$. That is,

$$z = (12 + c)x + 40y,$$

or

$$40y = -(12 + c)x + z,$$

which simplifies to

$$y = -\frac{12 + c}{40}x + \frac{z}{40}.$$

The line that represents the boundary of the constraint $x + 3y = 36$ has slope $-\frac{1}{3}$. If c begins to increase, forcing the slope of the isoprofit line to become more negative, eventually the slope of the isoprofit line corresponding to the optimal profit of $480 will have slope $-\frac{1}{3}$. If c continues to increase beyond this level, the optimal profit will occur at the corner point $(6, 10)$. That is, as long as the slope of the isoprofit line exceeds $-\frac{1}{3}$, the optimal solution will continue to be to raise 12 pigs and no goats. If, however, the slope of the isoprofit line becomes less than $-\frac{1}{3}$, then it will become profitable to raise goats as well. That is, if c increases to the point at which

$$-\frac{12 + c}{40} < -\frac{1}{3},$$

which simplifies to,

$$\frac{12 + c}{40} > \frac{1}{3},$$

or

$$c > \frac{40}{3} - 12 = \frac{4}{3},$$

the optimal solution changes from the corner point $(0, 12)$ to $(6, 10)$. Further analysis, as illustrated by Figure 24, shows that the optimal solution will remain at the corner point $(6, 10)$ as long as the slope of the isoprofit line stays between

$$-1 \leq -\frac{12 + c}{40} \leq -\frac{1}{3},$$

or when

$$\frac{4}{3} \leq c \leq 28.$$

Then the optimal solution will be to raise 6 goats and 10 pigs.

Beyond $c = \$28$ or a profit of $40 per goat, it will be optimal to raise 10 goats and 6 pigs. Note that this analysis can be used to completely determine the optimal solution for changes in a single cost coefficient for any two variable linear programming problem, without having to resolve the linear program.

CHANGES IN THE RIGHT HAND SIDE OF A CONSTRAINT

Sarah begins to wonder if the right-hand sides of any of the constraints might be changed so that the profit would increase. For example, the easiest thing to do would be for Sarah to increase the third constraint, corresponding to the restriction that no more than 10 goats are raised. Sarah considers the possibility of lifting this constraint. Notice, however, that if we increase the right-hand side of the third constraint, it has no affect on the optimal corner point. As you can see graphically with the red lines in Figure 25, increasing the right-hand side will not change the optimal solution. In fact, decreasing the third constraint even to zero will not change the optimal solution.

Now suppose that Sarah realizes that she has overestimated the total number of animals she can raise by 3 and wants to see how this will affect the optimal solution. The boundary of the first

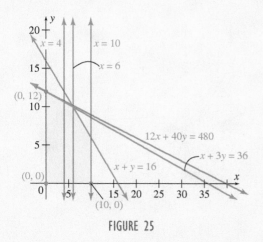

FIGURE 25

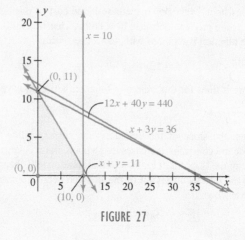

FIGURE 27

constraint can be written as the line $y = -x + 16$, which has y-intercept at the point $(0,16)$. Since Sarah has overestimated the total number of animals by three, the boundary line becomes $y = -x + 13$, which has y-intercept at the point $(0,13)$, as illustrated in Figure 26.

This change will not have an effect on the solution because raising 13 pigs is not feasible for the second constraint. That is, $(0, 13)$ is not a feasible corner point and cannot be a solution to the problem. In fact, as long as the total number of animals is at least 12 in the first constraint, the optimal solution is for Sarah to raise 12 pigs and no goats. In this case, we would say that the right-hand side of the first constraint is not sensitive to small changes. If, on the other hand, Sarah has overestimated the total number of animals she can raise and that, in fact, the total number is actually 11, then the optimal solution changes. As you can see in Figure 27, the feasible region has diminished to the point that the second constraint is now redundant and has no influence on the optimal solution. In fact, the optimal solution is to raise 11 pigs and no goats. This makes sense since the profit from raising pigs is so high that it does not become profitable to raise goats when a smaller total number of animals are raised. The same type of analysis can be performed on the right-hand side of the second constraint.

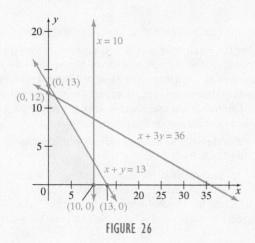

FIGURE 26

SHADOW PROFITS

Changes in the resources available in a linear programming problem usually result in a change in the value of the objective function in the optimal solution. For example, if an optimal solution uses all of the material available, then a sudden increase/decrease in the amount of that material available can change the objective function value. In the analysis above, decreasing the right-hand side of the first constraint from 16 to 12 did not change the optimal solution. In this case, we would say that the shadow profit, or the increase in the profit for changing the right-hand side of the first constraint by one unit is \$0. On the other hand, if we increase the amount of money available for the project by \$75, the optimal solution would change from raising 12 pigs to raising 13 pigs and thereby increase profit by \$40. This implies that for each dollar increase in the amount of money available, the profit will increase by \$40/75 or by about \$0.53. In this case, the shadow profit would be \$0.53.

CHANGES IN CONSTRAINT COEFFICIENTS

Sarah continues to explore reasons why the optimal policy is to only raise pigs. She wonders if any of the coefficients in the constraints are having an effect on the optimal solution. In the process, she realizes that it may cost more than \$75 to raise a pig. In the original statement of the problem, Sarah had up to \$900 to spend on her project, with each goat costing \$25 to raise and each pig costing \$75 to raise. This information was translated into the constraint $25x + 75y \leq 900$, which was then simplified by dividing the inequality by 25. Sarah wonders how much the \$75 would have to increase before the optimal solution would include raising goats. Letting b represent the change in the cost of raising a pig, the constraint becomes $25x + (75 + b)y \leq 900$, and the corresponding boundary line can then be simplified and written as

$$y = -\frac{25}{75 + b}x + \frac{900}{75 + b}.$$

To be consistent, every dollar increase in the cost of raising a pig also forces the profit to decrease by a dollar. That is, the 40 in the objective function is replaced with $40 - b$, becoming

$$z = 12x + (40 - b)y.$$

The isoprofit lines for this objective function will each have slope of $-\dfrac{12}{40 - b}$.

When the slope of the boundary line corresponding to the altered second constraint increases to the point that it is larger than the slope of the isoprofit lines, the optimal solution will change and move to the intersection point of the first and second constraints. This occurs when

$$-\frac{25}{75 + b} > -\frac{12}{40 - b},$$

which simplifies to

$$b > \frac{100}{37} \approx 2.70.$$

In other words, as long as the cost of raising a pig is at or below $75 + 2.70 = $77.70, the optimal policy is to only raise pigs. When the cost exceeds this amount the optimal solution will change, and it may become profitable to raise goats, too. For example, suppose the cost of raising a pig increases to $100. The new feasible region has corner points at (0, 0), (0, 9), (10, 0), (10, 6), and (28/3, 20/3), as indicated by Figure 28. It can be easily verified that the optimal

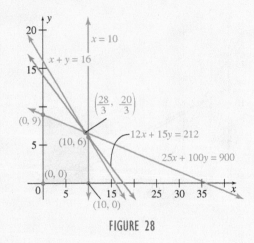

FIGURE 28

solution now occurs at (28/3, 20/3), with objective function value of $z = 12(\frac{28}{3}) + 15(\frac{20}{3}) = 212$. Of course, it is impossible to raise a fractional number of animals so some additional work is required to determine the optimal solution. Unfortunately, simply rounding the fractional solution downward to obtain $x = 9$ and $y = 6$ does not give the optimal solution. In fact, it can be shown that the optimal integer solution is $x = 10$ and $y = 6$ with an objective function value of $210. Thus, if the cost of raising a pig is $100 then the optimal policy is to raise 6 pigs and 10 goats.

EXERCISES

1. Use sensitivity analysis to find the optimal solution to the original 4-H problem, if the profit from raising a goat increases from $12 to $25.

2. Use sensitivity analysis to find the optimal solution to the original 4-H problem, if the profit from raising a pig decreases from $40 to $35.

3. Use sensitivity analysis to determine the smallest decrease in the cost of raising a goat, so that the optimal policy of raising 12 pigs and no goats changes. Note that changing this cost also changes the profit level for goats.

4. Katie's Landscaping Services weeds flower beds and mows lawns. Katie makes a profit of $8 for every hour she weeds and $25 for every hour she mows. Because Katie is also in college, she can only take on 18 jobs each week for her business. Katie has found that the flower beds in her neighborhood are very poorly maintained and that weeding a flower bed must be considered as two jobs. Each week, Katie sets aside $72 for her brother Nate to help her and feels that a fair price to pay Nate is $3 per hour for weeding and $9 per hour for mowing a lawn.

a. Show that this problem can be set up as follows:

Maximize $z = 8x + 25y$
Subject to: $2x + y \le 18$
                      $3x + 9y \le 72$
                      $x \ge 0, y \ge 0$

b. Use the graphical method to solve this linear program.

c. Alter the graph from part b to determine the new optimal solution if the right hand side of the second constraint increases to 81. (*Hint:* You shouldn't have to completely resolve this problem. Simply change the intercepts of one of the constraints and use isoprofit lines to identify the corner point where the new optimal solution occurs.)

d. What is the shadow profit associated with the change from 72 to 81 in part c?

e. Using the original problem, determine the smallest increase (to the nearest penny) in the objective function coefficient for variable x that will cause the value of x to increase in the optimal solution. In this case, we would say that the cost coefficient associated with variable x is sensitive to change.

    f. If the y-coefficient in the second constraint of the original problem begins to increase, forcing an equal decrease in the y-coefficient in the objective function, determine the smallest amount (to the nearest penny) that this coefficient can increase before it becomes optimal to produce positive quantities of variable x. For simplicity, assume that it is possible to have fractional amounts of each variable.

5. Go to the website WolframAlpha.com, and enter "minimize $8x + 25y$ with $2x + y <= 18, 3x + 9y <= 72, x >= 0, y >= 0$".

Study the solution provided by Wolfram|Alpha. Notice that the solution given is the same as the solution you found in Exercise 4b. Use Wolfram|Alpha to verify your answers to Exercises 4c–4f.

DIRECTIONS FOR GROUP PROJECT

Suppose that you are the manager of a company that manufactures two types of products. Develop a simple linear program with a solution that gives how many of each type of product the company should produce. Then perform sensitivity analysis on various aspects of the model. Use presentation software to report your model and your findings to the class.

LEARNING OBJECTIVES

1: Graphing Linear Inequalities

1. Graph linear inequalities
2. Graph a system of linear inequalities
3. Determine the feasible region for a system of linear inequalities
4. Solve application problems

2: Solving Linear Programming Problems Graphically

1. Determine corner points
2. Solve linear programming problems graphically

3: Applications of Linear Programming

1. Solve application problems

ANSWERS TO SELECTED EXERCISES

Answers to selected writing exercises are provided.

Exercises 1

For exercises . . .	1–20	21–32	33–36	38–45
Refer to example . . .	1,2	3–5	3	6

1.
$x + y \leq 2$

3.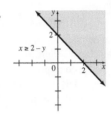
$x \geq 2 - y$

5.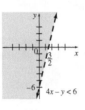
$4x - y < 6$

7.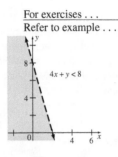
$4x + y < 8$

9.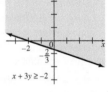
$x + 3y \geq -2$

11.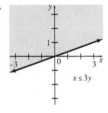
$x \leq 3y$

13.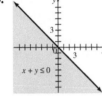
$x + y \leq 0$

15.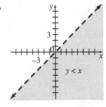
$y < x$

17.
$x < 4$

19.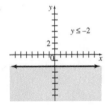
$y \leq -2$

21.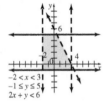
$x + y \leq 1$
$x - y \geq 2$
Unbounded

23.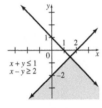
$x + 3y \leq 6$
$2x + 4y \geq 7$
Unbounded

25.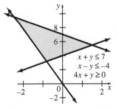
$x + y \leq 7$
$x - y \leq -4$
$4x + y \geq 0$
Bounded

27.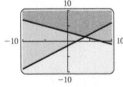
$-2 < x < 3$
$-1 \leq y \leq 5$
$2x + y < 6$
Bounded

29.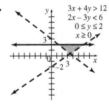
$y - 2x \leq 4$
$y \geq 2 - x$
$x \geq 0$
$y \geq 0$
Unbounded

31.
$3x + 4y > 12$
$2x - 3y < 6$
$0 \leq y \leq 2$
$x \geq 0$
Bounded

33.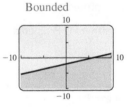

35.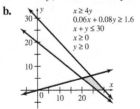

37. B: $\leq, \leq, \leq$; C: $\geq, \geq, \leq$; D: $\leq, \geq, \leq$; E: $\leq, \leq, \geq$; F: $\leq, \geq, \geq$; G: $\geq, \geq, \geq$

39. a.

	Shawls	Afghans		Total
Number Made	x	y		
Spinning Time	1	2	$\leq$	8
Dyeing Time	1	1	$\leq$	6
Weaving Time	1	4	$\leq$	14

b.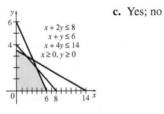
$x + 2y \leq 8$
$x + y \leq 6$
$x + 4y \leq 14$
$x \geq 0, y \geq 0$

c. Yes; no

41. a. $x \geq 4y$; $0.06x + 0.08y \geq 1.6$; $x + y \leq 30$; $x \geq 0$; $y \geq 0$

b.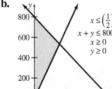
$x \geq 4y$
$0.06x + 0.08y \geq 1.6$
$x + y \leq 30$
$x \geq 0$
$y \geq 0$

43. a. $x \leq (1/2)y$; $x + y \leq 800$; $x \geq 0$; $y \geq 0$

b.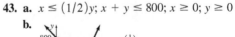
$x \leq \left(\frac{1}{2}\right)y$
$x + y \leq 800$
$x \geq 0$
$y \geq 0$

45. a. $x + y \geq 7$; $2x + y \geq 10$; $x + y \leq 9$; $x \geq 0$; $y \geq 0$ **b.**

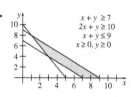

$$x + y \geq 7$$
$$2x + y \geq 10$$
$$x + y \leq 9$$
$$x \geq 0, y \geq 0$$

Exercises 2

1. a. Maximum of 29 at $(7, 4)$; minimum of 10 at $(0, 5)$ **b.** Maximum of 35 at $(3, 8)$; minimum of 8 at $(4, 1)$ **3. a.** Maximum of 9 at $(0, 12)$; minimum of 0 at $(0, 0)$ **b.** Maximum of 12 at $(8, 0)$; minimum of 0 at $(0, 0)$
5. a. No maximum; minimum of 16 at $(0, 8)$ **b.** No maximum; minimum of 18 at $(3, 4)$ **c.** No maximum; minimum of 21 at $(13/2, 2)$ **d.** No maximum; minimum of 12 at $(12, 0)$ **7.** Minimum of 24 when $x = 6$ and $y = 0$ **9.** Maximum of 46 when $x = 6$ and $y = 8$ **11.** Maximum of 1500 when $x = 150$ and $y = 0$, as well as when $x = 50$ and $y = 100$ and all points on the line between   **13.** No solution   **15. a.** Maximum of 204 when $x = 18$ and $y = 2$ **b.** Maximum of 588/5 when $x = 12/5$ and $y = 39/5$ **c.** Maximum of 102 when $x = 0$ and $y = 17/2$ **17.** b

Exercises 3

1. Let x be the number of product A produced and y be the number of product B. Then $3x + 5y \leq 60$.   **3.** Let x be the number of calcium carbonate supplements and y be the number of calcium citrate supplements. Then $600x + 250y \geq 1500$.   **5.** Let x be the number of pounds of $8 coffee and y be the number of $10 coffee. Then $x + y \geq 40$.   **7.** 51 to plant I and 32 to plant II, for a minimum cost of $2810   **9. a.** 6 units of policy A and 16 units of policy B, for a minimum premium cost of $940   **b.** 30 units of policy A and 0 units of policy B, for a minimum premium cost of $750   **11. a.** 500 type I and 1000 type II   **b.** Maximum revenue is $275.   **c.** If the price of the type I bolt exceeds 20¢, then it is more profitable to produce 1050 type I bolts and 450 type II bolts.   **13. a.** 120 kg of the half-and-half mix and 120 kg of the other mix, for a maximum revenue of $1980   **b.** 0 kg of the half-and-half mix and 200 kg of the other mix, for a maximum revenue of $2200   **15. a.** 40 gal from dairy I and 60 gal from dairy II, for a maximum butterfat of 3.4 gal   **b.** 10 gal from dairy I and 20 gal from dairy 2. No.   **17.** $10 million in bonds and $20 million in mutual funds, or $5 million in bonds and $22.5 million in mutual funds (or any solution on the line in between those two points), for a maximum annual interest of $2 million   **19.** a   **21. a.** Three of pill 1 and two of pill 2, for a minimum cost of $1.05 per day   **b.** 360 surplus IU of vitamin A. No.   **23.** 4 ounces of fruit and 2 ounces of nuts, for a minimum of 140 calories   **25.** 0 plants and 18 animals, for a minimum of 270 hours

Review Exercises

1. False   **2.** True   **3.** False   **4.** False   **5.** False
6. False   **7.** True   **8.** False   **9.** False   **10.** True   **11.** True   **12.** True   **13.** True

15.

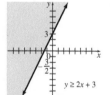

$y \geq 2x + 3$

17.

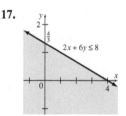

$2x + 6y \leq 8$

19.

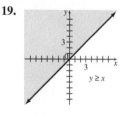

$y \geq x$

21.

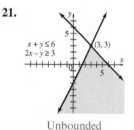

$x + y \leq 6$
$2x - y \geq 3$

$(3, 3)$

Unbounded

23.

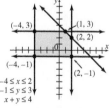

$(-4, 3)$ $(1, 3)$
$(2, 2)$
$(-4, -1)$
$(2, -1)$
$-4 \leq x \leq 2$
$-1 \leq y \leq 3$
$x + y \leq 4$

Bounded

25.

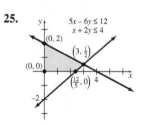

$5x - 6y \leq 12$
$x + 2y \leq 4$
$(0, 2)$
$\left(3, \frac{1}{2}\right)$
$(0, 0)$
$\left(\frac{12}{5}, 0\right)$

Bounded

27. Maximum of 22 at $(3, 4)$; minimum of 0 at $(0, 0)$
29. Maximum of 24 at $(0, 6)$ **31.** Minimum of 40 at any point on the segment connecting $(0, 20)$ and $(10/3, 40/3)$

35. a.

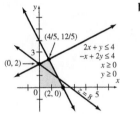

b.

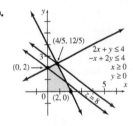

37. Let x = number of batches of cakes and y = number of batches of cookies. Then $x \geq 0$, $y \geq 0$, $2x + (3/2)y \leq 15$, and $3x + (2/3)y \leq 13$.

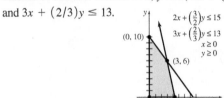

39. a. 3 batches of cakes and 6 batches of cookies, for a maximum profit of $210 **b.** If the profit per batch of cookies increases by more than $2.50 (to above $22.50), then it will be more profitable to make 10 batches of cookies and no batches of cake.
41. 7 packages of gardening mixture and 2 packages of potting mixture, for a maximum income of $31 **43.** Produce no runs of type I and 7 runs of type II, for a minimum cost of $42,000. **45.** 0 acres for millet and 2 acres for wheat, for a maximum harvest of 1600 lb

TEXT CREDITS

SOURCES

Section 2

1. Exercise 17 from Problem 5 from "November 1989 Course 130 Examination Operations Research" of the *Education and Examination Committee of The Society of Actuaries*. Reprinted by permission of The Society of Actuaries.

Section 3

1. Page 133 from *Uniform CPA Examinations and Unofficial Answers*, copyright © 1973, 1974, 1975 by the American Institute of Certified Public Accountants, Inc.; reprinted with permission.
2. Exercise 25 from Reidhead, Van A., "Linear Programming Models in Archaeology," *Annual Review of Anthropology*, Vol. 8, 1979, pp. 543–578.

Review Exercise

1. Exercise 45 from Joy, Leonard, "Barth's Presentation of Economic Spheres in Darfur," in *Themes in Economic Anthropology*, edited by Raymond Firth, Tavistock Publications, 1967, pp. 175–189.

Linear Programming: The Simplex Method

From Chapter 4 of *Finite Math,* Tenth Edition. Margaret L. Lial, Raymond N. Greenwell, Nathan P. Ritchey.Copyright © 2012 by Pearson Education, Inc. All rights reserved.

Linear Programming: The Simplex Method

Each type of beer has its own recipe and an associated cost per unit and brings in a specific revenue per unit. The brewery manager must meet a revenue target with minimum production costs. An exercise in Section 3 formulates the manager's goal as a linear programming problem and solves for the optimum production schedule when there are two beer varieties.

By now, you've discussed solving linear programming problems by the graphical method. This method illustrates the basic ideas of linear programming, but it is practical only for problems with two variables. For problems with more than two variables, or problems with two variables and many constraints, the *simplex method* is used. This method grew out of a practical problem faced by George B. Dantzig in 1947. Dantzig was concerned with finding the least expensive way to allocate supplies for the United States Air Force.

The **simplex method** starts with the selection of one corner point (often the origin) from the feasible region. Then, in a systematic way, another corner point is found that attempts to improve the value of the objective function. Finally, an optimum solution is reached, or it can be seen that no such solution exists.

The simplex method requires a number of steps. In this chapter we divide the presentation of these steps into two parts. First, a problem is set up in Section 1 and the method started; then, in Section 2, the method is completed. Special situations are discussed in the remainder of the chapter.

1 Slack Variables and the Pivot

Because the simplex method is used for problems with many variables, it usually is not convenient to use letters such as x, y, z, or w as variable names. Instead, the symbols x_1 (read "x-sub-one"), x_2, x_3, and so on, are used. These variable names lend themselves easily to use on the computer.

In this section we will use the simplex method only for problems such as the following:

$$\text{Maximize} \quad z = 2x_1 - 3x_2$$
$$\text{subject to:} \quad 2x_1 + x_2 \le 10$$
$$x_1 - 3x_2 \le 5$$
$$\text{with} \quad x_1 \ge 0, \quad x_2 \ge 0.$$

This type of problem is said to be in *standard maximum form*. All constraints must be expressed in the linear form

$$a_1x_1 + a_2x_2 + a_3x_3 + \cdots + a_nx_n \le b,$$

where $x_1, x_2, x_3, \ldots, x_n$ are variables and $a_1, a_2, \ldots, a_n$ and b are constants, with $b \ge 0$.

Standard Maximum Form

A linear programming problem is in **standard maximum form** if the following conditions are satisfied.

1. The objective function is to be maximized.
2. All variables are nonnegative ($x_i \ge 0$).
3. All remaining constraints are stated in the form

$$a_1x_1 + a_2x_2 + \cdots + a_nx_n \le b \quad \text{with } b \ge 0.$$

(Problems that do not meet all of these conditions are discussed in Sections 3 and 4.)

To use the simplex method, we start by converting the constraints, which are linear inequalities, into linear equations by adding a nonnegative variable, called a **slack variable**, to each constraint. For example, the inequality $x_1 + x_2 \leq 10$ is converted into an equation by adding the slack variable s_1 to get

$$x_1 + x_2 + s_1 = 10, \qquad \text{where } s_1 \geq 0.$$

The inequality $x_1 + x_2 \leq 10$ says that the sum $x_1 + x_2$ is less than or perhaps equal to 10. The variable s_1 "takes up any slack" and represents the amount by which $x_1 + x_2$ fails to equal 10. For example, if $x_1 + x_2$ equals 8, then s_1 is 2. If $x_1 + x_2 = 10$, then s_1 is 0.

CAUTION   A different slack variable must be used for each constraint.

EXAMPLE 1   Slack Variables

Restate the following linear programming problem by introducing slack variables.

$$\begin{aligned}
\text{Maximize} \quad & z = 3x_1 + 2x_2 + x_3 \\
\text{subject to:} \quad & 2x_1 + x_2 + x_3 \leq 150 \\
& 2x_1 + 2x_2 + 8x_3 \leq 200 \\
& 2x_1 + 3x_2 + x_3 \leq 320 \\
\text{with} \quad & x_1 \geq 0, \quad x_2 \geq 0, \quad x_3 \geq 0.
\end{aligned}$$

SOLUTION   Rewrite the three constraints as equations by adding slack variables s_1, s_2, and s_3, one for each constraint. Then the problem can be restated as follows.

$$\begin{aligned}
\text{Maximize} \quad & z = 3x_1 + 2x_2 + x_3 \\
\text{subject to:} \quad & 2x_1 + x_2 + x_3 + s_1 = 150 \\
& 2x_1 + 2x_2 + 8x_3 + s_2 = 200 \\
& 2x_1 + 3x_2 + x_3 + s_3 = 320 \\
\text{with} \quad & x_1 \geq 0, \quad x_2 \geq 0, \quad x_3 \geq 0, \quad s_1 \geq 0, \quad s_2 \geq 0, \quad s_3 \geq 0.
\end{aligned}$$

In Example 4, we will take another step toward solving this linear programming problem.

Adding slack variables to the constraints converts a linear programming problem into a system of linear equations. In each of these equations, all variables should be on the left side of the equal sign and all constants on the right. All the equations in Example 1 satisfy this condition except for the objective function, $z = 3x_1 + 2x_2 + x_3$, which may be written with all variables on the left as

$$-3x_1 - 2x_2 - x_3 + z = 0.$$

Now the equations in Example 1 can be written as the following augmented matrix.

$$
\begin{array}{ccccccc}
x_1 & x_2 & x_3 & s_1 & s_2 & s_3 & z \\
\end{array}
$$

$$
\left[
\begin{array}{ccccccc|c}
2 & 1 & 1 & 1 & 0 & 0 & 0 & 150 \\
2 & 2 & 8 & 0 & 1 & 0 & 0 & 200 \\
2 & 3 & 1 & 0 & 0 & 1 & 0 & 320 \\
-3 & -2 & -1 & 0 & 0 & 0 & 1 & 0
\end{array}
\right]
$$

Indicators

This matrix is called the initial **simplex tableau**. The numbers in the bottom row, which are from the objective function, are called **indicators** (except for the 1 and 0 at the far right).

EXAMPLE 2   Initial Simplex Tableau

Set up the initial simplex tableau for the following problem.

A farmer has 100 acres of available land on which he wishes to plant a mixture of potatoes, corn, and cabbage. It costs him \$400 to produce an acre of potatoes, \$160 to produce an acre of corn, and $280 to produce an acre of cabbage. He has a maximum of $20,000 to spend. He makes a profit of $120 per acre of potatoes, $40 per acre of corn, and $60 per acre of cabbage. How many acres of each crop should he plant to maximize his profit?

SOLUTION   Begin by summarizing the given information as follows.

Profits and Constraints for Crops				
	Potatoes	Corn	Cabbage	Total
Number of Acres	x_1	x_2	x_3 $\leq$	100
Cost (per acre)	$400	$160	$280 $\leq$	$20,000
Profit (per acre)	$120	$40	$60	

If the number of acres allotted to each of the three crops is represented by x_1, x_2, and x_3, respectively, then the constraint pertaining to the number of acres can be expressed as

$$x_1 + x_2 + x_3 \leq 100 \qquad \text{Number of acres}$$

where x_1, x_2, and x_3 are all nonnegative. This constraint says that $x_1 + x_2 + x_3$ is less than or perhaps equal to 100. Use s_1 as the slack variable, giving the equation

$$x_1 + x_2 + x_3 + s_1 = 100.$$

Here s_1 represents the amount of the farmer's 100 acres that will not be used (s_1 may be 0 or any value up to 100).

The constraint pertaining to the production cost can be expressed as

$$400x_1 + 160x_2 + 280x_3 \leq 20,000, \qquad \text{Production costs}$$

or if we divide both sides by 40, as

$$10x_1 + 4x_2 + 7x_3 \leq 500.$$

This inequality can also be converted into an equation by adding a slack variable, s_2.

$$10x_1 + 4x_2 + 7x_3 + s_2 = 500$$

If we had not divided by 40, the slack variable would have represented any unused portion of the farmer's $20,000 capital. Instead, the slack variable represents $1/40$ of that unused portion. (Note that s_2 may be any value from 0 to 500.)

The objective function represents the profit. The farmer wants to maximize

$$z = 120x_1 + 40x_2 + 60x_3.$$

The linear programming problem can now be stated as follows:

$$\begin{aligned}
\text{Maximize} \quad & z = 120x_1 + 40x_2 + 60x_3 \\
\text{subject to:} \quad & x_1 + x_2 + x_3 + s_1 \qquad\quad = 100 \\
& 10x_1 + 4x_2 + 7x_3 \qquad + s_2 = 500 \\
\text{with} \quad & x_1 \geq 0, \quad x_2 \geq 0, \quad x_3 \geq 0, \quad s_1 \geq 0, \quad s_2 \geq 0.
\end{aligned}$$

YOUR TURN 1 Set up the initial simplex tableau for Example 2 with the following two modifications. All the costs per acre are $100 less. Also, there are taxes of $5, $10, and $15 per acre of potatoes, corn, and cabbage, respectively, and the farmer does not want to pay more than $900 in taxes.

Rewrite the objective function as $-120x_1 - 40x_2 - 60x_3 + z = 0$, and complete the initial simplex tableau as follows.

$$\begin{array}{c}
\begin{array}{cccccc}
x_1 & x_2 & x_3 & s_1 & s_2 & z
\end{array} \\
\left[\begin{array}{cccccc|c}
1 & 1 & 1 & 1 & 0 & 0 & 100 \\
10 & 4 & 7 & 0 & 1 & 0 & 500 \\
\hline
-120 & -40 & -60 & 0 & 0 & 1 & 0
\end{array}\right]
\end{array}$$ TRY YOUR TURN 1

In Example 2 (which we will finish solving in the next section), the feasible region consists of the points (x_1, x_2, x_3) that satisfy the two inequalities for the number of acres and the production costs. It is difficult to draw such a region in three dimensions by hand. If there were a fourth crop, and hence a fourth dimension, plotting the region would be impossible. Nevertheless, as with the graphical method, the objective function is maximized at one of the corner points (or two corner points and all points on the line segment between the two points). With the simplex method, which we develop in this section and the next, we find that corner point using matrix methods that don't require drawing a graph of the feasible region.

After we have converted the two inequalities into equations by the addition of slack variables, the maximization problem in Example 2 consists of a system of two equations in five variables, together with the objective function. Because there are more variables than equations, the system will have an infinite number of solutions. To see this, solve the system for s_1 and s_2.

$$s_1 = 100 - x_1 - x_2 - x_3$$
$$s_2 = 500 - 10x_1 - 4x_2 - 7x_3$$

Each choice of values for x_1, x_2, and x_3 gives corresponding values for s_1 and s_2 that produce a solution of the system. But only some of these solutions are feasible.

In a feasible solution, all variables must be nonnegative. To get a unique feasible solution, we set three of the five variables equal to 0. In general, if there are m equations, then m variables can be nonzero. These m nonzero variables are called **basic variables**, and the corresponding solutions are called **basic feasible solutions**. Each basic feasible solution corresponds to a corner point. In particular, if we choose the solution with $x_1 = 0$, $x_2 = 0$, and $x_3 = 0$, then $s_1 = 100$ and $s_2 = 500$ are the basic variables. This solution, which corresponds to the corner point at the origin, is hardly optimal. It produces a profit of $0 for the farmer, since the equation that corresponds to the objective function becomes

$$-120(0) - 40(0) - 60(0) + 0s_1 + 0s_2 + z = 0.$$

In the next section we will use the simplex method to start with this solution and improve it to find the maximum possible profit.

Each step of the simplex method produces a solution that corresponds to a corner point of the region of feasible solutions. These solutions can be read directly from the matrix, as shown in the next example.

EXAMPLE 3 Basic Variables

Read a solution from the following simplex tableau.

$$\begin{bmatrix} x_1 & x_2 & x_3 & s_1 & s_2 & z & \\ 2 & 0 & 8 & 5 & 2 & 0 & 17 \\ 9 & 5 & 3 & 12 & 0 & 0 & 45 \\ -2 & 0 & -4 & 0 & 0 & 3 & 90 \end{bmatrix}$$

SOLUTION In this solution, the variables x_2 and s_2 are basic variables. They can be identified quickly because the columns for these variables have all zeros except for one nonzero entry. All variables that are not basic variables have the value 0. This means that in the tableau just shown, x_2 and s_2 are the basic variables, while x_1, x_3, and s_1 have the value 0. The nonzero entry for x_2 is 5 in the second row. Since x_1, x_3, and s_1 are zero, the second row of the tableau represents the equation $5x_2 = 45$, so $x_2 = 9$. Similarly, from the top row, $2s_2 = 17$, so $s_2 = 17/2$. From the bottom row, $3z = 90$, so $z = 30$. The solution is thus $x_1 = 0, x_2 = 9, x_3 = 0, s_1 = 0$, and $s_2 = 17/2$, with $z = 30$.

Pivots Solutions read directly from the initial simplex tableau are seldom optimal. It is necessary to proceed to other solutions (corresponding to other corner points of the feasible region) until an optimum solution is found. To get these other solutions, we use restricted

Three row operations:

1. interchanging any two rows;

2. multiplying the elements of a row by any nonzero real number; and

3. adding a multiple of the elements of one row to the corresponding elements of a multiple of any other row.

In this chapter we will only use operation 2 and a restricted version of operation 3; we will never interchange two rows.

versions of the row operations to change the tableau by using one of the nonzero entries of the tableau as a **pivot**. The row operations are performed to change to 0 all entries in the column containing the pivot (except for the pivot itself, which remains unchanged). Pivoting, explained in the next example, produces a new tableau leading to another solution of the system of equations obtained from the original problem.

CAUTION | In this chapter, when adding a multiple of one row to a multiple of another, we will never take a negative multiple of the row being changed. For example, when changing row 2, we might use $-2R_1 + 3R_2 \rightarrow R_2$, but we will never use $2R_1 - 3R_2 \rightarrow R_2$. If you get a negative number in the rightmost column, you will know immediately that you have made an error. The reason for this restriction is that violating it turns negative numbers into positive, and vice versa. This is disastrous in the bottom row, where we will seek negative numbers when we choose our pivot column. It will also cause problems with choosing pivots, particularly in the algorithm for solving nonstandard problems in Section 4.

When we are performing row operations by hand, we will postpone getting a 1 in each basic variable column until the final step. This will avoid fractions and decimals, which can make the operations more difficult and more prone to error. When using a graphing calculator, however, we must change the pivot to a 1 before performing row operations. The next example illustrates both of these methods.

EXAMPLE 4   Pivot

Pivot about the indicated 2 of the following initial simplex tableau.

$$
\begin{array}{ccccccc}
x_1 & x_2 & x_3 & s_1 & s_2 & s_3 & z \\
\end{array}
$$
$$
\left[
\begin{array}{ccccccc|c}
\mathbf{2} & 1 & 1 & 1 & 0 & 0 & 0 & 150 \\
1 & 2 & 8 & 0 & 1 & 0 & 0 & 200 \\
2 & 3 & 1 & 0 & 0 & 1 & 0 & 320 \\
-3 & -2 & -1 & 0 & 0 & 0 & 1 & 0 \\
\end{array}
\right]
$$

SOLUTION

Method 1
Calculating by Hand

Using the row operations indicated in color to get zeros in the column with the pivot, we arrive at the following tableau.

$$
\begin{array}{ccccccc}
x_1 & x_2 & x_3 & s_1 & s_2 & s_3 & z \\
\end{array}
$$
$$
\begin{array}{r}
\\
-R_1 + 2R_2 \rightarrow R_2 \\
-R_1 + R_3 \rightarrow R_3 \\
3R_1 + 2R_4 \rightarrow R_4
\end{array}
\left[
\begin{array}{ccccccc|c}
2 & 1 & 1 & 1 & 0 & 0 & 0 & 150 \\
0 & 3 & 15 & -1 & 2 & 0 & 0 & 250 \\
0 & 2 & 0 & -1 & 0 & 1 & 0 & 170 \\
0 & -1 & 1 & 3 & 0 & 0 & 2 & 450 \\
\end{array}
\right]
$$

In this simplex tableau, the variables x_1, s_2, and s_3 are basic variables. The solution is $x_1 = 75$, $x_2 = 0$, $x_3 = 0$, $s_1 = 0$, $s_2 = 125$, and $s_3 = 170$. Substituting these results into the objective function gives

$$0(75) - 1(0) + 1(0) + 3(0) + 0(125) + 0(170) + 2z = 450,$$

or $z = 225$. (This shows that the value of z can always be found using the number in the bottom row of the z column and the number in the lower right-hand corner.)

Finally, to be able to read the solution directly from the tableau, we multiply rows 1, 2, and 4 by $1/2$, getting the following tableau.

$$
\begin{array}{ccccccc}
x_1 & x_2 & x_3 & s_1 & s_2 & s_3 & z \\
\end{array}
$$
$$
\begin{array}{r}
\frac{1}{2}R_1 \rightarrow R_1 \\
\frac{1}{2}R_2 \rightarrow R_2 \\
\\
\frac{1}{2}R_4 \rightarrow R_4
\end{array}
\left[
\begin{array}{ccccccc|c}
1 & \frac{1}{2} & \frac{1}{2} & \frac{1}{2} & 0 & 0 & 0 & 75 \\
0 & \frac{3}{2} & \frac{15}{2} & -\frac{1}{2} & 1 & 0 & 0 & 125 \\
0 & 2 & 0 & -1 & 0 & 1 & 0 & 170 \\
0 & -\frac{1}{2} & \frac{1}{2} & \frac{3}{2} & 0 & 0 & 1 & 225 \\
\end{array}
\right]
$$

Method 2
Graphing Calculator

The row operations of the simplex method can also be done on a graphing calculator. Figure 1 shows the result when the tableau in this example is entered into a TI-84 Plus. The right side of the tableau is not visible but can be seen by pressing the right arrow key.

Recall that we must change the pivot to 1 before performing row operations with a graphing calculator. Figure 2 shows the result of multiplying row 1 of matrix A by $1/2$. In Figure 3 we show the same result with the decimal numbers changed to fractions.

We can now modify column 1 to agree with the tableau under Method 1. The result is shown in Figure 4.

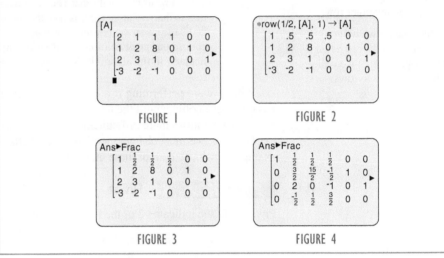

FIGURE 1   FIGURE 2

FIGURE 3   FIGURE 4

YOUR TURN 2 Pivot about the indicated 6 of the following initial simplex tableau, and then read a solution from the tableau.

$$\begin{array}{ccccccc|c} x_1 & x_2 & x_3 & s_1 & s_2 & s_3 & z & \\ 3 & \boxed{6} & 2 & 1 & 0 & 0 & 0 & 60 \\ 8 & 5 & 4 & 0 & 1 & 0 & 0 & 80 \\ 3 & 6 & 7 & 0 & 0 & 1 & 0 & 120 \\ -30 & -50 & -15 & 0 & 0 & 0 & 1 & 0 \end{array}$$

TRY YOUR TURN 2

In the simplex method, the pivoting process (without the final step of getting a 1 in each basic variable column when using Method 1) is repeated until an optimum solution is found, if one exists. In the next section we will see how to decide where to pivot to improve the value of the objective function and how to tell when an optimum solution either has been reached or does not exist.

EXERCISES

Convert each inequality into an equation by adding a slack variable.

1. $x_1 + 2x_2 \le 6$

2. $6x_1 + 2x_2 \le 50$

3. $2.3x_1 + 5.7x_2 + 1.8x_3 \le 17$

4. $8x_1 + 6x_2 + 5x_3 \le 250$

For Exercises 5–8, (a) determine the number of slack variables needed, (b) name them, and (c) use slack variables to convert each constraint into a linear equation.

5. Maximize $z = 5x_1 + 7x_2$

subject to: $2x_1 + 3x_2 \le 15$

$4x_1 + 5x_2 \le 35$

$x_1 + 6x_2 \le 20$

with $x_1 \ge 0, \quad x_2 \ge 0.$

6. Maximize $z = 1.2x_1 + 3.5x_2$

subject to: $2.4x_1 + 1.5x_2 \le 10$

$1.7x_1 + 1.9x_2 \le 15$

with $x_1 \ge 0, \quad x_2 \ge 0.$

7. Maximize $z = 8x_1 + 3x_2 + x_3$

subject to: $7x_1 + 6x_2 + 8x_3 \le 118$

$4x_1 + 5x_2 + 10x_3 \le 220$

with $x_1 \ge 0, \quad x_2 \ge 0, \quad x_3 \ge 0.$

8. Maximize $z = 12x_1 + 15x_2 + 10x_3$

subject to: $2x_1 + 2x_2 + x_3 \le 8$

$x_1 + 4x_2 + 3x_3 \le 12$

with $x_1 \ge 0, \quad x_2 \ge 0, \quad x_3 \ge 0.$

Introduce slack variables as necessary, then write the initial simplex tableau for each linear programming problem.

9. Find $x_1 \geq 0$ and $x_2 \geq 0$ such that

$$4x_1 + 2x_2 \leq 5$$
$$x_1 + 2x_2 \leq 4$$

and $z = 7x_1 + x_2$ is maximized.

10. Find $x_1 \geq 0$ and $x_2 \geq 0$ such that

$$2x_1 + 3x_2 \leq 100$$
$$5x_1 + 4x_2 \leq 200$$

and $z = x_1 + 3x_2$ is maximized.

11. Find $x_1 \geq 0$ and $x_2 \geq 0$ such that

$$x_1 + x_2 \leq 10$$
$$5x_1 + 2x_2 \leq 20$$
$$x_1 + 2x_2 \leq 36$$

and $z = x_1 + 3x_2$ is maximized.

12. Find $x_1 \geq 0$ and $x_2 \geq 0$ such that

$$x_1 + x_2 \leq 25$$
$$4x_1 + 3x_2 \leq 48$$

and $z = 5x_1 + 3x_2$ is maximized.

13. Find $x_1 \geq 0$ and $x_2 \geq 0$ such that

$$3x_1 + x_2 \leq 12$$
$$x_1 + x_2 \leq 15$$

and $z = 2x_1 + x_2$ is maximized.

14. Find $x_1 \geq 0$ and $x_2 \geq 0$ such that

$$10x_1 + 4x_2 \leq 100$$
$$20x_1 + 10x_2 \leq 150$$

and $z = 4x_1 + 5x_2$ is maximized.

Write the solutions that can be read from each simplex tableau.

15.

x_1	x_2	x_3	s_1	s_2	z	
1	0	4	5	1	0	8
3	1	1	2	0	0	4
−2	0	2	3	0	1	28

16.

x_1	x_2	x_3	s_1	s_2	z	
1	5	0	1	2	0	6
0	2	1	2	3	0	15
0	4	0	1	−2	1	64

17.

x_1	x_2	x_3	s_1	s_2	s_3	z	
6	2	2	3	0	0	0	16
2	2	0	1	0	5	0	35
2	1	0	3	1	0	0	6
−3	−2	0	2	0	0	3	36

18.

x_1	x_2	x_3	s_1	s_2	s_3	z	
0	2	0	5	2	2	0	15
0	3	1	0	1	2	0	2
7	4	0	3	5	0	0	35
0	−4	0	0	4	3	2	40

Pivot once as indicated in each simplex tableau. Read the solution from the result.

19.

x_1	x_2	x_3	s_1	s_2	z	
1	2	4	1	0	0	56
2	**2**	1	0	1	0	40
−1	−3	−2	0	0	1	0

20.

x_1	x_2	x_3	s_1	s_2	z	
2	3	4	1	0	0	18
6	**3**	2	0	1	0	15
−1	−6	−2	0	0	1	0

21.

x_1	x_2	x_3	s_1	s_2	s_3	z	
2	2	**1**	1	0	0	0	12
1	2	3	0	1	0	0	45
3	1	1	0	0	1	0	20
−2	−1	−3	0	0	0	1	0

22.

x_1	x_2	x_3	s_1	s_2	s_3	z	
4	2	3	1	0	0	0	22
2	2	**5**	0	1	0	0	28
1	3	2	0	0	1	0	45
−3	−2	−4	0	0	0	1	0

23.

x_1	x_2	x_3	s_1	s_2	s_3	z	
2	**2**	3	1	0	0	0	500
4	1	1	0	1	0	0	300
7	2	4	0	0	1	0	700
−3	−4	−2	0	0	0	1	0

24.

x_1	x_2	x_3	x_4	s_1	s_2	s_3	z	
1	2	3	1	1	0	0	0	115
2	1	8	5	0	1	0	0	200
1	0	1	0	0	0	1	0	50
−2	−1	−1	−1	0	0	0	1	0

25. Explain the purpose of a slack variable.

26. How can you tell by looking at a linear programming problem how many slack variables will be needed?

APPLICATIONS

Set up Exercises 27–31 for solution by the simplex method. First express the linear constraints and objective function, then add slack variables to convert each constraint into a linear equation, and then set up the initial simplex tableau. The solutions of some of these problems will be completed in the exercises for the next section.

Business and Economics

27. Royalties The authors of a best-selling textbook in finite mathematics are told that, for the next edition of their book, each simple figure would cost the project $20, each figure with additions would cost $35, and each computer-drawn sketch would cost $60. They are limited to 400 figures, for which they are allowed to spend up to $2200. The number of computer-drawn sketches must be no more than the number of the other two types combined, and there must be at least twice as many simple figures as there are figures with additions. If each simple figure increases the royalties by $95, each figure with additions increases royalties by $200, and each computer-drawn figure increases royalties by $325, how many of each type of figure should be included to maximize royalties, assuming that all art costs are borne by the publisher?

28. Manufacturing Bicycles A manufacturer of bicycles builds racing, touring, and mountain models. The bicycles are made of both aluminum and steel. The company has available 91,800 units of steel and 42,000 units of aluminum. The racing, touring, and mountain models need 17, 27, and 34 units of steel, and 12, 21, and 15 units of aluminum, respectively. How many of each type of bicycle should be made in order to maximize profit if the company makes $8 per racing bike, $12 per touring bike, and $22 per mountain bike? What is the maximum possible profit?

29. Production—Picnic Tables The manager of a large park has received many complaints about the insufficient number of picnic tables available. At the end of the park season, she has surplus cash and labor resources available and decides to make as many tables as possible. She considers three possible models: redwood, stained Douglas fir, and stained white spruce (all of which last equally well). She has carpenters available for assembly work for a maximum of 90 eight-hour days, while laborers for staining work are available for no more than 60 eight-hour days. Each redwood table requires 8 hours to assemble but no staining, and it costs $159 (including all labor and materials). Each Douglas fir table requires 7 hours to assemble and 2 hours to stain, and it costs $138.85. Each white spruce table requires 8 hours to assemble and 2 hours to stain, and it costs $129.35. If no more than $15,000 is available for this project, what is the maximum number of tables which can be made, and how many of each type should be made? *Source: Karl K. Norton.*

30. Production—Knives The Cut-Right Company sells sets of kitchen knives. The Basic Set consists of 2 utility knives and 1

chef's knife. The Regular Set consists of 2 utility knives, 1 chef's knife, and 1 slicer. The Deluxe Set consists of 3 utility knives, 1 chef's knife, and 1 slicer. Their profit is $30 on a Basic Set, $40 on a Regular Set, and $60 on a Deluxe Set. The factory has on hand 800 utility knives, 400 chef's knives, and 200 slicers. Assuming that all sets will be sold, how many of each type should be produced in order to maximize profit? What is the maximum profit?

31. Advertising The Fancy Fashions, an independent, local boutique, has $8000 available each month for advertising. Newspaper ads cost $400 each, and no more than 30 can run per month. Internet banner ads cost $20 each, and no more than 60 can run per month. TV ads cost $2000 each, with a maximum of 10 available each month. Approximately 4000 women will see each newspaper ad, 3000 will see each Internet banner, and 10,000 will see each TV ad. How much of each type of advertising should be used if the store wants to maximize its ad exposure?

YOUR TURN ANSWERS

1.

x_1	x_2	x_3	s_1	s_2	s_3	z	
1	1	1	1	0	0	0	100
15	3	9	0	1	0	0	1000
1	2	3	0	0	1	0	180
−120	−40	−60	0	0	0	1	0

2.

x_1	x_2	x_3	s_1	s_2	s_3	z	
1/2	1	1/3	1/6	0	0	0	10
11/2	0	7/3	−5/6	1	0	0	30
0	0	5	−1	0	1	0	60
−5	0	5/3	25/3	0	0	1	500

$x_1 = 0, x_2 = 10, x_3 = 0, s_1 = 0, s_2 = 30, s_3 = 60, z = 500$

2 Maximization Problems

APPLY IT How many racing, touring, and mountain bicycles should a bicycle manufacturer make to maximize profit?
We will answer this question in Exercise 27 of this section using an algorithm called the simplex method.

In the previous section we showed how to prepare a linear programming problem for solution. First, we converted the constraints to linear equations with slack variables; then we used the coefficients of the variables from the linear equation to write an augmented matrix. Finally, we used the pivot to go from one corner point to another corner point in the region of feasible solutions.

Now we are ready to put all this together and produce an optimum value for the objective function. To see how this is done, let us complete Example 2 from Section 1. In this example, we were trying to determine, under certain constraints, the number of acres of potatoes (x_1), corn (x_2), and cabbage (x_3) the farmer should plant in order to optimize his profit (z). In the previous section, we set up the following simplex tableau.

$$
\begin{array}{cccccc}
x_1 & x_2 & x_3 & s_1 & s_2 & z \\
\end{array}
$$

$$
\left[
\begin{array}{cccccc|c}
1 & 1 & 1 & 1 & 0 & 0 & 100 \\
10 & 4 & 7 & 0 & 1 & 0 & 500 \\
\hline
-120 & -40 & -60 & 0 & 0 & 1 & 0 \\
\end{array}
\right]
$$

This tableau leads to the solution $x_1 = 0$, $x_2 = 0$, $x_3 = 0$, $s_1 = 100$, and $s_2 = 500$, with s_1 and s_2 as the basic variables. These values produce a value of 0 for z. In this solution, the farmer is planting 0 acres and earning \$0 profit. We can easily see that there are other combinations of potatoes, corn, and cabbage that produce a nonzero profit, and thus we know that the farmer has better alternatives than planting nothing.

To decide which crops he should plant, we look at the original objective function representing profit,

$$z = 120x_1 + 40x_2 + 60x_3.$$

The coefficient of x_1 is the largest, which indicates that he will make the most profit per acre planting potatoes. It makes sense, then, to first try increasing x_1 to improve the profit.

To determine how much we can increase x_1, we look at the constraint equations:

$$
\begin{aligned}
x_1 + x_2 + x_3 + s_1 &= 100 \\
10x_1 + 4x_2 + 7x_3 + s_2 &= 500.
\end{aligned}
$$

Because there are two equations, only two of the five variables can be basic (and nonzero). If x_1 is nonzero in the solution, then x_1 will be a basic variable. Therefore, x_2 and x_3 will stay at 0, and the equations simplify to

$$
\begin{aligned}
x_1 + s_1 &= 100 \\
10x_1 + s_2 &= 500.
\end{aligned}
$$

Since s_1 and s_2 are both nonnegative, the first equation implies that x_1 cannot exceed 100, and the second implies that $10x_1$ cannot exceed 500, so x_1 cannot exceed 500/10, or 50. To satisfy both of these conditions, x_1 cannot exceed 50, the smaller of 50 and 100. If we let x_1 take the value of 50, then $x_1 = 50$, $x_2 = 0$, $x_3 = 0$, and $s_2 = 0$. Since $x_1 + s_1 = 100$, then $s_1 = 100 - x_1 = 100 - 50 = 50$. Therefore, s_1 is still a basic variable, while s_2 is no longer a basic variable, having been replaced in the set of basic variables by x_1. This solution gives a profit of

$$
\begin{aligned}
z &= 120x_1 + 40x_2 + 60x_3 + 0s_1 + 0s_2 \\
&= 120(50) + 40(0) + 60(0) + 0(50) + 0(0) = 6000,
\end{aligned}
$$

or \$6000, when 50 acres of potatoes are planted.

The same result could have been found from the initial simplex tableau given below. Recall that the indicators are the numbers in the bottom row in the columns labeled with real or slack variables. To use the tableau, we select the variable with the most negative indicator. (If no indicator is negative, then the value of the objective function cannot be improved.) In this example, the variable with the most negative indicator is x_1.

Basic variables

$$
\begin{array}{cccccc}
x_1 & x_2 & x_3 & s_1 & s_2 & z \\
\end{array}
$$

$$
\left[
\begin{array}{cccccc|c}
1 & 1 & 1 & 1 & 0 & 0 & 100 \\
10 & 4 & 7 & 0 & 1 & 0 & 500 \\
\hline
-120 & -40 & -60 & 0 & 0 & 1 & 0 \\
\end{array}
\right]
$$

Most negative indicator

The most negative indicator identifies the variable whose value is to be made nonzero, if possible, because it indicates the variable with the largest coefficient in the objective function. To find the variable that is now basic and will become nonbasic, calculate the quotients that were found above. Do this by dividing each number from the right side of the tableau by the corresponding number from the column with the most negative indicator.

Basic variables

		x_1	x_2	x_3	s_1	s_2	z	
Quotients					↓	↓		
$100/1 = 100$		1	1	1	1	0	0	100
Smaller → $500/10 = 50$		**10**	4	7	0	1	0	500
		−120	−40	−60	0	0	1	0

Notice that we do not form a quotient for the bottom row. Of the two quotients found, the smallest is 50 (from the second row). This indicates that x_1 cannot exceed $500/10 = 50$, so 10 is the pivot. Using 10 as the pivot, perform the appropriate row operations to get zeros in the rest of the column. We will use Method 1 from Section 1 (calculating by hand) to perform the pivoting, but Method 2 (graphing calculator) could be used just as well. The new tableau is as follows.

Basic variables

	x_1	x_2	x_3	s_1	s_2	z	
		↓		↓			
$-R_2 + 10R_1 \rightarrow R_1$	0	6	3	10	−1	0	500
	10	4	7	0	1	0	500
$12R_2 + R_3 \rightarrow R_3$	0	8	24	0	12	1	6000

The solution read from this tableau is

$$x_1 = 50, \qquad x_2 = 0, \qquad x_3 = 0, \qquad s_1 = 50, \qquad s_2 = 0,$$

with $z = 6000$, the same as the result found above.

None of the indicators in the final simplex tableau are negative, which means that the value of z cannot be improved beyond $6000. To see why, recall that the last row gives the coefficients of the objective function so that

$$0x_1 + 8x_2 + 24x_3 + 0s_1 + 12s_2 + z = 6000,$$

or
$$z = 6000 - 0x_1 - 8x_2 - 24x_3 - 0s_1 - 12s_2.$$

Since x_2, x_3, and s_2 are zero, $z = 6000$, but if any of these three variables were to increase, z would decrease.

This result suggests that the optimal solution has been found as soon as no indicators are negative. As long as an indicator is negative, the value of the objective function may be improved. If any indicators are negative, we just find a new pivot and use row operations, repeating the process until no negative indicators remain.

Once there are no longer any negative numbers in the final row, create a 1 in the columns corresponding to the basic variables and z. In the previous example, this is accomplished by dividing rows 1 and 2 by 10.

	x_1	x_2	x_3	s_1	s_2	z	
$R_1/10 \rightarrow R_1$	0	$\frac{6}{10}$	$\frac{3}{10}$	1	$-\frac{1}{10}$	0	50
$R_2/10 \rightarrow R_2$	1	$\frac{4}{10}$	$\frac{7}{10}$	0	$\frac{1}{10}$	0	50
	0	8	24	0	12	1	6000

It is now easy to read the solution from this tableau:

$$x_1 = 50, \qquad x_2 = 0, \qquad x_3 = 0, \qquad s_1 = 50, \qquad s_2 = 0,$$

with $z = 6000$.

We can finally state the solution to the problem about the farmer. The farmer will make a maximum profit of \$6000 by planting 50 acres of potatoes, no acres of corn, and no acres of cabbage. The value $s_1 = 50$ indicates that of the 100 acres of land available, 50 acres should be left unplanted. It may seem strange that leaving assets unused can produce a maximum profit, but such results actually occur often.

Note that since each variable can be increased by a different amount, the most negative indicator is not always the best choice. On average, though, it has been found that the most negative indicator is the best choice.

In summary, the following steps are involved in solving a standard maximum linear programming problem by the simplex method.

Simplex Method For Standard Maximization Problems

1. Determine the objective function.

2. Write all the necessary constraints.

3. Convert each constraint into an equation by adding a slack variable in each.

4. Set up the initial simplex tableau.

5. Locate the most negative indicator. If there are two such indicators, choose the one farther to the left.

6. Form the necessary quotients to find the pivot. Disregard any quotients with 0 or a negative number in the denominator. The smallest nonnegative quotient gives the location of the pivot. If all quotients must be disregarded, no maximum solution exists. If two quotients are both equal and smallest, choose the pivot in the row nearest the top of the matrix.

7. Use row operations to change all other numbers in the pivot column to zero by adding a suitable multiple of the pivot row to a positive multiple of each row.

8. If the indicators are all positive or 0, this is the final tableau. If not, go back to Step 5 and repeat the process until a tableau with no negative indicators is obtained.

9. Read the solution from the final tableau.

In Steps 5 and 6, the choice of the column farthest to the left or the row closest to the top is arbitrary. You may choose another row or column in case of a tie, and you will get the same final answer, but your intermediate results will be different.

> **CAUTION** In performing the simplex method, a negative number in the right-hand column signals that a mistake has been made. One possible error is using a negative value for c_2 in the operation $c_1 R_i + c_2 R_j \rightarrow R_j$.

EXAMPLE 1 Using the Simplex Method

To compare the simplex method with the graphical method, we use the simplex method to solve the problem is shown in Figure 5. The objective function to be maximized

$$z = 25x_1 + 30x_2. \quad \text{Revenue}$$

(Since we are using the simplex method, we use x_1 and x_2 instead of x and y as variables.) The constraints are as follows:

$$x_1 + x_2 \leq 65 \quad \text{Number}$$
$$4x_1 + 5x_2 \leq 300 \quad \text{Cost}$$

with

$$x_1 \geq 0, \quad x_2 \geq 0.$$

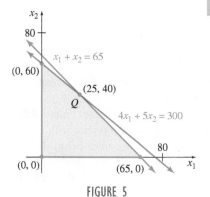

FIGURE 5

453

Add a slack variable to each constraint:

$$\begin{aligned} x_1 + x_2 + s_1 &= 65 \\ 4x_1 + 5x_2 + s_2 &= 300 \end{aligned}$$

with

$$x_1 \geq 0, \ x_2 \geq 0, \ s_1 \geq 0, \ s_2 \geq 0.$$

Write the initial tableau.

$$\begin{array}{ccccc|c} x_1 & x_2 & s_1 & s_2 & z & \\ \left[\begin{array}{ccccc|c} 1 & 1 & 1 & 0 & 0 & 65 \\ 4 & 5 & 0 & 1 & 0 & 300 \\ \hline -25 & -30 & 0 & 0 & 1 & 0 \end{array}\right] \end{array}$$

This tableau leads to the solution $x_1 = 0$, $x_2 = 0$, $s_1 = 65$, and $s_2 = 300$, with $z = 0$, which corresponds to the origin in Figure 5. The most negative indicator is -30, which is in column 2 of row 3. The quotients of the numbers in the right-hand column and in column 2 are

$$\frac{65}{1} = 65 \quad \text{and} \quad \frac{300}{5} = 60.$$

The smaller quotient is 60, giving 5 as the pivot. Use row operations to get the new tableau. For clarity, we will continue to label the columns with x_1, x_2, and so on, although this is not necessary in practice.

$$\begin{array}{l} \\ -R_2 + 5R_1 \rightarrow R_1 \\ \\ 6R_2 + R_3 \rightarrow R_3 \end{array} \quad \begin{array}{ccccc|c} x_1 & x_2 & s_1 & s_2 & z & \\ \left[\begin{array}{ccccc|c} 1 & 0 & 5 & -1 & 0 & 25 \\ 4 & 5 & 0 & 1 & 0 & 300 \\ \hline -1 & 0 & 0 & 6 & 1 & 1800 \end{array}\right] \end{array}$$

The solution from this tableau is $x_1 = 0$ and $x_2 = 60$, with $z = 1800$. (From now on, we will list only the original variables when giving the solution.) This corresponds to the corner point $(0, 60)$ in Figure 5. Verify that if we instead pivoted on the column with the indicator of -25, we would arrive at the corner point $(65, 0)$, where the objective function has the value 1625, which is smaller than its value at $(0, 60)$.

Because of the indicator -1, the value of z might be improved. We compare quotients and choose the 1 in row 1, column 1, as pivot to get the final tableau.

$$\begin{array}{l} \\ -4R_1 + R_2 \rightarrow R_2 \\ R_1 + R_3 \rightarrow R_3 \end{array} \quad \begin{array}{ccccc|c} x_1 & x_2 & s_1 & s_2 & z & \\ \left[\begin{array}{ccccc|c} 1 & 0 & 5 & -1 & 0 & 25 \\ 0 & 5 & -20 & 5 & 0 & 200 \\ \hline 0 & 0 & 5 & 5 & 1 & 1825 \end{array}\right] \end{array}$$

There are no more negative indicators, so the optimum solution has been achieved. Create a 1 in column 2 by multiplying row 2 by $1/5$.

$$(1/5)R_2 \rightarrow R_2 \quad \begin{array}{ccccc|c} x_1 & x_2 & s_1 & s_2 & z & \\ \left[\begin{array}{ccccc|c} 1 & 0 & 5 & -1 & 0 & 25 \\ 0 & 1 & -4 & 1 & 0 & 40 \\ \hline 0 & 0 & 5 & 5 & 1 & 1825 \end{array}\right] \end{array}$$

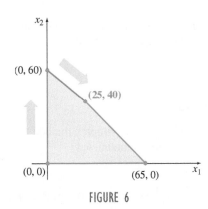

FIGURE 6

Here the solution is $x_1 = 25$ and $x_2 = 40$, with $z = 1825$. This solution, which corresponds to the corner point $(25, 40)$ in Figure 5, is the same as the solution found earlier.

Each simplex tableau above gave a solution corresponding to one of the corner points of the feasible region. As shown in Figure 6, the first solution corresponded to the origin, with $z = 0$. By choosing the appropriate pivot, we moved systematically to a new corner point, $(0, 60)$, which improved the value of z to 1800. The next tableau took us to $(25, 40)$, producing the optimum value of $z = 1825$. There was no reason to test the last corner point, $(65, 0)$, since the optimum value z was found before that point was reached. **TRY YOUR TURN 1**

It is good practice to verify your intermediate answers after each new tableau is calculated. You can check your answers by substituting these values for the original variables and the slack variables in the constraint equations and in the objective function.

> **CAUTION** Never choose a zero or a negative number as the pivot. The reason for this is explained in the next example.

EXAMPLE 2 Finding the Pivot

Find the pivot for the following initial simplex tableau.

$$\begin{array}{cccccc} x_1 & x_2 & s_1 & s_2 & s_3 & z \\ \left[\begin{array}{cccccc|c} 1 & -2 & 1 & 0 & 0 & 0 & 100 \\ 3 & 4 & 0 & 1 & 0 & 0 & 200 \\ 5 & 0 & 0 & 0 & 1 & 0 & 150 \\ \hline -10 & -25 & 0 & 0 & 0 & 1 & 0 \end{array}\right] \end{array}$$

SOLUTION The most negative indicator is -25. To find the pivot, we find the quotients formed by the entries in the rightmost column and in the x_2 column: $100/(-2)$, $200/4$, and $150/0$. The quotients predict the value of a variable in the solution. Thus, since we want all variables to be nonnegative, we must reject a negative quotient. Furthermore, we cannot choose 0 as the pivot, because no multiple of the row with 0, when added to the other rows, will cause the other entries in the x_2 column to become 0.

The only usable quotient is $200/4 = 50$, making 4 the pivot. If all the quotients either are negative or have zero denominators, no unique optimum solution will be found. Such a situation indicates an unbounded feasible region because the variable corresponding to that column can be made as large as you like. The quotients, then, determine whether an optimum solution exists.
TRY YOUR TURN 2

YOUR TURN 2 Pivot on the 4 in Example 2 and write the solution.

> **CAUTION** If there is a 0 in the right-hand column, do not disregard that row, unless the corresponding number in the pivot column is negative or zero. In fact, such a row gives a quotient of 0, so it will automatically have the smallest ratio. It will not cause an increase in z, but it may lead to another tableau in which z can be further increased.

TECHNOLOGY NOTE We saw earlier that graphing calculators can be used to perform row operations. A program to solve a linear programming problem with a graphing calculator is given in the *Graphing Calculator and Excel Spreadsheet Manual* available with this text.

TECHNOLOGY NOTE Spreadsheets often have a program for solving linear programming problems built in. Figure 7 on the next page shows the Solver feature of Microsoft Excel (under the Tools menu) for Example 1. (On some versions of Excel, the Solver must be installed from an outside source.) For details, see the *Graphing Calculator and Excel Spreadsheet Manual* available with this text.

In addition, Solver provides a **sensitivity analysis**, which allows us to see how much the constraints could be varied without changing the solution. Under the Solver options, make sure that "Assume Linear Model" and "Assume Non-Negative" are selected. Figure 8 on the next page shows a sensitivity analysis for Example 1. Notice that the value of the first coefficient in the objective function is 25, with an allowable increase of 5 and an allowable decrease of 1. This means that, while keeping the second coefficient at 30, the first coefficient of 25 could be increased by 5 (to 30) or decreased by 1 (to 24), and (25, 40) would still be a solution to the maximization problem. Similarly, for the second coefficient of 30, increasing it by 1.25 (to 31.25) or decreasing it by 5 (to 25) would still leave (25, 40) as a solution to the maximization problem. This would be useful to the owner who decides on the solution of (25, 40) (25 canoes and 40 kayaks) and wonders how much the objective function would have to change before the solution would no longer be optimal. The original revenue for a canoe was $25, which is the source of the first coefficient in the objective function. Assuming that everything else stays the same, the revenue could change to anything from $24 to $30, and the original decision would still be optimal.

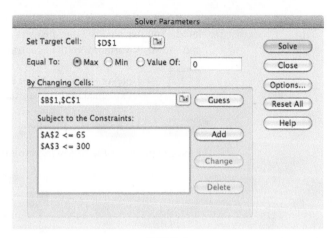

FIGURE 7

Notice, however, that any change in one of the revenues will change the total revenue in the optimal solution. For example, if the first coefficient of 25 is increased by 5 to 30, then the optimal objective value will increase by $5 \times 25 = 125$. One can perform similar changes to other parameters of the problem, but that is beyond the scope of this text.

Adjustable Cells

Cell	Name	Final Value	Reduced Cost	Objective Coefficient	Allowable Increase	Allowable Decrease
B1		25	0	25	5	1
C1		40	0	30	1.25	5

Constraints

Cell	Name	Final Value	Shadow Price	Constraint R.H. Side	Allowable Increase	Allowable Decrease
A2		65	5	65	10	5
A3		300	5	300	25	40

FIGURE 8

In many real-life problems, the number of variables and constraints may be in the hundreds, if not the thousands, in which case a computer is used to implement the simplex algorithm. Computer programs for the simplex algorithm differ in some ways from the algorithm we have shown. For example, it is not necessary for a computer to divide common factors out of inequalities to simplify the arithmetic. In fact, computer versions of the algorithm do not necessarily keep all the numbers as integers. As we saw in the previous section, dividing a row by a number may introduce decimals, which makes the arithmetic more difficult to do by hand, but creates no problem for a computer other than round-off error. Several linear programming models in actual use are presented on the website for this textbook.

If you use a graphing calculator to perform the simplex algorithm, we suggest that you review the pivoting procedure described in Method 2 of the previous section. It differs slightly from Method 1, because it converts each pivot element into a 1, but it works nicely with a calculator to keep track of the arithmetic details.

On the other hand, if you carry out the steps of the simplex method by hand, we suggest that you first eliminate fractions and decimals when setting up the initial tableau. For example, we would rewrite the constraint

$$\frac{2}{3}x_1 + \frac{5}{2}x_2 \leq 7$$

as
$$4x_1 + 15x_2 \leq 42,$$

by multiplying both sides of the equation by 6. Similarly, we would write

$$5.2x_1 + 4.4x_2 \le 8.5$$

as

$$52x_1 + 44x_2 \le 85$$

by multiplying both sides of the equation by 10. We must be cautious, however, in remembering that the value of the slack and surplus variables in the optimal solution must be adjusted by this factor to represent the original constraint.

NOTE Sometimes the simplex method cycles and returns to a previously visited solution, rather than making progress. Methods are available for handling cycling. In this text, we will avoid examples with this behavior. For more details, see Alan Sultan's *Linear Programming: An Introduction with Applications*, Academic Press, 1993. In real applications, cycling is rare and tends not to come up because of computer rounding.

2 EXERCISES

In Exercises 1–6, the initial tableau of a linear programming problem is given. Use the simplex method to solve each problem.

1.

x_1	x_2	x_3	s_1	s_2	z	
1	4	4	1	0	0	16
2	1	5	0	1	0	20
−3	−1	−2	0	0	1	0

2.

x_1	x_2	x_3	s_1	s_2	z	
3	3	2	1	0	0	18
2	2	3	0	1	0	16
−4	−6	−2	0	0	1	0

3.

x_1	x_2	s_1	s_2	s_3	z	
1	3	1	0	0	0	12
2	1	0	1	0	0	10
1	1	0	0	1	0	4
−2	−1	0	0	0	1	0

4.

x_1	x_2	x_3	s_1	s_2	s_3	z	
2	1	2	1	0	0	0	25
4	3	2	0	1	0	0	40
3	1	6	0	0	1	0	60
−4	−2	−3	0	0	0	1	0

5.

x_1	x_2	x_3	s_1	s_2	s_3	z	
2	2	8	1	0	0	0	40
4	−5	6	0	1	0	0	60
2	−2	6	0	0	1	0	24
−14	−10	−12	0	0	0	1	0

6.

x_1	x_2	x_3	s_1	s_2	z	
3	2	4	1	0	0	18
2	1	5	0	1	0	8
−1	−4	−2	0	0	1	0

Use the simplex method to solve each linear programming problem.

7. Maximize $z = 3x_1 + 5x_2$

subject to: $4x_1 + x_2 \le 25$

$2x_1 + 3x_2 \le 15$

with $x_1 \ge 0, \quad x_2 \ge 0.$

8. Maximize $z = 5x_1 + 2x_2$

subject to: $2x_1 + 4x_2 \le 15$

$3x_1 + x_2 \le 10$

with $x_1 \ge 0, \quad x_2 \ge 0.$

9. Maximize $z = 10x_1 + 12x_2$

subject to: $4x_1 + 2x_2 \le 20$

$5x_1 + x_2 \le 50$

$2x_1 + 2x_2 \le 24$

with $x_1 \ge 0, \quad x_2 \ge 0.$

10. Maximize $z = 1.5x_1 + 4.2x_2$

subject to: $2.8x_1 + 3.4x_2 \le 21$

$1.4x_1 + 2.2x_2 \le 11$

with $x_1 \ge 0, \quad x_2 \ge 0.$

11. Maximize $z = 8x_1 + 3x_2 + x_3$

subject to: $x_1 + 6x_2 + 8x_3 \le 118$

$x_1 + 5x_2 + 10x_3 \le 220$

with $x_1 \ge 0, \quad x_2 \ge 0, \quad x_3 \ge 0.$

12. Maximize $z = 8x_1 + 10x_2 + 7x_3$

subject to: $x_1 + 3x_2 + 2x_3 \le 10$

$x_1 + 5x_2 + x_3 \le 8$

with $x_1 \ge 0, \quad x_2 \ge 0, \quad x_3 \ge 0.$

13. Maximize $z = 10x_1 + 15x_2 + 10x_3 + 5x_4$

subject to: $x_1 + x_2 + x_3 + x_4 \le 300$

$x_1 + 2x_2 + 3x_3 + x_4 \le 360$

with $x_1 \ge 0, \quad x_2 \ge 0, \quad x_3 \ge 0, \quad x_4 \ge 0.$

14. Maximize $z = x_1 + x_2 + 4x_3 + 5x_4$

subject to: $x_1 + 2x_2 + 3x_3 + x_4 \le 115$

$2x_1 + x_2 + 8x_3 + 5x_4 \le 200$

$x_1 + x_3 \le 50$

with $x_1 \ge 0, \quad x_2 \ge 0, \quad x_3 \ge 0, \quad x_4 \ge 0.$

15. Maximize $\quad z = 4x_1 + 6x_2$

subject to: $\quad x_1 - 5x_2 \leq 25$

$\quad\quad\quad\quad 4x_1 - 3x_2 \leq 12$

with $\quad\quad x_1 \geq 0, \quad x_2 \geq 0.$

16. Maximize $\quad z = 2x_1 + 5x_2 + x_3$

subject to: $\quad x_1 - 5x_2 + 2x_3 \leq 30$

$\quad\quad\quad\quad 4x_1 - 3x_2 + 6x_3 \leq 72$

with $\quad\quad x_1 \geq 0, \quad x_2 \geq 0, \quad x_3 \geq 0.$

Use a graphing calculator, Excel, or other technology to solve the following linear programming problems.

17. Maximize $\quad z = 37x_1 + 34x_2 + 36x_3 + 30x_4 + 35x_5$

subject to: $\quad 16x_1 + 19x_2 + 23x_3 + 15x_4 + 21x_5 \leq 42{,}000$

$\quad\quad\quad\quad 15x_1 + 10x_2 + 19x_3 + 23x_4 + 10x_5 \leq 25{,}000$

$\quad\quad\quad\quad 9x_1 + 16x_2 + 14x_3 + 12x_4 + 11x_5 \leq 23{,}000$

$\quad\quad\quad\quad 18x_1 + 20x_2 + 15x_3 + 17x_4 + 19x_5 \leq 36{,}000$

with $\quad\quad x_1 \geq 0, \quad x_2 \geq 0, \quad x_3 \geq 0, \quad x_4 \geq 0, \quad x_5 \geq 0.$

18. Maximize $\quad z = 2.0x_1 + 1.7x_2 + 2.1x_3 + 2.4x_4 + 2.2x_5$

subject to: $\quad 12x_1 + 10x_2 + 11x_3 + 12x_4 + 13x_5 \leq 4250$

$\quad\quad\quad\quad 8x_1 + 8x_2 + 7x_3 + 18x_4 + 5x_5 \leq 4130$

$\quad\quad\quad\quad 9x_1 + 10x_2 + 12x_3 + 11x_4 + 8x_5 \leq 3500$

$\quad\quad\quad\quad 5x_1 + 3x_2 + 4x_3 + 5x_4 + 4x_5 \leq 1600$

with $\quad\quad x_1 \geq 0, \quad x_2 \geq 0, \quad x_3 \geq 0, \quad x_4 \geq 0, \quad x_5 \geq 0.$

19. The simplex algorithm still works if an indicator other than the most negative one is chosen. (Try it!) List the disadvantages that might occur if this is done.

20. What goes wrong if a quotient other than the smallest nonnegative quotient is chosen in the simplex algorithm? (Try it!)

21. Add lines corresponding to $z = 0$, $z = 1800$, and $z = 1825$ to Figure 6. Then explain how the increase in the objective function as we move from $(0, 0)$ to $(0, 60)$ to $(25, 40)$ relates to the discussion of the Corner Point Theorem in Section 3.2.

22. Explain why the objective function can be made larger as long as there are negative numbers in the bottom row of the simplex tableau. (*Hint:* Consider an example with negative numbers in the last row, and rewrite the last row as an equation.)

APPLICATIONS

Set up and solve Exercises 23–29 by the simplex method.

Business and Economics

23. Charitable Contributions Carrie Green is working to raise money for the homeless by sending information letters and making follow-up calls to local labor organizations and church groups. She discovers that each church group requires 2 hours of letter writing and 1 hour of follow-up, while for each labor union she needs 2 hours of letter writing and 3 hours of follow-up. Carrie can raise $100 from each church group and $200 from each union local, and she has a maximum of 16 hours of letter-writing

time and a maximum of 12 hours of follow-up time available per month. Determine the most profitable mixture of groups she should contact and the most money she can raise in a month.

24. Profit The Muro Manufacturing Company makes two kinds of plasma screen television sets. It produces the Flexscan set that sells for $350 profit and the Panoramic I that sells for $500 profit. On the assembly line, the Flexscan requires 5 hours, and the Panoramic I takes 7 hours. The cabinet shop spends 1 hour on the cabinet for the Flexscan and 2 hours on the cabinet for the Panoramic I. Both sets require 4 hours for testing and packing. On a particular production run, the Muro Company has available 3600 work-hours on the assembly line, 900 work-hours in the cabinet shop, and 2600 work-hours in the testing and packing department. (See Exercise 10 in Section 3.3.)

a. How many sets of each type should it produce to make a maximum profit? What is the maximum profit?

b. Find the values of any nonzero slack variables and describe what they tell you about any unused time.

25. Poker The Texas Poker Company assembles three different poker sets. Each Royal Flush poker set contains 1000 poker chips, 4 decks of cards, 10 dice, and 2 dealer buttons. Each Deluxe Diamond poker set contains 600 poker chips, 2 decks of cards, 5 dice, and one dealer button. The Full House poker set contains 300 poker chips, 2 decks of cards, 5 dice, and one dealer button. The Texas Poker Company has 2,800,000 poker chips, 10,000 decks of cards, 25,000 dice, and 6000 dealer buttons in stock. They earn a profit of $38 for each Royal Flush poker set, $22 for each Deluxe Diamond poker set, and $12 for each Full House poker set.

a. How many of each type of poker set should they assemble to maximize profit? What is the maximum profit?

b. Find the values of any nonzero slack variables and describe what they tell you about any unused components.

26. Income A baker has 150 units of flour, 90 of sugar, and 150 of raisins. A loaf of raisin bread requires 1 unit of flour, 1 of sugar, and 2 of raisins, while a raisin cake needs 5, 2, and 1 units, respectively.

a. If raisin bread sells for $1.75 a loaf and raisin cake for $4.00 each, how many of each should be baked so that gross income is maximized?

b. What is the maximum gross income?

c. Does it require all of the available units of flour, sugar, and raisins to produce the number of loaves of raisin bread and raisin cakes that produce the maximum profit? If not, how much of each ingredient is left over? Compare any leftover to the value of the relevant slack variable.

27. APPLY IT Manufacturing Bicycles A manufacturer of bicycles builds racing, touring, and mountain models. The bicycles are made of both aluminum and steel. The company has available 91,800 units of steel and 42,000 units of aluminum. The racing, touring, and mountain models need 17, 27, and 34 units of steel, and 12, 21, and 15 units of aluminum, respectively. (See Exercise 28 in Section 1.)

a. How many of each type of bicycle should be made in order to maximize profit if the company makes $8 per racing bike, $12 per touring bike, and $22 per mountain bike?

b. What is the maximum possible profit?

c. Does it require all of the available units of steel and aluminum to build the bicycles that produce the maximum profit? If not, how much of each material is left over? Compare any leftover to the value of the relevant slack variable.

d. There are many unstated assumptions in the problem given above. Even if the mathematical solution is to make only one or two types of the bicycles, there may be demand for the type(s) not being made, which would create problems for the company. Discuss this and other difficulties that would arise in a real situation.

28. Production The Cut-Right Company sells sets of kitchen knives. The Basic Set consists of 2 utility knives and 1 chef's knife. The Regular Set consists of 2 utility knives, 1 chef's knife, and 1 slicer. The Deluxe Set consists of 3 utility knives, 1 chef's knife, and 1 slicer. Their profit is $30 on a Basic Set, $40 on a Regular Set, and $60 on a Deluxe Set. The factory has on hand 800 utility knives, 400 chef's knives, and 200 slicers. (See Exercise 30 in Section 1.)

a. Assuming that all sets will be sold, how many of each type should be made up in order to maximize profit? What is the maximum profit?

b. A consultant for the Cut-Right Company notes that more profit is made on a Regular Set of knives than on a Basic Set, yet the result from part a recommends making up 100 Basic Sets but no Regular Sets. She is puzzled how this can be the best solution. How would you respond?

29. Advertising The Fancy Fashions, an independent, local boutique, has $8000 available each month for advertising. Newspaper ads cost $400 each, and no more than 30 can run per month. Internet banner ads cost $20 each, and no more than 60 can run per month. TV ads cost $2000 each, with a maximum of 10 available each month. Approximately 4000 women will see each newspaper ad, 3000 will see each Internet banner, and 10,000 will see each TV ad. (See Exercise 31 in Section 1.)

a. How much of each type of advertising should be used if the store wants to maximize its ad exposure?

b. A marketing analyst is puzzled by the results of part a. More women see each TV ad than each newspaper ad or Internet banner, he reasons, so it makes no sense to use the newspaper ads and Internet banners and no TV ads. How would you respond?

30. Profit A manufacturer makes two products, toy trucks and toy fire engines. Both are processed in four different departments, each of which has a limited capacity. The sheet metal department requires 2 hours for each truck and 3 hours for each fire engine and has a total of 24,000 hours available. The truck assembly department can handle at most 6600 trucks per week; and the fire engine assembly department assembles at most 5500 fire engines weekly. The painting department, which finishes both toys, has a maximum capacity of 10,000 per week.

a. If the profit is $8.50 for a toy truck and $12.10 for a toy fire engine, how many of each item should the company produce to maximize profit?

b. Keeping the profit for a toy truck at $8.50, use the graphical method to find the largest possible profit less than $12.10 for a toy fire engine that would result in an additional solution

besides the one found in part a. What is the additional solution? Verify this solution using the simplex method.

c. Keeping the profit for a toy truck at $8.50, use the graphical method to find the smallest possible profit greater than $12.10 for a toy fire engine that would result in an additional solution besides the one found in part a. What is the additional solution? Verify this solution using the simplex method.

Exercises 31 and 32 come from past CPA examinations. *Source: American Institute of Certified Public Accountants, Inc.* **Select the appropriate answer for each question.**

31. Profit The Ball Company manufactures three types of lamps, labeled A, B, and C. Each lamp is processed in two departments, I and II. Total available work-hours per day for departments I and II are 400 and 600, respectively. No additional labor is available. Time requirements and profit per unit for each lamp type are as follows:

	A	B	C
Work-hours in I	2	3	1
Work-hours in II	4	2	3
Profit per Unit	$5	$4	$3

The company has assigned you as the accounting member of its profit planning committee to determine the numbers of types of A, B, and C lamps that it should produce in order to maximize its total profit from the sale of lamps. The following questions relate to a linear programming model that your group has developed. (For each part, choose one of the four answers.)

a. The coefficients of the objective function would be

(1) 4, 2, 3.   (2) 2, 3, 1.

(3) 5, 4, 3.   (4) 400, 600.

b. The constraints in the model would be

(1) 2, 3, 1.   (2) 5, 4, 3.

(3) 4, 2, 3.   (4) 400, 600.

c. The constraint imposed by the available work-hours in department I could be expressed as

(1) $4X_1 + 2X_2 + 3X_3 \leq 400$.

(2) $4X_1 + 2X_2 + 3X_3 \geq 400$.

(3) $2X_1 + 3X_2 + 1X_3 \leq 400$.

(4) $2X_1 + 3X_2 + 1X_3 \geq 400$.

32. Profit The Golden Hawk Manufacturing Company wants to maximize the profits on products A, B, and C. The contribution margin for each product follows:

Product	Contribution Margin
A	$2
B	$5
C	$4

The production requirements and departmental capacities, by departments, are as follows:

Department	Production Requirements by Product (hours)			Departmental Capacity (total hours)
	A	B	C	
Assembling	2	3	2	30,000
Painting	1	2	2	38,000
Finishing	2	3	1	28,000

a. What is the profit-maximization formula for the Golden Hawk Company? (Choose one of the following.)

(1) $2A + $5B + $4C = X$ (where X = profit)

(2) $5A + 8B + 5C \leq 96,000$

(3) $2A + $5B + $4C \leq X$

(4) $2A + $5B + $4C = 96,000$

b. What is the constraint for the painting department of the Golden Hawk Company? (Choose one of the following.)

(1) $1A + 2B + 2C \geq 38,000$

(2) $2A + $5B + $4C \geq 38,000$

(3) $1A + 2B + 2C \leq 38,000$

(4) $2A + 3B + 2C \leq 30,000$

33. Sensitivity Analysis Using a computer spreadsheet, perform a sensitivity analysis for the objective function in Exercise 23. What are the highest and lowest possible values for the amount raised from each church group that would yield the same solution as the original problem? Answer the same question for the amount raised from each union local.

34. Sensitivity Analysis Using a computer spreadsheet, perform a sensitivity analysis for the objective function in Exercise 24. What are the highest and lowest possible values for profit on a Flexscan set that would yield the same solution as the original problem? Answer the same question for a Panoramic I set.

Set up and solve Exercises 35–40 by the simplex method.

Life Sciences

35. Calorie Expenditure Rachel Reeve, a fitness trainer, has an exercise regimen that includes running, biking, and walking. She has no more than 15 hours per week to devote to exercise, including at most 3 hours running. She wants to walk at least twice as many hours as she bikes. According to a website, a 130-pound person like Rachel will burn on average 531 calories per hour running, 472 calories per hour biking, and 354 calories per hour walking. How many hours per week should Rachel spend on each exercise to maximize the number of calories she burns? What is the maximum number of calories she will burn? (*Hint:* Write the constraint involving walking and biking in the form ≤ 0.) *Source: NutriStrategy.com.*

36. Calorie Expenditure Joe Vetere's exercise regimen includes light calisthenics, swimming, and playing the drums. He has at most 10 hours per week to devote to these activities. He wants the total time he does calisthenics and plays the drums to be at least twice as long as he swims. His neighbors, however, will tolerate no more than 4 hours per week on the drums. According to a website, a 190-pound person like Joe will burn an average of 388 calories per hour doing calisthenics, 518 calories per hour swimming, and 345 calories per hour playing the drums. *Source: NutriStrategy.com.*

a. How many hours per week should Joe spend on each exercise to maximize the number of calories he burns? What is the maximum number of calories he will burn?

b. What conclusions can you draw about Joe's selection of activities?

37. Resource Management The average weights of the three species stocked in the lake referred to in Section 2.2, Exercise 59, are 1.62, 2.14, and 3.01 kg for species A, B, and C, respectively.

a. If the largest amounts of food that can be supplied each day are as given in Exercise 59, how should the lake be stocked to maximize the weight of the fish supported by the lake?

b. Does it require all of the available food to produce the maximum weight of fish? If not, how much of each type of food is left over?

c. Find a value for each of the average weights of the three species that would result in none of species B or C being stocked to maximize the weight of the fish supported by the lake, given the constraints in part a.

d. Find a value for each of the average weights of the three species that would result in none of species A or B being stocked to maximize the weight of the fish supported by the lake, given the constraints in part a.

38. Blending Nutrients A biologist has 500 kg of nutrient A, 600 kg of nutrient B, and 300 kg of nutrient C. These nutrients will be used to make four types of food, whose contents (in percent of nutrient per kilogram of food) and whose "growth values" are as shown in the table.

	P	Q	R	S
A	0	0	37.5	62.5
B	0	75	50	37.5
C	100	25	12.5	0
Growth Value	90	70	60	50

a. How many kilograms of each food should be produced in order to maximize total growth value?

b. Find the maximum growth value.

c. Does it require all of the available nutrients to produce the four types of food that maximizes the total growth value? If not, how much of each nutrient is left over?

Social Sciences

39. Politics A political party is planning a half-hour television show. The show will have at least 3 minutes of direct requests for money from viewers. Three of the party's politicians will be on the show—a senator, a congresswoman, and a governor. The senator, a party "elder statesman," demands that he be on screen at least twice as long as the governor. The total time taken by the senator and the governor must be at least twice the time taken by the congresswoman. Based on a pre-show survey, it is believed that 35, 40, and 45 (in thousands) viewers will watch the program for each minute the senator, congresswoman, and governor, respectively, are on the air. Find the time that should be allotted to each politician in order to get the maximum number of viewers. Find the maximum number of viewers.

40. Fund Raising The political party in Exercise 39 is planning its fund-raising activities for a coming election. It plans to raise money through large fund-raising parties, letters requesting funds, and dinner parties where people can meet the candidate personally. Each large fund-raising party costs $3000, each mailing costs $1000, and each dinner party costs $12,000. The party can spend up to $102,000 for these activities. From

experience, the planners know that each large party will raise $200,000, each letter campaign will raise $100,000, and each dinner party will raise $600,000. They are able to carry out a total of 25 of these activities.

a. How many of each should the party plan in order to raise the maximum amount of money? What is the maximum amount?

b. Dinner parties are more expensive than letter campaigns, yet the optimum solution found in part a includes dinner parties but no letter campaigns. Explain how this is possible.

YOUR TURN ANSWERS

1. $x_1 = 0$, $x_2 = 12$, for a maximum value of $z = 480$.

2. $x_1 = 0$, $x_2 = 50$, $s_1 = 200$, $s_2 = 0$, $s_3 = 150$, $z = 1250$

3 Minimization Problems; Duality

APPLY IT How many units of different types of feed should a dog breeder purchase to meet the nutrient requirements of her golden retrievers at a minimum cost? *Using the method of duals, we will answer this question in Example 5.*

Minimization Problems The definition of a problem in standard maximum form was given earlier in this chapter. Now we can define a linear programming problem in *standard minimum form*, as follows.

Standard Minimum Form

A linear programming problem is in **standard minimum form** if the following conditions are satisfied.

1. The objective function is to be minimized.
2. All variables are nonnegative.
3. All remaining constraints are stated in the form

$$a_1 y_1 + a_2 y_2 + \cdots + a_n y_n \geq b, \quad \text{with } b \geq 0.$$

NOTE
In this section, we require that all coefficients in the objective function be positive, so $c_1 \geq 0$, $c_2 \geq 0, \ldots, c_n \geq 0$.

The difference between maximization and minimization problems is in conditions 1 and 3: In problems stated in standard minimum form, the objective function is to be *minimized*, rather than maximized, and all constraints must have $\geq$ instead of $\leq$.

We use y_1, y_2, etc., for the variables and w for the objective function as a reminder that these are minimizing problems. Thus, $w = c_1 y_1 + c_2 y_2 + \cdots + c_n y_n$.

Duality An interesting connection exists between standard maximization and standard minimization problems: any solution of a standard maximization problem produces the solution of an associated standard minimization problem, and vice versa. Each of these associated problems is called the **dual** of the other. One advantage of duals is that standard minimization problems can be solved by the simplex method discussed in the first two sections of this chapter. Let us explain the idea of a dual with an example.

EXAMPLE 1 Duality

Minimize $w = 8y_1 + 16y_2$

subject to: $y_1 + 5y_2 \geq 9$

                  $2y_1 + 2y_2 \geq 10$

with $y_1 \geq 0, \quad y_2 \geq 0.$

SOLUTION   Without considering slack variables just yet, write the augmented matrix of the system of inequalities and include the coefficients of the objective function (not their negatives) as the last row in the matrix.

Constants

Objective function ⟶ $\begin{bmatrix} 1 & 5 & | & 9 \\ 2 & 2 & | & 10 \\ 8 & 16 & | & 0 \end{bmatrix}$

Now look at the following matrix, which we obtain from the one above by interchanging rows and columns.

Constants

Objective function ⟶ $\begin{bmatrix} 1 & 2 & | & 8 \\ 5 & 2 & | & 16 \\ 9 & 10 & | & 0 \end{bmatrix}$

The *rows* of the first matrix (for the minimization problem) are the *columns* of the second matrix.

The entries in this second matrix could be used to write the following maximization problem in standard form (again ignoring the fact that the numbers in the last row are not negative):

Maximize $z = 9x_1 + 10x_2$

subject to: $x_1 + 2x_2 \leq 8$

            $5x_1 + 2x_2 \leq 16$

with all variables nonnegative.

Figure 9(a) shows the region of feasible solutions for the minimization problem just given, while Figure 9(b) shows the region of feasible solutions for the maximization problem produced by exchanging rows and columns. The solutions of the two problems are given below.

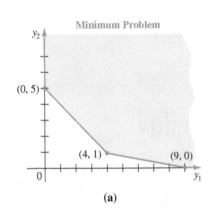

Minimum Problem

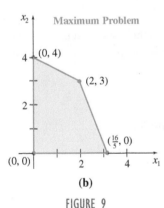

Maximum Problem

FIGURE 9

Minimum Problem	
Corner Point	$w = 8y_1 + 16y_2$
$(0, 5)$	80
$(4, 1)$	48 Minimum
$(9, 0)$	72

The minimum is 48 when $y_1 = 4$ and $y_2 = 1$.

Maximum Problem	
Corner Point	$z = 9x_1 + 10x_2$
$(0, 0)$	0
$(0, 4)$	40
$(2, 3)$	48 Maximum
$(16/5, 0)$	28.8

The maximum is 48 when $x_1 = 2$ and $x_2 = 3$.

The two feasible regions in Figure 9 are different and the corner points are different, but the values of the objective functions are equal—both are 48. An even closer connection between the two problems is shown by using the simplex method to solve this maximization problem.

Maximization Problem

$$\begin{array}{ccccc} x_1 & x_2 & s_1 & s_2 & z \\ \end{array}$$
$$\left[\begin{array}{ccccc|c} 1 & 2 & 1 & 0 & 0 & 8 \\ 5 & 2 & 0 & 1 & 0 & 16 \\ \hline -9 & -10 & 0 & 0 & 1 & 0 \end{array}\right]$$

$$\begin{array}{ccccc} x_1 & x_2 & s_1 & s_2 & z \\ \end{array}$$
$-R_1 + R_2 \rightarrow R_2$
$5R_1 + R_3 \rightarrow R_3$
$$\left[\begin{array}{ccccc|c} 1 & 2 & 1 & 0 & 0 & 8 \\ 4 & 0 & -1 & 1 & 0 & 8 \\ \hline -4 & 0 & 5 & 0 & 1 & 40 \end{array}\right]$$

$$\begin{array}{ccccc} x_1 & x_2 & s_1 & s_2 & z \\ \end{array}$$
$-R_2 + 4R_1 \rightarrow R_1$

$R_2 + R_3 \rightarrow R_3$
$$\left[\begin{array}{ccccc|c} 0 & 8 & 5 & -1 & 0 & 24 \\ 4 & 0 & -1 & 1 & 0 & 8 \\ \hline 0 & 0 & 4 & 1 & 1 & 48 \end{array}\right]$$

$$\begin{array}{ccccc} x_1 & x_2 & s_1 & s_2 & z \\ \end{array}$$
$R_1/8 \rightarrow R_1$
$R_2/4 \rightarrow R_2$
$$\left[\begin{array}{ccccc|c} 0 & 1 & \frac{5}{8} & -\frac{1}{8} & 0 & 3 \\ 1 & 0 & -\frac{1}{4} & \frac{1}{4} & 0 & 2 \\ \hline 0 & 0 & 4 & 1 & 1 & 48 \end{array}\right]$$

The maximum is 48 when
$x_1 = 2$ and $x_2 = 3$.

Notice that the solution to the *minimization problem* is found in the bottom row and slack variable columns of the final simplex tableau for the maximization problem. This result suggests that standard minimization problems can be solved by forming the dual standard maximization problem, solving it by the simplex method, and then reading the solution for the minimization problem from the bottom row of the final simplex tableau.

Before using this method to actually solve a minimization problem, let us find the duals of some typical linear programming problems. The process of exchanging the rows and columns of a matrix, which is used to find the dual, is called *transposing* the matrix, and each of the two matrices is the **transpose** of the other. The transpose of an $m \times n$ matrix A, written A^T, is an $n \times m$ matrix.

EXAMPLE 2 Transposes

Find the transpose of each matrix.

(a) $A = \begin{bmatrix} 2 & -1 & 5 \\ 6 & 8 & 0 \\ -3 & 7 & -1 \end{bmatrix}$

SOLUTION Both matrix A and its transpose are 3×3 matrices. Write the rows of matrix A as the columns of the transpose.

$$A^T = \begin{bmatrix} 2 & 6 & -3 \\ -1 & 8 & 7 \\ 5 & 0 & -1 \end{bmatrix}$$

(b) $B = \begin{bmatrix} 1 & 2 & 4 & 0 \\ 2 & 1 & 7 & 6 \end{bmatrix}$

SOLUTION The matrix B is 2×4, so B^T is the 4×2 matrix

$$B^T = \begin{bmatrix} 1 & 2 \\ 2 & 1 \\ 4 & 7 \\ 0 & 6 \end{bmatrix}.$$

EXAMPLE 3 Duals

Write the dual of each standard linear programming problem.

(a) Maximize $z = 2x_1 + 5x_2$

subject to: $x_1 + x_2 \leq 10$

$2x_1 + x_2 \leq 8$

with $x_1 \geq 0, \quad x_2 \geq 0.$

SOLUTION   Begin by writing the augmented matrix for the given problem.

$$\begin{bmatrix} 1 & 1 & | & 10 \\ 2 & 1 & | & 8 \\ 2 & 5 & | & 0 \end{bmatrix}$$

Form the transpose of the matrix as follows:

$$\begin{bmatrix} 1 & 2 & | & 2 \\ 1 & 1 & | & 5 \\ 10 & 8 & | & 0 \end{bmatrix}.$$

The dual problem is stated from this second matrix as follows (using y instead of x):

Minimize $w = 10y_1 + 8y_2$

subject to: $y_1 + 2y_2 \geq 2$

$y_1 + y_2 \geq 5$

with $y_1 \geq 0, \quad y_2 \geq 0.$

(b) Minimize $w = 7y_1 + 5y_2 + 8y_3$

subject to: $3y_1 + 2y_2 + y_3 \geq 10$

$4y_1 + 5y_2 \qquad \geq 25$

with $y_1 \geq 0, \quad y_2 \geq 0, \quad y_3 \geq 0.$

SOLUTION   The dual problem is stated as follows.

Maximize $z = 10x_1 + 25x_2$

subject to: $3x_1 + 4x_2 \leq 7$

$2x_1 + 5x_2 \leq 5$

$x_1 \qquad \leq 8$

with $x_1 \geq 0, \quad x_2 \geq 0.$ TRY YOUR TURN 1

YOUR TURN 1 Write the dual of the following linear programming problem.

Minimize $w = 25y_1 + 12y_2 + 27y_3$

subject to: $3y_1 + 3y_2 + 4y_3 \geq 24$

$5y_1 + y_2 + 3y_3 \geq 27$

with $y_1 \geq 0, y_2 \geq 0, y_3 \geq 0.$

NOTE   You might find it easier to set up the dual if you put the objective function *after* the constraints in the original problem, and then line up the variables, as in the following rewriting of Example 3 (b):

$$3y_1 + 2y_2 + y_3 \geq 10$$

$$4y_1 + 5y_2 \qquad \geq 25$$

Minimize $7y_1 + 5y_2 + 8y_3.$

Notice that you can read down the first column to get the coefficients of the first constraint in the dual $(3x_1 + 4x_2 \leq 7)$. Reading down the second and third columns gives the coefficients of the next two constraints, and the last column gives the coefficients of the objective function.

In Example 3, all the constraints of the given standard maximization problems were $\leq$ inequalities, while all those in the dual minimization problems were $\geq$ inequalities. This is generally the case; inequalities are reversed when the dual problem is stated.

The following table shows the close connection between a problem and its dual.

Duality	
Given Problem	**Dual Problem**
m variables	n variables
n constraints	m constraints
Coefficients from objective function	Constraint constants
Constraint constants	Coefficients from objective function

NOTE
To solve a minimization problem with duals, all of the coefficients in the objective function must be positive. (To investigate what would happen without this requirement, see Exercise 18). For a method that does not have this restriction, see the next section.

The next theorem, whose proof requires advanced methods, guarantees that a standard minimization problem can be solved by forming a dual standard maximization problem.

Theorem of Duality

The objective function w of a minimization linear programming problem takes on a minimum value if and only if the objective function z of the corresponding dual maximization problem takes on a maximum value. The maximum value of z equals the minimum value of w.

This method is illustrated in the following example.

EXAMPLE 4   Duality

Minimize $w = 3y_1 + 2y_2$

subject to: $y_1 + 3y_2 \geq 6$

            $2y_1 + \; y_2 \geq 3$

with $y_1 \geq 0, \quad y_2 \geq 0.$

SOLUTION   Use the given information to write the matrix.

$$\left[\begin{array}{cc|c} 1 & 3 & 6 \\ 2 & 1 & 3 \\ \hline 3 & 2 & 0 \end{array}\right]$$

Transpose to get the following matrix for the dual problem.

$$\left[\begin{array}{cc|c} 1 & 2 & 3 \\ 3 & 1 & 2 \\ \hline 6 & 3 & 0 \end{array}\right]$$

Write the dual problem from this matrix, as follows:

Maximize $z = 6x_1 + 3x_2$

subject to: $x_1 + 2x_2 \leq 3$

            $3x_1 + \; x_2 \leq 2$

with $x_1 \geq 0, \quad x_2 \geq 0.$

Solve this standard maximization problem using the simplex method. Start by introducing slack variables to give the system

$$\begin{aligned} x_1 + 2x_2 + \; s_1 \qquad\qquad &= 3 \\ 3x_1 + \; x_2 \qquad + \; s_2 \qquad &= 2 \\ -6x_1 - 3x_2 \qquad\qquad + z &= 0 \end{aligned}$$

with $x_1 \geq 0, \quad x_2 \geq 0, \quad s_1 \geq 0, \quad s_2 \geq 0.$

The first tableau for this system is given below, with the pivot as indicated.

$$\begin{array}{c} \text{Quotients} \\ 3/1 = 3 \\ 2/3 \end{array} \begin{array}{cccccc} & x_1 & x_2 & s_1 & s_2 & z \\ \left[\begin{array}{ccccc|c} 1 & 2 & 1 & 0 & 0 & 3 \\ \mathbf{3} & 1 & 0 & 1 & 0 & 2 \\ \hline -6 & -3 & 0 & 0 & 1 & 0 \end{array}\right] \end{array}$$

The simplex method gives the following as the final tableau.

$$\begin{array}{ccccc} x_1 & x_2 & s_1 & s_2 & z \\ \left[\begin{array}{ccccc|c} 0 & 1 & \frac{3}{5} & -\frac{1}{5} & 0 & \frac{7}{5} \\ 1 & 0 & -\frac{1}{5} & \frac{2}{5} & 0 & \frac{1}{5} \\ \hline 0 & 0 & \frac{3}{5} & \frac{9}{5} & 1 & \frac{27}{5} \end{array}\right] \end{array}$$

YOUR TURN 2

Minimize $w = 15y_1 + 12y_2$

subject to: $3y_1 + 5y_2 \geq 20$

$3y_1 + y_2 \geq 18$

with $y_1 \geq 0, y_2 \geq 0.$

Since a 1 has been created in the z column, the last row of this final tableau gives the solution to the minimization problem. The minimum value of $w = 3y_1 + 2y_2$, subject to the given constraints, is 27/5 and occurs when $y_1 = 3/5$ and $y_2 = 9/5$. The minimum value of w, 27/5, is the same as the maximum value of z. **TRY YOUR TURN 2**

Let us summarize the steps in solving a standard minimization linear programming problem by the method of duals.

Solving a Standard Minimum Problem with Duals

1. Find the dual standard maximization problem.
2. Solve the maximization problem using the simplex method.
3. The minimum value of the objective function w is the maximum value of the objective function z.
4. The optimum solution to the minimization problem is given by the entries in the bottom row of the columns corresponding to the slack variables, so long as the entry in the z column is equal to 1.

CAUTION (1) If the final entry in the z column is a value other than 1, divide the bottom row through by that value so that it will become 1. Only then can the solution of the minimization problem be found in the bottom row of the columns corresponding to the slack variables.

(2) Do not simplify an inequality in the dual by dividing out a common factor. For example, if an inequality in the dual is $3x_1 + 3x_2 \leq 6$, do not simplify to $x_1 + x_2 \leq 2$ by dividing out the 3. Doing so will give an incorrect solution to the original problem.

Further Uses of the Dual

The dual is useful not only in solving minimization problems but also in seeing how small changes in one variable will affect the value of the objective function.

EXAMPLE 5 Nutrition

Suppose a dog breeder needs at least 6 units per day of nutrient A and at least 3 units of nutrient B for her golden retrievers, and that the breeder can choose between two different feeds, feed 1 and feed 2. Find the minimum cost for the breeder if each bag of feed 1 costs \$3 and provides 1 unit of nutrient A and 2 units of B, while each bag of feed 2 costs \$2 and provides 3 units of nutrient A and 1 of B.

APPLY IT

SOLUTION If y_1 represents the number of bags of feed 1 and y_2 represents the number of bags of feed 2, the given information leads to the following problem.

$$\text{Minimize} \qquad w = 3y_1 + 2y_2$$
$$\text{subject to:} \qquad y_1 + 3y_2 \geq 6 \qquad \text{Nutrient A}$$
$$2y_1 + y_2 \geq 3 \qquad \text{Nutrient B}$$
$$\text{with} \qquad y_1 \geq 0, \quad y_2 \geq 0.$$

This standard minimization linear programming problem is the one solved in Example 4 of this section. In that example, the dual was formed and the following tableau was found.

$$
\begin{array}{ccccc}
x_1 & x_2 & s_1 & s_2 & z
\end{array}
$$
$$
\left[
\begin{array}{ccccc|c}
0 & 1 & \frac{3}{5} & -\frac{1}{5} & 0 & \frac{7}{5} \\
1 & 0 & -\frac{1}{5} & \frac{2}{5} & 0 & \frac{1}{5} \\
\hline
0 & 0 & \frac{3}{5} & \frac{9}{5} & 1 & \frac{27}{5}
\end{array}
\right]
$$

This final tableau shows that the breeder will obtain minimum feed costs by using 3/5 bag of feed 1 and 9/5 bags of feed 2 per day, for a daily cost of 27/5 = $5.40.

Notice that the solution to the dual (maximization) problem is

$$x_1 = \frac{1}{5} = 0.20 \qquad \text{and} \qquad x_2 = \frac{7}{5} = 1.40.$$

These represent the **shadow costs** of nutrients A and B. The nutrients don't have actual costs because you can't buy a unit of nutrient A or B; all you can buy is a bag of Feed 1 or Feed 2, each of which contains both nutrients A and B. Shadow costs, however, are a convenient way of allocating costs. Suppose that a unit of nutrient A is said to cost $0.20, its shadow cost, and a unit of nutrient B is said to cost $1.40. Then the minimum daily cost, which we previously found to be $5.40 (providing 6 units of A and 3 units of B), can be found by the following procedure.

$$(\$0.20 \text{ per unit of A}) \times (6 \text{ units of A}) = \$1.20$$
$$\underline{+ \ (\$1.40 \text{ per unit of B}) \times (3 \text{ units of B}) = \$4.20}$$
$$\text{Minimum daily cost} = \$5.40$$

Furthermore, the shadow costs allow the breeder to calculate feed costs for small changes in nutrient requirements. For example, an increase of one unit in the requirement for each nutrient would produce a total cost of $7.00:

$5.40	6 units of A, 3 of B
0.20	1 extra unit of A
+ 1.40	1 extra unit of B
$7.00	Total cost per day

Shadow costs only give the exact answer for a limited range. Unfortunately, finding that range is somewhat complicated. In the dog feed example, we can add up to 3 units or delete up to 4 units of A, and shadow costs will give the exact answer. If, however, we add 4 units of A, shadow costs give an answer of $6.20, while the true cost is $6.67.

NOTE Shadow costs become shadow profits in maximization problems. For example, see Exercises 21 and 22.

CAUTION If you wish to use shadow costs, do not simplify an inequality in the original problem by dividing out a common factor. For example, if an inequality in the original problem is $3y_1 + 3y_2 \geq 6$, do not simplify to $y_1 + y_2 \geq 2$ by dividing out the 3. Doing so will give incorrect shadow costs.

TECHNOLOGY NOTE The Solver in Microsoft Excel provides the values of the dual variables. See the *Graphing Calculator and Excel Spreadsheet Manual* available with this text for more details.

Courtesy of Raymond N. Greenwell

3 EXERCISES

Find the transpose of each matrix.

1. $\begin{bmatrix} 1 & 2 & 3 \\ 3 & 2 & 1 \\ 1 & 10 & 0 \end{bmatrix}$

2. $\begin{bmatrix} 3 & 4 & -2 & 0 & 1 \\ 2 & 0 & 11 & 5 & 7 \end{bmatrix}$

3. $\begin{bmatrix} 4 & 5 & -3 & 15 \\ 7 & 14 & 20 & -8 \\ 5 & 0 & -2 & 23 \end{bmatrix}$

4. $\begin{bmatrix} 1 & 11 & 15 \\ 0 & 10 & -6 \\ 4 & 12 & -2 \\ 1 & -1 & 13 \\ 2 & 25 & -1 \end{bmatrix}$

State the dual problem for each linear programming problem.

5. Maximize $z = 4x_1 + 3x_2 + 2x_3$

subject to:
$$x_1 + x_2 + x_3 \le 5$$
$$x_1 + x_2 \le 4$$
$$2x_1 + x_2 + 3x_3 \le 15$$

with $x_1 \ge 0, \quad x_2 \ge 0, \quad x_3 \ge 0.$

6. Maximize $z = 2x_1 + 7x_2 + 4x_3$

subject to:
$$4x_1 + 2x_2 + x_3 \le 26$$
$$x_1 + 7x_2 + 8x_3 \le 33$$

with $x_1 \ge 0, \quad x_2 \ge 0, \quad x_3 \ge 0.$

7. Minimize $w = 3y_1 + 6y_2 + 4y_3 + y_4$

subject to:
$$y_1 + y_2 + y_3 + y_4 \ge 150$$
$$2y_1 + 2y_2 + 3y_3 + 4y_4 \ge 275$$

with $y_1 \ge 0, \quad y_2 \ge 0, \quad y_3 \ge 0, \quad y_4 \ge 0.$

8. Minimize $w = y_1 + y_2 + 4y_3$

subject to:
$$y_1 + 2y_2 + 3y_3 \ge 115$$
$$2y_1 + y_2 + 8y_3 \ge 200$$
$$y_1 + y_3 \ge 50$$

with $y_1 \ge 0, \quad y_2 \ge 0, \quad y_3 \ge 0.$

Use the simplex method to solve.

9. Find $y_1 \ge 0$ and $y_2 \ge 0$ such that
$$2y_1 + 3y_2 \ge 6$$
$$2y_1 + y_2 \ge 7$$
and $w = 5y_1 + 2y_2$ is minimized.

10. Find $y_1 \ge 0$ and $y_2 \ge 0$ such that
$$2y_1 + 3y_2 \ge 15$$
$$5y_1 + 6y_2 \ge 35$$
and $w = 2y_1 + 3y_2$ is minimized.

11. Find $y_1 \ge 0$ and $y_2 \ge 0$ such that
$$10y_1 + 5y_2 \ge 100$$
$$20y_1 + 10y_2 \ge 150$$
and $w = 4y_1 + 5y_2$ is minimized.

12. Minimize $w = 29y_1 + 10y_2$

subject to:
$$3y_1 + 2y_2 \ge 2$$
$$5y_1 + y_2 \ge 3$$

with $y_1 \ge 0, \quad y_2 \ge 0.$

13. Minimize $w = 6y_1 + 10y_2$

subject to:
$$3y_1 + 5y_2 \ge 15$$
$$4y_1 + 7y_2 \ge 20$$

with $y_1 \ge 0, \quad y_2 \ge 0.$

14. Minimize $w = 3y_1 + 2y_2$

subject to:
$$y_1 + 2y_2 \ge 10$$
$$y_1 + y_2 \ge 8$$
$$2y_1 + y_2 \ge 12$$

with $y_1 \ge 0, \quad y_2 \ge 0.$

15. Minimize $w = 2y_1 + y_2 + 3y_3$

subject to:
$$y_1 + y_2 + y_3 \ge 100$$
$$2y_1 + y_2 \ge 50$$

with $y_1 \ge 0, \quad y_2 \ge 0, \quad y_3 \ge 0.$

16. Minimize $w = 4y_1 + 7y_2 + 9y_3$

subject to:
$$2y_1 + 3y_2 + 4y_3 \ge 45$$
$$y_1 + 5y_2 + 2y_3 \ge 40$$

with $y_1 \ge 0, \quad y_2 \ge 0, \quad y_3 \ge 0.$

17. You are given the following linear programming problem (P):

Minimize $z = x_1 + 2x_2$

subject to:
$$-2x_1 + x_2 \ge 1$$
$$x_1 - 2x_2 \ge 1$$
$$x_1 \ge 0, \quad x_2 \ge 0.$$

The dual of (P) is (D). Which of the statements below is true? *Source: Society of Actuaries.*

a. (P) has no feasible solution and the objective function of (D) is unbounded.

b. (D) has no feasible solution and the objective function of (P) is unbounded.

c. The objective functions of both (P) and (D) are unbounded.

d. Both (P) and (D) have optimal solutions.

e. Neither (P) nor (D) has feasible solutions.

18. Suppose the coefficient of 3 in the objective function of Example 4 is changed to -3 and all the constraints are kept the same. Explain why the objective function now has no minimum.

APPLICATIONS

Business and Economics

19. Production Costs A brewery produces regular beer and a lower-carbohydrate "light" beer. Steady customers of the brewery buy 10 units of regular beer and 15 units of light beer monthly. While setting up the brewery to produce the beers, the management decides to produce extra beer, beyond that needed to satisfy customers. The cost per unit of regular beer is $32,000 and the cost per unit of light beer is $50,000. Every unit of regular beer brings in $120,000 in revenue, while every unit of light beer brings in $300,000 in revenue. The brewery wants at least $9,000,000 in revenue. At least 20 additional units of beer can be sold.

a. How much of each type of beer should be made so as to minimize total production costs?

b. Suppose the minimum revenue is increased to $9,500,000. Use shadow costs to calculate the total production costs.

20. Supply Costs The chemistry department at a local college decides to stock at least 900 small test tubes and 600 large test tubes. It wants to buy at least 2700 test tubes to take advantage of a special price. Since the small test tubes are broken twice as often as the large, the department will order at least twice as many small tubes as large.

a. If the small test tubes cost 18 cents each and the large ones, made of a cheaper glass, cost 15 cents each, how many of each size should be ordered to minimize cost?

b. Suppose the minimum number of test tubes is increased to 3000. Use shadow costs to calculate the total cost in this case.

In most examples of this section, the original problem is a minimization problem and the dual is a maximization problem whose solution gives shadow costs. The reverse is true in Exercises 21 and 22. The dual here is a minimization problem whose solution can be interpreted as shadow profits.

21. Agriculture Refer to the original information in Example 2, Section 1.

a. Give the dual problem.

b. Use the shadow profits to estimate the farmer's profit if land is cut to 90 acres but capital increases to $21,000.

c. Suppose the farmer has 110 acres but only $19,000. Find the optimum profit and the planting strategy that will produce this profit.

22. Toy Manufacturing A small toy manufacturing firm has 200 squares of felt, 600 oz of stuffing, and 90 ft of trim available to make two types of toys, a small bear and a monkey. The bear requires 1 square of felt and 4 oz of stuffing. The monkey requires 2 squares of felt, 3 oz of stuffing, and 1 ft of trim. The firm makes $1 profit on each bear and $1.50 profit on each monkey.

a. Set up the linear programming problem to maximize profit.

b. Solve the linear programming problem in part a.

c. What is the corresponding dual problem?

d. What is the optimal solution to the dual problem?

e. Use the shadow profits to calculate the profit the firm will make if its supply of felt increases to 210 squares.

f. How much profit will the firm make if its supply of stuffing is cut to 590 oz and its supply of trim is cut to 80 ft?

g. Explain why it makes sense that the shadow profit for trim is 0.

23. Interview Time Joan McKee has a part-time job conducting public opinion interviews. She has found that a political interview takes 45 min and a market interview takes 55 min. She needs to minimize the time she spends doing interviews to allow more time for her full-time job. Unfortunately, to keep her part-time job, she must complete at least 8 interviews each week. Also, she must earn at least $60 per week at this job; she earns $8 for each political interview and $10 for each market interview. Finally, to stay in good standing with her supervisor, she must earn at least 40 bonus points per week; she receives 6 bonus points for each political interview and 5 points for each market interview. How many of each interview should she do each week to minimize the time spent?

24. Animal Food An animal food must provide at least 54 units of vitamins and 60 calories per serving. One gram of soybean meal provides 2.5 units of vitamins and 5 calories. One gram of meat byproducts provides 4.5 units of vitamins and 3 calories. One gram of grain provides 5 units of vitamins and 10 calories. A gram of soybean meal costs 8¢, a gram of meat byproducts 9¢, and a gram of grain 10¢.

a. What mixture of these three ingredients will provide the required vitamins and calories at minimum cost?

b. What is the minimum cost?

c. There is more than one optimal basic solution to this problem. The answer found in part a depends on whether the tie in the minimum ratio rule was broken by pivoting on the second row or third row of the dual. Find the other solution.

25. Feed Costs Refer to Example 5 in this section on minimizing the daily cost of feeds.

a. Find a combination of feeds that will cost $7 and give 7 units of A and 4 units of B.

b. Use the dual variables to predict the daily cost of feed if the requirements change to 5 units of A and 4 units of B. Find a combination of feeds to meet these requirements at the predicted price.

26. Pottery Karla Harby makes three items in her pottery shop: large bowls, small bowls, and pots for plants. A large bowl requires 3 lb of clay and 6 fl oz of glaze. A small bowl requires 2 lb of clay, and 6 fl oz of glaze. A pot requires 4 lb of clay and 2 fl oz of glaze. She must use up 72 lb of old clay and 108 fl oz of old glaze; she can order more if necessary. If Karla can make a large bowl in 5 hours, a small bowl in 6 hours, and a pot in 4 hours, how many of each should she make to minimize her time? What is the minimum time?

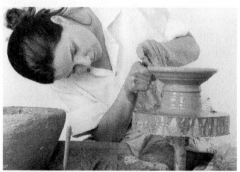

Iko/Shutterstock

Life Sciences

27. Calorie Expenditure Francesca wants to start exercising to burn at least 1500 extra calories per week, but she does not have much spare time for exercise. According to a website, she can burn an average of 3.5 calories per minute walking, 4 calories per minute cycling, and 8 calories per minute swimming. She would like her total time walking and cycling to be at least 3 times as long as she spends swimming. She would also like to walk at least 30 minutes per week. How much time should she spend on each activity not only to meet her goals but also to minimize her total exercise time per week? What is her minimum exercise time per week? *Source: BrianMac.co.uk.*

28. Health Care Marty McDonald takes vitamin pills. Each day he must have at least 3200 IU of vitamin A, 5 mg of vitamin B_1, and 200 mg of vitamin C. He can choose between pill 1, which costs 10¢ and contains 1600 IU of A, 1 mg of B_1, and 20 mg of C; and pill 2, which costs 20¢ and contains 400 IU of A, 1 mg of B_1, and 70 mg of C. How many of each pill should he buy in order to minimize his cost?

29. Blending Nutrients A biologist must make a nutrient for her algae. The nutrient must contain the three basic elements D, E, and F, and must contain at least 10 kg of D, 12 kg of E, and 20 kg of F. The nutrient is made from three ingredients, I, II, and

III. The quantity of D, E, and F in one unit of each of the ingredients is as given in the following chart.

		Ingredient		
		I	II	III
Kilograms of	D	4	1	10
Elements (per	E	3	2	1
unit of ingredient)	F	0	4	5
Cost per unit (in $)		4	7	5

How many units of each ingredient are required to meet the biologist's needs at minimum cost?

YOUR TURN ANSWERS

1. Maximize $z = 24x_1 + 27x_2$

subject to: $3x_1 + 5x_2 \le 25$

$3x_1 + x_2 \le 12$

$4x_1 + 3x_2 \le 27$

with $x_1 \ge 0, \quad x_2 \ge 0.$

2. Minimum is 187/2 when $y_1 = 35/6$ and $y_2 = 1/2.$

4 Nonstandard Problems

APPLY IT

How many cars should an auto manufacturer send from each of its two plants to each of two dealerships in order to minimize the cost while meeting each dealership's needs?

We will learn techniques in this section for answering questions like the one above, which will be answered in Example 2.

So far we have used the simplex method to solve linear programming problems in standard maximum or minimum form only. Now this work is extended to include linear programming problems with mixed $\le$ and $\ge$ constraints.

For example, suppose a new constraint is added to the farmer problem in Example 2 of Section 1: To satisfy orders from regular buyers, the farmer must plant a total of at least 60 acres of the three crops. Notice that our solution from Section 2 (plant 50 acres of potatoes, no acres of corn, and no acres of cabbage) does not satisfy this constraint, which introduces the new inequality

$$x_1 + x_2 + x_3 \ge 60.$$

As before, this inequality must be rewritten as an equation in which the variables all represent nonnegative numbers. The inequality $x_1 + x_2 + x_3 \ge 60$ means that

$$x_1 + x_2 + x_3 - s_3 = 60$$

for some nonnegative variable s_3. (Remember that s_1 and s_2 are the slack variables in the problem.)

The new variable, s_3, is called a **surplus variable**. The value of this variable represents the excess number of acres (over 60) that may be planted. Since the total number of acres planted is to be no more than 100 but at least 60, the value of s_3 can vary from 0 to 40.

We must now solve the system of equations

$$
\begin{aligned}
x_1 + x_2 + x_3 + s_1 \qquad\qquad\qquad &= 100 \\
10x_1 + 4x_2 + 7x_3 \qquad + s_2 \qquad\qquad &= 500 \\
x_1 + x_2 + x_3 \qquad\qquad - s_3 \qquad &= 60 \\
-120x_1 - 40x_2 - 60x_3 \qquad\qquad\qquad + z &= 0,
\end{aligned}
$$

with $x_1, x_2, x_3, s_1, s_2,$ and s_3 all nonnegative.

Set up the initial simplex tableau.

$$
\begin{array}{ccccccc|c}
x_1 & x_2 & x_3 & s_1 & s_2 & s_3 & z & \\
1 & 1 & 1 & 1 & 0 & 0 & 0 & 100 \\
10 & 4 & 7 & 0 & 1 & 0 & 0 & 500 \\
1 & 1 & 1 & 0 & 0 & -1 & 0 & 60 \\
\hline
-120 & -40 & -60 & 0 & 0 & 0 & 1 & 0
\end{array}
$$

This tableau gives the solution

$$x_1 = 0, \quad x_2 = 0, \quad x_3 = 0, \quad s_1 = 100, \quad s_2 = 500, \quad s_3 = -60.$$

But this is not a feasible solution, since s_3 is negative. This means that the third constraint is not satisfied; we have $x_1 + x_2 + x_3 = 0$, but the sum is supposed to be at least 60. All the variables in any feasible solution must be nonnegative if the solution is to correspond to a point in the feasible region.

When a negative value of a variable appears in the solution, row operations are used to transform the matrix until a solution is found in which all variables are nonnegative. Here the problem is the -1 in a column corresponding to a basic variable. If the number in that row of the right-hand column were 0, we could simply multiply this row by -1 to remove the negative from the column. But we cannot do this with a positive number in the right-hand column. Instead, we find the positive entry that is farthest to the left in the third row (the row containing the -1); namely, the 1 in row 3, column 1. We will pivot using this column. (Actually, any column with a positive entry in row 3 will do; we chose the column farthest to the left arbitrarily.*) Use quotients as before to find the pivot, which is the 10 in row 2, column 1. Then use row operations to get the following tableau.

$$
\begin{array}{l}
-R_2 + 10R_1 \to R_1 \\
\\
\\
-R_2 + 10R_3 \to R_3 \\
12R_2 + R_4 \to R_4
\end{array}
\begin{array}{ccccccc|c}
x_1 & x_2 & x_3 & s_1 & s_2 & s_3 & z & \\
0 & 6 & 3 & 10 & -1 & 0 & 0 & 500 \\
10 & 4 & 7 & 0 & 1 & 0 & 0 & 500 \\
0 & 6 & 3 & 0 & -1 & -10 & 0 & 100 \\
\hline
0 & 8 & 24 & 0 & 12 & 0 & 1 & 6000
\end{array}
$$

Notice from the s_3 column that $-10s_3 = 100$, so s_3 is still negative. Therefore, we apply the procedure again. The 6 in row 3, column 2, is the positive entry farthest to the left in row 3, and by investigating quotients, we see that it is also the pivot. This leads to the following tableau.

$$
\begin{array}{l}
-R_3 + R_1 \to R_1 \\
-2R_3 + 3R_2 \to R_2 \\
\\
-4R_3 + 3R_4 \to R_4
\end{array}
\begin{array}{ccccccc|c}
x_1 & x_2 & x_3 & s_1 & s_2 & s_3 & z & \\
0 & 0 & 0 & 10 & 0 & 10 & 0 & 400 \\
30 & 0 & 15 & 0 & 5 & 20 & 0 & 1300 \\
0 & 6 & 3 & 0 & -1 & -10 & 0 & 100 \\
\hline
0 & 0 & 60 & 0 & 40 & 40 & 3 & 17{,}600
\end{array}
$$

The value of s_3 is now 0 and the solution is feasible. We now continue with the simplex method until an optimal solution is found. We check for negative indicators, but since

---

*We use this rule for simplicity. There are, however, more complicated methods for choosing the pivot element that require, on average, fewer pivots to find the solution.

there are none, we have merely to create a 1 in each column corresponding to a basic variable or z.

$$\begin{array}{c} R_1/10 \rightarrow R_1 \\ R_2/30 \rightarrow R_2 \\ R_3/6 \rightarrow R_3 \\ R_4/3 \rightarrow R_4 \end{array} \begin{array}{cccccccc} x_1 & x_2 & x_3 & s_1 & s_2 & s_3 & z & \\ \left[\begin{array}{ccccccc|c} 0 & 0 & 0 & 1 & 0 & 1 & 0 & 40 \\ 1 & 0 & \frac{1}{2} & 0 & \frac{1}{6} & \frac{2}{3} & 0 & \frac{130}{3} \\ 0 & 1 & \frac{1}{2} & 0 & -\frac{1}{6} & -\frac{5}{3} & 0 & \frac{50}{3} \\ 0 & 0 & 20 & 0 & \frac{40}{3} & \frac{40}{3} & 1 & \frac{17,600}{3} \end{array}\right] \end{array}$$

The solution is

$$x_1 = \frac{130}{3} = 43\frac{1}{3}, \quad x_2 = \frac{50}{3} = 16\frac{2}{3}, \quad x_3 = 0, \quad z = \frac{17,600}{3} = 5866.67.$$

For maximum profit with this new constraint, the farmer should plant $43\frac{1}{3}$ acres of potatoes, $16\frac{2}{3}$ acres of corn, and no cabbage. The profit will be \$5866.67, less than the \$6000 profit if the farmer were to plant only 50 acres of potatoes. Because of the additional constraint that at least 60 acres must be planted, the profit is reduced. Notice that $s_1 = 40$. This is the slack variable for the constraint that no more than 100 acres are available. It indicates that 40 of the 100 available acres are still unused.

The procedure we have followed is a simplified version of the **two-phase method**, which is widely used for solving problems with mixed constraints. To see the complete method, including how to handle some complications that may arise, see *Linear Programming: An Introduction with Applications* by Alan Sultan, Academic Press, 1993.

In the previous section we solved standard minimum problems using duals. If a minimizing problem has mixed $\leq$ and $\geq$ constraints, the dual method cannot be used. We solve such problems with the method presented in this section. To see how, consider the simple fact: When a number t gets smaller, then $-t$ gets larger, and vice versa. For instance, if t goes from 6 to 1 to 0 to -8, then $-t$ goes from -6 to -1 to 0 to 8. Thus, if w is the objective function of a minimizing linear programming problem, the feasible solution that produces the minimum value of w also produces the maximum value of $z = -w$, and vice versa. Therefore, to solve a minimization problem with objective function w, we need only solve the maximization problem with the same constraints and objective function $z = -w$.

In summary, the following steps are involved in solving the nonstandard problems in this section.

NOTE
If we ever reach a point where a surplus variable still has a negative solution, but there are no positive elements left in the row, then we have no way to make the surplus variable positive, so the problem has no feasible solution.

Solving a Nonstandard Problem

1. If necessary, convert the problem to a maximization problem.
2. Add slack variables and subtract surplus variables as needed.
3. Write the initial simplex tableau.
4. If any basic variable has a negative value, locate the nonzero number in that variable's column, and note what row it is in.
5. In the row located in Step 4, find the positive entry that is farthest to the left, and note what column it is in.
6. In the column found in Step 5, choose a pivot by investigating quotients.
7. Use row operations to change the other numbers in the pivot column to 0.
8. Continue Steps 4 through 7 until all basic variables are nonnegative. If it ever becomes impossible to continue, then the problem has no feasible solution.
9. Once a feasible solution has been found, continue to use the simplex method until the optimal solution is found.

In the next example, we use this method to solve a minimization problem with mixed constraints.

EXAMPLE 1 Minimization

Minimize $\quad w = 3y_1 + 2y_2$

subject to: $\quad y_1 + 3y_2 \le 6$

$\qquad\qquad 2y_1 + y_2 \ge 3$

with $\qquad\quad y_1 \ge 0, \quad y_2 \ge 0.$

SOLUTION Change this to a maximization problem by letting z equal the *negative* of the objective function: $z = -w$. Then find the *maximum* value of

$$z = -w = -3y_1 - 2y_2.$$

The problem can now be stated as follows.

Maximize $\quad z = -3y_1 - 2y_2$

subject to: $\quad y_1 + 3y_2 \le 6$

$\qquad\qquad 2y_1 + y_2 \ge 3$

with $\qquad\quad y_1 \ge 0, \quad y_2 \ge 0.$

To begin, we add slack and surplus variables, and rewrite the objective function.

$$y_1 + 3y_2 + s_1 \qquad\qquad = 6$$
$$2y_1 + y_2 \qquad - s_2 \qquad = 3$$
$$3y_1 + 2y_2 \qquad\qquad + z = 0$$

NOTE
1) Slack variables are used for $\le$ constraints, while surplus variables are used for $\ge$ constraints
2) Remember to convert from z to w as the last step in solving a minimization problem.

Set up the initial simplex tableau.

$$
\begin{array}{ccccc}
y_1 & y_2 & s_1 & s_2 & z \\
\end{array}
$$
$$
\left[
\begin{array}{ccccc|c}
1 & 3 & 1 & 0 & 0 & 6 \\
2 & 1 & 0 & -1 & 0 & 3 \\
3 & 2 & 0 & 0 & 1 & 0 \\
\end{array}
\right]
$$

The solution $y_1 = 0$, $y_2 = 0$, $s_1 = 6$, and $s_2 = -3$, is not feasible. Row operations must be used to get a feasible solution. We start with s_2, which has a -1 in row 2. The positive entry farthest to the left in row 2 is the 2 in column 1. The element in column 1 that gives the smallest quotient is 2, so it becomes the pivot. Pivoting produces the following matrix.

$$
\begin{array}{ccccc}
y_1 & y_2 & s_1 & s_2 & z \\
\end{array}
$$

$-R_2 + 2R_1 \rightarrow R_1$

$-3R_2 + 2R_3 \rightarrow R_3$

$$
\left[
\begin{array}{ccccc|c}
0 & 5 & 2 & 1 & 0 & 9 \\
2 & 1 & 0 & -1 & 0 & 3 \\
0 & 1 & 0 & 3 & 2 & -9 \\
\end{array}
\right]
$$

Now $s_2 = 0$, so the solution is feasible. Furthermore, there are no negative indicators, so the solution is optimal. Divide row 1 by 2, row 2 by 2, and row 3 by 2 to find the final solution: $y_1 = 3/2$ and $y_2 = 0$. Since $z = -w = -9/2$, the minimum value is $w = 9/2$.

TRY YOUR TURN 1

YOUR TURN 1

Minimize $\quad w = 6y_1 + 4y_2$

subject to: $\quad 3y_1 + 4y_2 \ge 10$

$\qquad\qquad 9y_1 + 7y_2 \le 18$

with $\qquad\quad y_1 \ge 0, \quad y_2 \ge 0.$

An important application of linear programming is the problem of minimizing the cost of transporting goods. This type of problem is often referred to as a *transportation problem* or *warehouse problem*. Some problems of this type were included in the exercise sets in previous chapters. In the next example, the transportation costs were set equal to $10,640. We will now use the simplex method to minimize the transportation costs.

EXAMPLE 2 Transportation Problem

An auto manufacturer sends cars from two plants, I and II, to dealerships A and B located in a midwestern city. Plant I has a total of 28 cars to send, and plant II has 8. Dealer A needs 20 cars, and dealer B needs 16. Transportation costs per car based on the distance of each dealership from each plant are \$220 from I to A, \$300 from I to B, \$400 from II to A, and \$180 from II to B. How many cars should be sent from each plant to each of the two dealerships to minimize transportation costs? Use the simplex method to find the solution.

SOLUTION To begin, let

$$y_1 = \text{the number of cars shipped from I to A;}$$
$$y_2 = \text{the number of cars shipped from I to B;}$$
$$y_3 = \text{the number of cars shipped from II to A;}$$

and
$$y_4 = \text{the number of cars shipped from II to B.}$$

Plant I has only 28 cars to ship, so

$$y_1 + y_2 \leq 28.$$

Similarly, plant II has only 8 cars to ship, so

$$y_3 + y_4 \leq 8.$$

Since dealership A needs 20 cars and dealership B needs 16 cars,

$$y_1 + y_3 \geq 20 \quad \text{and} \quad y_2 + y_4 \geq 16.$$

The manufacturer wants to minimize transportation costs, so the objective function is

$$w = 220y_1 + 300y_2 + 400y_3 + 180y_4.$$

Now write the problem as a system of linear equations, adding slack or surplus variables as needed, and let $z = -w$.

$$
\begin{aligned}
y_1 + y_2 \qquad\qquad\qquad + s_1 \qquad\qquad\qquad &= 28 \\
y_3 + y_4 \qquad + s_2 \qquad\qquad\qquad &= 8 \\
y_1 \qquad + y_3 \qquad\qquad\qquad - s_3 \qquad\qquad &= 20 \\
y_2 \qquad + y_4 \qquad\qquad\qquad - s_4 \qquad &= 16 \\
220y_1 + 300y_2 + 400y_3 + 180y_4 \qquad\qquad + z &= 0
\end{aligned}
$$

Set up the initial simplex tableau.

Alma Sacra/Fotolia

	y_1	y_2	y_3	y_4	s_1	s_2	s_3	s_4	z	
	1	1	0	0	1	0	0	0	0	28
	0	0	1	1	0	1	0	0	0	8
	1	0	1	0	0	0	−1	0	0	20
	0	1	0	1	0	0	0	−1	0	16
	220	300	400	180	0	0	0	0	1	0

Because $s_3 = -20$, we choose the positive entry farthest to the left in row 3, which is the 1 in column 1. After forming the necessary quotients, we find that the 1 is also the pivot, leading to the following tableau.

	y_1	y_2	y_3	y_4	s_1	s_2	s_3	s_4	z	
$-R_3 + R_1 \rightarrow R_1$	0	**1**	−1	0	1	0	1	0	0	8
	0	0	1	1	0	1	0	0	0	8
	1	0	1	0	0	0	−1	0	0	20
	0	1	0	1	0	0	0	−1	0	16
$-220R_3 + R_5 \rightarrow R_5$	0	300	180	180	0	0	220	0	1	−4400

We still have $s_4 = -16$. Verify that the 1 in row 1, column 2, is the next pivot, leading to the following tableau.

$$\begin{array}{c} \\ \\ \\ -R_1 + R_4 \rightarrow R_4 \\ -300R_1 + R_5 \rightarrow R_5 \end{array} \begin{array}{ccccccccc} y_1 & y_2 & y_3 & y_4 & s_1 & s_2 & s_3 & s_4 & z \\ \left[\begin{array}{ccccccccc|c} 0 & 1 & -1 & 0 & 1 & 0 & 1 & 0 & 0 & 8 \\ 0 & 0 & 1 & 1 & 0 & 1 & 0 & 0 & 0 & 8 \\ 1 & 0 & 1 & 0 & 0 & 0 & -1 & 0 & 0 & 20 \\ 0 & 0 & \boxed{1} & 1 & -1 & 0 & -1 & -1 & 0 & 8 \\ 0 & 0 & 480 & 180 & -300 & 0 & -80 & 0 & 1 & -6800 \end{array}\right] \end{array}$$

We still have $s_4 = -8$. Choosing column 3 to pivot, there is a tie between rows 2 and 4. Ordinarily in such cases, we arbitrarily choose the pivot in the row nearest to the top of the matrix. With surplus variables, however, we have the immediate goal of making all basic variables nonnegative. Because choosing row 4 will remove s_4 from the set of basic variables, we will choose as the pivot the 1 in column 3, row 4. The result is the following tableau.

$$\begin{array}{c} R_4 + R_1 \rightarrow R_1 \\ -R_4 + R_2 \rightarrow R_2 \\ -R_4 + R_3 \rightarrow R_3 \\ \\ -480R_4 + R_5 \rightarrow R_5 \end{array} \begin{array}{ccccccccc} y_1 & y_2 & y_3 & y_4 & s_1 & s_2 & s_3 & s_4 & z \\ \left[\begin{array}{ccc|cccccc|c} 0 & 1 & 0 & 1 & 0 & 0 & 0 & -1 & 0 & 16 \\ 0 & 0 & 0 & 0 & 1 & 1 & 1 & 1 & 0 & 0 \\ 1 & 0 & 0 & -1 & 1 & 0 & 0 & 1 & 0 & 12 \\ 0 & 0 & 1 & 1 & -1 & 0 & -1 & -1 & 0 & 8 \\ 0 & 0 & 0 & -300 & 180 & 0 & 400 & 480 & 1 & -10640 \end{array}\right] \end{array}$$

We now have the feasible solution

$$y_1 = 12, \quad y_2 = 16, \quad y_3 = 8, \quad y_4 = 0, \quad s_1 = 0, \quad s_2 = 0, \quad s_3 = 0, \quad s_4 = 0,$$

with $w = 10{,}640$. But there are still negative indicators in the bottom row, so we can keep going. After two more tableaus, we find that

$$y_1 = 20, \quad y_2 = 8, \quad y_3 = 0, \quad y_4 = 8,$$

with $w = 8240$. Therefore, the manufacturer should send 20 cars from plant I to dealership A and 8 cars to dealership B. From plant II, 8 cars should be sent to dealership B and none to dealership A. The transportation cost will then be $8240, a savings of $2400 over the original stated cost of $10,640. **TRY YOUR TURN 2**

YOUR TURN 2 Finish the missing steps in Example 2 and show the final tableau.

When one or more of the constraints in a linear programming problem is an equation, rather than an inequality, we add an **artificial variable** to each equation, rather than a slack or surplus variable. The first goal of the simplex method is to eliminate any artificial variables as basic variables, since they must have a value of 0 in the solution. We do this exactly the way we changed the surplus variables from having negative values to being zero. The only difference is that once an artificial variable is made nonbasic, we must never pivot on that column again, because that would change it to a basic variable. We must never carry out any pivot that would result in an artificial variable becoming nonzero.

EXAMPLE 3 **Artificial Variables**

In the transportation problem discussed in Example 2, it would be more realistic for the dealerships to order exactly 20 and 16 cars, respectively. Solve the problem with these two equality constraints.

SOLUTION Using the same variables, we can state the problem as follows.

$$\begin{aligned} \text{Minimize} \quad & w = 220y_1 + 300y_2 + 400y_3 + 180y_4 \\ \text{subject to:} \quad & y_1 + y_2 \le 28 \\ & y_3 + y_4 \le 8 \\ & y_1 + y_3 = 20 \\ & y_2 + y_4 = 16 \end{aligned}$$

with all variables nonnegative.

The corresponding system of equations requires slack variables s_1 and s_2 and two artificial variables that we shall call a_1 and a_2, to remind us that they require special handling. The system

$$
\begin{array}{rcrcrcrcrcrcrcr}
y_1 &+& y_2 & & & & &+& s_1 & & & & & & & & &=& 28 \\
& & & & y_3 &+& y_4 & & &+& s_2 & & & & & & &=& 8 \\
y_1 & & & & &+& y_3 & & & & &+& a_1 & & & & &=& 20 \\
& & y_2 & & &+& y_4 & & & & & & &+& a_2 & & &=& 16 \\
220y_1 &+& 300y_2 &+& 400y_3 &+& 180y_4 & & & & & & & & &+& z &=& 0
\end{array}
$$

produces a tableau exactly the same as in Example 2, except that the columns labeled s_3 and s_4 in that example are now labeled a_1 and a_2, and there is initially a 1 rather than a -1 in the columns for a_1 and a_2. The first three pivots are the same as in Example 2, resulting in the following tableau.

y_1	y_2	y_3	y_4	s_1	s_2	a_1	a_2	z	
0	1	0	1	0	0	0	1	0	16
0	0	0	0	1	1	-1	-1	0	0
1	0	0	-1	1	0	0	-1	0	12
0	0	1	1	-1	0	1	1	0	8
0	0	0	-300	180	0	-400	-480	1	-10640

NOTE
Another way to handle this situation is by solving for y_3 and y_4 in terms of y_1 and y_2. Then proceed with the usual method for standard problems.

Ordinarily our next step would be to pivot on the column with the indicator of -480, but that is not allowed because it would make a_2 a basic variable. Similarly, we cannot pivot on the column with the indicator of -400. Instead, we pivot on the column with the indicator of -300. Verify that after this step and one more tableau, we reach the same solution as in Example 2. In other problems, equality constraints can result in a higher cost.

CAUTION   If the artificial variables cannot be made equal to zero, the problem has no feasible solution.

Applications requiring the simplex method often have constraints that have a zero on the right-hand side. For example, in Exercise 35 of Section 2 a person wants to walk at least twice as many hours as she bikes. This results in one of the constraints $x_1 - 2x_2 \leq 0$ or $-x_1 + 2x_2 \geq 0$. For the purposes of using the simplex method to solve problems in the standard maximum form, it is always better to write constraints in the first form, since the first constraint can be readily handled by the basic simplex method by adding a slack variable.

Several linear programming models in actual use are presented on the Web site for this textbook. These models illustrate the usefulness of linear programming. In most real applications, the number of variables is so large that these problems could not be solved without using methods (like the simplex method) that can be adapted to computers.

4   EXERCISES

Rewrite each system of inequalities as a system of linear equations, adding slack variables or subtracting surplus variables as necessary.

1. $2x_1 + 3x_2 \leq 8$
   $x_1 + 4x_2 \geq 7$

2. $3x_1 + 7x_2 \leq 9$
   $4x_1 + 5x_2 \geq 11$

3. $2x_1 + x_2 + 2x_3 \leq 50$
   $x_1 + 3x_2 + x_3 \geq 35$
   $x_1 + 2x_2 \geq 15$

4. $2x_1 + x_3 \leq 40$
   $x_1 + x_2 \geq 18$
   $x_1 + x_3 \geq 20$

Convert each problem into a maximization problem.

5. Minimize $w = 3y_1 + 4y_2 + 5y_3$
   subject to: $y_1 + 2y_2 + 3y_3 \geq 9$
                $y_2 + 2y_3 \geq 8$
                $2y_1 + y_2 + 2y_3 \geq 6$
   with $y_1 \geq 0, \quad y_2 \geq 0, \quad y_3 \geq 0.$

6. Minimize $\quad w = 8y_1 + 3y_2 + y_3$

subject to: $\quad 7y_1 + 6y_2 + \ 8y_3 \geq 18$

$\qquad\qquad 4y_1 + 5y_2 + 10y_3 \geq 20$

with $\qquad\quad y_1 \geq 0, \quad y_2 \geq 0, \quad y_3 \geq 0.$

7. Minimize $\quad w = y_1 + 2y_2 + y_3 + 5y_4$

subject to: $\quad y_1 + y_2 + \ y_3 + y_4 \geq \ 50$

$\qquad\qquad 3y_1 + y_2 + 2y_3 + y_4 \geq 100$

with $\qquad\quad y_1 \geq 0, \quad y_2 \geq 0, \quad y_3 \geq 0, \quad y_4 \geq 0.$

8. Minimize $\quad w = y_1 + y_2 + 7y_3$

subject to: $\quad 5y_1 + 2y_2 + \ y_3 \geq 125$

$\qquad\qquad 4y_1 + \ y_2 + 6y_3 \leq \ 75$

$\qquad\qquad 6y_1 + 8y_2 \qquad\quad \geq \ 84$

with $\qquad\quad y_1 \geq 0, \quad y_2 \geq 0, \quad y_3 \geq 0.$

Use the simplex method to solve.

9. Find $x_1 \geq 0$ and $x_2 \geq 0$ such that

$$x_1 + 2x_2 \geq 24$$
$$x_1 + \ x_2 \leq 40$$

and $z = 12x_1 + 10x_2$ is maximized.

10. Find $x_1 \geq 0$ and $x_2 \geq 0$ such that

$$2x_1 + \ x_2 \geq 20$$
$$2x_1 + 5x_2 \leq 80$$

and $z = 6x_1 + 2x_2$ is maximized.

11. Find $x_1 \geq 0$, $x_2 \geq 0$, and $x_3 \geq 0$ such that

$$x_1 + x_2 + x_3 \leq 150$$
$$x_1 + x_2 + x_3 \geq 100$$

and $z = 2x_1 + 5x_2 + 3x_3$ is maximized.

12. Find $x_1 \geq 0$, $x_2 \geq 0$, and $x_3 \geq 0$ such that

$$x_1 + \ x_2 + \ x_3 \leq 15$$
$$4x_1 + 4x_2 + 2x_3 \geq 48$$

and $z = 2x_1 + x_2 + 3x_3$ is maximized.

13. Find $x_1 \geq 0$ and $x_2 \geq 0$ such that

$$x_1 + \ x_2 \leq 100$$
$$2x_1 + 3x_2 \leq \ 75$$
$$x_1 + 4x_2 \geq \ 50$$

and $z = 5x_1 - 3x_2$ is maximized.

14. Find $x_1 \geq 0$ and $x_2 \geq 0$ such that

$$x_1 + 2x_2 \leq 18$$
$$x_1 + 3x_2 \geq 12$$
$$2x_1 + 2x_2 \leq 24$$

and $z = 5x_1 - 10x_2$ is maximized.

15. Find $y_1 \geq 0$, $y_2 \geq 0$, and $y_3 \geq 0$ such that

$$5y_1 + \ 3y_2 + 2y_3 \leq 150$$
$$5y_1 + 10y_2 + 3y_3 \geq \ 90$$

and $w = 10y_1 + 12y_2 + 10y_3$ is minimized.

16. Minimize $\quad w = 3y_1 + 2y_2 + 3y_3$

subject to: $\quad 2y_1 + 3y_2 + 6y_3 \leq 60$

$\qquad\qquad y_1 + 4y_2 + 5y_3 \geq 40$

with $\qquad\quad y_1 \geq 0, \quad y_2 \geq 0, \quad y_3 \geq 0.$

Solve using artificial variables.

17. Maximize $\quad z = 3x_1 + 2x_2$

subject to: $\quad x_1 + \ x_2 = \ 50$

$\qquad\qquad 4x_1 + 2x_2 \geq 120$

$\qquad\qquad 5x_1 + 2x_2 \leq 200$

with $\qquad\quad x_1 \geq 0, \quad x_2 \geq 0.$

18. Maximize $\quad z = 5x_1 + 7x_2$

subject to: $\quad x_1 + \ x_2 = 15$

$\qquad\qquad 2x_1 + 4x_2 \geq 30$

$\qquad\qquad 3x_1 + 5x_2 \geq 10$

with $\qquad\quad x_1 \geq 0, \quad x_2 \geq 0.$

19. Minimize $\quad w = 32y_1 + 40y_2 + 48y_3$

subject to: $\quad 20y_1 + 10y_2 + \ 5y_3 = 200$

$\qquad\qquad 25y_1 + 40y_2 + 50y_3 \leq 500$

$\qquad\qquad 18y_1 + 24y_2 + 12y_3 \geq 300$

with $\qquad\quad y_1 \geq 0, \quad y_2 \geq 0, \quad y_3 \geq 0.$

20. Minimize $\quad w = 15y_1 + 12y_2 + 18y_3$

subject to: $\qquad y_1 + 2y_2 + 3y_3 \leq 12$

$\qquad\qquad 3y_1 + \ y_2 + 3y_3 \geq 18$

$\qquad\qquad y_1 + \ y_2 + \ y_3 = 10$

with $\qquad\quad y_1 \geq 0, \quad y_2 \geq 0, \quad y_3 \geq 0.$

21. Explain how, in any linear programming problem, the value of the objective function can be found without using the number in the lower right-hand corner of the final tableau.

22. Explain why, for a maximization problem, you write the negative of the coefficients of the objective function on the bottom row, while, for a minimization problem, you write the coefficients themselves.

APPLICATIONS

Business and Economics

23. Transportation   Southwestern Oil supplies two distributors in the Northwest from two outlets, S_1 and S_2. Distributor D_1 needs at least 3000 barrels of oil, and distributor D_2 needs at least 5000 barrels. The two outlets can each furnish up to 5000 barrels of oil. The costs per barrel to ship the oil are given in the table.

		Distributors	
		D_1	D_2
Outlets	S_1	$30	$20
	S_2	$25	$22

There is also a shipping tax per barrel as given in the table below. Southwestern Oil is determined to spend no more than $40,000 on shipping tax.

	D_1	D_2
S_1	$2	$6
S_2	$5	$4

a. How should the oil be supplied to minimize shipping costs?

b. Find and interpret the values of any nonzero slack or surplus variables.

24. Transportation Change Exercise 23 so that the two outlets each furnish exactly 5000 barrels of oil, with everything else the same. Use artificial variables to solve the problem, following the steps outlined in Example 3.

25. Finance A bank has set aside a maximum of $25 million for commercial and home loans. Every million dollars in commercial loans requires 2 lengthy application forms, while every million dollars in home loans requires 3 lengthy application forms. The bank cannot process more than 72 application forms at this time. The bank's policy is to loan at least four times as much for home loans as for commercial loans. Because of prior commitments, at least $10 million will be used for these two types of loans. The bank earns 10% on commercial loans and 12% on home loans. What amount of money should be allotted for each type of loan to maximize the interest income?

26. Blending Seed Topgrade Turf lawn seed mixture contains three types of seed: bluegrass, rye, and Bermuda. The costs per pound of the three types of seed are 16 cents, 14 cents, and 12 cents, respectively. In each batch there must be at least 25% bluegrass seed, and the amount of Bermuda must be no more than 2/3 the amount of rye. To fill current orders, the company must make at least 6000 lb of the mixture. How much of each kind of seed should be used to minimize cost?

27. Blending Seed Change Exercise 26 so that the company must make exactly 6000 lb of the mixture. Use artificial variables to solve the problem.

28. Investments Lynda Rago has decided to invest a $100,000 inheritance in government securities that earn 7% per year, municipal bonds that earn 6% per year, and mutual funds that earn an average of 10% per year. She will spend at least $40,000 on government securities, and she wants at least half the inheritance to go to bonds and mutual funds. Government securities have an initial fee of 2%, municipal bonds have an initial fee of 1%, and mutual funds have an initial fee of 3%. Lynda has $2400 available to pay initial fees. How much should be invested in each way to maximize the interest yet meet the constraints? What is the maximum interest she can earn?

29. Transportation The manufacturer of a popular personal computer has orders from two dealers. Dealer D_1 wants at least 32 computers, and dealer D_2 wants at least 20 computers. The manufacturer can fill the orders from either of two warehouses, W_1 or W_2. There are 25 computers on hand at W_1, and 30 at W_2. The costs (in dollars) to ship one computer to each dealer from each warehouse are given in the following table.

		Dealer	
		D_1	D_2
Warehouse	W_1	$14	$12
	W_2	$12	$10

a. How should the orders be filled to minimize shipping costs?

b. Find and interpret the values of any nonzero slack or surplus variables.

30. Calorie Expenditure Joe Vetere's exercise regimen includes light calisthenics, swimming, and playing the drums. He has at most 10 hours per week to devote to these activities. He wants the total time he does calisthenics and plays the drums to be at least twice as long as he swims. His neighbors, however, will tolerate no more than 4 hours per week on the drums. According to a website, a 190-pound person like Joe will burn an average of 388 calories per hour doing calisthenics, 518 calories per hour swimming, and 345 calories per hour playing the drums. In Section 2, Exercise 36, Joe found that he could maximize calories burned in an exercise routine that did not include playing the drums as part of his exercise plan. *Source: NutriStrategy.com.*

a. Joe really likes to play the drums and insists that his exercise plan include at least 1 hour of playing the drums per week. With this added constraint, now how many hours per week should Joe spend on each exercise to maximize the number of calories he burns? What is the maximum number of calories he will burn?

b. Without the added constraint from part a, Joe's maximum calorie expenditure was $4313\frac{1}{3}$ calories. Compare this number with the new optimal solution. What conclusions can you draw when additional constraints are placed on a problem?

c. Show how the solution from part a can be found without using the simplex method by considering the constraints and the number of calories for each activity.

31. Blending Chemicals Natural Brand plant food is made from three chemicals, labeled I, II, and III. In each batch of the plant food, the amounts of chemicals II and III must be in the ratio of 4 to 3. The amount of nitrogen must be at least 30 kg. The percent of nitrogen in the three chemicals is 9%, 4%, and 3%, respectively. If the three chemicals cost $1.09, $0.87, and $0.65 per kilogram, respectively, how much of each should be used to minimize the cost of producing at least 750 kg of the plant food?

32. Blending a Soft Drink A popular soft drink called Sugarlo, which is advertised as having a sugar content of no more than 10%, is blended from five ingredients, each of which has some sugar content. Water may also be added to dilute the mixture. The sugar content of the ingredients and their costs per gallon are given below.

	Ingredient					
	1	2	3	4	5	Water
Sugar Content (%)	0.28	0.19	0.43	0.57	0.22	0
Cost ($/gal)	0.48	0.32	0.53	0.28	0.43	0.04

At least 0.01 of the content of Sugarlo must come from ingredients 3 or 4, 0.01 must come from ingredients 2 or 5, and 0.01 from ingredients 1 or 4. How much of each ingredient should be used in preparing 15,000 gal of Sugarlo to minimize the cost?

33. Blending Gasoline A company is developing a new additive for gasoline. The additive is a mixture of three liquid ingredients, I, II, and III. For proper performance, the total amount of additive must be at least 10 oz per gal of gasoline. However, for safety reasons, the amount of additive should not exceed 15 oz per gal of gasoline. At least 1/4 oz of ingredient I must be used for every ounce of ingredient II, and at least 1 oz of ingredient III must be used for every ounce of ingredient I. If the costs of I, II, and III are \$0.30, \$0.09, and \$0.27 per oz, respec-

tively, find the mixture of the three ingredients that produces the minimum cost of the additive. How much of the additive should be used per gal of gasoline?

YOUR TURN ANSWERS

1. Minimum is 10 when $y_1 = 0$ and $y_2 = 5/2$.

2.
$$
\left[
\begin{array}{ccccccccc|c}
0 & 1 & -1 & 0 & 0 & -1 & 0 & -1 & 0 & 8 \\
0 & 0 & 0 & 0 & 1 & 1 & 1 & 1 & 0 & 0 \\
1 & 0 & 1 & 0 & 0 & 0 & -1 & 0 & 0 & 20 \\
0 & 0 & 1 & 1 & 0 & 1 & 0 & 0 & 0 & 8 \\
\hline
0 & 0 & 300 & 0 & 0 & 120 & 220 & 300 & 1 & -8240
\end{array}
\right]
$$

CHAPTER REVIEW

SUMMARY

In this chapter, we introduced the simplex method, which is a procedure for solving any linear programming problem. To apply this method, we first had to write the problem as a standard maximization problem in matrix form. This form tells us an initial basic feasible solution, which the simplex method uses to determine other basic feasible solutions. Each successive iteration of the simplex method gives us a new basic feasible solution, whose objective function value is greater than or equal to the objective function value of the previous basic feasible solution. We then

introduced duality, which tells us that every time we solve a linear programming problem, we are actually solving two problems—a maximization problem and a minimization problem. This has far-reaching consequences in the fields of operations research and decision sciences, including the fact that standard minimization problems can be solved by the simplex method. Finally, we extended the simplex method to solve problems that are not standard because they have inequalities going in both directions (and perhaps equalities as well).

Standard Maximum Form A linear programming problem is in standard maximum form if the following conditions are satisfied.

1. The objective function is to be maximized.

2. All variables are nonnegative.

3. All remaining constraints are stated in the form

$$a_1x_1 + a_2x_2 + \cdots + a_nx_n \le b \qquad \text{with } b \ge 0.$$

Simplex Method
1. Determine the objective function.

2. Write all the necessary constraints.

3. Convert each constraint into an equation by adding a slack variable in each.

4. Set up the initial simplex tableau.

5. Locate the most negative indicator. If there are two such indicators, choose the one farther to the left.

6. Form the necessary quotients to find the pivot. Disregard any quotients with 0 or a negative number in the denominator. The smallest nonnegative quotient gives the location of the pivot. If all quotients must be disregarded, no maximum solutions exist. If two quotients are both equal and smallest, choose the pivot in the row nearest the top of the matrix.

7. Use row operations to change all other numbers in the pivot column to zero by adding a suitable multiple of the pivot row to a positive multiple of each row.

8. If the indicators are all positive or 0, this is the final tableau. If not, go back to step 5 and repeat the process until a tableau with no negative indicators is obtained.

9. Read the solution from the final tableau.

Standard Minimum Form   A linear programming problem is in standard minimum form if the following conditions are satisfied.

1. The objective function is to be minimized.

2. All variables are nonnegative.

3. All remaining constraints are stated in the form

$$a_1 y_1 + a_2 y_2 + \cdots + a_n y_n \geq b \qquad \text{with } b \geq 0.$$

Theorem of Duality   The objective function w of a minimization linear programming problem takes on a minimum value if and only if the objective function z of the corresponding dual maximization problem takes on a maximum value. The maximum value of z equals the minimum value of w.

Solving a Standard Minimum Problem with Duals

1. Find the dual standard maximization problem.

2. Solve the maximization problem using the simplex method.

3. The minimum value of the objective function w is the maximum value of the objective function z.

4. The optimum solution is given by the entries in the bottom row of the columns corresponding to the slack variables, as long as the entry in the z column is equal to 1.

Solving a Nonstandard Problem

1. If necessary, convert the problem to a maximization problem.

2. Add slack variables and subtract surplus variables as needed.

3. Write the initial simplex tableau.

4. If any basic variable has a negative value, locate the nonzero number in that variable's column, and note what row it is in.

5. In the row located in step 4, find the positive entry that is farthest to the left, and note what column it is in.

6. In the column found in step 5, choose a pivot by investigating quotients.

7. Use row operations to change the other numbers in the pivot column to 0.

8. Continue steps 4 through 7 until all basic variables are nonnegative. If it ever becomes impossible to continue, then the problem has no feasible solution.

9. Once a feasible solution has been found, continue to use the simplex method until the optimal solution is found.

Artificial Variables   When one or more of the constraints in a linear programming problem is an equation, rather than an inequality, an artificial variable is added to each equation. Artificial variables are handled in the same way as surplus variables, except that once an artificial variable is no longer basic, never pivot on its column. If in the optimal solution an artificial variable has a positive value, then the original problem does not have a solution.

KEY TERMS

simplex method
1
standard maximum form
slack variable
simplex tableau
indicators

basic variable
basic feasible solution
pivot
2
sensitivity analysis

3
standard minimum form
dual
transpose
shadow costs

4
surplus variable
two-phase method
artificial variable

REVIEW EXERCISES

CONCEPT CHECK

Determine whether each of the following statements is true or false, and explain why.

1. The simplex method can be used to solve all linear programming problems.

2. If the feasible region of a linear programming problem is unbounded, then the objective function value is unbounded.

3. A linear programming problem in standard maximization form always has a feasible solution.

4. A linear programming problem in standard minimization form always has a feasible solution.

5. A linear programming problem in standard maximization form always has a finite optimal solution.

6. The tableau below for a linear program in standard maximization form shows that it has no finite maximum value.

$$\begin{array}{ccccc} x_1 & x_2 & s_1 & s_2 & z \\ \left[\begin{array}{ccccc|c} -1 & 1 & 0 & 1 & 0 & 1 \\ \hline -4 & 0 & 1 & -2 & 0 & 3 \\ \hline -1 & 0 & 0 & 2 & 1 & 4 \end{array}\right] \end{array}$$

7. One must always use the minimum quotient when choosing a pivot row.

8. If there is a 0 in the right-hand column, we can disregard it when determining the quotients used to choose the pivot row.

9. One must always pick the most negative number in the indicator row when choosing the pivot column.

10. A basic variable can be assigned a value of zero by the simplex method.

11. A slack variable of a linear programming problem in standard maximization form may become negative during the intermediate stages of the simplex method.

12. The dual of the dual of a linear programming problem is the original problem.

13. The simplex method guarantees that each iteration will yield a feasible solution whose objective function value is bigger than the objective function value of all previous solutions.

14. Standard maximization problems can only have slack variables, and standard minimization problems (not solved by the dual method) can only have surplus variables.

PRACTICE AND EXPLORATIONS

15. When is it necessary to use the simplex method rather than the graphical method?

16. What can you conclude if a surplus variable cannot be made nonnegative?

For each problem, (a) add slack variables or subtract surplus variables, and (b) set up the initial simplex tableau.

17. Maximize $\quad z = 2x_1 + 7x_2$

subject to: $\quad 4x_1 + 6x_2 \le 60$

$\qquad\qquad 3x_1 + x_2 \le 18$

$\qquad\qquad 2x_1 + 5x_2 \le 20$

$\qquad\qquad x_1 + x_2 \le 15$

with $\qquad x_1 \ge 0, \quad x_2 \ge 0.$

18. Maximize $\quad z = 25x_1 + 30x_2$

subject to: $\quad 3x_1 + 5x_2 \le 47$

$\qquad\qquad x_1 + x_2 \le 25$

$\qquad\qquad 5x_1 + 2x_2 \le 35$

$\qquad\qquad 2x_1 + x_2 \le 30$

with $\qquad x_1 \ge 0, \quad x_2 \ge 0.$

19. Maximize $\quad z = 5x_1 + 8x_2 + 6x_3$

subject to: $\quad x_1 + x_2 + x_3 \le 90$

$\qquad\qquad 2x_1 + 5x_2 + x_3 \le 120$

$\qquad\qquad x_1 + 3x_2 \ge 80$

with $\qquad x_1 \ge 0, \quad x_2 \ge 0, \quad x_3 \ge 0.$

20. Maximize $\quad z = 4x_1 + 6x_2 + 8x_3$

subject to: $\quad x_1 + x_2 + 2x_3 \ge 200$

$\qquad\qquad 8x_1 + 6x_3 \le 400$

$\qquad\qquad 3x_1 + 5x_2 + x_3 \le 300$

with $\qquad x_1 \ge 0, \quad x_2 \ge 0, \quad x_3 \ge 0.$

Use the simplex method to solve each maximization linear programming problem with the given initial tableau.

21.
$$\begin{array}{cccccc} x_1 & x_2 & x_3 & s_1 & s_2 & z \\ \left[\begin{array}{cccccc|c} 4 & 5 & 2 & 1 & 0 & 0 & 18 \\ \hline 2 & 8 & 6 & 0 & 1 & 0 & 24 \\ \hline -5 & -3 & -6 & 0 & 0 & 1 & 0 \end{array}\right] \end{array}$$

22.
$$\begin{array}{ccccc} x_1 & x_2 & s_1 & s_2 & z \\ \left[\begin{array}{ccccc|c} 2 & 7 & 1 & 0 & 0 & 14 \\ \hline 2 & 3 & 0 & 1 & 0 & 10 \\ \hline -2 & -4 & 0 & 0 & 1 & 0 \end{array}\right] \end{array}$$

23.
$$\begin{array}{ccccccc} x_1 & x_2 & x_3 & s_1 & s_2 & s_3 & z \\ \left[\begin{array}{ccccccc|c} 1 & 2 & 2 & 1 & 0 & 0 & 0 & 50 \\ 3 & 1 & 0 & 0 & 1 & 0 & 0 & 20 \\ 1 & 0 & 2 & 0 & 0 & -1 & 0 & 15 \\ \hline -5 & -3 & -2 & 0 & 0 & 0 & 1 & 0 \end{array}\right] \end{array}$$

24.
$$\begin{array}{cccccc} x_1 & x_2 & s_1 & s_2 & s_3 & z \\ \left[\begin{array}{cccccc|c} 3 & 6 & -1 & 0 & 0 & 0 & 28 \\ 1 & 1 & 0 & 1 & 0 & 0 & 12 \\ 2 & 1 & 0 & 0 & 1 & 0 & 16 \\ \hline -1 & -2 & 0 & 0 & 0 & 1 & 0 \end{array}\right] \end{array}$$

Convert each problem into a maximization problem and then solve each problem using both the dual method and the method of Section 4.

25. Minimize $\quad w = 10y_1 + 15y_2$

subject to: $\quad y_1 + y_2 \ge 17$

$\qquad\qquad 5y_1 + 8y_2 \ge 42$

with $\qquad y_1 \ge 0, \quad y_2 \ge 0.$

26. Minimize $\quad w = 22y_1 + 44y_2 + 33y_3$

subject to: $\quad y_1 + 2y_2 + y_3 \ge 3$

$\qquad\qquad y_1 + y_3 \ge 3$

$\qquad\qquad 3y_1 + 2y_2 + 2y_3 \ge 8$

with $\qquad y_1 \ge 0, \quad y_2 \ge 0, \quad y_3 \ge 0.$

27. Minimize $\quad w = 7y_1 + 2y_2 + 3y_3$

subject to: $\quad y_1 + y_2 + 2y_3 \ge 48$

$\qquad\qquad y_1 + y_2 \ge 12$

$\qquad\qquad y_3 \ge 10$

$\qquad\qquad 3y_1 + y_3 \ge 30$

with $\qquad y_1 \ge 0, \quad y_2 \ge 0, \quad y_3 \ge 0.$

28. Minimize $w = 3y_1 + 4y_2 + y_3 + 2y_4$

subject to: $4y_1 + 6y_2 + 3y_3 + 8y_4 \geq 19$

$13y_1 + 7y_2 + 2y_3 + 6y_4 \geq 16$

with $y_1 \geq 0, \quad y_2 \geq 0, \quad y_3 \geq 0, \quad y_4 \geq 0.$

Use the simplex method to solve each problem. (You may need to use artificial variables.)

29. Maximize $z = 20x_1 + 30x_2$

subject to: $5x_1 + 10x_2 \leq 120$

$10x_1 + 15x_2 \geq 200$

with $x_1 \geq 0, \quad x_2 \geq 0.$

30. Minimize $w = 4y_1 + 2y_2$

subject to: $y_1 + 3y_2 \geq 6$

$2y_1 + 8y_2 \leq 21$

with $y_1 \geq 0, \quad y_2 \geq 0.$

31. Maximize $z = 10x_1 + 12x_2$

subject to: $2x_1 + 2x_2 = 17$

$2x_1 + 5x_2 \geq 22$

$4x_1 + 3x_2 \leq 28$

with $x_1 \geq 0, \quad x_2 \geq 0.$

32. Minimize $w = 24y_1 + 30y_2 + 36y_3$

subject to: $5y_1 + 10y_2 + 15y_3 \geq 1200$

$y_1 + y_2 + y_3 \leq 50$

with $y_1 \geq 0, \quad y_2 \geq 0, \quad y_3 \geq 0.$

33. What types of problems can be solved using slack, surplus, and artificial variables?

34. What kind of problems can be solved using the method of duals?

35. In solving a linear programming problem, you are given the following initial tableau.

$$\begin{bmatrix} 4 & 2 & 3 & 1 & 0 & 0 & | & 9 \\ 5 & 4 & 1 & 0 & 1 & 0 & | & 10 \\ \hline -6 & -7 & -5 & 0 & 0 & 1 & | & 0 \end{bmatrix}$$

a. What is the problem being solved?

b. If the 1 in row 1, column 4 were a -1 rather than a 1, how would it change your answer to part a?

c. After several steps of the simplex algorithm, the following tableau results.

$$\begin{bmatrix} 3 & 0 & 5 & 2 & -1 & 0 & | & 8 \\ 11 & 10 & 0 & -1 & 3 & 0 & | & 21 \\ \hline 47 & 0 & 0 & 13 & 11 & 10 & | & 227 \end{bmatrix}$$

What is the solution? (List only the values of the original variables and the objective function. Do not include slack or surplus variables.)

d. What is the dual of the problem you found in part a?

e. What is the solution of the dual you found in part d? (Do not perform any steps of the simplex algorithm; just examine the tableau given in part c.)

36. In Chapter 2 we wrote a system of linear equations using matrix notation. We can do the same thing for the system of linear inequalities in this chapter.

a. Find matrices A, B, C, and X such that the maximization problem in Example 1 of Section 1 can be written as

Maximize CX

subject to: $AX \leq B$

with $X \geq O.$

(*Hint:* Let B and X be column matrices, and C a row matrix.)

b. Show that the dual of the problem in part a can be written as

Minimize YB

subject to: $YA \geq C$

with $Y \geq O,$

where Y is a row matrix.

c. Show that for any feasible solutions X and Y to the original and dual problems, respectively, $CX \leq YB$. (*Hint:* Multiply both sides of $AX \leq B$ by Y on the left. Then substitute for YA.)

d. For the solution X to the maximization problem and Y to the dual, it can be shown that

$$CX = YB$$

is always true. Verify this for Example 1 of Section 1. What is the significance of the value in CX (or YB)?

APPLICATIONS

For Exercises 37–40, (a) select appropriate variables; (b) write the objective functions; (c) write the constraints as inequalities.

Business and Economics

37. Production The Bronze Forge produces and ships three different hand-crafted bronze plates: a dogwood-engraved cake plate, a wheat-engraved bread plate, and a lace-engraved dinner plate. Each cake plate requires \$15 in materials, 5 hours of labor, and \$6 to ship. Each bread plate requires \$10 in materials, 4 hours of labor, and \$5 to ship. Each dinner plate requires \$8 in materials, 4 hours of labor, and \$5 to deliver. The profit on the cake plate is \$15, on the bread plate is \$12, and on the dinner plate is \$5. The company has available up to 2700 hours of labor per week. Each week, they can spend at most \$1500 on materials and \$1200 on delivery. How many of each plate should the company produce to maximize their weekly profit? What is their maximum profit?

38. Investments An investor is considering three types of investments: a high-risk venture into oil leases with a potential return of 15%, a medium-risk investment in stocks with a 9% return, and a relatively safe bond investment with a 5% return. He has \$50,000 to invest. Because of the risk, he will limit his investment in oil leases and stocks to 30% and his investment in oil leases and bonds to 50%. How much should he invest in each to maximize his return, assuming investment returns are as expected?

39. Profit The Aged Wood Winery makes two white wines, Fruity and Crystal, from two kinds of grapes and sugar. One gallon of Fruity wine requires 2 bushels of Grape A, 2 bushels of Grape B, and 2 lb of sugar, and produces a profit of $12. One gallon of Crystal wine requires 1 bushel of Grape A, 3 bushels of Grape B, and 1 lb of sugar, and produces a profit of $15. The winery has available 110 bushels of grape A, 125 bushels of grape B, and 90 lb of sugar. How much of each wine should be made to maximize profit?

40. Production Costs Cauchy Canners produces canned whole tomatoes and tomato sauce. This season, the company has available 3,000,000 kg of tomatoes for these two products. To meet the demands of regular customers, it must produce at least 80,000 kg of sauce and 800,000 kg of whole tomatoes. The cost per kilogram is $4 to produce canned whole tomatoes and $3.25 to produce tomato sauce. Labor agreements require that at least 110,000 person-hours be used. Each kilogram can of sauce requires 3 minutes for one worker, and each kilogram can of whole tomatoes requires 6 minutes for one worker. How many kilograms of tomatoes should Cauchy use for each product to minimize cost? (For simplicity, assume production of y_1 kg of canned whole tomatoes and y_2 kg of tomato sauce requires $y_1 + y_2$ kg of tomatoes.)

41. Solve Exercise 37.   **42.** Solve Exercise 38.

43. Solve Exercise 39.   **44.** Solve Exercise 40.

45. Canning Cauchy Canners produces canned corn, beans, and carrots. Demand for vegetables requires it to produce at least 1000 cases per month. Based on past sales, it should produce at least twice as many cases of corn as of beans, and at least 340 cases of carrots. It costs $10 to produce a case of corn, $15 to produce a case of beans, and $25 to produce a case of carrots.

a. Using the method of surplus variables, find how many cases of each vegetable should be produced to minimize costs. What is the minimum cost?

b. Using the method of duals, find how many cases of each vegetable should be produced to minimize costs. What is the minimum cost?

c. Suppose the minimum number of cases that must be produced each month rises to 1100. Use shadow costs to calculate the total cost in this case.

46. Food Cost A store sells two brands of snacks. A package of Sun Hill costs $3 and contains 10 oz of peanuts, 4 oz of raisins, and 2 oz of rolled oats. A package of Bear Valley costs $2 and contains 2 oz of peanuts, 4 oz of raisins, and 8 oz of rolled oats. Suppose you wish to make a mixture that contains at least 20 oz of peanuts, 24 oz of raisins, and 24 oz of rolled oats.

a. Using the method of surplus variables, find how many packages of each you should buy to minimize the cost. What is the minimum cost?

b. Using the method of duals, find how many packages of each you should buy to minimize the cost. What is the minimum cost?

c. Suppose the minimum amount of peanuts is increased to 28. Use shadow costs to calculate the total cost in this case.

d. Explain why it makes sense that the shadow cost for rolled oats is 0.

Life Sciences

47. Calorie Expenditure Ginger's exercise regimen includes doing tai chi, riding a unicycle, and fencing. She has at most 10 hours per week to devote to these activities. Her fencing partner can work with her at most only 2 hours per week. She wants the total time she does tai chi to be at least twice as long as she unicycles. According to a website, a 130-pound person like Ginger will burn an average of 236 calories per hour doing tai chi, 295 calories per hour riding a unicycle, and 354 calories per hour fencing. *Source: NutriStrategy.com.*

a. How many hours per week should Ginger spend on each activity to maximize the number of calories she burns? What is the maximum number of calories she will burn?

b. Show how the solution from part a can be found without using the simplex method by considering the constraints and the number of calories for each activity.

EXTENDED APPLICATION

USING INTEGER PROGRAMMING IN THE STOCK-CUTTING PROBLEM

Some problems require solutions in integers because the resources to be allocated are items that can't be split into pieces, like cargo containers or airplanes. These *integer programming* problems are generally harder than the linear programming problems we have been solving by the simplex method, but often linear programming can be combined with other techniques to solve integer problems. Even if the number of variables and constraints is small, some help from software is usually required. We will introduce integer programming with the basic but important *stock-cutting problem*. (To get a feeling for the issues involved, you may want to try the simple stock-cutting problem given in Exercise 1.)

A paper mill produces rolls of paper that are much wider than most customers require, often as wide as 200 in. The mill then cuts these wide rolls into smaller widths to fill orders for paper rolls to

Source: Northwestern University and the Special Interest Group on Cutting and Packing

be used in printing and packaging and other applications. The stock-cutting problem is the following:

Given a list of roll widths and the number of rolls ordered for each width, decide how to cut the raw rolls that come from the paper-making machine into smaller rolls so as to fill all the orders with a minimum amount of waste.

Another way to state the problem is: What is the minimum number of raw rolls required to fill the orders? This is an integer problem because the customers have ordered whole numbers of rolls, and each roll is cut in a single piece from one of the raw rolls.

As an example, suppose the paper machine produces rolls 100 in. wide. The manufacturer offers rolls in the following six widths: 14 in., 17 in., 31 in., 33 in., 36 in., and 45 in. (We'll call these the standard widths.) The current orders to be filled are as follows:

	Rolls of Paper Ordered					
Width in Inches	14	17	31	33	36	45
Number Ordered	100	123	239	121	444	87

The cutting machine can make four simultaneous cuts, so a raw roll can be cut into as many as five pieces. With luck, all five pieces might be usable for filling orders, but there will usually be unusable waste on the end, and we also might end up with more rolls of some standard width than we need. We'll consider both the end pieces that are too narrow and any unused standard-width rolls as waste, and this is the waste we want to minimize.

The first question is, what are the possible cutting patterns? We're restricted to at most five standard rolls from any given raw roll, and we'll elect to use as much as possible in each raw roll so that the waste remaining at the end will always be less than 14 in. So, for example, 14|36|45| is a possible pattern, but 14|14|14|14|14| is not, because it has too many cuts, and 45|36| is not, because more than 14 in. is left at the end. (Each vertical bar represents a cut; if the piece on the end happens to be a standard width, then we don't need a cut after it, since we've reached the end of the roll.) This is already a tricky problem, and variations of it appear in many industrial applications involving packing objects of different sizes into a fixed space (for example, packing crates into a container for shipment overseas). In the Exercises we'll ask you to write down some more possible patterns, but finding all of them is a job for a computer, and it turns out that there are exactly 33 possible cutting patterns.

The next question is, what's the best we can do? We have to use an integral number of 100-in. raw rolls, and we can find the total "roll-inches" ordered by multiplying the width of each standard roll by the number ordered for this width. This computation is a natural one for the matrix notation that you have learned. If W and O are 6×1 column matrices, then the total roll inches used is $W^{T}O$:

$$W = \begin{bmatrix} 14 \\ 17 \\ 31 \\ 33 \\ 36 \\ 45 \end{bmatrix} \quad O = \begin{bmatrix} 100 \\ 123 \\ 239 \\ 121 \\ 444 \\ 87 \end{bmatrix} \quad W^{T}O = 34{,}792$$

Since each raw roll is 100 in., the best we can do is to use 348 rolls with a total width of 34,800. As a percentage of the raw material, the corresponding waste is

$$\frac{8}{34{,}800} \approx 0.02\%,$$

which represents very low waste. Of course, we'll only reach this target if we can lay out the cutting with perfect efficiency.

As we noted previously, these integer programming problems are difficult, but many mathematical analysis and spreadsheet programs have built-in optimization routines that can handle problems of modest size. We submitted this problem to one such program, giving it the lists of orders and widths and a list of the 33 allowable cutting patterns. Figure 10 shows the seven cutting patterns chosen by the minimizer software, with a graphical representation, and the total number of times each pattern was used.

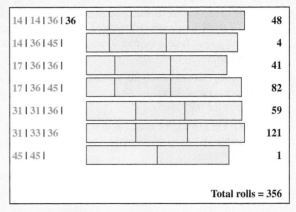

FIGURE 10

With these cutting choices we generate the following numbers of each standard width:

	Solution to Stock-cutting Problem					
Width	14	17	31	33	36	45
Quantity Produced	100	123	239	121	444	88
Quantity Ordered	100	123	239	121	444	87

We figured that the minimum possible number of raw rolls was 348, so we have used only 8 more than the minimum. In the Exercises you'll figure the percentage of waste with this cutting plan.

Manufacturers of glass and sheet metal encounter a two-dimensional version of this problem: They need to cut the rectangular pieces that have been ordered from a larger rectangular piece of glass or metal, laying out the ordered sizes so as to minimize waste.

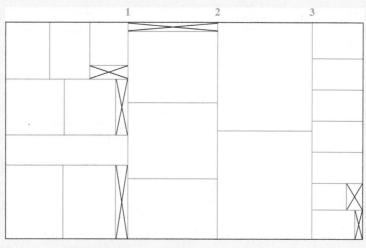

FIGURE 11

Besides the extra dimension, this problem is complicated by another constraint: The typical cutting machine can make only "guillotine cuts" that go completely across the sheet being cut, so a cutting algorithm must usually begin with a few long cuts that cut the original rectangle into strips, followed by crossways cuts that begin to create the order sizes. A typical finished cutting layout might look like Figure 11.

The first cuts would be the three vertical cuts labeled 1, 2, and 3, followed by horizontal cuts in each of the four resulting strips, then vertical cuts in these new rectangles, and so on. Areas of waste are marked with X. An additional complication in designing the layout is that any given stock rectangle can be oriented in two different directions (unless it's square), so the packing problem has many alternative solutions.

In three dimensions, a comparable problem is to fill a shipping container with smaller boxes (rectangular prisms) with the minimum wasted space. These packing problems are complicated geometric versions of a basic problem called the *knapsack problem*:

Given n objects with weights $w_1, w_2, \ldots, w_n$ and cash values $v_1, v_2, \ldots, v_n$ and a knapsack that can hold a weight of at most W, choose the objects that will pack in the greatest value. In the Exercises you can try a small example, but as soon as n gets large, this problem "explodes," that is, the number of possibilities becomes too large for a trial-and-error solution, even with a computer to do the bookkeeping. The development of good algorithms for cutting and packing problems is an active research specialty in the field of optimization.

EXERCISES

1. Suppose you plan to build a raised flower bed using landscape timbers, which come in 8-ft lengths. You want the bed's outer dimensions to be 6 ft by 4 ft, and you will use three layers of timbers. The timbers are 6 in. by 6 in. in cross section, so if you make the bottom and top layers with 6-ft lengths on the sides and 3-ft lengths on the ends, and the middle layer with 5-ft lengths on the sides and 4-ft lengths on the ends, you could build the bed out of the following lengths.

Plan A	
Length	Number Needed
3 ft	4
4 ft	2
5 ft	2
6 ft	4

a. What is the smallest number of timbers you can buy to build your bed? How will you lay out the cuts? How much wood will you waste?

b. If you overlap the corners in a different way, you can build the bed with this plan:

Plan B	
Length	Needed
3 ft	2
4 ft	4
5 ft	4
6 ft	2

Does plan B allow you to build the bed with fewer 8-ft timbers?

c. What is the smallest length for the uncut timbers that would allow you to build the bed with no waste?

2. For the list of standard paper roll widths given earlier, write down four more possible cutting patterns that use at most four cuts and leave less than 14 in. of waste on the end. See if you can find ones that aren't in the list of patterns returned by the optimizer.

3. Four of the 33 possible patterns use up the raw roll with no waste, that is, the widths add up to exactly 100 in. Find these four patterns.

4. For the computer solution of the cutting problem, figure out the percent of the 356 rolls used that is wasted.

5. In our cutting plan, we elected to use up as much as possible of each 100-in, roll with standard widths. Why might it be a better idea to allow leftover rolls that are *wider* than 14 in.?

6. The following table shows the weights of six objects and their values.

Weight	2	2.5	3	3.5	4	4.5
Value	12	11	7	13	10	11

If your knapsack holds a maximum weight of 9, what is the highest value you can pack in?

7. Suppose that of the original 33 cutting patterns, we allow only the 7 that occur in the final solution. Let y_1 = the number of copies of the first pattern, and similarly define y_2 through y_7. Write the integer programming problem that we are trying to solve.

8. Try solving the problem from Exercise 7 with the Solver in Microsoft Excel. First try it only requiring that the variables be nonnegative, not that they be integers. Then add constraints in the constraint box that the variables be integers.

9. Compare your two answers from Exercise 8 with each other and with the answer given in Figure 10. Discuss the effect on the minimum value of the requirement that the variables take on integer values. Also discuss what these solutions tell you about uniqueness of this integer programming problem.

10. Go to the website WolframAlpha.com and enter: "Minimize $y_1 + y_2$ with $2y_1 + y_2 \geq 100$, $y_1 \geq 0$, $y_2 \geq 0$". Study the solution provided by Wolfram|Alpha. As of this writing, Wolfram|Alpha cannot solve linear programming problems with more than five variables nor does it provide a way to do integer programming. Investigate whether this is still true. If these restrictions no longer exist, try Exercise 8 with Wolfram|Alpha and discuss how it compares with Microsoft Excel.

DIRECTIONS FOR GROUP PROJECT

Suppose you and three of the students from class have met at your house to study and your father questions each of you on what you are learning in college. While this is happening, your mother is busy planning a new raised-bed garden and your sister is attempting to choose which items she will put in a backpack for a field trip. Using the data in Exercises 1 and 6, prepare a presentation for your family on the value of what you're learning in college.

LEARNING OBJECTIVES

1: Slack Variables and the Pivot

1. Determine the number of slack variables needed for a linear programming problem
2. Add slack variables to a linear programming problem
3. Generate the initial simplex tableau
4. Identify the pivot and find the resulting matrix
5. Solve linear programming problems using the simplex tableau
6. Solve application problems

2: Maximization Problems

1. Solve maximization problems using the simplex tableau and simplex method
2. Solve maximization application problems

3: Minimization Problems; Duality

1. Find the transpose of a matrix
2. Generate the dual problem
3. Solve minimization problems using the simplex method
4. Solve minimization application problems

4: Nonstandard Problems

1. Solve nonstandard linear programming problems

ANSWERS TO SELECTED EXERCISES

Answers to selected writing exercises are provided.

Exercises I

1. $x_1 + 2x_2 + s_1 = 6$ **3.** $2.3x_1 + 5.7x_2 + 1.8x_3 + s_1 = 17$ **5. a.** 3

For exercises . . .	1–14	15–18	19–24	27–31
Refer to example . . .	1	3	4	2

b. s_1, s_2, s_3 **c.** $2x_1 + 3x_2 + s_1 = 15; 4x_1 + 5x_2 + s_2 = 35; x_1 + 6x_2 + s_3 = 20$ **7. a.** 2   **b.** s_1, s_2

c. $7x_1 + 6x_2 + 8x_3 + s_1 = 118; 4x_1 + 5x_2 + 10x_3 + s_2 = 220$

9.
$$\begin{array}{ccccc|c}
x_1 & x_2 & s_1 & s_2 & z & \\
4 & 2 & 1 & 0 & 0 & 5 \\
1 & 2 & 0 & 1 & 0 & 4 \\
-7 & -1 & 0 & 0 & 1 & 0
\end{array}$$

11.
$$\begin{array}{cccccc|c}
x_1 & x_2 & s_1 & s_2 & s_3 & z & \\
1 & 1 & 1 & 0 & 0 & 0 & 10 \\
5 & 2 & 0 & 1 & 0 & 0 & 20 \\
1 & 2 & 0 & 0 & 1 & 0 & 36 \\
-1 & -3 & 0 & 0 & 0 & 1 & 0
\end{array}$$

13.
$$\begin{array}{ccccc|c}
x_1 & x_2 & s_1 & s_2 & z & \\
3 & 1 & 1 & 0 & 0 & 12 \\
1 & 1 & 0 & 1 & 0 & 15 \\
-2 & -1 & 0 & 0 & 1 & 0
\end{array}$$

15. $x_1 = 0, x_2 = 4, x_3 = 0, s_1 = 0, s_2 = 8, z = 28$ **17.** $x_1 = 0, x_2 = 0, x_3 = 8, s_1 = 0, s_2 = 6, s_3 = 7, z = 12$
19. $x_1 = 0, x_2 = 20, x_3 = 0, s_1 = 16, s_2 = 0, z = 60$ **21.** $x_1 = 0, x_2 = 0, x_3 = 12, s_1 = 0, s_2 = 9, s_3 = 8, z = 36$
23. $x_1 = 0, x_2 = 250, x_3 = 0, s_1 = 0, s_2 = 50, s_3 = 200, z = 1000$

27. If x_1 is the number of simple figures, x_2 is the number of figures with additions, and x_3 is the number of computer drawn sketches, find $x_1 \geq 0, x_2 \geq 0$, and $x_3 \geq 0$ such that $20x_1 + 35x_2 + 60x_3 \leq 2200$, $x_1 + x_2 + x_3 \leq 400$, $x_3 \leq x_1 + x_2, x_1 \geq 2x_2$, and
$z = 95x_1 + 200x_2 + 325x_3$ is maximized;
$20x_1 + 35x_2 + 60x_3 + s_1 = 2200, x_1 + x_2 + x_3 + s_2 = 400$,
$-x_1 - x_2 + x_3 + s_3 = 0, -x_1 + 2x_2 + s_4 = 0$.

$$\begin{array}{cccccccc|c}
x_1 & x_2 & x_3 & s_1 & s_2 & s_3 & s_4 & z & \\
20 & 35 & 60 & 1 & 0 & 0 & 0 & 0 & 2200 \\
1 & 1 & 1 & 0 & 1 & 0 & 0 & 0 & 400 \\
-1 & -1 & 1 & 0 & 0 & 1 & 0 & 0 & 0 \\
-1 & 2 & 0 & 0 & 0 & 0 & 1 & 0 & 0 \\
-95 & -200 & -325 & 0 & 0 & 0 & 0 & 1 & 0
\end{array}$$

29. If x_1 is the number of redwood tables made, x_2 is the number of stained Douglas fir tables made, and x_3 is the number of stained white spruce tables made, find $x_1 \geq 0, x_2 \geq 0$, and $x_3 \geq 0$ such that $8x_1 + 7x_2 + 8x_3 \leq 720, 2x_2 + 2x_3 \leq 480$,
$159x_1 + 138.85x_2 + 129.35x_3 \leq 15,000$, and $z = x_1 + x_2 + x_3$
is maximized; $8x_1 + 7x_2 + 8x_3 + s_1 = 720$,
$2x_2 + 2x_3 + s_2 = 480, 159x_1 + 138.85x_2 + 129.35x_3 + s_3 = 15,000$.

$$\begin{array}{ccccccc|c}
x_1 & x_2 & x_3 & s_1 & s_2 & s_3 & z & \\
8 & 7 & 8 & 1 & 0 & 0 & 0 & 720 \\
0 & 2 & 2 & 0 & 1 & 0 & 0 & 480 \\
159 & 138.85 & 129.35 & 0 & 0 & 1 & 0 & 15,000 \\
-1 & -1 & -1 & 0 & 0 & 0 & 1 & 0
\end{array}$$

31. If x_1 is the number of newspaper ads run, x_2 is the number of Internet banner ads run, and x_3 is the number of TV ads run, find $x_1 \geq 0, x_2 \geq 0$, and $x_3 \geq 0$, such that $400x_1 + 20x_2 + 2000x_3 \leq 8000, x_1 \leq 30, x_2 \leq 60, x_3 \leq 10$, and $z = 4000x_1 + 3000x_2 + 10,000x_3$ is maximized;
$400x_1 + 20x_2 + 2000x_3 + s_1 = 8000, x_1 + s_2 = 30, x_2 + s_3 = 60$,
$x_3 + s_4 = 10$.

$$\begin{array}{cccccccc|c}
x_1 & x_2 & x_3 & s_1 & s_2 & s_3 & s_4 & z & \\
400 & 20 & 2000 & 1 & 0 & 0 & 0 & 0 & 8000 \\
1 & 0 & 0 & 0 & 1 & 0 & 0 & 0 & 30 \\
0 & 1 & 0 & 0 & 0 & 1 & 0 & 0 & 60 \\
0 & 0 & 1 & 0 & 0 & 0 & 1 & 0 & 10 \\
-4000 & -3000 & -10,000 & 0 & 0 & 0 & 0 & 1 & 0
\end{array}$$

Exercises 2

1. Maximum is 30 when $x_1 = 10, x_2 = 0, x_3 = 0, s_1 = 6$, and $s_2 = 0$.   **3.** Maximum is 8 when

For exercises . . .	1–40
Refer to example . . .	1

$x_1 = 4, x_2 = 0, s_1 = 8, s_2 = 2$, and $s_3 = 0$.   **5.** Maximum is 264 when $x_1 = 16, x_2 = 4, x_3 = 0, s_1 = 0, s_2 = 16$, and $s_3 = 0$.
7. Maximum is 25 when $x_1 = 0, x_2 = 5, s_1 = 20$, and $s_2 = 0$.   **9.** Maximum is 120 when $x_1 = 0, x_2 = 10, s_1 = 0, s_2 = 40$, and
$s_3 = 4$.   **11.** Maximum is 944 when $x_1 = 118, x_2 = 0, x_3 = 0, s_1 = 0$, and $s_2 = 102$.   **13.** Maximum is 3300 when $x_1 = 240$,
$x_2 = 60, x_3 = 0, x_4 = 0, s_1 = 0$, and $s_2 = 0$.   **15.** No maximum   **17.** Maximum is 70,818.18 when $x_1 = 181.82, x_2 = 0$,
$x_3 = 454.55, x_4 = 0, x_5 = 1363.64, s_1 = 0, s_2 = 0, s_3 = 0$, and $s_4 = 0$.   **23.** 6 churches and 2 labor unions, for a maximum of
$1000 per month   **25. a.** Assemble 1000 Royal Flush poker sets, 3000 Deluxe Diamond poker sets, and 0 Full House poker sets,
for a maximum profit of $104,000.   **b.** $s_4 = 1000$; there are 1000 unused dealer buttons.   **27. a.** No racing or touring bicycles and
2700 mountain bicycles   **b.** Maximum profit is $59,400   **c.** No; there are 1500 units of aluminum left; $s_2 = 1500$.   **29. a.** 17
newspaper ads, 60 Internet banner ads, and no TV ads, for a maximum exposure of 248,000   **31. a.** 3   **b.** 4   **c.** 3   **33.** $200,
$66.67, $300, $100   **35.** Rachel should run 3 hours, bike 4 hours, and walk 8 hours, for a maximum calorie expenditure of 6313
calories.   **37. a.** None of species A, 114 of species B, and 291 of species C, for a maximum combined weight of 1119.72 kg
b. No; there are 346 units of Food II available.   **c.** Many answers are possible.   **d.** Many answers are possible.   **39.** 12 minutes
to the senator, 9 minutes to the congresswoman and 6 minutes to the governor, for a maximum of 1,050,000 viewers.

Exercises 3

1. $\begin{bmatrix} 1 & 3 & 1 \\ 2 & 2 & 10 \\ 3 & 1 & 0 \end{bmatrix}$ **3.** $\begin{bmatrix} 4 & 7 & 5 \\ 5 & 14 & 0 \\ -3 & 20 & -2 \\ 15 & -8 & 23 \end{bmatrix}$ **5.** Minimize $w = 5y_1 + 4y_2 + 15y_3$ subject to $y_1 + y_2 + 2y_3 \geq 4$, $y_1 + y_2 + y_3 \geq 3$, $y_1 + 3y_3 \geq 2$, with $y_1 \geq 0$, $y_2 \geq 0$, and $y_3 \geq 0$. **7.** Maximize $z = 150x_1 + 275x_2$ subject to $x_1 + 2x_2 \leq 3$, $x_1 + 2x_2 \leq 6$, $x_1 + 3x_2 \leq 4$, $x_1 + 4x_2 \leq 1$, with $x_1 \geq 0$ and $x_2 \geq 0$.

9. Minimum is 14 when $y_1 = 0$ and $y_2 = 7$. **11.** Minimum is 40 when $y_1 = 10$ and $y_2 = 0$. **13.** Minimum is 30 when $y_1 = 5$ and $y_2 = 0$ or when $y_1 = 0$ and $y_2 = 3$, or any point on the line segment between (5, 0) and (0,3). **15.** Minimum is 100 when $y_1 = 0$, $y_2 = 100$, and $y_3 = 0$. **17.** a **19. a.** 25 units of regular beer and 20 units of light beer, for a minimum cost of \$1,800,000 **b.** The shadow cost is \$0.10; total production cost is \$1,850,000. **21. a.** Minimize $w = 100y_1 + 20,000y_2$ subject to $y_1 + 400y_2 \geq 120$, $y_1 + 160y_2 \geq 40$, $y_1 + 280y_2 \geq 60$, with $y_1 \geq 0$, $y_2 \geq 0$. **b.** 52.5 acres of potatoes and no corn or cabbage, for a profit of \$6300. **c.** 47.5 acres of potatoes and no corn or cabbage, for a profit of \$5700. **23.** 8 political interviews and no market interviews are done, for a minimum of 360 minutes. **25. a.** 1 bag of feed 1 and 2 bags of feed 2 **b.** 1.4 (or 7/5) bags of feed 1 and 1.2 (or 6/5) bags of feed 2 should be used, for a minimum cost of \$6.60 **27.** She should spend 30 minutes walking, 197.25 minutes cycling, and 75.75 minutes swimming, for a minimum time of 303 minutes per week. **29.** 8/3 units of ingredient I and 4 units of ingredient III, for a minimum cost of \$30.67.

Exercises 4

1. $2x_1 + 3x_2 + s_1 = 8$; $x_1 + 4x_2 - s_2 = 7$
3. $2x_1 + x_2 + 2x_3 + s_1 = 50$; $x_1 + 3x_2 + x_3 - s_2 = 35$; $x_1 + 2x_2 - s_3 = 15$ **5.** Change the objective function to maximize $z = -3y_1 - 4y_2 - 5y_3$. The constraints are not changed. **7.** Change the objective function to maximize $z = -y_1 - 2y_2 - y_3 - 5y_4$. The constraints are not changed. **9.** Maximum is 480 when $x_1 = 40$ and $x_2 = 0$. **11.** Maximum is 750 when $x_1 = 0$, $x_2 = 150$, and $x_3 = 0$. **13.** Maximum is 135 when $x_1 = 30$ and $x_2 = 5$. **15.** Minimum is 108 when $y_1 = 0$, $y_2 = 9$, and $y_3 = 0$. **17.** Maximum is 400/3 when $x_1 = 100/3$ and $x_2 = 50/3$. **19.** Minimum is 512 when $y_1 = 6$, $y_2 = 8$, and $y_3 = 0$. **23. a.** Ship 200 barrels of oil from supplier S_1 to distributor D_1; ship 2800 barrels of oil from supplier S_2 to distributor D_1; ship 2800 barrels of oil from supplier S_1 to distributor D_2; ship 2200 barrels of oil from supplier S_2 to distributor D_2. Minimum cost is \$180,400. **b.** $s_3 = 2000$; S_1 could furnish 2000 more barrels of oil. **25.** Make \$3,000,000 in commercial loans and \$22,000,000 in home loans, for a maximum return of \$2,940,000. **27.** Use 1500 lb of bluegrass, 2700 lb of rye, and 1800 lb of Bermuda, for a minimum cost of \$834. **29. a.** Ship 2 computers from W_1 to D_1, 20 computers from W_1 to D_2, 30 computers from W_2 to D_1, and 0 computers from W_2 to D_2, for a minimum cost of \$628. **b.** $s_3 = 3$; warehouse W_1 has 3 more computers that it could ship. **31.** Use 59.21 kg of chemical I, 394.74 kg of chemical II, and 296.05 kg of chemical III, for a minimum cost of \$600.39 **33.** 5/3 oz of I, 20/3 oz of II, and 5/3 oz of III, for a minimum cost of \$1.55 per gal; 10 oz of the additive should be used per gal of gasoline.

Review Exercises

1. True **2.** False **3.** True **4.** False **5.** False **6.** True **7.** True **8.** False **9.** False **10.** True **11.** False **12.** True **13.** False **14.** True **15.** When the problem has more than two variables **17. a.** $4x_1 + 6x_2 + s_1 = 60$; $3x_1 + x_2 + s_2 = 18$; $2x_1 + 5x_2 + s_3 = 20$; $x_1 + x_2 + s_4 = 15$ **b.**

x_1	x_2	s_1	s_2	s_3	s_4	z	
4	6	1	0	0	0	0	60
3	1	0	1	0	0	0	18
2	5	0	0	1	0	0	20
1	1	0	0	0	1	0	15
-2	-7	0	0	0	0	1	0

19. a. $x_1 + x_2 + x_3 + s_1 = 90$; $2x_1 + 5x_2 + x_3 + s_2 = 120$; $x_1 + 3x_2 - s_3 = 80$ **b.**

x_1	x_2	x_3	s_1	s_2	s_3	z	
1	1	1	1	0	0	0	90
2	5	1	0	1	0	0	120
1	3	0	0	0	-1	0	80
-5	-8	-6	0	0	0	1	0

21. Maximum is 33 when $x_1 = 3$, $x_2 = 0$, $x_3 = 3$, $s_1 = 0$, and $s_2 = 0$.   **23.** Maximum is 76.67 when $x_1 = 6.67$, $x_2 = 0$, $x_3 = 21.67$, $s_1 = 0$, $s_2 = 0$, and $s_3 = 35$.   **25. Dual Method** Solve the dual problem: Maximize $17x_1 + 42x_2$ subject to $x_1 + 5x_2 \leq 10$, $x_1 + 8x_2 \leq 15$.   **Method of Section 4** Change the objective function to maximize $z = -10y_1 - 15y_2$. The constraints are not changed. Minimum is 170 when $y_1 = 17$ and $y_2 = 0$.   **27. Dual Method** Solve the dual problem: Maximize $48x_1 + 12x_2 + 10x_3 + 30x_4$ subject to $x_1 + x_2 + 3x_4 \leq 7$, $x_1 + x_2 \leq 2$, $2x_1 + x_3 + x_4 \leq 3$.   **Method of Section 4** Change the objective function to maximize $z = -7y_1 - 2y_2 - 3y_3$. The constraints are not changed. Minimum is 98 when $y_1 = 4$, $y_2 = 8$, and $y_3 = 18$.   **29.** Maximum of 480 when $x_1 = 24$ and $x_2 = 0$ **31.** Maximum of 102 when $x_1 = 0$ and $x_2 = 8.5$ **33.** Problems with constraints involving "≤" can be solved using slack variables, while those involving "≥" or "=" can be solved using surplus and artificial variables, respectively.   **35. a.** Maximize $z = 6x_1 + 7x_2 + 5x_3$, subject to $4x_1 + 2x_2 + 3x_3 \leq 9$, $5x_1 + 4x_2 + x_3 \leq 10$, with $x_1 \geq 0$, $x_2 \geq 0$, $x_3 \geq 0$.   **b.** The first constraint would be $4x_1 + 2x_2 + 3x_3 \geq 9$.   **c.** $x_1 = 0$, $x_2 = 2.1$, $x_3 = 1.6$, and $z = 22.7$ **d.** Minimize $w = 9y_1 + 10y_2$, subject to $4y_1 + 5y_2 \geq 6$, $2y_1 + 4y_2 \geq 7$, $3y_1 + y_2 \geq 5$, with $y_1 \geq 0$, $y_2 \geq 0$.   **e.** $y_1 = 1.3$, $y_2 = 1.1$, and $w = 22.7$ **37. a.** Let $x_1 =$ number of cake plates, $x_2 =$ number of bread plates, and $x_3 =$ number of dinner plates.   **b.** $z = 15x_1 + 12x_2 + 5x_3$ **c.** $15x_1 + 10x_2 + 8x_3 \leq 1500$; $5x_1 + 4x_2 + 4x_3 \leq 2700$; $6x_1 + 5x_2 + 5x_3 \leq 1200$ **39. a.** Let $x_1 =$ number of gallons of Fruity wine and $x_2 =$ number of gallons of Crystal wine to be made.   **b.** $z = 12x_1 + 15x_2$ **c.** $2x_1 + x_2 \leq 110$; $2x_1 + 3x_2 \leq 125$; $2x_1 + x_2 \leq 90$ **41.** Produce no cake plates, 150 bread plates, and no dinner plates, for a maximum profit of $1800.   **43.** 36.25 gal of Fruity and 17.5 gal of Crystal, for a maximum profit of $697.50

45. a and b Produce 660 cases of corn, 0 cases of beans, and 340 cases of carrots, for a minimum cost of $15,100.   **c.** $16,100

47. Ginger should do $5\frac{1}{3}$ hours of tai chi, $2\frac{2}{3}$ hours of riding a unicycle, and 2 hours of fencing, for a maximum calorie expenditure of $2753\frac{1}{3}$ calories.

TEXT CREDITS

Exercise 29: Professor Karl K. Norton, Husson College
Exercises 31 and 32: Copyright 1973-1991, American Institute of Certified Public Accountants, Inc. All Rights Reserved. Used with permission.
Exercise 17: Copyright © Society of Actuaries. Used by permission.

SOURCES

Section 1

1. Exercise 29 was provided by Professor Karl K. Norton, Husson University.

Section 2

1. Exercise 31 from *Uniform CPA Examination Questions and Unofficial Answers*, copyright ©1973, 1974, 1975 by the American Institute of Certified Public Accountants, Inc., is reprinted with permission.
2. Exercise 35 from http://www.nutristrategy.com/activitylist4.htm.
3. Exercise 36 from http://www.nutristrategy.com/activitylist4.htm.

Section 3

1. Exercise 17 from Problem 2 from "November 1989 Course 130 Examination Operations Research" of the *Education and Examination Committee of The Society of Actuaries*. Reprinted by permission of The Society of Actuaries.
2. Exercise 27 from http://www.brianmac.demon.co.uk/energyexp.htm.

Section 4

1. Exercise 30 from http://www.nutristrategy.com/activitylist4.htm.

Review Exercise

1. Exercise 47 from http://www.nutristrategy.com/activitylist4.htm.

Extended Application

1. This application based on material from the following online sources: The website of the Optimization Technology Center at Northwestern University at http://www.ece.nwu.edu/OTC/. There is a link to a thorough explanation of the stock-cutting problem. Home page of the Special Interest Group on Cutting and Packing at http://prodlog.wiwi.uni-halle.de/sicup/index.html. The linear programming FAQ at http://www.faqs.org/faqs/linear-programming-faq/.

Index

Page references followed by "f" indicate illustrated figures or photographs; followed by "t" indicates a table.

492